LOBLOLLY PINE

This elite loblolly pine tree in Rankin County, Mississippi, had these dimensions at 68 years: Diameter at breast height 25 inches, height 125 feet, clear stem 79 feet, number of 16-foot logs 6, volume 1150 board feet. It would make a 100-foot piling. (By permission from Ed Hoover, Forester, International Paper Company. The climber is Hoy Grigsby.)

Loblolly Pine

ITS USE, ECOLOGY, REGENERATION, PROTECTION,
GROWTH AND MANAGEMENT

BY

W. G. Wahlenberg
SENIOR RESEARCH ASSOCIATE
DUKE UNIVERSITY

''Many ideas grow better when transplanted into
another mind than the one where they sprang up.
. . . . Knowledge and timber should not be much
used until seasoned.''

OLIVER WENDELL HOLMES

PUBLISHED BY

THE SCHOOL OF FORESTRY
DUKE UNIVERSITY

IN COOPERATION WITH FOREST INDUSTRY AND THE
FOREST SERVICE, U. S. DEPARTMENT OF AGRICULTURE

1960

MANUFACTURED IN THE UNITED STATES OF AMERICA
BY THE SEEMAN PRINTERY INCORPORATED, DURHAM, N. C.

DEDICATED TO

CLARENCE FERDINAND KORSTIAN

TO WHOSE INSIGHT, KNOWLEDGE,

VISION, AND LEADERSHIP, THOSE INTERESTED IN THE ART,

SCIENCE, AND BUSINESS OF FORESTRY

IN THE SOUTHEAST ARE PERMANENTLY INDEBTED.

WITHOUT HIS DEVOTED SUPPORT

THIS MONOGRAPH WOULD NOT HAVE MATERIALIZED

FOREWORD

THE LOBLOLLY FORESTS of the South may truthfully be said to be that expansive region's greatest renewable resource. The botanical range of the species extends in a great crescent southwestward through fourteen states, from Delaware to Texas, interrupted only by the wide flood plain of the Mississippi River. Trees of this species are found in all manner of soils, sites, and situations from the sandy reaches of the Coastal Plain through the fertile bottom lands to the warm, washed-out slopes of the Piedmont Plateau. They are found mixed with hardwoods, with other pines, and in pure stands. All of which is to say that the culture, protection, and management of loblolly pines is not a simple matter easily determined and responsive to a few uniform rules of thumb.

It may be said too, that because of the almost universal presence of this species and the equally universal economic pressure for its production, few indeed of the many forest managers of the South are not faced, today, with the complexities involved in its continued growth and utilization.

So it is that this new comprehensive monograph by W. G. Wahlenberg on loblolly pine comes, as it were, as a timely answer to a forester's prayer. The book is a worthy companion volume to his monumental Longleaf Pine, published in 1946.

In Loblolly Pine, Wahlenberg puts into print the results of 12 years of patient, painstaking research on the rich field of reported experimentation, observation, and experience having to do with all phases of the management of the species from seedlings to saw logs. The work is particularly valuable in that his intimate contact with the subject in the field has allowed a degree of discrimination and up-to-dateness in choice of reported results not to be expected of an author farther removed from the scene.

Obviously the book is designed, in the main, as a reference book, and a silvicultural tool for forest managers. Although it is scientific in its approach and technical throughout, it is expressed clearly and simply, with a minimum of the jargon of the profession. It moves fast and is easy to read and to understand. It can be predicted that Wahlenberg's Loblolly Pine will for many years to come be and remain a well-thumbed reference book on the shelves of foresters-in-boots throughout the South, as well as a standard item in forest school reading and libraries generally.

Inman F. Eldredge, Sr.

AUTHOR'S PREFACE

THE LEADING COMMERCIAL TIMBER species in the southern United States is loblolly pine (*Pinus taeda* L.). This species has even been referred to as the second most important timber species in the world. Loblolly pine clearly merits monographic treatment on the basis of its wide range over the South, its prominent place in southern forestry, and the mass of new information about it added in the past 10 years. Each year now more researchers are learning to understand its peculiarities, more managers are gaining experience in handling it skillfully, and more landowners are recognizing its culture as a sound business proposition. Because of these promising developments, loblolly pine was chosen and accepted as the subject of this monograph. As W. W. Ashe said many years ago: "Loblolly pine combines all the essentials for an ideal forest-management tree."

Only in recent years, however, has forest management begun to take its place throughout the South. Widespread failure to apply accumulated silvical knowledge resulted in extensive forest deterioration.

A prominent European forester, G. L. Hartig, once admonished his colleagues that "each compartment must be kept in such condition that it cannot, before seeding takes place, grow up to grass and weeds." Inferior species of trees were, of course, regarded as weeds. Southeastern United States today shows scant evidence that this bit of wisdom had been heeded. Why not? As economist Henry George remarked, "Until there is correct thought there can not be correct action." And correct thought is based on information. Incorrect thought, however, stems less from the scarcity of information than from its relative inaccessibility. Therein lies the real need for assembling in one place all the essential information about a tree species.

Nor has there been any disagreement on the obvious need to gather widely dispersed information on loblolly pine. How best to fulfill this need was another matter. Nearly everyone wanted a book, but hardly anyone relished an assignment to produce the kind we desired. It had been my hope that someone else would take on the job. In the absence of any volunteers I agreed to attempt it. I have found the task appealing and challenging, but formidable and not without frustrations.

Two concepts of a species monograph were abandoned early as both unworkable and undesirable. The first called for the production of a book composed largely of general principles with little or no supporting evidence. This concept proved impractical because insufficient general principles have been formulated or accepted to make a book. And to attempt a book without including quantitative facts and supporting local experience would scarcely be a worthy goal.

The second concept would have confined this treatise to those things which are peculiar to loblolly pine. This could not be done because so many things that the species has in common with the other yellow pines of the South are of prime importance to forest managers. To leave these out would result in a disappointingly brief and fragmentary treatment of loblolly pine forestry.

The present collation involved four main phases as follows: (1) to collect scattered information based on research or practice and to summarize the facts assembled; (2) to correlate, sort, and organize them systematically; (3) to evaluate, interpret, illustrate, and report them clearly; and (4) to publish a comprehensive treatise for use by timber growers, foresters, researchers, and educators.

In recent years the first monograph of a tree species comprehensive enough to have been based on review of nearly all pertinent forestry literature to date was Longleaf Pine, published by the Charles Lathrop Pack Forestry Foundation in January 1946. This is the second. Of the reams of printed experiences with loblolly pine—popular leaflets, brochures, articles in trade and technical journals, scientific notes, and bulletins—only a small part can be found outside the largest libraries. A good start was made in locating source materials on loblolly pine when, in 1949, Dorman and Sims issued their bibliography of about 650 titles. Listed, in 11 subject-matter sections, were papers by 330 authors contributing to our knowledge of loblolly pine forestry between 1890 and 1949. This second review of the literature on southern pine has covered nearly 1,500 articles concerned with loblolly pine.

More material was published between 1950 and June 1959, the

cutoff date for literature to be listed in the bibliography, than in the previous 60 years. It has been difficult to keep abreast of this continuing stream of new contributions to forest knowledge in recent years, and to prevent a monograph from becoming too badly out of date during the extended period needed to compile it.

Positive answers to many vitally important silvicultural questions are not yet possible. Numerous methods of management, now being suggested as practical measures, need further testing in different localities. Within this profusion of existing information it is often difficult and time consuming to locate the solid and pertinent facts that are needed to resolve many local problems. Inaccessibility of essential information continues to retard the application of effective forest management.

In my present endeavor to crystallize all pertinent information the most baffling features were the following five: (1) abundant repetitious versions in the literature due to multiple reporting of useful findings, (2) almost universal verbosity and circumlocution found in college theses, (3) lack of segregation of species in much of the data for southern yellow pines, (4) relative inaccessibilty of recent technical advances made through private industrial research, and (5) situations in which many current problems obviously remain unresolved.

In spite of these features and my own limitations, I have nevertheless enjoyed the job. We hope the present monograph will serve us now as well as the one by Ashe in 1915 served those before us. Ralph Waldo Emerson said: "That book is good which puts me in a working mood." This one did for me; would that it may do so for others.

Let me close with just one more quotation—an old German saying: "The forest is a blessing of God's creation; to be a servant of the forest is a fine vocation."

Asheville, N. C.
March 1960

ACKNOWLEDGMENTS

THE AUTHOR IS MUCH INDEBTED to the School of Forestry at Duke University for beginning the project that resulted in this book; to the Southeastern Forest Experiment Station and other units of the U. S. Forest Service for making available many published and unpublished sources of information, for office space, typing, and other facilities.

Information for the monograph has been obtained mainly from specialists in four fields: (1) the economic and silvicultural aspects of timber management, (2) the problem of injurious agents, (3) the influence of tree physiology and soils, and (4) the nature of range, wildlife, and watershed values. The author desires to thank about seventy of his forestry colleagues working in these four fields for their helpful comments. In scanning parts of early versions of the text these men have brightened the arduous task of portraying facts properly and expounding procedures clearly. Although original source material was used insofar as possible the author alone is responsible for any misinterpretations that may still be included.

Advice received from several members of the U. S. Forest Service deserves special recognition here. Silviculture measures for the Coastal Plain were reviewed by G. F. Gruschow, K. W. Wenger, T. Lotti, and R. J. Riebold; those for inland areas by E. V. Brender, R. Zahner, and R. R. Reynolds. P. C. Wakeley and F. M. Cossitt improved the report on regeneration; P. R. Wheeler supplied useful data on measurements; and Walton R. Smith and P. J. Bois contributed sections on log grades and on treatments to season and preserve timber products. All the other data on uses and properties of wood were reviewed by specialists at the Forest Products Laboratory at Madison, Wis. David F. Olson, Jr., scanned the rough draft of each chapter.

Two men who read the entire manuscript deserve special thanks for outstanding help: G. K. Stephenson, Research Center Leader in

Texas, for constructive review of the first version, and F. H. Eyre, a member of the editorial board of Forest Science, for an overall professional criticism of the revised draft.

Editors of several copyrighted periodicals have kindly granted permission to reprint certain tables and illustrations from their pages. The graphs—adopted or adapted from originals—were nearly all drafted in final form by M. L. McCormack, School of Forestry, Duke University. The bibliography was checked by C. E. Folckemer, and typed at the Duke School of Forestry. The entire manuscript was edited by W. P. Everard.

CONTENTS

8. Management of Mature Timber   342

9. Management for Other Purposes   392

Appendix   489

SPONSORS

Angelina County Lumber Company, Keltys, Texas
Allis-Chalmers Manufacturing Company, Milwaukee, Wisconsin
Asten-Hill Manufacturing Company, Philadelphia, Pennsylvania
Beloit Iron Works, Beloit, Wisconsin
Bowaters Southern Paper Corporation, Calhoun, Tennessee
Brunswick Pulp and Paper Company, Brunswick, Georgia
The Buckeye Cellulose Corporation, Memphis, Tennessee
Cary Lumber Company, Durham, North Carolina
The Champion Paper and Fibre Company, Hamilton, Ohio
Duke University School of Forestry, Durham, North Carolina
E. F. Craven Company, Greensboro, North Carolina
East Texas Pulp and Paper Company, Silsbee, Texas
Frost Lumber Industries, Shreveport, Louisiana
Gaylord Container Corporation, Bogalusa, Louisiana
Georgia Kraft Company, Macon, Georgia
Gulf States Paper Corporation, Tuscaloosa, Alabama
International Harvester Foundation, Chicago, Illinois
Lightsey Brothers, Miley, South Carolina
Mr. Richard W. Lloyd, Camden, South Carolina
The Lutcher and Moore Lumber Company, Orange, Texas
North Carolina Equipment Company, Raleigh, North Carolina
Prior Chemical Corporation, New York, New York
Resources for the Future, Washington, D. C.
Riegel Paper Corporation, New York, New York
Rome Kraft Company, Rome, Georgia
Southeastern Forest Experiment Station, U. S. Forest Service, Asheville, North Carolina
Southern Forest Experiment Station, U. S. Forest Service, New Orleans, Louisiana
Southland Paper Mills, Inc., Lufkin, Texas
St. Regis Paper Company, New York, New York
Stowe-Woodward, Inc., Newton Upper Falls, Massachusetts
Union Bag-Camp Paper Corporation, New York, New York

Chapter 1

Introduction

Loblolly pine (*Pinus taeda* L.) stands high among the natural resources of the South. For half a century southern yellow pine has provided an average harvest of some 10 billion board feet a year; at least half of this has been loblolly pine. Today the growing stock volume of this species stands at nearly 90 billion board feet, and the lands suitable for growing it promise a much greater volume. Foresters, land managers, landowners, industrialists, and many others have seen the benefits loblolly pine has already provided and they are becoming increasingly aware of the innumerable possibilities the future holds. But these men face many problems involving resource maintenance and renewal, competition for growing space and markets, protection, management practices, and a multiplicity of uses. The characteristics of loblolly pine, its habitat, its needs and limitations, its treatment from seed to maturity—of these much is known that can help solve such problems.

A PROBLEM OF RESOURCE MAINTENANCE

Until the 19th century the natural loblolly pine forest of the southern United States was but little influenced by men. Since then it has been modified decidedly, if inadvertently, by the expanding civilization. Now that the migratory rush of lumbermen from one region of virgin timber to another is ended, the temptation to "cut out and get out" is past. From the reversal of our traditional practice of forest land exploitation new problems and opportunities have emerged. The future of the loblolly pine forest will depend on how well existing and newly acquired knowledge of natural laws governing its growth and renewal can be utilized. Although this forest is still being depleted in many places, the overall trend toward better forestry has turned decidedly upward. The loblolly pine forest (fig. 1) continues to supply essential raw materials abundantly at

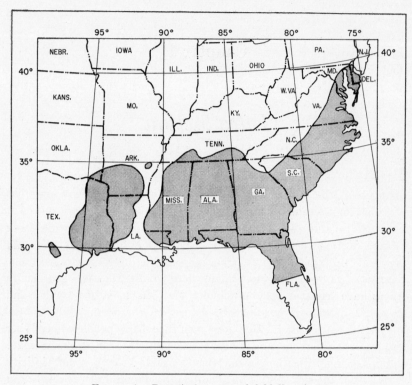

FIGURE 1.—Botanical range of loblolly pine.

reasonable cost, and it remains the greatest renewable resource in the South.

Renewal of the loblolly pine forest type is a challenge foresters expect to meet. Here is what one eminent Southern forester says on that point. "Forestry with us is certain to grow and prosper, because at last it has joined a cause greater than itself and nearer to the human heart—the liberation of millions from the tyranny of poor-land farming, and the launching of a new South, proud of the strength it will add to our nation" (Eldredge 1947). Wise utilization of the renewed forest is a related challenge, involving the stabilization of wood-using industries and forest communities by balancing the cut with the growth of loblolly pine.

The underlying problem of renewal is ecological, in that the natural laws of plant succession generally militate against success with pine, the pine type being but a temporary stage in a long-term progression favoring certain hardwood species. The better hardwood trees can be sold, but any surplus of poor trees should be destroyed. Because they lack the technical qualities that make up feasible raw materials for most mass-demand products, full utilization of most of these hardwoods is nowhere in sight. In the manufacturing process lumber produced per unit of time spent is 30 to 40 percent greater for pine than for hardwood.

There is a tremendous volume of cellulose contained in little-used, hard-textured, broad-leaved forest trees within the loblolly pine belt. These hardwoods need not, cannot, and should not be eradicated completely by those who grow loblolly pine, but their natural tendency to usurp growing space on pine lands must be curbed.[1]

COMPETITION BY OTHER REGIONS
AND FROM OTHER CROPS

Opportunities to invest capital to grow loblolly pine saw logs and timbers, and to dispose of these structural materials in nationwide markets, meet with about as much competition from Douglas-fir out of the Northwest as they do from other softwood species within the loblolly pine range.

A valid comparison of rates of growth has been made between loblolly pine and Douglas-fir based on the yields from each when grown on sites of average quality in its own region (Worthington 1954). Loblolly pine, for example, reaches 85 feet at 50 years and Douglas-fir 140 feet at 100 years. Greater average increment and yield accrue from the fir, but earlier returns and more clear lumber from the pine. Natural pruning of loblolly pine is rapid, resulting in one-quarter of the wood being knot-free by 50 years. For the first 25 or 30 years loblolly pine grows faster in both diameter and height.[2]

In the loblolly pine belt, cotton has long been "king" of cellulose production on agricultural land, but the pine can excel on the forest land. Cellulose from cotton can be processed in manufacturing plants more economically than cellulose from pine, but the latter

[1] The ramifications of this problem of regenerating the pine adequately are such that they were topics discussed in at least 200 of the basic papers and had to be treated in half of the chapters in this book.

[2] It averages 2 inches larger than Douglas-fir at 25 years, 1 inch larger at 55 years, and is equal at 75 years; the fir excels later. The peaks in mean annual increments indicate rotations of 35 years for pine and 70 years for Douglas-fir in producing pulpwood. Firs produce more logs per tree and more trees per acre—twice as many at 100 years—at which time the yield in board feet may exceed loblolly pine by 40 percent.

can be grown at less cost, particularly on old fields that have lost over half their topsoil from erosion (Hostetter 1943). A cord of pine wood contains about 1,000 pounds of cellulose. On average sites loblolly pine yields from 600 to 700 pounds of cellulose per acre annually, which is 4 or 5 times the usual yield from cotton (Bull 1939a, Reynolds 1948b). If any forest tree species can depose "King cotton" in plantations to produce cellulose, loblolly pine is a promising candidate.

Loblolly pine is the leading forest tree species to be managed for successive timber crops in the South for four principal reasons: (1) effective natural or easy artificial regeneration on extensive areas, (2) rapid growth on a wide range of sites, (3) ease of handling products in forest and mill, and (4) steady demand and rising prices for a variety of commodities made from its wood.

Among other tree species in the South loblolly pine competes well. Except on true bottom lands within the pine belt hardwoods yield less than loblolly pine. Elsewhere on deep moist soil, and under proper management, loblolly pine and yellow-poplar (*Liriodendron tulipifera*) make comparable development. On medium and shallow soils the loblolly pine is superior in diameter growth and merchantable height (Hocker 1953). On well-drained upland sites in central Louisiana loblolly pine outgrows its southern yellow pine associates (slash, longleaf, and shortleaf) in mixed species plantations (Mann 1953a).

FOREST HISTORY

Southern pines are the base for the oldest industry in America. The first hand-operated pit type of sawmill in the colonies was set up at Jamestown, Virginia, in 1608.[3] The colonists soon harnessed their waterpower to mills of the sash-saw type, each cutting about 500 board feet per day. Such mills continued to operate throughout the 18th century. The first of many steam mills was established at Wilmington, North Carolina, about 1818, but steam was not in common use until the time of the war between the states.

The early lumber business in the South was dominated by longleaf pine, primarily for export, and was concentrated on the coast or near river transportation. The exhaustion of white pine in the Northeast sent lumbermen from that section to the Midwest and

[3] The first description of loblolly pine was published by Plukenet in 1696. This species was introduced into Europe before 1713 by Bishop Compton, and specimens have grown to large size in European collections (Sargent 1897).

South. But the supply of longleaf pine began to run low, first in the Carolinas about 1860 and later in the deep South in the early nineteen hundreds.

This depletion brought loblolly pine—first marketed in the Carolinas because of freight advantages—into prominence in the lumber trade. Old growth of this species, together with shortleaf pine, then became the mainstay of the industry. Of some 437 million board feet of pine cut in North Carolina in 1893 nearly two-thirds was loblolly pine. In the Carolinas old-growth stumpage of this species was available at 50 cents per M board feet, and the land with 1,500 to 4,000 board feet could be purchased for $1 to $4 an acre (Spring 1902, Silcox 1904). In Arkansas loblolly pine stands varied from 5 to 15 M board feet, averaging 7 M per acre. In spite of the advantages of cheap land, rapid growth, and low taxes—one cent per acre—forestry was not then attractive (Ames 1906).

An economy of abundance still prevailed for this timber during the first decade of the present century. The South held the lead in lumber production from 1900 to 1925, and when the peak was reached in 1909, the South was producing about 45 percent of the total. In 1910 loblolly pine, occurring over an area of some 200,000 square miles, occupied 75 percent of the area. Of this loblolly pine forest, 10 to 13 percent, or 15,000 to 19,500 square miles, was then estimated to be second-growth of natural or old-field origin (Ashe 1910).

Harvest operations, sweeping southwestward from the Atlantic seaboard, still left about 15 billion board feet in mature loblolly pine on some 5 million acres in North Carolina (Ashe 1915). And 10 years after the peak of production, about 23 million acres of old-growth southern pine and 60 million of new growth supported 260 billion board feet (Forbes 1923).

The progressive shift by the lumber industry to the use of second growth, much of it loblolly pine, brought significant change. Liquidation of promising young growth gave way in many locations to plans to conserve remaining supplies and grow more of the same. This stabilizing transformation of policy was evident among many of the more strongly financed firms, and among those smaller mills that were affiliated with them. The development of roads and the widespread use of trucks, however, also brought in many more independent small mills, semiportable plants handling the smaller logs from scattered tracts with low volumes per acre. The small portable mill remains popular because its operation is flexible, no land need be owned, stumpage can be purchased in small amounts, there are no costly overhead expenses and no fixed responsibilities toward labor. Useful as these mills have been to many rural communities, they nevertheless became the "problem children" of the lumber industry.[4]

Today the South has more than 40 million acres of commercial forest land poorly stocked as a result of past misuse. Much of this land will grow loblolly pine. On the plus side, though, more than 50 million acres are owned by forest industries or are in public ownership, and most of this area is under some form of management. And too, nearly one-third of the Nation's annual sawtimber growth is in southern yellow pine, including billions of board feet from second (or third) growth loblolly pine.

RESOURCES

The softwoods of the United States cover some 234 million acres in various types of forest. About a third of this area is in the South which has had the distinction of remaining a continuous major source of softwood lumber longer than has any other timber growing region. More pine lumber was manufactured in the South in the first half of the 20th century during each year (except 1931) than in any other producing section of the country.

Much of that lumber came from loblolly pine that developed without benefit of forestry or any artificial aids, except some protection from fire in a few states. Loblolly pine, therefore, should be able to maintain its position. If the demand for pulpwood is not overwhelming, the species could even improve its position through the application of silvicuture.

Within the 14 states where loblolly pine grows naturally, this species occurs most abundantly in the loblolly-shortleaf pine type. This type occupies about 53 million acres or 27 percent of the commercial forest land, the coverage (fig. 5, p. 20) varying from only 3 percent in Florida to 48 percent in South Carolina (table 1). Roughly two-thirds of the pine volume in this type and about half of the yellow pine in the South is loblolly pine.

Within the 20 million acres of oak-pine type in the South, loblolly pine can be increased under management, and some of that area

---

[4] The chief offenders were to be found among mills cutting less than 5 million board feet annually, or 1,000 board feet per day per worker. Many of these do business intermittently on a "shoe-string" basis, using unskilled labor to harvest timber in "fly-by-night" enterprises that are seldom in any way related to the capacity of pine lands to sustain yields. These situations are unfortunate—and we hope temporary.

TABLE 1.—*Prevalence of the principal type of forest in which loblolly pine was found in surveys from 1947 to 1957*[1]

State	Commercial forest land	Portion included in the loblolly-short-leaf pine type	State	Commercial forest land	Portion included in the loblolly-short-leaf pine type
	Acres	*Percent*		*Acres*	*Percent*
Alabama.....	20,756,200	38.6	N. Carolina...	19,341,400	27.3
Arkansas.....	19,292,000	30.5	S. Carolina...	11,899,500	48.0
Delaware.....	391,100	37.8	Oklahoma....	5,632,000	18.9
Florida.......	21,451,100	3.1	Tennessee....	12,300,700	17.7
Georgia......	23,969,100	29.1	Texas........	12,171,900	43.8
Louisiana.....	16,038,000	25.0	Virginia......	15,449,900	18.9
Maryland....	2,897,000	13.9			
Mississippi....	17,193,600	26.7	All 14 states..	198,783,500	26.7

[1] Forest Service, U.S.D.A., survey data.

may be converted into pine forest. When some 29 million acres of idle pine lands are reforested, as much as two-thirds of them could be planted with loblolly pine, although if present trends in planting continue, only one third (about 10 million acres) may be restored to loblolly pine.

It is commonly necessary, and wholly feasible, to manage loblolly pine along with its associate shortleaf pine. In timber volume these two species together were far in the lead in 1953 with nearly 131 billion board feet of sawtimber in the South (table 2). At the same time the total commercial volume of growing stock in loblolly pine alone was estimated at nearly 22 billion cubic feet. The saw-log portion of this volume amounted to about 89 billion board feet (table 3), about half of it in trees of medium size. Approximations of annual growth rates vary from 5 percent in large timber to 8 percent in pole-sized trees, averaging possibly 6 percent in the Southeast.[5]

The harvests of southern yellow pine for lumber have averaged nearly 10 billion board feet a year for about a century (Lotti and McCulley 1951). Although the per capita use of lumber continues to decrease, total consumption is increasing. The value of many trees has increased several fold while the wood-using industries have grown into a 5-billion-dollar-a-year business in the South since World War II. Lumber is no longer the principal commodity; parts of many stands and certain trees make pulp for paper. Multiple-product harvests are increasing and now permit utilization of 72

[5] Survey data reported in Southeastern Forest Experiment Station Notes 2, 3, 6, and 7 (1952). Estimates of how natural increases offset commercial drain are beyond the scope of this report.

TABLE 2.—*Timber stocks of the two principal species of southern yellow pine in the range of loblolly pine, and the proportion of loblolly pine, 1947 to 1957*[1]

State	Shortleaf and loblolly pine growing stock	Portion that is loblolly pine	Sawtimber volume in shortleaf and loblolly pines	Portion that is loblolly pine	Period of estimate
	M. cu. ft.	*Percent*	*M. bd. ft.*	*Percent*	*Years*
Alabama	3,912,200	67	15,296,500	74	1951-53
Arkansas	4,136,600	39	16,977,800	45	1953
Delaware	226,200	74	536,600	80	1957
Florida	323,700	88	1,301,500	90	1949
Georgia	3,344,000	66	9,531,800	71	1951-53
Louisiana	3,327,000	77	15,883,100	78	1953-54
Maryland	612,000	75	1,239,000	85	1953
Mississippi	2,449,400	62	9,959,600	67	1956-57
North Carolina	5,460,100	67	18,811,100	75	1955
South Carolina	3,374,600	72	12,497,600	79	1947
Oklahoma	492,700	4	1,992,700	5	1955-56
Tennessee	373,300	4	1,065,800	3	1953
Texas	3,774,200	63	16,374,700	67	1953-55
Virginia	2,931,900	64	9,259,600	71	1957
Total	34,737,900	63	130,727,400	68	1947-57

[1] Forest Service, U.S.D.A., survey data. All pines 5 inches in d.b.h. and larger are included in the cubic volume estimates, whereas only pines 9 inches and larger are counted as sawtimber.

TABLE 3.—*Growing stock and saw-log volume*[1] *of loblolly pine and the distribution of sawtimber in three diameter groups, by states, 1947 to 1957*

State	Growing stock volume	Saw-log volume	Proportion of sawtimber when d.b.h. in inches is—		
			10-12	14-18	20+
	Thousand cubic feet	*Million board feet*	*Percent*	*Percent*	*Percent*
North Carolina	3,643,800	14,112	40	47	13
Alabama	2,605,900	11,307	40	44	16
Louisiana	2,561,800	12,443	30	52	18
South Carolina	2,417,239	9,917	31	46	23
Texas	2,375,100	10,926	34	49	17
Georgia	2,202,900	6,781	48	41	11
Virginia	1,867,800	6,611	47	44	9
Arkansas[2]	1,633,900	7,623	35	49	16
Mississippi[3]	1,514,300	6,680	32	49	19
Maryland	449,000	1,116	48	44	8
Florida	286,200	1,168	37	50	13
Delaware	178,000	459	50	37	13
Oklahoma	20,300	108	20	70	10
Tennessee[2]	16,000	32	61	27	12
Total	21,772,239	89,283	37	47	16

[1] The saw-log volume is a part of—not in addition to—the growing stock volume. The table includes volumes found in the Texas "Pine Fringe" area; in addition there are possibly 100 million board feet or 20,000 M cubic feet of loblolly pine growing stock scattered in the so-called "lost pines" area of Texas.
[2] Data from Timber Resource Review work sheets.
[3] Data from third survey report tabulations.

percent of the volume cut. Sometimes nearly half of the saw-log-size trees cut are used wholly for some purpose other than lumber (McCormack 1952). Volume increase of high-grade saw logs tends to exceed commercial drain only in regions where silviculture is a prevailing practice.

With adequate supply, active demand, and rising prices for loblolly pine wood, there is a vigorous trade in the products of this species. The improved markets for relatively small pines made into posts, poles, and pulpwood have become extensive within, and adjacent to, the loblolly pine belt (figs. 2 and 3). More than half of all the pulpwood produced in the United States is made at about 75 southern mills having a total capacity of over 44,000 tons per day.

The pulp and paper industry, through rapid technical development and lowered costs, has made tremendous progress. Annual

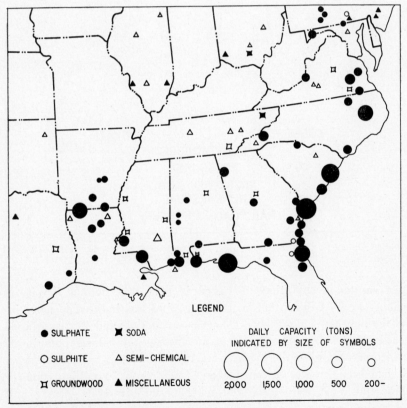

LEGEND

● SULPHATE   ✖ SODA   DAILY CAPACITY (TONS)
                                  INDICATED BY SIZE OF SYMBOLS
○ SULPHITE   △ SEMI-CHEMICAL

◻ GROUNDWOOD ▲ MISCELLANEOUS   2,000   1,500   1,000   500   200-

FIGURE 2.—Size and location of mills and the principal types of woodpulp produced in 1958 in southeastern United States (based on Lockwood's 1958 directory of the paper and allied trades and other sources).

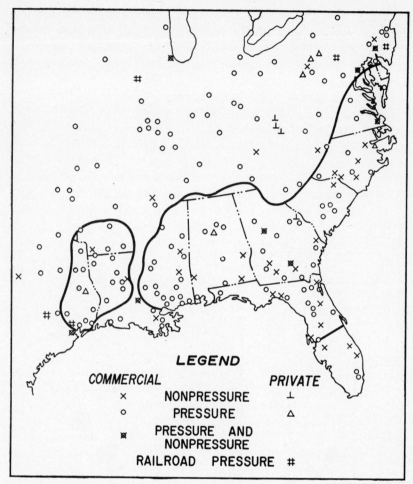

FIGURE 3.—Type and location of wood-preserving plants in eastern United
    States.

per capita consumption of paper is over 400 pounds. With a
chance to cut costs in half northern capital was induced to move into the South (Calder 1946). There between 1939 and 1952 pulpwood
production increased steadily at an average annual compound rate
of 8.5 percent (Worrell 1955a). By 1953 production was double what
it had been 7 years earlier (Moon 1956). Over 15 million cords of
pine pulpwood were harvested in the South in 1955—nearly half
of it in Georgia, Florida, and Alabama (Jeffords 1956). Millions
of dollars have been invested in new manufacturing plants. As a

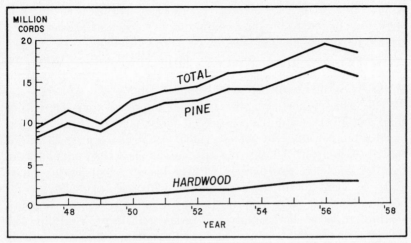

FIGURE 4.—The trend of utilization of round wood for pulp in the South; by 1957 the amounts shown here were increased 5 to 7 percent by the use of wood residues for pulp (Forest Survey data).

result of the phenomenal growth of this industry the market for pine is extensive and increasing (fig. 4).[6]

Most of the southern pulp mills either already own or intend to acquire enough forest land to supply half their wood requirements continuously. The other half of their requirements provides a market important to small woodland owners. If all forests within a radius of about 40 miles of each mill were well stocked and properly managed they might fill the need, but some of the wood goes into other uses, so actually the wood for a mill is gathered from a much wider area. The industry, in need of a perpetual supply, employs nearly 150 foresters who work exclusively, and free of charge, with local woodland owners to make their forests more productive. About 10,000 owners with some 5 million acres of forest land benefit from industry assistance.

SUMMARY

The rebuilding of the loblolly pine forest, in the face of natural sucession toward hardwoods, is a challenge to the South. It is likewise an attractive silvicultural opportunity. This is true because

[6] Throughout the loblolly pine belt pulpwood is abundantly available from broad-leaved species at prices per unit of volume that are well below those for softwood, but the demand for hardwood is low. Hardwoods contribute only about 13 percent of the wood used for pulp in the South. Hence this market is insufficient to absorb all the hardwood that needs to be harvested to permit full growth of the valuable softwoods such as loblolly pine.

of increases in the accessibility of the forest resource, advances in knowledge of its culture, and continuing expansion of market outlets for all its principal and some of its minor products.

Loblolly pine yields more than do its own hardwood associates in the South, and on short rotations it excels even the Douglas-fir of the West in producing merchantable cellulose.

The loblolly-shortleaf pine type of forest occupies 53 million acres or 27 percent of the commercial forest land in 14 states. The merchantable volume of loblolly pine alone was nearly 22 billion cubic feet in 1953. Of this the saw-log volume was 89 billion board feet. Annual harvests, largely without benefit of silviculture, have averaged about 10 billion board feet for half a century. High-grade poles, piles, and clear lumber, produced only in limited amounts, continue to be in short supply and rather high in price. Pulpwood, though still abundant, is now being deliberately grown on relatively short rotations for an expanding market. The expansion justifies intensive silviculture on the better lands. Professional foresters are now assisting this development by increasing their research and extension work in the South.

Chapter 2

The Species and Its Environment

How did loblolly pine get its scientific and its peculiar common name; which of its features identify it as a botanical species; and what are the results of basic studies made to facilitate its culture? This chapter attempts to answer such questions.

Because the loblolly pine type over extensive areas is an intermediate stage in plant succession and tends to be replaced by hardwoods, the forester or land manager needs to know about the various factors that affect the maintenance and regeneration of loblolly pine. The lay of the land, available moisture, soil makeup, root response, and the relationships of photosynthesis all play their part in determining the survival of the species. The quality of sites and their ability to grow loblolly pine satisfactorily are measured by site index. An understanding of natural forces that underly the behavior of a crop species during reproduction and the capacity of young trees to survive and develop normally are essential to success in silviculture. Among the fundamental biological contributions to this basic understanding are the more highly specialized research studies reported in this chapter. The review here includes productive work in laboratory and greenhouse as well as in the pine forest.

NAMES FOR LOBLOLLY PINE

Carolus Linnaeus gave loblolly pine its scientific name, *Pinus taeda,* over 200 years ago. *Taeda,* the ancient name for resinous pines, comes from the Latin word meaning *torch,* and in Roman times *taeda* was applied to several of the hard, pitchy pines.

How did *Pinus taeda* acquire the common name *loblolly?* We cannot be sure, for, like many names, its roots lie buried in the obscurity of unrecorded customs, fancies, and slang usage. Seemingly unrelated elements are involved in the derivation of this peculiar word, loblolly. Its application in the New World appears closely linked with certain topographic features of the eastern seaboard, the travel to it, and the first probing by seafaring men and early settlers.

We know that *lob* is from *lobe,* a curved object, bay, or trajectory. One old English meaning for the syllable *lolly,* as in lollypop, is lump candy (especially in Australia) or a lumpy substance. "Lolly" in the 18th century maritime circles referred to the ship's doctor's drench, a lumpy broth or soup. The "loblolly boy" on a ship was the doctor's assistant in charge of drugs dispensed from the sick bay or storage nook (curved object, bay) aboard the vessel ferrying seasick colonists across the ocean. Such colonists, exploring the terra firma of the present central Atlantic seaboard states, remembering, perhaps, the distasteful and lumpy gruel they had tried to stomach on their ships, applied the name *loblolly* to mud holes, moist depressions, swales, swamps, baygalls, and lowland stream borders or "branches." The colonists called one of the flowering broad-leaved trees found in such locations "loblolly bay" (*Gordonia lasianthus*) and one of the needle-leaved trees "loblolly pine" (*Pinus taeda*). Thus, the evidence points to a strong association between lumpy mud in a baygall and the name of this pine.

In the original 13 states other names sometimes used for the species were sap pine, corn-stalk pine, swamp pine, spruce pine, Indian pine, foxtail pine, slash pine, frankincense pine, and torch pine. Locally from Delaware to North Carolina it was called Rosemary pine, longstraw pine, long-shat pine, longchat pine, longshucks pine, or longtag pine. Often its designation changed with associated species. For example, *Pinus taeda* was called longleaf pine if found together with *P. echinata, P. rigida,* or *P. virginiana,* but called shortleaf pine if it occurred with *P. palustris.* In the colonial markets it was most often designated merely southern pine or North Carolina pine, but occasionally it was referred to as Virginia pine or Delaware pine.

In the Gulf states and in Arkansas it was occasionally called meadow pine, black pine, black slash pine, bastard pine, or Arkansas pine, but more often it was named sap pine, yellow pine, or bull pine. Its commonest name, however, as in the Atlantic states, was LOBLOLLY. A term very widely used has been "old-field pine" because it reseeded so many abandoned fields, and that characteristic is one reason for the great importance of the species in present-day southern industry.

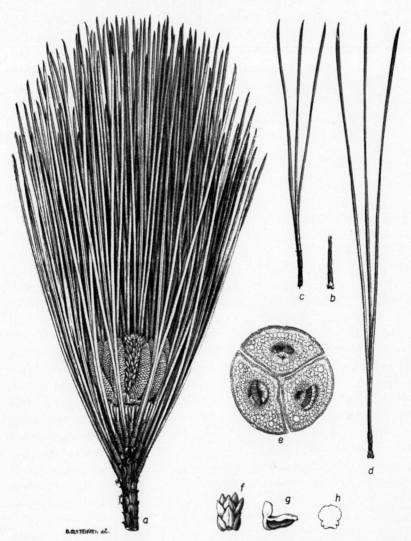

PLATE 1.—Male flowers and leaves of loblolly pine: *a*, Branch with staminate
flowers; *b*, a young fascicle of leaves in the spring; *c*, *d*, mature leaves;
e, cross section at base of leaf bundle magnified to show central fibrovascular
bundles, and resin ducts surrounded by parenchyma (Mohr 1897); *f*, an
involucre—bracts surrounded by a cluster of staminate flowers; *g*, an anther,
the polliniferous part of a stamen, side view enlarged; and *h*, an anther,
front view enlarged (Sargent 1897).

SPECIES CHARACTERISTICS

There is evidence that within the family Pinaceae, in which loblolly pine belongs, the pines (*Pinus*) occupy an intermediate position, whereas, for example, the larch (*Larix*) is low and cypress (*Taxodium*) high in the scale of development (Doak 1935). Within its genus, loblolly pine (*P. taeda*) belongs with the other hard pines in the group *Australes* (Shaw 1914).

Loblolly pine foliage consists of needles 6 to 9 inches long in clusters of 3 (occasionally 2) persistent normally until the second autumn, though some may enter the third growing season (plate 1). There are 10 to 12 rows of large stomata on each face. The distinguishing characters are miscroscopic—resin canals medial, rarely both medial and internal, endosperm triangular, hypoderm not projecting far into the green tissue, and outer walls of the endosperm mostly thin (Doi and Morikawa 1929).

The cones, 6 to 10 inches long, may be recognized in both years of their growth by the spines on their scales. The whole umbo forms a stout triangular spine with slightly concave sides. These spines are, with one exception (*Pinus pungens*), the strongest and most persistent of all pine species in eastern North America (Shaw 1914) (plate 2).

The bark resembles that of the other hard pines in the South. It can usually be distinguished from that of shortleaf pine (*Pinus echinata*) because the surface shows few, if any, of the resin blisters so abundant on most specimens of that species. Beneath the surface of the bark there is a layer (the *periderm*) with a sheet of cells called *phellogen* (or cork cambium) that, together with other evidence, may possibly help in the recognition of loblolly pine. Loblolly pine phellogen, like that of pond pine (*P. serotina*), is an inconspicuous slate gray, whereas the same tissue in several of the other hard pines (*P. palustris, P. echinata, P. elliottii, P. glabra,* and *P. clausa*) is by contrast a conspicuous ivory white (DeVall 1944).

The wood has few characteristics sufficiently distinctive to differentiate it from other southern yellow pines, with the possible exception of longleaf pine (*Pinus palustris*). When a cross section close to stump height is available, longleaf pine wood shows the large pith typical of its seedlings. On any cross section longleaf pine wood usually shows a more distinct line between spring and summer wood than does loblolly pine. Loblolly pine wood rays are less prominent and closer together (Bitting 1909).

An early analysis of loblolly pine turpentine showed it to be

PLATE 2.—Female flowers, cone, and seed of loblolly pine: *a*, Branch with two
subterminal aments of female flowers at the end of seasonal shoot; *b*, immature yearling cone; *c*, mature 2-year cone closed; *d*, mature cone open
after shedding seed; *e*, dorsal side of cone scale with stout reflexed prickle;
f, ventral view of same with seed in place; *g*, seed and wing detached
(Mohr 1897).

dextrorotatary (+ 46°), its density 0.8525, and its index of refraction 1.4700.   Later tests (Mirov, Wang, and Haagen-Smit 1949) showed the oleoresin to consist of 85 percent d — α — pinene and 12 percent l — β — pinene.   Limonene was not found.   On distillation the oleoresin yielded 18 percent turpentine.

SPECIES DISTRIBUTION

Loblolly pine reaches merchantable size throughout its natural range and can be found in commercial concentrations in many areas, according to the latest available survey information on timber volume by counties (fig. 5).   Stands of loblolly pine timber today

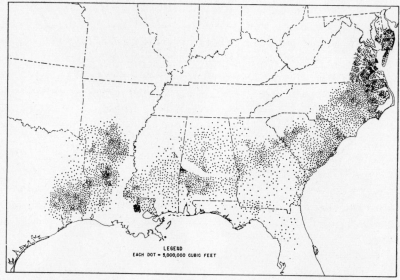

LEGEND
EACH DOT = 5,000,000 CUBIC FEET

FIGURE 5.—Distribution of timber volume within the natural range of the species—each dot representing 5 million cubic feet of loblolly pine timber (Forest Survey data).

are relatively heavy in southern Delaware and Maryland, as well as in eastern Virginia and northeastern North Carolina from the coast westward to about 78° west longitude.   More southerly concentrations are found in various Gulf states, as for example in Winn and Livingston Parishes in Louisiana.

Natural limits

Loblolly pine forests thrive with 6 to 10 frost-free months a year, 40 to 50 inches of fairly well-distributed annual rainfall, and enough humidity for a favorable precipitation-evaporation ratio

(Carmean 1947).   Although 500 feet is its usual altitudinal limit it reaches nearly 700 feet in central North Carolina (Ashe 1915). The species disappears altogether at latitude 39°21′ N., or about 20 miles north of Dover, Del. (Crow 1941), and at about 97° west longitude in eastern Texas.

Prominent among the climatic factors that limit the botanical range of a species are temperature and moisture.   Water that the soil can supply for the growth of trees and the flow of streams depends on the relation between precipitation (P) which adds water and evapotranspiration (E) which removes it.   Hence Thornthwaite (1941) uses the ratio P over E, each term expressed in inches, to estimate the effectiveness of precipitation,[7] and to classify climates. The sum of 12 monthly ratios supplies an annual "P–E index." Average values of this index range within the loblolly pine belt from 64 to 111.   Where the P-E index is low the soluble materials in the soil become concentrated a short distance below the surface and in the root zone.   Where it is high these solutes are rapidly leached out leaving relatively insoluble materials like compounds of iron and aluminum.

Summer rainfall is low in the western part of the range as contrasted with the extremely high summer rainfall in the southeastern part.   Winter temperature is appreciably lower in the northern than in the southern parts of the range.   Relatively mild winters appear to make more soil moisture available (Hocker 1956).   Such differences can easily affect the results from efforts to obtain either natural or artificial reproduction.   Summer temperature shows less geographic variation.

Just as temperatures depend on both latitude and altitude, available moisture depends on both rain and the capacity of soil to retain water.   At its northern natural limit loblolly pine is confined to the flat Coastal Plain, whereas farther south it occupies rolling inland sites as well (Lotti and McCulley 1951).   On the western shore of Chesapeake Bay commercial quantities of loblolly pine were found only in St. Mary's County, Md., and in the southern part of Calvert and Charles Counties on poorly drained soils not over 60 feet above sea level (Cope 1923a).   Individual tree outposts of loblolly pine were found by Gifford Pinchot at Town Bank, Cape

---

[7] Direct measurements of the term E are difficult and not available for any extensive areas. Accordingly Thornthwaite derived values of E indirectly using the formula $\dfrac{P}{E} = 11.5 \left(\dfrac{P}{T-10}\right)^{10\%}$, where T is the mean monthly temperature in degrees F., except that no mean less than 28.4°F. is used. This formula, based on studies at 21 western U. S. stations, has been widely applied.

May County, N. J. (Hollick 1897), and planted stands have produced merchantable box bolts in southern New Jersey (Anonymous
1928). An outpost is reported also on the banks of the Delaware-
Chesapeake Canal at Summit Bridge, New Castle County, Del.
(Taber 1939).

One student of transpiration from trees (Kozlowski 1941) be-
lieves that the reduction in absorption of moisture from cold soil,
which is greater for loblolly than for white pine, may well limit
the ability of loblolly pine to survive in colder regions. The species
crosses the fall line and advances into the Virginia Piedmont at
a point just south of Washington and a few miles west of Alexandria
(Crow 1941). Within the Piedmont and on the eastern edge of that
plateau loblolly pine is confined to a strip 40-50 miles wide in North
Carolina and 20-30 miles wide in Virginia. In the salt marshes
along the coast loblolly pine is able to grow for long periods, but it
does not tolerate salt spray. It occurs on the outerbanks of North
Carolina, reaching substantial development on old dunes near Bux-
ton on Hatteras.

Southward, frequent fires have been most effective in limiting
the original range of loblolly pine. The southernmost outposts of
the species were scattered, well-developed trees along streams within
the coastal belt of longleaf pine. Here fine specimens were occasionally found in naturally protected spots of climax forest called
hammocks where they were associated with such species as laurel
oak, water oak, and beech (Mohr 1901). The hardwood bottom
lands of the lower Mississippi River Valley form a complete break
in the loblolly pine belt.

At the western limits of the range, what appears to be a drought-
hardy strain of loblolly pine is isolated in the so-called "Lost Pine"
areas. These are in Colorado, Fayette, and Bastrop Counties, Texas,
where the annual rainfall is 10 to 20 inches less than it is 200 miles
farther east. Loblolly pine plantations have survived in central
Texas.

Situations occupied

Loblolly pine originally occupied lowlands, bordering or within
swamps, savannas, pocosins, or hammocks on a wide variety of moist
topsoils, but was most abundant on the best quality loams, silts,
clays, and peaty soils seldom flooded but with a water table 5 to 8
feet below the surface (Ashe 1915).

Before the South was settled there would have been little pine
forest had it not been for fire (Chapman 1944a). After settlement

agricultural failures increased pine stands. Within the outer limits
for loblolly pine, as described above, natural controls, including
untimely fire, continued to restrict pine distribution, but land use
had the most pronounced effect in modifying its pattern. A bit of
history can clarify these trends.

The first settlers to leave the coastal strip faced a forest of oak,
hickory, and other hardwoods, with scattered individual specimens
of loblolly pine. The clearings made by colonists, however, were
largely confined to the lower Coastal Plain until the Revolutionary
War period. Thereafter, cotton farming spread inland to the Piedmont Plateau, where the peak of agricultural development was
reached by 1840, with 87 percent of the land in cultivation. According to studies in Georgia about 10 percent of these Piedmont
farm lands reverted to forest during the Civil War; another 30
percent was abandoned to the natural reseeding of pine during the
depression of the late eighteen-eighties (Brender 1952a). Since the
rough estimate of the distribution of timber volumes in 1884 (fig. 6)
loblolly pine has increased southward into the Gulf coastal areas
formerly occupied largely by longleaf and slash pines.

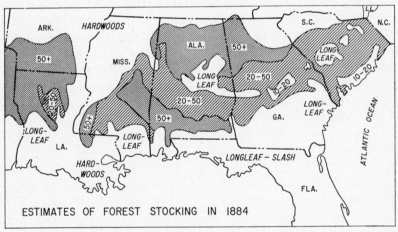

FIGURE 6.—Part of the present loblolly pine belt showing approximate stand
    density of forest cover in cords per acre as estimated by C. S. Sargent
    in 1884.

A large acreage of the new pine forest was cleared again for
growing cotton during World War I, but with the advent of the
boll weevil in 1920 about one-third of the new farm land was abandoned, and now roughly two-thirds of the Georgia Piedmont is once
more in pine forest. When abandoned fields became available to

loblolly pine it promptly invaded many sites to mingle over extensive areas with various other species, and to form numerous pure stands in the lower Piedmont.

The history of land use elsewhere in the Piedmont and coastal areas has similarly affected the forests. For example, Harper (1913) studying trends in some 15 physiographic subdivisions of Alabama, found that the loblolly pine cover types had increased in all but two districts. Some of this advance was into heavily cut-over forest land, but more of it was natural reseeding of abandoned fields. Loblolly became popularly known as "old-field pine." Thus, land use greatly increased the area of loblolly pine forests.

This trend has been temporarily reversed in the loblolly pine belt east of the Mississippi River for three principal reasons: (1) agriculture—at least in the Coastal Plain—is now more stable, (2) better markets for pine still exist and loggers indulge in over-cutting on many small tracts, and (3) organized protection has eliminated the widespread light burning that previously minimized the competition from hardwood brush (Lotti and McCulley 1951).

West of the Mississippi River the early trend toward an increase in pine area and volume continues in Arkansas, Louisiana, Texas, and Oklahoma. The increase in volume is especially noticeable in Oklahoma. Much of the improvement in this general area arises from an increased application of silviculture to extensive tracts of pine land (Sternitzke and Wheeler 1955). Similar increases in loblolly pine timber resources are to be expected now on the Atlantic seaboard as a result of rising interest in industrial forestry there.

The introduction of partial cutting and the curtailment of the traditional practice of frequently burning over the forest floor had various effects along the fringes of the original loblolly pine forest. In parts of southeastern Texas fire protection resulted in the development of a dense understory of yaupon (Hartman 1949). Encroachment of loblolly pine into the Coastal Prairie as reported over 50 years ago (Zon 1905) appears to be continuing. This, however, has not happened to the small treeless prairies within the loblolly pine forest in Arkansas; here the prairies are on the flat, poorly drained divides that lie between divergent drainage lines extending into surrounding forest.

Along the southern fringes of loblolly pine forest in the Gulf states, this species has captured much of the loamy flatwood land formerly held by longleaf pine (Pessin 1933), and where hogs had destroyed much longleaf pine regeneration. This tendency for loblolly pine to take over devastated longleaf pine cutover lands was extensive, but not universal. On sterile sands loblolly pine becomes established with difficulty, if at all, and then produces short, knotty trees (Ashe 1895, Pinchot and Ashe 1897). In countless other locations the reduced use of fire—like the commercial preference for pine products—places loblolly pine at a disadvantage in competition with its deciduous competitors. Currently a large area is being lost to less valuable hardwood forest.

Loblolly pine, however, is capable of growing in a great variety of soils, rich and poor, wet and dry. It may even grow in places subject to inundation by muddy waters (Harper 1928). Ashe (1915) listed its characteristic occurrence in six situations as follows:

1. River swamps, as single trees with hardwoods.
2. Deep or shallow interior swamps, in small groups with hardwoods.
3. Hammocks, sparingly with other pines.
4. Well-drained uplands, in compact groups.
5. Peaty soils, with hardwoods, or in pure stands following fires.
6. Narrow stream swamps in eastern Piedmont and scattered westward.

Associated species

In the old-growth forests in the South, loblolly pine was a minor component on the dry longleaf pine lands and on the wet bottom lands, but a major species on the upper Coastal Plain and other moist inland sites not frequently burned over. Before abandoned fields became available to loblolly pine, other species mingled with it nearly everywhere except on areas devastated by hurricanes. Under protection from fire loblolly pine took over extensive longleaf pine lands where the water table was seldom below 20 feet. The remaining longleaf pine on many of these areas formed less than 1 percent of stand volume in the second growth.

Associated species vary by locality. At the western and northern limits of its range loblolly pine is generally replaced by shortleaf pine, and at the northeastern limit by shortleaf and Virginia pine. In the Georgia Piedmont the original stands with a heavy proportion of pine were more prevalent west of the Atlantic-Gulf divide than east of it (Nelson 1957).

The original forest in Arkansas was about half and half shortleaf and loblolly pines (Betts 1909). In a 1905 study of old-growth forests in Alabama, Reed reported that on well-drained shale and schist soils the pine forest was longleaf with only 2 percent loblolly. But on the lower slopes, where the soil was deeper, and more moist, the loblolly pine increased to 67 percent. Lower still, on land bordering the principal creek and river bottoms, loblolly pine was found only in groups of 3 or 4 trees or singly among the hardwoods. Maximum individual development was best where the chance for natural regeneration of pine was least.

Loblolly pine was largely excluded from wet lowlands by hardwoods and from dry longleaf pine lands by frequent fire. Between these extremes it was able to hold extensive areas of intermediate topography where fires occurred less frequently. On these areas loblolly pine usually dominated the overstory, but seldom dominated the understory. This stand condition was typical of the virgin forest, and remains highly significant silviculturally, as will be shown in the following section. The mixture of species found in the understory included only a few, like shortleaf pine, sweetgum, or white oak, that were able to penetrate the pine overstory. In capacity to develop timber trees of top quality, loblolly pine appears inferior to yellow-poplar on the best sites, and inferior to longleaf pine timber only on the poorest of the deep dry sands. Elsewhere, with an even start it surpasses nearly all competitors.

The associated species vary also with topographic situation. For example, where there is plenty of moisture in South Carolina, sweetgum, blackgum, water oak, red maple, and occasionally yellow-poplar, ash, beech, hickory, and slash pine are the associates (Chapman 1905), whereas on dryer soils longleaf or shortleaf pines may be found along with certain scrubby oaks, such as blackjack, southern red, and post oak. In the North Carolina Piedmont loblolly pine and shortleaf pine together often occupy the best sites and Virginia pine the poorest. Although no complete list exists, the following is a partial list of associated species:

Principal associates of loblolly pine[1]

Scientific name	Common name
Acer rubrum L. (and varieties)	Red maple
Albizzia julibrissin Durazz	Mimosa*
Carpinus caroliniana Walt	American hornbeam*
Carya cordiformis (Wangenh.) K. Koch	**Bitternut hickory**
C. glabra (Mill.) Sweet	**Pignut hickory**
C. pallida (Ashe) Engl. & Graebn.	Sand hickory
C. texana Buckl.	Black hickory
C. tomentosa Nutt.	**Mockernut hickory**
Cercis canadensis L.	Eastern redbud*

Scientific name	Common name
Chamaecyparis thyoides (L.) B.S.P.	Atlantic white-cedar
Cornus florida L.	Flowering dogwood*
Crataegus spp. L.	Hawthorn* (many species)
Diospyros virginiana L.	Persimmon
Fagus grandifolia Ehrh.	American beech
Fraxinus americana L.	White ash
F. caroliniana Mill.	Carolina ash
F. pennsylvanica Marsh.	Green ash
F. profunda (Bush) Bush	Pumpkin ash
Gleditsia triacanthos L.	Honeylocust
Ilex opaca Ait.	American holly*
Juniperus virginiana L.	Eastern redcedar
Liquidambar styraciflua L.	Sweetgum
Liriodendron tulipifera L.	Yellow-poplar
Maclura pomifera (Raf.) Schneid.	Osage-orange
Magnolia grandiflora L.	Southern magnolia
M. virginiana L.	Sweetbay
Morus rubra L.	Red mulberry
Nyssa aquatica L.	Water tupelo
N. sylvatica Marsh.	Blackgum
Ostrya virginiana (Mill.) K. Koch	Eastern hophornbeam*
Oxydendrum arboreum (L.) DC.	Sourwood*
Persea barbonia (L.) Spreng.	Redbay
Pinus echinata Mill.	Shortleaf pine
P. elliottii var. *elliottii* Engelm.	Slash pine
P. glabra Walt.	Spruce pine*
P. palustris Mill.	Longleaf pine
P. rigida Mill.	Pitch pine
P. serotina Michx.	Pond pine
P. virginiana Mill.	Virginia pine
Populus deltoides Bartr.	Eastern cottonwood
P. heterophylla L.	Swamp cottonwood
Prunus serotina Ehrh.	Black cherry
Quercus alba L.	White oak
Q. coccinea Muenchh.	Scarlet oak
Q. falcata Michx.	Southern red oak
Q. falcata var. *pagodaefolia* Ell.	Cherrybark oak
Q. laevis Walt.	Turkey oak
Q. laurifolia Michx.	Laurel oak
Q. marilandica Muenchh.	Blackjack oak*
Q. michauxii Nutt.	Swamp chestnut oak
Q. nigra L.	Water oak
Q. palustris Muenchh.	Pin oak
Q. phellos L.	Willow oak
Q. rubra L.	Northern red oak
Q. shumardii Buckl.	Shumard oak
Q. stellata Wangenh.	Post oak
Q. stellata var. *margaretta* (Ashe) Sarg.	Sand post oak
Q. velutina Lam.	Black oak
Q. virginiana Mill.	Live oak
Robinia pseudoacacia L.	Black locust
Sassafras albidum (Nutt.) Nees.	Sassafras*
Taxodium distichum (L.) Rich.	Baldcypress

Ulmus alata Michx............................Winged elm
U. americana L...............................**American elm**
U. thomasii Sarg............................Rock elm*

[1] Boldface indicates species of commercial importance within the type, and asterisks indicate species that seldom develop to saw-log size. All are native except one. Mimosa is nonindigenous—an introduced species that escaped. (References: Ashe 1915, Cope 1923a, U. S. Forest Service Southern Forest Expt. Sta. 1933.)

The Society of American Foresters (1926) listed four variants of the loblolly pine type: (1) flatwood stands with associated oaks, hickories, gum, etc.; (2) pine-barren stands—formerly cutover longleaf pine areas on coarse sandy-loam sites; (3) old-field stands on well-drained soils of fair quality; and (4) loblolly-shortleaf pine stands, with the species mixed individually or groupwise. In addition, however, the presence of localized groups of certain associated species causes many differences in the loblolly pine type.

SUCCESSIONAL TRENDS

A basic problem in silviculture the world over is the maintenance of a forest cover that will provide the maximum in human benefits consistent with the ecological limitations of the site (Lotti and McCulley 1951). Many of the world's most valuable timber trees neither reproduce well in their own shade, nor compete successfully in mixture with many aggressive associate species of less value.

In the loblolly pine belt the natural replacement of pine with more shade-tolerant and less valuable hardwoods is reducing timber yields in many places. This trend is most serious on sites of medium or low productivity. Good hardwoods can readily be produced on fertile bottom lands; elsewhere the extent to which pine is being replaced by inferior hardwoods is alarming. It is reported that by 1951 in coastal Virginia low-grade hardwoods occupied one-fifth of a 2,000,000-acre pine site, and in South Carolina the hardwood types covered a 59 percent larger area than they did 10 years earlier (Lotti and McCulley 1951).

The period of middle-aged stablization in composition of many pine stands is more apparent than real. Actually a rough "thumbnail" sketch of typical pine-hardwood relations over a long undisturbed period would be two crossing J-shaped stand curves (fig. 7, *A*) (Oosting 1942). Pine stands thinned by cutting, or naturally at maturity, are replaced by hardwoods at accelerating rates. The natural decline in pine density is such that the number of pine stems is in direct proportion to the reciprocal of stand age (fig. 7, *B*) (Coile 1940).

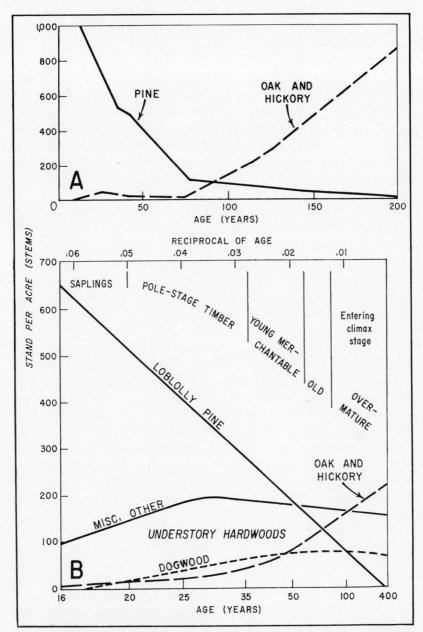

FIGURE 7.—Trends of long-term change in the pine and hardwood components of a forest during natural succession: *A*, An old-field stand reverting to hardwoods (Oosting 1942) and, *B*, the direct linear relation between the decreasing density of loblolly pine and the reciprocal of its age (Coile 1940).

In loblolly pine stands unburned for about 10 years deciduous trees and shrubs are relatively abundant in the understory. They attain more stems per acre as the age of the pine overstory increases. The pine component of the understory, however, decreases as the overstory density increases, or as site quality decreases. Oaks and hickories are accepted as the principal species in the final or "climax" stage of forest succession in the southern pine belt. Their capacity to increase in competition with the other associated understory hardwoods is manifest. Often they become more numerous while the pine seedling stand diminishes with overwood crown closure, though coexistence may be possible for some time on the better sites.

On pine sites of index 60 and 70 the oaks and hickories outnumber the pine seedlings beneath the older timber. On pine sites of index 80 and 90 the amount of pine reproduction exceeds that of the climax hardwoods except in the oldest and densest stands. In this analysis by Barrett and Downs (1943) observations made on areas burned accidentally at least once in 10 years did not disclose any significant differences in regeneration. The use of, or exclusion of, fire must be planned wisely to be helpful. Once burning is stopped the existing underbrush, plus possibly some additional shrubs, develops into thickets on good sites even under a fairly heavy overstory. In this manner much pine reproduction in the past has been deprived of an equal start with that of the hardwoods. Then when a large pine died (or was removed) there often were no recruits to replace it; consequently deciduous understory species then grew into the upper canopy (Oosting 1942). This type of conversion has taken place on a large scale. Three practices have aided the natural succession: (1) fire exclusion, (2) indiscriminate cutting, and (3) pine harvests that leave hardwoods standing (Haig 1950a and 1950b).

This trend should not, and need not, continue; silviculture can reverse it. If the forest, where hardwood understories have developed on good sites in spite of an overwood, is undisturbed for 10 to 20 years, a high percentage of the hardwood stems naturally will be eliminated while the minority grows up. With the forest floor relatively clear again, the pine stand can reproduce itself. A thorough chemical treatment to release the pine seedlings then can practically eradicate the remaining hardwoods.

Although the tendency for unmanaged eastern forests to revert to broad-leaved types cannot be changed, the trend in that direction can and must be widely arrested if pine is to be perpetuated as a commercial crop of timber.

Stages of succession

The fact of forest succession is unavoidable; the trend toward hardwoods is unmistakable. Less is known of the exact number and duration of its stages. Yet, any forester who tries to arrest the process in favor of pine needs some knowledge of the tenure of less desirable species that seize the pine land. What happens locally varies on fields abandoned in different regions. In the Piedmont region, the succession of dominants on abandoned lands where cultivation has given reseeding a fresh start by destroying native root systems can be outlined as follows:

Forest succession typical of old fields on the Piedmont Plateau in North Carolina[1]

Invasion stage	Dominant vegetation
Autumn following last cultivation	Crabgrass
During first year	Horseweed[2]
During second year	Aster[2]
Within 3 to 5 years	Broomsedge
Within 10 years	Pine[3]
Anytime after 20 or 30 years	Hardwoods

[1] Adapted from several sources, mainly Wells 1928, Coile 1940, Oosting 1942, and Keever 1950.
[2] Ragweed may dominate these stages.
[3] Usually in the first half decade.

The succession does not represent, as might be inferred, a relay of distinctly separate stages. The reason for the sequence of dominants hinges on relative timing of events significant in the life cycle of each species. In the example, the crabgrass started prior to complete abandonment. The horseweed became dominant because its seeds were ready to germinate when much of the land was cultivated for the last time. Aster dominance was delayed because the seeds did not germinate until the spring following maturity. The dominance of broomsedge was delayed because of inadequate seed supply for a full stand until the first invaders had produced seeds (Keever 1950). Where seeds of both are available, loblolly pine usually precedes sweetgum in occupying old fields because of the superior drought resistance of its seedlings during germination and throughout the first year (Bormann 1953). Obviously, these relations vary with the differences in climate and local flora within the loblolly pine belt.

The chain of events on cut-over forest lands normally short-cuts the timetable of natural succession for abandoned fields because of

residual hardwood trees, sprouting stumps with firmly established
root systems, or both. Owing to its origin from sprouts, rather than
from disseminated seeds, the composition of the first resurgent hardwood stand following a cutting often corresponds closely to that of
the original hardwood component in the pine stand. This is
confirmed by recent excavation studies of the initial regeneration
of broad-leaved species on cut-over pine lands in Arkansas. It
showed nearly all individual hardwood stems to be old residents
rather than sudden invaders (Reynolds 1956).

The final stage of succession is rarely reached in a single step.
Some shrubs (e.g., *Crataegus*) and some vines (e.g., *Smilax* and
Rhus) may come in early in the life of a stand and persist through
all succeeding stages (Oosting 1942), but not all the first invaders
are apt to be of species capable of holding the land permanently
(Boyce, S.G., 1951). Only the true climax forest can re-establish itself naturally when and where its mature trees still dominate the
site. Unfortunately, however, the earlier stages in hardwood succession may be just as undesirable commercially as the final stage.

In both pure and mixed stands loblolly pine now occupies such
a wide variety of sites that it is of little use to plant scientists in
classifying natural forest associations of the region. Clearly, however, its place in succession of cover types is an intermediate one,
often designated as "fire subclimax" (Haig 1938) in both the Piedmont and the Coastal Plain. Wells (1928) says it naturally occupies
a vanishing role.

With increased and reasonably satisfactory control of wildfire
and use of prescribed fire, however, the pine type of forest now
can be extensively perpetuated by natural means. Under intensive
management the same end is achieved by using the more artificial
measures of hardwood control, seedbed preparation, or planting of
pine.

Soils influence

Natural succession is slower on dry coarse soil than on moist
fine soil (Oosting 1942). Fewer oak and hickory seedlings are found
in the Piedmont on sandy loam soil types than on silt loam and
clay loam types (Diftler 1947). Pines grow faster on a porous loam
or sandy loam surface soil than on a compact clay soil or on a coarse
siliceous one (Ashe 1915). In the Coastal Plain sweetgum and red
maple are more abundant where the drainage is imperfect or poor
than on either water-logged or well-drained soils (Coile 1950a).
Shrubs also increase under these conditions, and especially where

the clay content of the subsoil is greater. On ungrazed lands following fire these species and shrubs increase with time, while under
grazing they decrease.

Coile (1940) did not find any significant changes in soil characteristics accompanying succession on loblolly pine land. Carbon-
nitrogen ratios usually increase during succession, except in stands
with well-developed understories, but total nitrogen content of the
surface 5 inches of soil does not change greatly. Nitrogen is highest
in those old-field stands with a hardwood understory of species
whose litter is high in calcium. Physical characteristics of soil such
as bulk density, water-holding capacity, and air space likewise change
very slowly and do not appear to be influenced by succession.

Existing differences in soil clearly may modify the rate of plant
succession, but the soil itself does not change measurably from one
vegetal stage to the next. The rate of change in the vegetation may
also be influenced, first by the character of a given cover type and
then by what happens to it. The current events most often significant in forest succession are its acceleration by indiscriminate
cutting and its retardation by fire.

Arresting succession

Where pine is the objective, retarding succession in the Coastal
Plain is helpful—arresting it is better, but in the Piedmont some
hardwoods are probably necessary for the maintenance of soil
fertility. Recognition of this need has developed slowly and experiments to resolve the problem are still underway.

Burning in the loblolly type where pine saplings were over 6 feet
tall was suggested early (Record 1907) merely to lessen the danger
of subsequent conflagrations, but even 30 years later little was
known of its use for other purposes. Oosting (1944) contrasted the
temporary benefits from surface fire with the serious setback (type
conversion) after a crown fire, and Chapman (1943) reported that,
with the exception of the pure stands of pine on old fields or hurricane areas, loblolly pine was preponderant where fire burned on
the average about once in 10 years. He stated unequivocally that
". . . if there is one thing that menaces the future success of pine
in the South it is reversion to hardwoods in the absence of fire."

During the early years after complete protection was started the
improvements observed in the pine forest were traceable to changes
wrought by previous fires. Thereafter seedbeds deteriorated and
understory competition increased. Where hardwood sprouts had
2 to 3 years' start over pine seedlings, the pines were suppressed

everywhere except in openings that happened to be clear of expanding hardwood crowns. But where fire-killed brush must start sprouting at the same time that pine seedlings start to grow, the pines emerge successfully in many situations.

Controlled burning is a latter-day development in managing the loblolly pine type of forest. Modern silviculture using chemicals or machines as well as fire will succeed to the degree that it effectively retards the natural succession toward hardwoods. These matters will be discussed further in the chapter on natural regeneration.

PHYSIOGRAPHY AND MOISTURE

In ancient time the Atlantic and Gulf Coastal Plains were under the sea. In South Carolina, for example, the coastline was inland about 60 miles, reaching the northwest boundaries of the Brandywine terrace and formation. The old shoreline, now about 270 feet above sea level, extends westward at one point to Columbia (Cooke 1936). The southeastern Coastal Plain, 120 to 150 miles wide in the Carolinas, has a sandy mantle that originated as the ocean receded, leaving at least six recognized terraces: the La Fayette, Coharie, Sunderland, Wicomico, Chowan (Talbot), and Pamlico (Wells 1942).

In the upper part of the northeastern Coastal Plain many of the best pine sites are in the valleys of small streams. Poorly drained moisture-holding clays and clay loams seem to bring maximum growth (Cope 1923a), but regeneration may be more difficult on fine-textured than on coarse soils (Diftler 1947). Westward loblolly pine occupies extensive uplands—much of the Piedmont Plateau, the Ridge and Valley Province in Alabama, Tennessee, and northwest Georgia, and sections of the Cumberland plateau in Tennessee.

In studies of physiography and pine growth in Arkansas, Turner (1937b) found that soil features affecting available water were most influential in determining the rate of growth. These features were degree of slope with its effect on drainage, exposure as it affects evaporation loss, and the character of the soil horizons—their depth, position, and physical structure. The steeper the slope above 3 percent the slower the growth of pine. In Arkansas loblolly pine is seldom found on slopes greater than 7 percent (Turner 1938). In this study three qualities of loblolly pine lands were recognized as follows:

Quality	Site index (feet)
I. Superior	96-115
II. Intermediate	76- 95
III. Inferior	56- 75

Quality I, found in the flood plains of small streams, consisted of fine sandy or silt loams without marked profile development and with plenty of moisture and good drainage. Quality II sites showed distinct profile development, shallower surface soil, and, in some series, imperfect drainage. Quality III showed thin surface soil because of erosion losses, clay or gravel subsoils, and sandy profiles having excessive internal drainage. A change in the type of soil frequently, but not always, is reflected in rates of timber growth.

Within the range of loblolly pine the Piedmont Plateau is more varied in type of forest, quality of soil, and rates of timber growth than any other province. The physiographic aspect of forest sites in the southern part is associated with the rate of succession toward hardwoods and the difficulty of perpetuating the loblolly pine without planting. The relationship is discernible in the effects of slope and exposure on the prevalence of broad-leaved underbrush. The hardwood associates are most abundant in bottom lands and on steep slopes. For example, on the upper part of slopes with a northeastern exposure the underwood composition in natural second-growth stands is typically as follows:

Gradient	Hardwood (percent)	Pine (percent)	Mixed (percent)
Gentle.............	8	71	21
Moderate..........	20	45	35
Steep..............	63	13	24

It has been observed on the Hitchiti Experimental Forest in central Georgia that loblolly pine can usually be perpetuated without hardwood control on all gentle upper slopes and on moderate upper slopes with a southwestern exposure. Measures to control hardwoods are needed on steep upper slopes with a southwestern exposure, moderate upper slopes with a northeastern exposure, and on all moderate lower slopes. Because of hardwood competition loblolly pine is difficult to perpetuate naturally on steep upper slopes with a northeastern exposure and on bottom lands.

Moisture and soils

Many loblolly pines, as they become larger and need more room, die from lack of adequate growing space. But whether the principal direct cause of death is a deficiency in light or of moisture has long been a controversial question. Usually both are involved in a manner that makes it difficult to distinguish between them. In tests reported by Mann (1950c, 1952f) competition for moisture first seemed to be the more intense, but later some evidence indicated that a deficiency in light was the more critical. The physiological balance of pine is easily disturbed by decreased light when soil moisture is adequate, or by drought when light is adequate (Kozlowski 1947). Under natural conditions the effects are interdependent (Ferrell 1953). Although other factors are often involved, it is clear that competition for both light and moisture exerts a major influence on thrift. Moisture is probably the more important for survival and light for the growth of pine seedlings. Death of the "intolerant" pine permits the more shade-tolerant and commonly slower growing hardwoods ultimately to dominate the stand and become the climax in the natural succession (Korstian and Bilan 1957).

Temperature-moisture relations, often important in drought, have been observed in connection with loblolly pine growth in southwestern Louisiana (Coile 1936). Annual growth of the timber in a given year was influenced most by fluctuations of rainfall during January to May of the same year. Increases in rainfall above the mean usually resulted in an increase in growth under any condition of temperature; high temperatures were associated with low growth and low temperatures with more than average growth (fig. 8), possibly an effect of loss of soil moisture through evaporation.[8]

A general concept of the relationship of soil moisture and the site quality of pine land may be based first on observation of soil drainage. Within certain limits, poor drainage, either on the surface or within the soil, may be associated with good quality pine sites in the eastern Coastal Plain. However, poor internal drainage in Piedmont soils usually is associated with lower quality sites.

A more precise concept of soil and site in the eastern part of the loblolly pine range[9] requires measurement or estimates of (1) the depth of the surface soil as an indication of the space available to roots, and (2) the capacity of the subsoil to imbibe water.

[8] Nelson (1959) suggests that moisture lost to the atmosphere from forest soils may be estimated on the basis of its relation to average air temperatures as follows:

Daily mean temperature (degrees F.)	Evaporation loss (inches)	Daily mean temperature (degrees F.)	Evaporation loss (inches)
50	0.02	70	0.14
55	.05	75	.19
60	.07	80	.25
65	.10	85	.32

[9] This concept does not apply to the upper Coastal Plain west of the Mississippi River, and probably does not hold for north Mississippi. Such areas are more like the Piedmont.

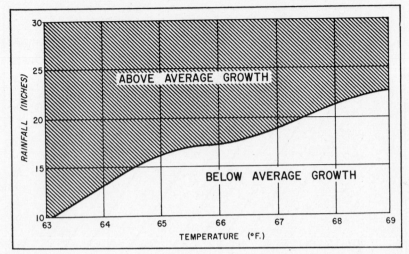

FIGURE 8.—Combinations of temperature and rainfall associated with above average and below average radial growth of loblolly pine at DeRidder, La. (Coile 1936).

The imbibed water, or imbibitional water value (IWV)[10] usually increases with increased "fines" (i.e., silt and clay particles). IWV reflects plasticity in soil, but is used largely as a measure of internal drainage and aeration. The subsoils of the Piedmont are usually finer textured than those of the eastern Coastal Plain, and as high site quality is usually associated with medium-textured subsoils, it seems reasonable that the site quality of these Coastal Plain soils should increase with a rise in imbibitional water values, at least up to a point, whereas site quality of Piedmont soil should generally decrease with rising values of imbibitional water (fig. 9). However, part of the reason that the site quality of eastern Coastal Plain soils increases with an increase in IWV is that on gently sloping land the more dense subsoil helps to maintain a constant water supply in a "perched" position, whereas in the hilly Piedmont the water drains away more rapidly along the top of the subsoil and does not remain in its perched position so long. In the rolling uplands of the western part of the loblolly pine range, the soil moisture relations resemble those of the Piedmont Plateau more closely than those of southeastern Coastal Plain. The use of IWV in

[10] IWV—the capacity of a soil to imbibe water—is associated with colloidal content. It is a useful indication of the physical properties of B horizons favorable to pine trees on the Piedmont Plateau (Coile 1942). In laboratory determinations it is the difference between the moisture equivalent and the xylene equivalent.

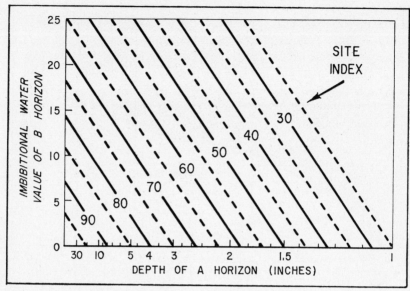

FIGURE 9.—Site index of loblolly pine in the lower Piedmont region as influenced by two significant soil variables: IWV of subsoil and thickness of surface soil (Coile 1948).

quantitative estimates of site quality is discussed in the final section of this chapter.

Transpiration

The evaporation of moisture from foliage or other living plant tissue into the air is called transpiration. The formation of 100 grams of cellulose requires 55 grams of water, but while a tree increases its weight by 100 grams, it loses in transpiration perhaps 50,000 grams of water. Loblolly pine trees use about 750,000 gallons of water to grow a cord, or about 2,000 tons of water to grow a ton of dry wood. In a normal growing season in the mid-South, transpiration and evaporation from pine forests return about 30 acre-inches of water to the atmosphere (Zahner 1956).

Differences in per-acre transpiration between evergreen and deciduous trees are small in loblolly pine forest (Zahner 1955a). Moisture loss per unit of leaf surface is higher for hardwoods than for loblolly pine, but the loss per unit of crown volume may be no higher for hardwoods. It is fortunate for pine seedlings that, when the harvest of larger trees floods the forest floor with light, the cutting also temporarily reduces the transpiration drain on soil moisture supplies. Release cuttings may be necessary subsequently to check the tendency for transpiration to rise once more with the regrowth of sprouting hardwoods and again make heavy demands on soil moisture.

The rate of transpiration increases with soil moisture, the saturation deficit of the air, and also with light intensity, provided there is an abundant supply of moisture (Raber 1937) and roots remain uninjured by flooding.

The transpiration of pine seedlings as affected by their own development, time of year, and condition of air and soil can be listed as follows:

Transpiration rate tends to be—

Greater for—	Than for—
Light-grown[1]	Shade-grown
Second-year[2]	Third-year
High temperature[3]	Low temperature (fig. 10, *A*)
Good root development[2]	Poor root development (fig. 10, *B*)
Moist soil	Dry soil (fig. 10, *C*)
Well-aerated soil	Poorly aerated soil
Warm soil	Cold soil
October-November[2]	December-January
Low humidity	High humidity
Good light[4]	Poor light (fig. 10, *A* and *C*)
Sun leaves	Shade leaves
Windy weather	Calm weather

[1] If atmospheric conditions are favorable.
[2] If it is computed per unit of area of foliage.
[3] Through its effect on humidity.
[4] Provided the moisture supply is abundant.
Basis: Raber 1937, Kramer 1942, Kozlowski 1943 and 1947, and Parker 1949 and 1950a.

Air and soil temperatures are important factors influencing the rate of transpiration. In one test with loblolly pine seedlings, autumn (October-November) transpiration rate averaged more than twice the winter (December-January) average maximum rate (Kozlowski 1941 and 1943). As soil gradually cools transpiration decreases as follows (Kramer 1942):

Soil temperature (degrees C.)	Transpiration (percent of rate at 25° C.)
25	100
20	80
15	60
10	40
5	30
0	12

Below 5°C. (41°F.) the transpiration rate drops rapidly. Plants native to warm climates and normally growing in warm soils reduce their intake of water when the soil is chilled more than do the plants

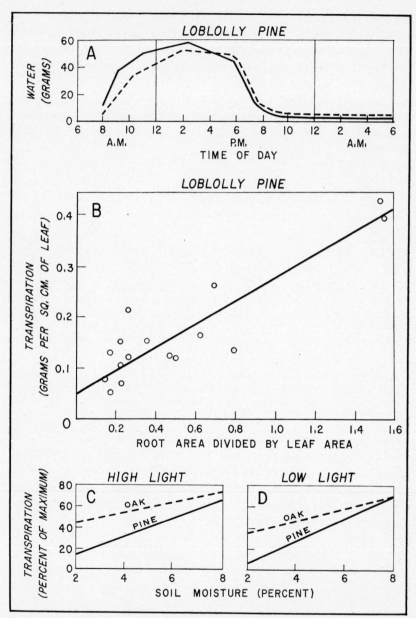

FIGURE 10.—The rate at which moisture moves through loblolly pine seedlings varies with time of day, root-top ratios, and soil moisture: *A*, Diurnal variation on a hot summer day showing absorption (dotted line) lagging behind transpiration (solid line) (Kramer 1936); *B*, increase in transpiration with root-foliage surface ratios (Parker 1949); *C* and *D*, increase with moisture in the soil for oak and pine at two intensities of light (Kozlowski 1947).

that normally grow in cool soil. The lag in absorption behind transpiration for loblolly pine (fig. 10, A) is similar to that of other species. Pines transpire more per unit of leaf area when they are well rooted (fig. 10, B), but approach the maximum only when soil moisture is high (fig. 10, C).[11]

The transpiration rate of a forest may be estimated from measurements of the rate of soil moisture depletion. Zahner (1955a) estimated water loss during hot weather to be about 0.25 inch per day. He calculated further that a single loblolly pine tree 10 inches in d.b.h., whose crown occupies 300 square feet of forest area, will transpire about 50 gallons of water in one 24-hour period on a hot summer day when the ground is moist.

In view of the practical difficulty in estimating transpiration accurately in forests, an understanding of the conditions that tend to raise or lower it, as listed above for pine seedlings, is more useful than any quantitative estimate of moisture loss.

Flooding and drainage

For pine trees a uniformly moist or damp soil is preferable to either a dry or wet one or to one subject to great extremes of moisture or drought (Ashe 1915). Unlike cypress, the roots of loblolly pine are relatively susceptible to injury by flooding.

Where loblolly pine seedlings were observed standing in saturated soil for 10 months the tops were not visibly affected but the roots were severely injured. A 12-week study to observe the effects of various degrees and methods of flooding on loblolly pine tested (1) continuous flooding with standing water, (2) with flowing water, (3) 2 weeks flood alternating with 2 weeks in soil with moisture at field capacity, and (4) drainage control with moisture at field capacity (Hunt 1951). The seedlings proved surprisingly resistant to

---

[11] Studies of pine transpiration, all based on small seedlings, fail to reveal the water loss from larger trees. To approximate this it is necessary to estimate amount of foliage. Branch by branch foliage estimates may be made somewhat laboriously using this formula (Young 1948) for loblolly pine:

Needle volume in cubic centimeters for a branch equals
$-70.9 + 255.3$ diameter (inches) $+ 5.3$ diameter times length (inches)
$- 7.4$ position $+ 1.1$ site index (feet)

where position is determined by counting branches or whorls back from the tip (considered position 1). Actually, however, transpiration is probably more closely correlated with the surface than with the volume of leaves. The surface area of loblolly pine needles is related to their volume as follows (Kozlowski and Schumacher 1943):

$$S = 6.078 + 70.880 \ (V - 0.0621) \quad \text{where}$$
$S =$ transpiring surface in square centimeters,
$V =$ volume of needles in cubic centimeters.

injury by flooding. A continuous flood with stagnant water for 12 weeks produced seedlings with a lower oven dry weight, but it reduced growth only slightly. Alternate drying and flooding with running water for 7 months reduced growth and injured the roots but not the tops.

The development of loblolly pine trees in the Coastal Plain is also influenced by the degree of surface drainage and the depth of relatively impermeable layers of soil. Growth is best where drainage is "poor," the permeable soil layers deep (fig. 11), and fluctuations of ground water moderate.

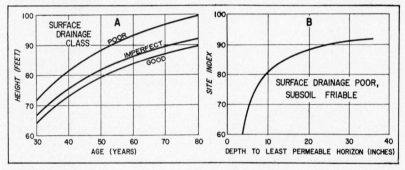

FIGURE 11.—Moisture relations on Coastal Plain soils: *A*, Effect of drainage on height attained by loblolly pine at various ages; *B*, effect of soil depth on site index for one class of soil (Gaiser 1950).

Site quality for pine may be reduced, however, by unfavorable average levels of ground water. Drainage can be so poor that the water table often lingers close to the surface too long for the development of a healthy root system. Under moderate drainage ample layers of soil with moisture above the wilting point are available to the pines. Where drainage is "good" the water table is frequently too deep to supply any of the moisture needed by tree roots—a difficulty most apparent where the deep soil is all coarse sand and where droughts occur. Hence on the best pine sites the ground-water depth is intermediate between these extremes with an average of 5 to 10 feet (Ashe 1915).

Many pine stands in the Coastal Plain remove enough water from the soil through transpiration to keep the ground water down to a safe level. The water table is much lower and less fluctuating under selection cutting of pine than under clear cutting. This was shown by observation in the autumn of 1953 of a series of ground-water wells 8 feet deep in a forest on rather impermeable Bladen soil in Hertford County, N. C. (Trousdell and Hoover 1955) (fig.

12). Here during one 2-week period, a rainfall of 3.21 inches raised the water table in the clear-cut area 3 feet and in the selection cutting less than 1 foot. Forest transpiration appears to have a natural stabilizing effect on ground-water levels.

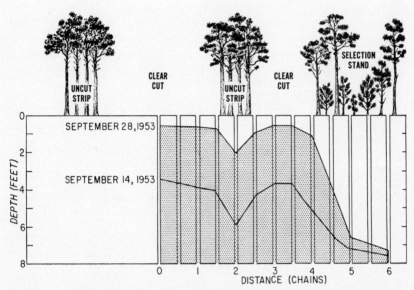

FIGURE 12.—Effect of the forest itself on the measured depth of ground water in impermeable Bladen soil, Hertford County, N. C., on two dates in the autumn of 1953 (Trousdell and Hoover 1955).

Artificial control of the water table, as in rice culture, is seldom used in forestry, but is being applied with striking effect in the culture of loblolly pine at one point in South America. A private company is planting this species for pulpwood in deep silt on Parana delta land in Argentina. There the water table normally fluctuates up to or above the surface as the river level rises with each flow of the tide, but is artificially controlled by flood gates in drainage ditches. The favorable effect of this control is reflected in outstanding growth of pine—the dominant trees exceeding 7 inches in d.b.h. and reaching 40 feet in height in 8 years. The yield from trees spaced 6 by 6 feet was over 4,000 cubic feet per acre at 10 years.[12] Such growth surpasses the best to be expected of pine from upland sites.

The reclamation of certain swamp lands in the United States likewise presents opportunity to grow pine rapidly. Maki (1955)

[12] Personal communication to the author from Lamberto Golfari, Las Carabelas S.A. Commercial E Industrial de Tierras Y Bosques, May 31, 1955.

has reported the need for drainage of extensive wet lands in eastern North Carolina. These are half-bog "pocosin-margin" lands with deep organic loam soils. They now support pond pine, but are suitable for loblolly pine if drained. The potential site index for loblolly pine is high. Where a canal lowered the water table back 1,000 feet and improved the physical properties of the soil the growth of pine was increased in a border strip at least 600 feet wide. The growth study plots there, supplying the data for table 4, are in a plantation still too young to have approached the culmination point in mean annual growth.

TABLE 4.—*Effect of distance from a drainage canal on depth of ground water and on the growth and yield of loblolly pine planted on organic soil (Maki 1955)*

Distance from canal (feet)	Depth of water table[1]	Loblolly pine at 17 years			
		Average d.b.h.	Average height	Yield per acre	Mean annual increment per acre
	Inches	Inches	Feet	Cu. ft.	Cu. ft.
200..............	20.1	5.9	38	2,600	153
300..............	17.5	5.4	33	2,000	118
400..............	15.5	5.1	32	1,550	91
500..............	13.8	4.8	29	1,200	71
600..............	....	4.7	28	1,000	59
Not drained.......	....	3.0	17	199	12

[1] Average depth as sampled in 3 compartments in the 9th year in the Hofmann Forest, Onslow County, N. C. (Pruitt 1947).

Although the outstanding effects of drainage were confined to a strip within 300 feet of the canal, the response was obtained without the benefit of lateral ditches. It would appear that wherever subsoils are sufficiently permeable and the lay of the land favorable, a drainage system is warranted in terms of expected increases in wood production.

NUTRITION AND SOILS

Trees, like other plants, make use of a dozen or more chemical elements (principally C, O, H, N, P, K, but also Ca, Mg, S, and Fe). Other so-called trace elements are needed by loblolly pine only in the minute quantities found in nearly all soils. Sixty percent of the wood is cellulose $(C_6H_{10}O_5)x$. Carbon, oxygen, and hydrogen, readily available from air or water, form the bulk of the tree, but phosphorus, potassium, and especially nitrogen, obtainable from soil, may be deficient. Phosphorus is needed especially for growing points and seeds; potassium for synthesis of sugar and for cell division;

and nitrogen for the formation of protoplasm. Of the minor elements magnesium is important because it is an essential element in the formation of chlorophyl. Dark green healthy foliage is one response of loblolly pine when the absorption of nitrogen is adequate. From 25 to 100 parts per million is sufficient in a nutrient solution (Fowells and Krause 1959). Any surplus that may be deposited in the needles in the current year may be translocated to foliage formed the following year. Height growth may not be affected, but the stimulation of diameter growth in saplings may last 2 years from a single application of nitrate fertilizer. As shown by analysis of the ash, minerals from the soil are less than 1 percent of the whole tree.

Nutrients for pine

Nutrition for pine has not been extensively studied, but a few results using loblolly pine are on record. These scattered tests are reported here to aid in understanding instances of malnutrition or judging the need for, or feasibility of, fertilization. Mycorrhizae may supply vitamins, auxins, and amino compounds as well as carbohydrates to the roots.[13]

Total reserve food per plant is greater in sun-grown than in shade-grown pine. In forests specific differences in nutrition affect the competitive relations of trees. Deciduous species have their maximum food reserves accumulated by early autumn, whereas southern pines have a minimum in reserve at that time—accumulating carbohydrates later in winter while hardwoods are devoid of leaves (Hepting 1945a, Kozlowski 1947). A close relation appears to exist between slash and loblolly pines in their uptake of such elements as aluminum and phosphorus, though the nutritional requirements appear to be different.

Both pine and oak litter have an acid reaction, though it may be less evident where the climate is dry. In a study made in the Bastrop region of Texas—a "pine island" of about 40 square miles—the soil was sampled in 17 places where loblolly pines were dominant. The observed pH values ranged from 4.6 to 7.3, and were typically

---

[13] A laboratory experiment in Queensland (Young 1947) showed that loblolly pine can exist and even grow in an atmosphere free of carbon dioxide if the source of nutrients is under control. Mycorrhizal fungi were able to produce soluble carbohydrate from cellulose in sufficient quantities to support the growth of seedlings in sand culture in the absence of photosynthesis. Also maltose in the absence of mycorrhizae can, as a soil nutrient, substitute for photosynthetic activity to some extent.

6.7 (Berkman 1928). These high values are associated with low rainfall.

Loblolly pine soils normally have a medium acid reaction near the surface and tend to be less acid with increasing depth (Wherry 1922). An example of the pH of the forest floor and mineral soil beneath is found in the following acid reaction of a soil profile under a loblolly pine stand on the Duke Forest in the Piedmont (Coile 1933 and 1937a):

Soil layer	Average reaction		Range of reaction, pH	Basis: No. of samples
	pH	Active acidity		
Litter..............	4.2	630	3.8-4.8	18
Fermentation.......	4.2	630	3.8-5.1	18
Humus.............	4.7	200	4.2-5.9	17
0-2 inches.........	6.0	10	5.4-6.5	17
6-8 inches.........	5.8	16	5.7-6.5	18
16-18 inches.......	6.1	8	5.9-7.0	17

Calcium helps make other components of fertility more readily available from the soil, and the indications of its deficiency have been observed in loblolly pine. Two sets of seedlings were grown one year at 2 to 5 p.p.m. versus 200 p.p.m. of calcium (Davis 1949). The symptoms of calcium deficiency in pine were six: (1) terminal buds were smaller and had dead scales, (2) stem tips were smaller and pointed, (3) leaf cells were fewer and smaller, (4) areas of xylem and phloem were smaller, (5) epidermal and hypodermal cell walls were thicker, (6) root tips were blunt and cell division was retarded.

It was observed in Australia that a light top dressing of copper sulfate stimulated loblolly pine and reduced the incidence of the fused needle disease (Young 1940). Zinc is a trace element essential in small, or poisonous in large amounts. As a group, the pines are relatively resistant to zinc poisoning, and loblolly pine requires zinc at approximately 0.1 p.p.m. for continued normal growth. It usually gets this, but it can tolerate a low concentration of nutrient zinc somewhat better than can shortleaf pine (Wilson 1953). In parts of southern Australia the application of zinc to needles in the form of a 2½ percent solution of zinc sulphate has become a standard step in plantation practice (Moulds 1957) to avoid a number of growth disorders.

The principal elements (N, P, and K) cannot be economically supplied in a complete fertilizer as in agriculture, and may be deficient in the forest though the amount needed is relatively small. Australian experience with loblolly pine indicates the limiting minimum amount of phosphorus pentoxide content in surface soil to be 135 p.p.m. The fertilizer practice is to add enough P_2O_5 to the top 4 inches to bring its content up to 150 p.p.m. In the United States comparable studies of deficiencies in specific elements have not been made. Harper (1917) suggests, however, that at least in the Virginia part of the loblolly pine belt, where the metamorphic rocks are high in potassium content, such deficiencies are unlikely to develop. Parts of South Carolina are probably above the average in calcium, phosphorus, and iron on account of the occurrence of these elements in underlying soil parent materials.

Our knowledge, now scanty, of the absorption and utilization of nutrients by trees may soon be increased through the modern technique of using radioactive isotopes as tracers. Already some studies with loblolly pine have indicated that the mycorrhizal parts of its roots can accumulate much larger quantities of phosphorus than the nonmycorrhizal parts (Kramer and Wilbur 1949). When an 11-year-old loblolly pine plantation near Franklin, Va., was studied with P 32 as a tracer, the rate of translocation in stem and roots together was 1.20 meters per hour and the rate in roots was 1.42 meters per hour (Moreland 1950a and 1950b). Many more such studies and fundamental experiments with fertilizers are needed before any nutrition problems can be resolved in actual practice.

Current studies with fertilizers on upland Coastal Plain soils of moderate fertility in south Arkansas indicate that the height growth on 5- to 8-year-old loblolly pines is unresponsive to any fertilizer, and that diameter growth responds to nitrogen only (Zahner 1957a). A single application of 100 pounds of nitrogen per acre brought an increase of 10 percent in five-year diameter growth. Foliar analysis showed that the trees absorbed and stored nitrogen in proportion to the amount applied. During the second season this extra nitrogen was translocated from the old to the new foliage.

The availability of nitrogen to pines is affected both by soil acidity and by the form of nitrogen. Loblolly pine can utilize ammoniacal nitrogen more readily from a neutral soil and nitrate nitrogen more successfully from an acid soil (Addoms 1937). Where it is desired to increase the content of nitrogen and calcium in the surface soil, it can be done by favoring an understory of hardwoods. A study at the Calhoun Experimental Forest near Union, S. C., showed the following turnover in quantities per acre of elements returned to the soil in falling litter:

	11-year-old loblolly pine (pounds)	Average of three hardwood stands (pounds)
Nitrogen	15	26
Calcium	21	88
Leaf fall	4,476	3,818
All litter (leaves, twigs, bark, and fruit)	5,619	4,502

Thus for hardwoods the nitrogen returned to the soil is nearly double and the calcium four times that for loblolly (Metz 1952b).

Soils under pure and mixed stands

Early evidence seemed to indicate that, in European forests where species were planted in pure stands outside their natural ranges, a slow decline in timber yields might be attributed to monoculture. However, there seems to be little basis for believing that purity in stands of native species inevitably, or even generally in the Coastal Plain, leads to soil deterioration and lowered production, although it may possibly do so on the Piedmont Plateau.

In recognizing soil characteristics that have most effect on forest growth, it is well to distinguish between those which are not readily changed and those which can be improved. The inherent and relatively static characteristics of soils are those resulting from the parent material, its topographic position, and the amount of erosion that has taken place. The changeable characteristics concern the nature of organic debris and the environment under which it decomposes—for this influences the nature of decomposition products, humus types, and soil fertility (Coile 1937b).

Most conifers have less beneficial influence on the soil than the hardwoods (Chandler 1939). Leaf fall from many species of deciduous trees is helpful. The chemical nature of litter from certain ones, particularly the high calcium ones, is such that decomposition is rapid and relatively complete; included in this group are dogwood, ash, yellow-poplar, redbud, sweetgum, and hickory. The litter from other trees decomposes slowly and incompletely; these species include white oak, post oak, red oak, black oak, blackjack oak, shortleaf pine, and loblolly pine (Coile 1940). The soil building superiority of the first group is indicated by relative dry weight of constituents of the mature undecomposed litter of dogwood as compared with that of pine.

	Loblolly pine (percent)	Flowering dogwood (percent)
Nitrogen	0.891	0.999
Carbon	53.0	48.3
Ash	3.0	7.7
Calcium	0.4	3.3

Extensive research on soils in connection with the littleleaf disease of pines has shown that where calcium is high in surface soils, the calcium-potassium ratio is favorable, the soil favors utilization of nitrogen in the form of ammonia, the nitrification process remains normal, and the physical structure is favorable. Furthermore in such soils the rate of incorporation of organic matter in the mineral soil is relatively rapid because of the favorable build-up among bacteria, actinomycetes, and soil fauna generally. This all leads to comparatively high availability of nutrients where the high calcium hardwoods are retained as a component of the loblolly pine forest.

Organic matter

The oven-dry weight of litter under loblolly pine—either pure or mixed with shortleaf—may vary from 20,000 to 30,000 pounds per acre (Korstian 1939). Metz (1952a, 1954), studying the quality of Piedmont soils in the Calhoun Experimental Forest near Union, S. C., found the annual litter fall per acre from two loblolly pine stands of 103 square feet of basal area each to be as follows:

Origin and age of stand	Pine needles only (pounds)[1]	All species: twigs, bark, and fruit (pounds)[1]	Total for all species (pounds)[1]
Planted, 10 years.	3,771±127	288±122	4,059±245
Natural, 25 years[2]	4,476±108	1,143±145	5,619±246

[1] Second figure is standard error of mean.
[2] Composition: 75 percent pine and 25 percent hardwood.

On the Duke Forest Coile (1940) found the thickness of litter under loblolly pine on Georgeville stony clay loam to be 1.25 inches at 10 years. Under undisturbed conditions, accumulation there may be expected to continue for at least 30 years at the rate of about 0.025 inch annually. Generally at a given age in pine stands, not only the depth of surface litter, but also the amount of organic matter entering the soil, are greater for fine-textured soils and sites of high timber-growing quality. Korstian (1939) found the amount of organic matter in the upper 2 inches to be 6.4 percent in a fine-textured soil and only 3.6 percent in a coarse soil.

The amount of litter decreases as succession towards hardwoods progresses. The quantity of organic matter and nitrogen in the surface foot of mineral soil is appreciably less under the pine stands than under the hardwoods, while the mixed stands are intermediate (fig. 13). Organic matter decomposes more rapidly beneath the hardwoods. Where soils have been depleted by past agricultural use, where pines are growing poorly, and where understory soil builders

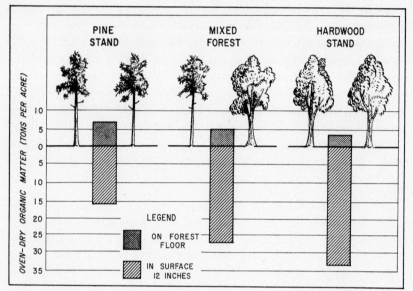

FIGURE 13.—Distribution of organic matter on and in the ground under three types of Piedmont forest in South Carolina (adapted from Metz 1954).

like dogwood and redbud can be grown, they should be favored because they benefit the site.

Soil fauna

The mantle of undecomposed litter over forest soils serves as a mulch moderating the rate of change in temperature and moisture at the surface of the soil—effects that are largely physical. Few chemical changes benefiting soil fertility accrue until the raw organic debris has decomposed and become incorporated as humus within the mineral soil. In this process the soil fauna is most valuable.

The many animals in forest litter and soil induce much of the decomposition that improves soil for the growth of trees. Through these organisms the soil is turned over and aerated, and its minerals are made more readily available.

In a loblolly pine stand in the Duke Forest, Pearse (1943, 1946) collected macroscopic animals in litter and soil every 3 months for 5 years. In the litter on an undisturbed forest area he found numerous earthworms, centipedes, millipedes, beetles, scarabaeid larvae, tenebreonid and elaterid larvae, roaches, Machilis, mites, and spiders. Some of these small creatures often migrate from the litter up tree trunks to seek food or avoid excessive moisture. In another study in the same forest Ramsay (1941) examined 147 square feet of pine bark at all seasons. Some 1,479 animals were found—about 10 per square foot. A total of 137 identified species included 78 insects, 48 spiders, 6 centipedes, 1 snail, 1 phalangid, and 3 mites. The numbers were progressively fewer from 1 to 3 feet above ground—indicating a home base in or under the forest floor.

The organisms in the soil have a more stable habitat than the ones in the litter. Those in the soil suffer less from extremes of temperature, radiation, and desiccation. Many of them can live with low concentrations of oxygen and therefore have slow rates of metabolism. Probably less than 5 percent of them penetrate clay or sand deeper than 2 inches. Organic remains in soil usually make it more favorable for animals by providing food and by making soil more porous, aerated, and penetrable. Variations in temperature and acidity influence distribution less than does moisture. The layer of litter serves as a loose organic blanket valuable as shelter for soil animals that may be temporarily deprived of air during rain storms.

The effect of human interference on this habitat was observed in one of the Duke University experiments (Pearse 1943). One loblolly pine plot was left intact, one burned over every 2 years, and another cleared of litter every 2 years. From each of these plots the soil animals obtained in collections made every 3 months during 5 years from 35 square feet of litter and soil to a depth of 3 inches were as follows:

Surface	Animals (number)	In litter (percent)	In soil (percent)
Intact............	2,278	74	26
Burned over.....	868	76	24
Raked..........	718	21	79

Surface burning was apparently not as detrimental as complete removal of forest litter. Without litter and with few soil animals forest soils tend to become barren and unproductive.

ROOT AND SHOOT GROWTH

Living roots provide the water, minerals, and anchorage trees need to survive; dead roots supply the soil with humus, improve its physical structure, and leave channels for deep percolation of water. For loblolly pine, the quantity of roots produced, the competition they face, the soil conditions encountered, the temperatures involved, all have an effect on growth. Shoot development, too, is limited by such factors as moisture, light, and temperature.

Root adequacy

Among the southern pines loblolly and shortleaf have the greatest quantity of absorbing roots in proportion to the top, and young loblolly has the most diffuse root system (Wakeley 1935b).

The roots formed by small plants like loblolly pine seedlings in their first season, or early years before they become firmly established, are vital to survival in the forest. The silviculturist, who may be able to offer "first aid," needs to understand the competitive status of pine seedlings and their associates during this critical period. For example, pine seedlings may be lost by withholding a release operation, or money may be wasted on unnecessary release.

Unlike the hardwoods, loblolly pine seedlings in the shade cannot manufacture sufficient food to build root systems extensive enough to make them drought hardy. Shading reduces both the dry weight and the root-shoot ratio of seedlings more in pine than in several other species. In a greenhouse comparison of potted seedlings, no significant differences between loblolly and shortleaf pines appeared, but sweetgum was different. Pine shoots and laterals grew more than those of the gum, but sweetgum excelled in fresh weight increase of the entire plant and in the root-top ratio as determined from oven-dry weights (Wenger 1952). Other greenhouse studies (Kozlowski and Scholtes 1948) showed that at 6 months dogwood seedlings had 3 roots to each 1 on loblolly pine. At 4 months black locust had 17 times as many roots as loblolly pine. At 3 years white oak seedlings had more dry weight of foliage than did loblolly pine seedlings, and much larger root systems. At comparable ages where the total roots produced by dogwood amounted to 168 to 305 feet, loblolly pines grew only 7 to 20 feet of roots (Kozlowski 1947).

Shade apparently does not reduce the root-shoot ratio of hardwood seedlings. Loblolly pines, however, in abandoned fields where Andropogon predominates, develop relatively deep and spreading root systems (Coile 1940), while they have less well-developed roots under pine stands and even more poorly developed roots in oak stands.

At normal field moisture contents, very little capillary water moves toward roots, and continual extension of the pine roots into new regions of soil is necessary for absorption of adequate quantities of soil moisture (Kozlowski 1947). This extension proceeds more readily in some soils than in others. In well-aerated soil both roots and tops of pines usually grow best where moisture is abundant. In relatively dry soil roots tend to outgrow the tops; however, as soil

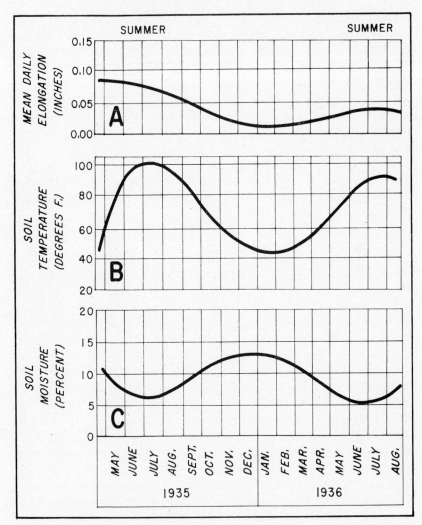

FIGURE 14.—The trend of average daily root elongation, *A*, was greatest in
    summer when the daily maximum of soil temperatures were highest, *B;*
    although there was less soil moisture, *C*, present in summer (Reed 1939;
    Kramer 1949).

moisture approaches the permanent wilting percentage, root growth
slows down or stops.   Thus, in soils which are droughty during the
middle portion of the growing season there may be two peaks of
root growth, one in late spring or early summer and another in late
summer or early autumn (Turner 1936b).   Within a range of favorable moisture contents, temperature seems to control root extension.

Seasonal response of loblolly pine roots to temperature and moisture (fig. 14) was observed by Reed (1939).

Thinning in a pine stand releases new soil space and old root channels for remaining roots to enter. The rate at which roots spread into new areas may sometimes be gaged by the expanding border in which the soil is dried by their invasion. This was observed at Crossett, Ark., where a heavy thinning was made in a 9-year-old plantation of loblolly pine. When the thinning reduced the stand from 1,100 to 100 trees per acre only 10 percent of the total soil area was fully occupied by roots to a depth of 2 feet. Two years later they occupied 30 percent of the area of soil as indicated by the progressive depletion of soil moisture at greater distances from the trees (Zahner 1956).

Root systems

The character of a soil can modify the general development of loblolly pine root systems. A taproot 4 or 5 feet long may be found on mature trees standing on deep sandy or loamy soils. On stiff clay the taproot tends to be stout but short. In marshy locations lateral roots are prominent in a superficial system (Zon 1905). When either the water table or an impenetrable hardpan confines the roots to surface layers of soil, growth is retarded (Broadfoot 1951a) and wind resistance lowered. Ashe (1915) was the first to illustrate the typical variation in loblolly pine root systems as modified by age and soil (fig. 15). The lateral spread of large loblolly pines is greater for the roots than for the crowns. That is one reason why even fairly light stands of old timber often do not contain much young pine in the openings. Some observations on root distribution were made in the course of excavations for studying the littleleaf disease (Copeland 1952). Loblolly pine roots were dispersed more deeply throughout the soil than those of shortleaf pine. The greatest mean diameter of roots was at a depth of 4 to 5 inches for the older shortleaf pines whereas for loblolly pines on the same sites it was found at 8 to 10 inches. The loblolly pine roots also penetrated deeply into rather heavy subsoils. When root elongation is rapid and soil resistance high the roots develop pointed tips; where it is slower and resistance is lower the roots have blunt tips (Addoms 1950).

The number of roots in the A_1 horizon increases rapidly with age until stands are 20 to 30 years old. After 30 years the increase is much slower (Coile 1937c). The development of roots in the A_2 horizon follows the same trend as in the A_1 although the numbers

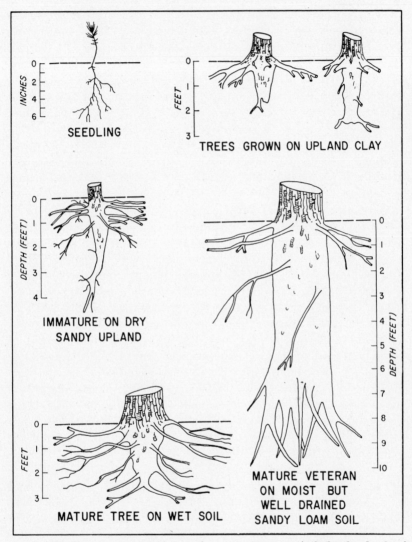

FIGURE 15.—The inherent character of root systems, particularly the depth of penetration, is materially influenced by both age and site. The deep-seated feeding roots on the veteran loblolly pine extended to the water table. The seedling is 2 years old (Ashe 1915).

are smaller. In the B and C horizons the number of roots remains constant after about 20 years. In a 31- to 35-year-old loblolly pine stand on Alamance stony loam in the Duke Forest the frequency with which pine roots were severed at different depths was counted on the vertical walls of trenches in two plots (Korstian and Coile

1938). Numbers of pine roots less than 0.1 inch in diameter, per square foot of each profile face, were determined. These feeder roots were found apportioned to soil layers as follows:

Soil horizon	Fine roots per square foot (number)
A_1	105-111
A_2	49-55
B_1	4-11
B_2	5-8
C_1	0.2-0.6

Although considerable sheet erosion had left this old field with only 5 inches of A horizon, the concentration of roots near the surface is manifest.

The close network of surface roots in well-stocked uncut stands leaves little opportunity for seedlings to develop under the canopy. When a stand matures and thinning—natural or artificial—starts, space becomes available for regeneration in the open spots. There pine seedlings are often handicapped in competition with hardwood sprouts that have the advantage of previously established root systems. These old roots are absent from the soil in many old-field pine stands, but, to a lesser extent, the pine seedlings are handicapped there also. Their first-year root systems are inferior to those of many hardwood seedlings of the same age. A yearling white oak, for example, has a well-developed root system, including a taproot, capable of early penetration below the surface zone of intense competition for moisture during periods of drought. According to Coile (1940) these differences in initial root habit of forest-grown seedlings go far to explain the persistent tendency of oak and hickory to invade and hold pine lands.

Inadequacy of the root systems of pine seedlings increases with the shade in which they grow. Low light intensity decreases, and may even stop, root elongation in forest-grown loblolly pine seedlings. The minimum intensity of light just sufficient for root growth is between 120 and 295 foot-candles (Barney 1947, 1951). Unit increases in light add more growth at low than at high intensities (fig. 17, *B*, p. 65).

Response of roots to temperature

The seasonal differences in the daily elongation of roots (fig. 14) may result in part from length of day, but are attributed largely to moisture and temperature changes. Barney (1947, 1951) found that roots of loblolly pine $2\frac{1}{2}$ weeks old grow most rapidly at 20° to 25°C; the rates at 5°C and 35°C were less than 10 percent of the maximum rate. In winter with soil at 5°C or warmer the roots can grow. At 35°C most of the roots appeared to be dormant. The observed response to heat and cold was as follows:

Soil temperature (degrees Centigrade)	Daily root growth (millimeters)
5	0.2
10	1.1
15	2.8
20	4.2
25	5.2
30	4.3
35	0.2

In Arkansas two periods of marked dormancy for loblolly pine roots have been noted (Turner 1936b): December to March and July to September. The reasons appeared to be low temperature in winter and low moisture in summer. In the deep South the roots of loblolly pine may grow throughout the year, the high soil temperatures that preclude root growth in summer on the barren areas being confined to a thin zone near the surface (Greene 1953).

Root hairs and mycorrhizae

Absorbing roots of pine—those about 1 millimeter in diameter—comprise less than 3 percent of the total root surface (Roberts 1948). These roots, however, are supplemented on some trees by two variations that aid them in absorbing moisture and mineral nutrients: (1) root hairs, and (2) mycorrhizae.

Root hairs are single-cell protuberances on the youngest absorbing roots. Where these hairs are numerous they multiply the surface several fold, but one observation (Kozlowski 1947) revealed only 217 of them per square centimeter of loblolly pine roots. This is but a small fraction of the number possessed by many of the deciduous associates of the pines.

Mycorrhizae are structures composed of root and fungous tissue in a symbiotic relationship. The rapid growing long roots of loblolly pine are typically without these structures, though they often have mycorrhizal branches farther back (Addoms 1950). The shorter roots, that are mycorrhizal, are the main absorbing roots. The mycorrhizae themselves may occupy less than 2 percent of the total root length (Roberts 1948), but these structures are particularly effective in the absorption of certain mineral elements (Kramer and Hodgson 1954). Mycorrhizae are most abundant on loblolly pine seedlings grown in full light and in situations where the A horizon of a soil is present (Wenger 1955d). Helpful as root hairs and mycorrhizae may be, drought resistance results mainly from the advance of root tips from dry soil into adjacent undepleted soil masses.

Shoot development

On the Gulf Coast, pine shoots start growth before the vernal equinox on March 31, and continue into midsummer forming nodes or partial whorls (Reed 1939). The average number is 3, but the individual nodes are not a reliable indication of age, nor do they seem to be synchronized with any rest periods within a growing season. However, recognition of the flush of spring growth, normally each season's longest internode, permits estimates of the age of free-growing saplings to be based on observation of branch whorls.

Near Crossett, Ark., the average annual height growth of loblolly pine is 86 to 88 percent complete by July 4 and 93 to 96 percent complete by August 1 (Williston 1951). There the rainfall seems to increase the amount, but not the period, of growth. At Durham, N. C., loblolly pine starts growing in late March, making roughly 15 to 20 percent of total growth each month from April through August. Its distribution there by months in 1939 on 2- and 3-year-old seedlings was as follows (Kramer 1943):

	Distribution of growth (percent)		Distribution of growth (percent)
March	2	July	14
April	14	August	13
May	27	September	6
June	23	October	1

In larger trees also, height growth was observed to start a few days before the diameter growth, but it ceased about August 1, or at least 2 months before the growth in d.b.h. ceased (Young and Kramer 1952). Spring height growth of loblolly pines from local seed sources is normally uninjured by frost and the growth ceases in mid or late summer.

The course of shoot growth in local strains of loblolly pine appears to be relatively independent of the length of growing season and normal fluctuations in the environmental factors during the season. Severe drought with hot nights in late summer or very low temperature at other times may check growth, and artificial light can stimulate it, but otherwise the usual natural variation in moisture and temperature has little effect (Kramer 1936, 1943). In a test with a local strain of loblolly pine seedlings (Kramer 1957) the best growth was made with the widest spread (12° or 13°C.) between day and night temperatures and poorest growth with nights as warm as the days. The hot nights of mid and late summer may tend to bring about a cessation of shoot growth.

In the spring low air temperature appears to be more important than low soil temperature in retarding the resumption of growth. This was determined by means of tests (Hahn 1942) wherein greenhouse soil was cooled to match that in outside beds, while the outdoor soil was heated to match that in the greenhouse. Out of doors all species were observed to start growth earlier in warm than in cold soil, and loblolly pine began spring growth 1 to 4 weeks earlier in the warm greenhouse regardless of soil temperature.

Although with favorable temperatures the leading shoots can be induced to grow in a greenhouse during winter by providing artificial light, [14] genetic research (Perry and Wang 1957a) indicates clearly that variations in the duration of natural outdoor shoot growth are controlled largely by differences in photoperiodism associated with the latitude of their racial origin. Furthermore, ancestral adaptation to long days tends not only to extend the period of growth for the progeny of loblolly pine, but also to increase the number of whorls and branches. Thus, within the seasonal limitations of a new location, such an adaptation tends to increase the total growth attained.

Seedling size and thrift increase with a decrease in the overstory. The increase is reflected in the dimensions of buds, foliage, and branches. At full stocking with about 81 percent crown cover near Crossett, Ark., the seedlings average less than a foot high at 3 years and two-thirds of them are still without branches. Under well-stocked overstories and 60 percent cover, the third-year seedlings are nearly a foot tall and half of them possess one or more branches. In relatively open places with less than 5 percent cover the 3-year-old seedlings are over 2 feet tall, branches numerous, needles and buds long, and the stems well foliated. These responses to various degrees of opening in an overwood canopy are stimulated by an increase from about 25 percent to 85 percent of sunlight reaching the forest floor (table 5), and made possible by the relative scarcity of competition from roots left alive in the open spots. Effects on survival are discussed in the chapter on natural regeneration.

[14] Within certain limits, variation in the length of day controls duration of a growing season. Kramer (1936) noted that with normal length of day loblolly pine ceased to grow as early in the autumn in a warm greenhouse as out of doors. It grew all winter with a 14½-hour day, but made better growth with continuous light.

TABLE 5.—*Effect of an overwood on the development of 3-year-old loblolly pine seedlings at Crossett, Ark.*[1]

	Overwood											
Cover (percent)	Light (percent)	Density (S.D.I.)	Basis: Plots	Diameter	Height	Foliated stem	Bearing branches	Branch frequency	Branch length	Needle length	Bud length
			No.	In.	Ft.	Percent	Percent	No.	Ft.	In.	In.
. .	100	0	. .	0.37	2.15	69	100	9.2	2.43	6.6	0.58
5	85	50	17	.28	2.03	63	93	5.5	1.73	6.1	.52
14	69	100	26	.22	1.73	58	79	3.1	1.02	5.7	.47
36	54	150	33	.18	1.28	52	65	1.9	.59	5.2	.42
60	40	200	35	.15	.98	46	52	1.2	.44	4.7	.37
76	28	250	32	.12	.81	40	38	0.6	.37	4.2	.32
85	18	300	25	.11	.69	34	24	0.2	.27	3.8	.27
92	8	350	16	.10	.60	29	10	0.1	.10	3.3	.22
98	3	400	5	. . . .	.53	23	0	0	0	2.8	.17

[1] Branches of negligible length—i.e. branch buds—were not counted. Seedlings without branches were not included in computing average length of branches. The overwood was 30 percent hardwood and measured to a radius of 31.2 feet. Stand density index (S.D.I.) may be conceived as the number of trees per acre that a stand will (or did) have at the time when the trees average 10 inches in d.b.h. Numerically it may be computed from factors in appendix table 86 or from the original formula (Reineke 1933).

PHOTOSYNTHESIS

Intensity of light

Only about 1 percent of the solar energy that falls on leaves is used for photosynthesis. A low intensity of insolation in a dense stand may retard growth of seedlings, although the light needed for their survival is very low—less than 40 foot-candles. Loblolly pine is able to survive for 6 months under light in which it is barely able to increase in weight. In dense shade the dry weight produced by loblolly pine is almost directly proportional to the intensity of illumination up to about 20 percent of full sunlight (Shirley 1928). In this situation moderate variations in soil moisture are not likely to cause any significant changes in dry weight provided the moisture content is not so low that it approaches the wilting coefficient, or so high that it approaches saturation.

Pines are noticeably more tolerant of shade as seedlings than as saplings or larger trees. Measurements of photosynthesis in 16-week-old loblolly pine indicated that maximum rates were attained at light intensities far below those required by pines more than 2 years old (Bormann 1956). This decreasing photosynthetic efficiency as seedlings grow up helps to explain why the thrift of young loblolly pine stands is sustained on old fields, whereas under a partial canopy a vigorous start is often followed by ultimate failure. The amount of light reaching the forest floor varies appreciably with the distribution of the larger trees, but under a uniform cover it varies inversely with basal area (Anderson 1941). A stand with an over-wood density (S.D.I.) of 100 admits 70 percent of full sunlight; one with a density of 200 admits 37 percent (fig. 16). Under these conditions there is a marked difference in the development of pines near Crossett, Ark. At 5 years of age, for example, the seedlings receiving 70 percent light had 18 branches averaging about 1 foot long, whereas those receiving 37 percent light had only half as many branches averaging about 7 inches long. The average height in the first group was 4.2 feet, in the second 2.4 feet. At 5 years also the survival with 70 percent light was 75 percent; with 37 percent light it was 62 percent.

Concentration of carbon dioxide

Carbon dioxide is a heavy gas given off in respiration of plants, but absorbed in greater amounts in photosynthesis. Experiments with ten potted 2-year-old loblolly pine seedlings (Decker 1947) have shown the apparent rate of photosynthesis increasing with the supply of air and the concentration of carbon dioxide as follows:[15]

Air supply (liters per minute)	Photosynthesis (mgs. CO_2 per minute)	Concentration (mgs. CO_2 per liter)	Photosynthesis (mgs. CO_2 per minute)
2	0.34	0.46	0.37
3	.43	.47	.40
4	.47	.48	.43
5	.50	.49	.47
6	.52	.50	.50
7	.53	.51	.53
8	.54	.52	.56
9	.55		
10	.55		

Because carbon dioxide is a relatively heavy component of the atmosphere its concentration is somewhat greater (possibly 10 per-cent) at low elevations and close to the ground. This may explain, in part, the superior shade tolerance of small seedlings close to the ground. In loblolly pine respiration is doubled when air temperature is increased from 20° to 30°C., though photosynthesis apparently remains about the same (Decker 1944). But for an increase from 30° to 40°C. respiration increases about 50 percent, while photosynthesis decreases about 45 percent. Exactly how these functions are related to growth behavior remains to be shown.

Continuity and kind of illumination

The timing and the quality of light influence the growth of lob-lolly pine. After a period of dormancy, resumption of growth can

[15] All seedlings were exposed to all rates of supply, and results gaged through analysis of variance using a Latin square.

be hastened by additional light and retarded by shortening the photoperiod below the normal length of day (fig. 17, D).[16] Zahner (1955b) showed that the height growth of yearling loblolly pines may be more than doubled by an interruption of the period of darkness. Beween March and September while his short-day control seedlings became 7 centimeters tall, others provided with a half-hour of artificial light in the middle of each night became 17 centimeters tall.

There is slight evidence that red rays may stimulate and blue rays retard the growth of loblolly pine seedlings. According to Phillips (1941), the effect of color of light on height of loblolly pine seedlings was as follows:

	Red (cm.)	White[1] (cm.)	Blue (cm.)
1936:			
October 31	34	33	35
December 3	35	33	35
December 21	37	33	35
1937:			
January 8	41	33	35
February 1	46	33	35
March 1	48	38	37
March 13	48	40	39

[1] Control—entire solar spectrum.

In this study loblolly pine broke dormancy almost immediately when placed under 18 hours of light, part of which was supplemental red irradiation, whereas under short normal winter days they failed to break dormancy until about February 1—2½ months later. The pines grew more rapidly when nights were shortened by the use of red light than under other conditions. Additional irradiation with blue light resulted in less growth. Fortunately the wave length of white light that filters through a forest canopy is not changed enough to lower its quality for photosynthesis.

Pine versus hardwood response

Tree species characteristically differ in their capacity to endure shade. This capacity decreases somewhat with both age and deterioration in site quality. Shade tolerance, however, is a relative character, not subject to precise quantitative measurement. Yellow-poplar, for example, is recognized as an intolerant hardwood, yet regardless of age or soil depth, it maintains a somewhat greater ratio of live crown to total height than does loblolly pine (Hocker

[16] Length of day is affected by some 10 degrees difference in latitude between the northern and southern parts of the range of loblolly pine. In the north the species has about an hour more of daylight available for photosynthesis during the middle of the growing season.

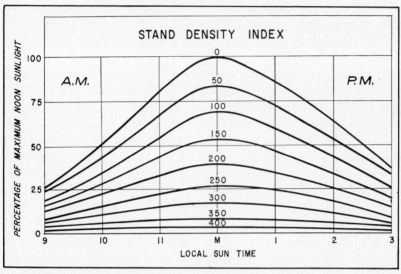

FIGURE 16.—Effect of time of day on the quantity of light reaching the forest floor under loblolly pine stands of different stand density indices as compared with full sunlight in the open at noon. Based on measurements by photoelectric meter on clear days, when no clouds or haze were near the sun, during July and August at Crossett, Ark.

1953), which is an indication of possibly greater shade tolerance. These two timber species are sufficiently alike in silvical character and in value, however, to be planted in small-block even-aged mixtures on some of the better sites.

To maintain pine on the much larger areas in need of natural regeneration, a knowledge of the relative tolerance of the pine and its competitors is essential. One advantage the pines do have is that, to some extent, photosynthesis is possible during mild winter weather when their competitors are leafless. Few tests, however, have compared directly under forest canopies the capacity of hardwood seedlings (not sprouts) to outlive pine seedlings of the same age.[17] Numerous laboratory tests indicate that deciduous species commonly associated with loblolly pine do have that capacity. For

[17] By contrast many observations have indicated probable failure of pine seedlings to survive in adequate numbers within an understory where the hardwood *sprouts* arose simultaneously. Much life persists in residual hardwood roots that may remain hidden in the soil many years before shoots emerge. Some of these roots, through original or natural root-graft connections with living trees, may well have unsuspected sources of nourishment to sustain them. Thus many sprouts are not wholly dependent on photosynthesis in their own leaves. Where sprouts with vital connections are 3 years or more older than the associated pine seedlings unaided regeneration of pine commonly fails.

example shading reduces the rate of photosynthesis of seedlings more in pine than in oak. When soil dries out, photosynthesis, as well as transpiration, is reduced sooner in pine than in oak.

The fact that oak seedlings have a smaller percentage of their total weight in foliage signifies their greater photosynthetic efficiency (Kozlowski 1947). The difference is most noticeable under partial light. With full sunlight, for instance, both oak and pine appear to attain about 80 percent of their maximum photosynthesis, but with only one-tenth as much light oak reaches 93 percent of its maximum, while pine functions at only 57 percent of its capacity. With somewhat less extreme variation in light, as in most pine forests, the photosynthetic superiority of oak is less pronounced, but ever present. The decrease in photosynthesis, as the moisture supplying power of forest soil decreases, begins earlier for pine than for oak (Kozlowski 1947). Such responses account for the inferior shade tolerance of pine. Proper functioning of pine seedling tops in heavy shade is hindered by inadequate elaboration of the food needed for good root growth, and consequently absorption from the soil of water and minerals essential to thrift and further development of the tops is insufficient.

Under competition in the forest, insufficient light and moisture tend to suppress loblolly pine seedlings. The fundamental superiority of hardwoods over pine in capacity to endure shade is confirmed and has been demonstrated in several studies at Duke University (Kramer et al. 1942, 1949). In these studies potted specimens of loblolly pine and northern red oak seedlings were observed at an air temperature of 25°C. Photosynthesis was measured at seven intensities of light from 300 to 9,300 foot-candles. Maximum photosynthesis in oak occurred at about 3,300 foot-candles and decreased slightly in brighter light. In pine, photosynthesis increased constantly up to the highest intensity used, 9,300 foot-candles, or almost that of full sunlight (fig. 17, A and B). White oak and dogwood likewise reached a maximum at about ⅓ or ¼ of full sunlight (Kramer and Decker 1942, 1944). Greenhouse tests have shown that loblolly pine responds to increased light (fig. 17, C) by producing heavier and taller seedlings.

The failure of pine seedlings to grow as well as hardwoods do in one-third sunlight appears not to arise from any deficiency in leaf tissue, but rather from the arrangement of their needles, i.e., their inferiority in deploying their foliage to catch the sunlight. Pine needles individually tested under full exposure to light function much like hardwood leaves. In the natural fascicle and branch clusters, however, they suffer considerable mutual shading (Kramer and Clark 1947).

Whatever the cause, it appears that a critical "threshold" condition of low photosynthesis exists below which pine cannot maintain itself. In the Piedmont, at least, this condition is normally a function of the combined effect of decreased light intensity and less moisture under forest stands (Kozlowski 1949). By contrast, the hardwood associates of pine achieve sufficient photosynthesis in the shade to grow rather extensive root systems that enable them to survive droughts.

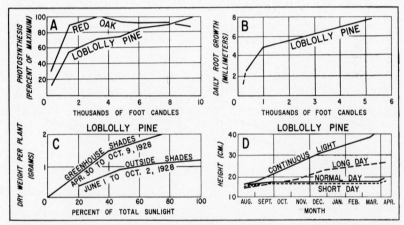

FIGURE 17.—Light in relation to growth of loblolly pine seedlings: *A*, red oak attains maximum photosynthesis with only a third as much light as is required by loblolly pine (Kramer and Clark 1947); *B*, effect on elongation of roots from light intensity to which the shoot was exposed (Barney 1947); *C*, effect of shade on dry weight of seedlings (Shirley 1928); *D*, effect of modifying the period of illumination on shoot growth of loblolly pine from North Carolina during different seasons (Kramer 1936).

SITE QUALITY

Plant indicators

There is a universal need in silviculture to classify land according to its capacity to produce timber. In Finland and adjacent countries the ground-cover types of minor vegetation have been extensively used to indicate the quality of sites for growing pine. This method appears to be useful under the relatively stable virgin forest conditions in northern latitudes with a limited flora.

It would seem that the relative abundance of certain understory species in the loblolly pine type of forest might betoken the quality of the local soil. Some investigation of this possibility has been made by Coile (1950b). He found that density and coverage by several understory species in the Piedmont is greatest on the better sites and tends to increase with age in a pine stand (fig. 18). Deep surface soil favors an understory, as it does the overstory.

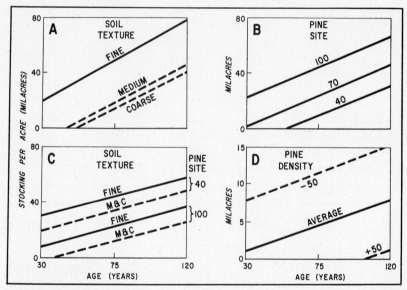

FIGURE 18.—Area occupied by understory species as influenced by soil properties, site quality, and density and age of pine overwood in the Piedmont: *A*, Dogwood on subsoil with imbibitional water value at a high level (24) with three different surface soil textures; *B*, sweetgum on fine-textured surface soil; *C*, redcedar; *D*, certain moist-site oaks (white, willow, and both northern and southern red oak) (Coile 1950b).

The numbers of oaks, specifically the white and willow oaks and both the northern and southern species of red oak, increase as stands become older and the overwood less dense (fig. 18, *D*). Dogwood is most abundant on sites which have a low imbibitional water value for the subsoil and a fine-textured surface soil. Sweetgum is more common on good pine sites, whereas redcedar is more prevalent on the poorer pine sites.

Within the loblolly pine belt the subordinate vegetation as a whole is materially modified not only by the quality of the site, but also by the currently dominant cover, including its density and condition as a result of treatment (Coile 1938). In consequence no useful plant indicator species have yet been recognized.

Site determination

Three possible ways of determining the producing power of forest land remain. We may judge it by the loblolly pine trees, other species of trees, or the soil itself (Coile 1937b, 1938, 1942). When thrifty, pole-sized, uninjured loblolly pines are available, their average height at 50 years indicates site quality. The best sample trees for this purpose are dominant specimens from well-stocked even-aged pine stands 30 to 70 years old. Average age may be taken from increment borings and site index interpolated from a chart such as the one based on a formula by Gaiser (1950) (fig. 19), wherein the logarithm of site index equals the logarithm of height (feet) plus 7.11 over age (years) minus 0.142. An earlier site index chart in the same form (U. S. Forest Service 1929—Misc. Pub. 50) included more gulf coastal timber, but often leads to poor estimates when young trees are sampled. Below 50 years those curves need correction according to the following equation (Coile and Schumacher 1953b):

$$\text{Log}\, \frac{y}{Y} = 1.2892 \left(\frac{1}{A} - 0.02 \right)$$

where y is the tree site index, Y is the soil site index, and A is age in years.

Where the only material for such an estimate consists of scattered 8- to 20-year-old pines the growth intercept method, now under development, can be used. A 5-year intercept for any one tree is the length of trunk formed in 5 consecutive years, during the first of which the tree attains breast height (Wakeley 1958). An average of these intercepts as measured on a number of young trees indicates the quality of the site.

In the absence of suitable 30- to 70-year-old loblolly pines for site determination, other species can be used as indicators only if previous study has determined quantitative interspecies relationships. Work in Arkansas by Turner (1936a) indicated that the site indices for shortleaf pine were about 95 percent of those for the loblolly. Similar observations in the East (Coile 1948) show that the site index for shortleaf pine is commonly 89 percent of that for loblolly pine. At site index 40 for shortleaf pine, the index for loblolly pine is only about 5 feet higher, but the superiority of loblolly pine increases with site quality. Where the index for shortleaf pine is 80, that for loblolly pine is 10 feet higher. Zahner (1957b) found a similar relationship between height growth of loblolly and shortleaf pine on the same site.

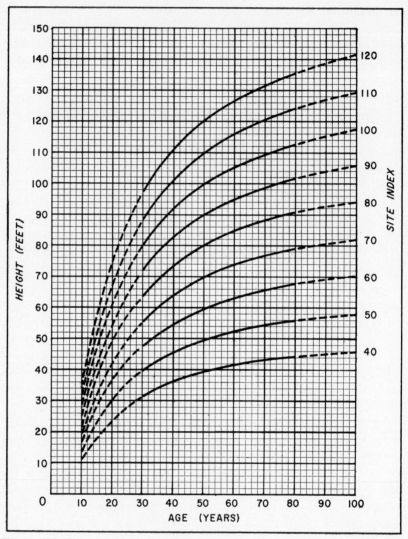

FIGURE 19.—Site quality for loblolly pine in the Coastal Plain of Virginia and the Carolinas (Gaiser 1950).

His equation is—

Loblolly pine S.I. = 1.30 (shortleaf S.I.) — 17.4

Because few interspecies growth relationships of this kind have been worked out, an ability to estimate site quality without reference to existing vegetation is useful.

Hardwood species supply optional crop trees on some of these soils. Those with a pine site index of 60, however, can produce only hardwoods of extremely low and doubtful value. Those with an index of 70 or 80 are also distinctly inferior for hardwood timber; 90-foot sites are intermediate; but the 100- and 110-foot sites can produce superior hardwood (Turner 1937a).

Site indices of soil series

A soil series is a group of soils having horizons similar in characteristics and arrangement in the profile, except for the texture of the surface soil. Each series is developed from a particular type of parent material. The designation of forest soils by series is useful to the extent that they are recognized, mapped, and correlated with site quality for timber.

Some research on this was done west of the Mississippi. Turner (1936a), studying the physical properties and aeration of soils, reported from Arkansas that the best sites for loblolly pine were found on flat land where the soils were immature sandy loams and silt loams with permeable subsoil, fair drainage, and an adequate water supply. Table 6 indicates that loblolly pine does best on very gently sloping land.

A similar study in Texas (Chandler, Schoen, and Anderson 1943) also gives top rank to Ochlockone sandy loam in the following list of soil types:

	Mean site index for loblolly pine
Ochlockonee fine sandy loam............	103
Lufkin fine sand......................	82
Segno fine sandy loam.................	81
Ruston fine sandy loam................	80
Caddo fine sandy loam.................	78
Susquehanna fine sandy loam...........	73
Segno fine sand......................	58

Site indices for shortleaf pine were 6 ± 3 feet lower on these soils with one exception. On Segno fine sand the index was 4 feet higher for shortleaf.

More recently a comparable study on the Atlantic Coastal Plain (Gaiser 1950) has added observation of subsoil imbibitional water values within two drainage groups of other soil series (table 7). Site indices in relation to depth to the least permeable layer of the B horizon, and for eight soil series are shown in figures 20 and 21.

It is clearly inadvisable, however, to depend solely on soil series as an indication of site quality. This is apparent from the within-series variation shown in table 7, from the slope of the curves in figures 20 and 21, and from Zahner's work in Arkansas where cer-

TABLE 6.—*Relation of certain Arkansas soils to site quality of two native pines (Turner 1936a)*

| Soil type | Slope | Loblolly pine site | | Shortleaf pine site | |
		Range	Average	Average	Ratio to loblolly
	Percent	Feet	Feet	Feet	Percent
Ocklockonee sandy loam......	1	102-110	108	92	85
Vicksburg silt loam..........	1	100-108	107	..	...
Boeuf fine sandy loam........	1	91-96	94	..	...
Caddo silt loam..............	2	84-100	92	90	98
Caddo-Ruston transition......	2	85-90	89	89	100
Lufkin silt loam..............	1	83-95	85	..	...
Ruston fine sandy loam.......	2½	83-90	84	83	99
Caddo very fine sandy loam...	3	77-85	83	78	94
Susquehanna fine sandy loam..	4	71-81	77	75	97
Hanceville fine sandy loam....	5	74-75	77	65	84
Susquehanna fine sandy loam..	9	75-77	76	73	96
Ruston fine sandy loam.......	6	......	74	72	97
Norfolk fine sandy loam.......	2½	65-75	69	68	98

tain other characteristics of the soil were essential to good estimates of site indices.

Soil-site evaluation

Site quality results from the interaction of numerous factors, including several that can safely be ignored in practice. Within a single climatic region the climatic and biotic characteristics of site can usually be disregarded (except in planting), but physiographic and edaphic influences must be recognized. Among these, certain soil factors are keys to site quality because they directly influence the growing space for roots or the moisture available to them or both. Such attributes are, for example, the thickness of surface soil, the depth to mottling (a varicolored zone indicative of poor drainage), and the nature of the subsoil, its texture and consistence.

An increase in surface soil down to a depth of 10 inches causes a pronounced increase in site quality in the Piedmont. Friable subsoil is favorable there also. In the Coastal Plain surface drainage is involved and may be judged by relative topographic position. The more poorly drained soils near the Atlantic coast in Virginia and the Carolinas have the higher site indices (Gaiser 1950, Coile 1952b).[18] They often contain a layer of mineral soil where aeration

---

[18] The following observation—possibly surprising and seemingly paradoxical—has been made at widely separated points: Pine timber growth improves as soil drainage becomes poorer. In the southern Coastal Plain an increase in the imbibitional water value of the subsoil has a favorable influence on height growth in pine (Metz 1950). This is confirmed by Grigsby (1952) working in Louisiana.

TABLE 7.—*Imbibitional water values of plastic subsoil by soil series arrayed in descending order of site quality for loblolly pine on soils in the Coastal Plain of Virginia and the Carolinas (Gaiser 1950)*

Soil series	Basis: Number of observations	Imbibitional water value	Site index
Drainage imperfect:			
Roanoke	2	11.5±0.19	102
Scranton	4	1.6±0.36	89
Moyock	12	7.4±0.51	86
Lenoir	12	9.2±0.73	83
Atlee	3	5.2±0.24	82
Craven[1]	14	7.4±0.59	82
Norfolk[1]	37	3.6±0.34	80
Dunbar	20	6.4±0.34	80
Onslow	4	6.7±1.16	76
Others[1]	9	. . . .	75
Leon	2	1.7±0.41	59
Drainage poor:			
Elkton	6	11.5±0.74	95
Coxville	19	10.5±0.78	89
Portsmouth[2]	29	5.1±0.25	89
Bladen	17	10.0±0.72	88
Bayboro	2	8.8±0.43	88
Fallsington[2]	5	6.5±0.68	84
Others	3	. . . .	75

[1] Well-drained soils.
[2] Subsoils friable in these 2 series, but plastic in the other 4 of this group.

is poor, infiltration slow, and root penetration difficult. The influence of intractable layers on site quality may be reversed by their location in the profile. The position of a plastic layer of soil tends to be beneficial if it helps to maintain a constant water supply, or it may be detrimental if located so that it restricts space available for growing roots.

Coile (1948 and 1950b) was the first to develop effective methods of loblolly pine site determinations directly from quantitative measurements of soil properties themselves. He perceived that topographic situation—ridge, upper or lower slope, and bottom land—are alone insufficient to account for variation in site quality. At least two of the numerous soil properties involved must be recognized for a definitive estimate of site quality. These appear in Coile's equation for the lower Piedmont region of North Carolina:

$$\text{Site index for loblolly pine} = 100.04 - \frac{75}{T} - 1.39 \text{ IWV}$$

where T is the thickness of surface soil in inches and IWV is imbibitional water value of the subsoil (fig. 9). This equation is generally satisfactory, but it does give (Stoehr 1946) low values when used to estimate the quality of poor sites in the lower Piedmont of the

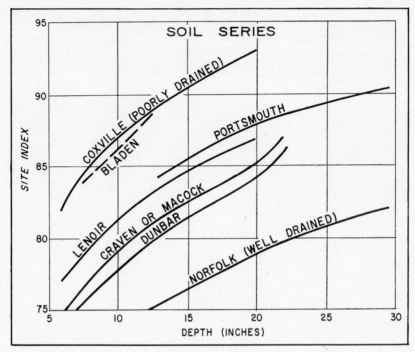

FIGURE 20.—Relation of soil series and depth to the quality of loblolly pine sites in Virginia and the Carolinas (Gaiser 1950).

Carolinas and Georgia.[19] An inadequate appraisal of the drainage situation may produce inaccuracy in soil-site determinations. It is pointed out by Hodgkins (1956) that neglect of one or more significant features, such as internal drainage, may lead to considerable error.[20]

[19] Conversely the results from this formula may appear to be high if it is applied where the pines frequently have suffered foliar damage and retardation from recurrent fires. In such cases some figure between 71 and 78, depending on intensity of the damage, may be substituted for the constant 100.04 (Coile 1952a). On areas unburned or properly treated with prescribed fires, however, no change is needed.

In some situations in the lower Piedmont where alluvial soils are unusually deep Coile's formula is not readily applicable. An example of this was found in Wake County, North Carolina, where the soil depth measurements had to be somewhat arbitrary because of poorly defined profiles (Ralston 1955). In general the unproductive soils are those with a shallow A and an impervious B horizon.

[20] Some additional precision can be achieved by modifying formulas to recognize local differences in surface drainage. Thus, according to Gaiser (1950) working in the Coastal Plain, the logarithm of site index for loblolly pine varies with drainage class as follows: For good or imperfectly drained soils it is $1.692 + 0.110$ times $(\log T + \log \text{IWV})$; for poorly drained soils with plastic

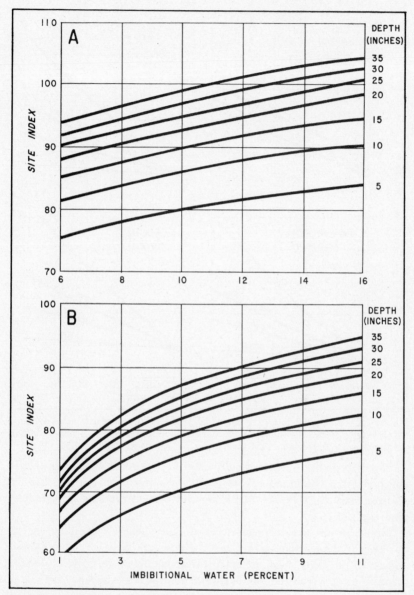

FIGURE 21.—Estimated site index of loblolly pine on Coastal Plain soils of (A) poor surface drainage with plastic subsoils, and (B) good or imperfect surface drainage. Depths were measured to the least permeable horizon (Gaiser 1950).

subsoil it is $1.715 + 0.110$ times $(\log T + \log \text{IWV})$; and for soils of poor surface drainage and friable subsoils it is 1.983 minus $(0.772 \text{ over } T)$ where T is in inches in each instance.

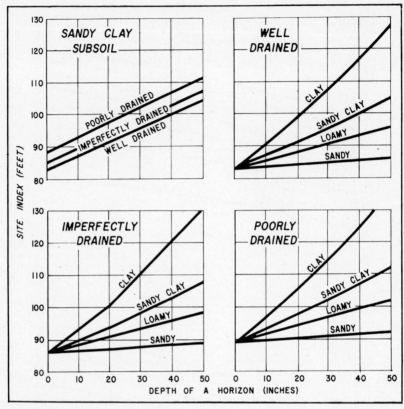

FIGURE 22.—Height of loblolly pine at 50 years of age in the Coastal Plain as affected by the depth of the A horizon and the textural grade of the B horizon in four situations that differ in drainage (Metz 1950).

Working in the southeastern Coastal Plain, Metz (1950) has clearly portrayed the combined effects of surface drainage, the depth of A horizon, and the texture of B horizon on site quality for loblolly pine (fig. 22).

Research on this problem is certain to continue region by region. So far, for the southeastern Coastal Plain, the data for loblolly pine appear in the form most useful to forest managers in Coile's (1952b) tabulation, in which the northern and southern sections are separated (table 8). Analogous data for use in the Piedmont are in table 9. Note that the corresponding site indices for shortleaf pine on these soils are 6 percent lower for the 2-inch depth to subsoil and about 20 percent lower for the deeper surface soils.

To implement similar estimates of soil-site quality for loblolly pine west of the Mississippi we have the results of studies by Zahner

TABLE 8.—*Relation of Coastal Plain soils to site quality for loblolly pine in the Southeast (Coile 1952b)*

VIRGINIA, NORTH CAROLINA, AND NORTHEASTERN SOUTH CAROLINA

Drainage and subsoil consistence	Subsoil texture	Site index when depth to subsoil in inches is—						
		6	12	18	24	30	36	42
		Ft.	Ft.	Ft.	Ft.	Ft.	Ft.	Ft.
Well and imperfectly drained soils:								
Very friable......	Sands	65	70	73	75	77	79	...
Friable..........	Loamy sands to light sandy loams	70	75	79	81	83	85	...
	Sandy loams	73	79	82	85	87	89	...
	Loams	75	81	85	88	90	92	...
Semiplastic......	Sandy clay loams to clay loams	77	83	87	90	92	94	...
Plastic..........	Sandy clays to clays	78	85	89	92	94	96	...
Poorly drained soils:								
Friable..........	Sandy loams to sandy clays	75	81	85	88	90	92	93
Semiplastic to plastic.......	Sandy clays	81	88	92	95	97	99	101
Very plastic.....	Clays	85	92	96	99	102	104	106

SOUTH CAROLINA, GEORGIA, FLORIDA, AND ALABAMA

Subsoil texture	Surface drainage	Site index when depth to subsoil in inches is—						
		6	12	18	24	30	36	42
		Ft.	Ft.	Ft.	Ft.	Ft.	Ft.	Ft.
Sand and loamy sand...	Good	80	85	85	85	85	90	90
	Imperfect	90	90	90	90	90	90	95
	Poor	90	90	90	90	95	95	95
Sandy loam and sandy clay loam...........	Good	85	85	90	90	90	95	95
	Imperfect	90	90	90	95	95	100	100
	Poor	90	90	95	95	100	100	100
Loam, clay loam, sandy clay, and light clay..	Good	85	90	90	95	100	105	105
	Imperfect	90	95	95	100	105	105	110
	Poor	90	95	100	100	105	110	115
Silty clay and heavy clay...............	Good	85	90	95	105	110	110	115
	Imperfect	90	95	100	105	110	115	120
	Poor	95	100	105	110	115	120	125
Silty clay loam and silt loam...............	Good	90	90	95	100	105	110	115
	Imperfect	90	95	100	105	110	115	120
	Poor	95	100	105	110	115	120	125

(1954) working in south and central Louisiana and southeastern Texas. How the characteristics of these soils are related to site quality is shown in table 10.

Zahner (1957b) has recently extended this work to the Coastal Plain uplands and terrace soils of north Louisiana and south Ar-

TABLE 9.—*Relation of Piedmont Plateau soils in the Carolinas to site quality for loblolly and shortleaf pines (Coile 1952a)*

Soil consistence when moist	Species	Site index when depth to subsoil in inches is—						
		2	4	6	8	10	12	18
		Ft.	Ft.	Ft.	Ft.	Ft.	Ft.	Ft.
Very friable............	Loblolly	57	79	82	86	88	89	91
	Shortleaf	51	62	66	68	69	70	71
Friable................	Loblolly	52	74	77	81	83	84	86
	Shortleaf	47	59	62	64	65	66	67
Semiplastic............	Loblolly	46	68	71	75	76	77	79
	Shortleaf	43	54	58	60	61	62	63
Plastic................	Loblolly	38	60	63	68	69	70	72
	Shortleaf	38	49	53	55	56	57	58
Very plastic...........	Loblolly	32	54	57	61	62	64	66
	Shortleaf	33	44	48	50	51	52	53

TABLE 10.—*Relation of site quality for loblolly pine to the soils of south and central Louisiana and southeast Texas (Zahner 1954)*

Subsoil characteristics			Site quality[2] when depth to subsoil in inches is—		
Consistence class with range of IWV[1]	Textural grade	Surface drainage	0-10	10-20	20+
Very friable, IWV 0 to 5............	Sands to sandy loams	Good	Low	Medium	Medium
		Poor	Medium	Medium	High
Friable to semiplastic, IWV 6 to 15......	Clay loams to light clays	Good	Medium	High	High
		Poor	High	High	High
Plastic, IWV 16 to 25.	Silty clays to heavy clays	Good	Low	Low	Medium
		Poor	Medium	Medium	High

[1] Imbibitional water value (IWV) may be determined in the laboratory or estimated in the field from the consistence of the subsoil.
[2] Ranges of site indices within each quality class: Low 70 to 80, medium 80 to 90, and high 90 to 100. Zahner's formula was as follows: Logarithm of site index equals C plus $0.00156T$ plus 0.00679 (IWV) minus 0.000368 (IWV)^2, where C is 1.8872 for well-drained sites or 1.9124 for poor drainage, T is thickness of surface soil in inches, and IWV is imbibitional water value of the subsoil.

kansas. Site estimates may be had by distinguishing between soils with or without visible "horizons" in the profile, by recognizing slope of the land, and by substituting more specific measures of surface and subsoil textures. These site characteristics can be related to site index (table 11). The ability to use a soil auger to determine site quality in quantitative terms is a most practical achievement because it provides the basis for valid estimates of potential timber yields from bare lands.

Regional distribution of sites

Site index is the best single indication of the capacity of forest land to produce a given species of timber. Hence the prevalence of

TABLE 11.—*Loblolly pine site index on upland and terrace soils in north Louisiana and south Arkansas (Zahner 1957b)*[1]

ZONAL SOILS (HORIZONS VISIBLE)

Textural grade of subsoil	Slope	Site index when depth of surface soil in inches is—				
		6	12	18	24	30
	Percent	Ft.	Ft.	Ft.	Ft.	Ft.
Loam......................	1-5	74	81	84	82	75
	6-10	70	77	80	78	72
	11-15	67	74	76	74	68
Sandy clay loam.............	1-5	81	87	90	88	82
	6-10	77	84	86	84	78
	11-15	73	80	83	81	74
Clay loam..................	1-5	80	87	89	87	81
	6-10	76	83	86	84	77
	11-15	72	79	82	80	73
Light clay and sandy clay.....	1-5	76	83	85	83	77
	6-10	72	79	82	80	73
	11-15	68	75	78	76	69
Heavy clay (over 50 percent clay)....................	1-5	72	79	82	80	73
	6-10	69	75	78	76	70
	11-15	65	72	74	72	66

AZONAL SOILS (HORIZON INVISIBLE)

Textural grade of subsoil	Slope	Site index when textural grade of surface soil is—		
		Sandy loam	Loam	Silt loam
	Percent	Ft.	Ft.	Ft.
Sandy loam to sandy clay loam	0	80	73	(2)
	2	87	79	(2)
	4	81	74	(2)
Loam to clay loam...........	0	90	85	(2)
	2	96	91	(2)
	4	91	86	(2)
Clay......................	0	86	82	79
	2	92	89	83
	4	86	83	80
Silty clay loam to silty clay....	0	(2)	70	69
	2	(2)	77	75
	4	(2)	71	70

[1] Zahner's equations are as follows:

Site index on upland *zonal* soils equals $33.58 + 3.174 \ (CP) - 0.0827 \ (CP)^2 + 0.00063 \ (CP)^3 + 2.257 \ (T) - 0.0615 \ (T)^2 - 0.739 \ (SP)$

Site index on upland *azonal* soils equals $69.51 + 1.805 \ (Sa) - 0.0062 \ (Sa)(Si) - 0.0215 \ (Sa)^2 - 2.77 \ (SP + 0.1) - 1.227 \left(\frac{1}{SP} + 0.1\right)$ where

T = thickness of surface soil or depth to subsoil (inches)
CP = percentage of clay in subsoil
Sa = percentage of sand in subsoil
Si = percentage of silt in surface soil
SP = percent of slope

[2] Combination of surface silt and subsoil silt plus clay which does not occur in nature.

various quality classes of land is important to consumers of wood from extensive areas. The average quality and the relative abundance of common site-index classes for loblolly pine in the eastern part of its range are given in table 12.

TABLE 12.—*Relative abundance of land by quality classes for growing loblolly pine in each of two physiographic regions in five southeastern states (Cruikshank 1954b)*

Physiographic region and state	Site index class (feet)				
	50 —	*60*	*70*	*80+*	*Average*
	Percent	*Percent*	*Percent*	*Percent*	*Feet*
Coastal Plain:					
Virginia	8	16	50	26	70
North Carolina	1	19	58	22	71
South Carolina	—	8	46	46	76
Georgia	—	8	26	66	80
Florida	—	14	23	63	80
All	2	14	48	36	73
Piedmont:					
Virginia	6	30	34	30	70
North Carolina	—	9	55	36	73
South Carolina	2	15	55	28	72
Georgia	—	11	54	35	73
All	(¹)	12	54	34	73

¹ Negligible.

In general, site quality is better in the Coastal Plain than in the hilly country and the better sites are found on the wetter and more poorly drained soil. In many sections of the Coastal Plain slight variations in drainage and soil cause much local variation in site quality. Still more pronounced differences in terrain in the Piedmont Plateau produce a mosaic arangement of site quality governed largely by differences in subsoil characteristics, slope, past erosion, and present drainage. Over closely dissected rolling topography the pattern of site differences may be so intricate as to defy portrayal on any small map.

Intensive maps of site quality for individual timber properties should be very useful in silviculture. The principles and procedures for utilizing topography and soil-site survey data to construct precise large-scale site-index maps for properties under forest management have been reported by Coile (1948) and by Zahner (1957a).

SUMMARY

A complex of environmental influences limits the natural range of loblolly pine. Chief among them are three: low temperature at the northern extremity, low rainfall in Texas, and, until recently, fires at too frequent intervals along the Gulf coast. In the northeastern part of its range loblolly pine is confined to the Coastal Plain, but farther south it enters the Piedmont as well. In the past both abusive use of fire and abandonment of cleared fields have modified the pattern of today's pine forest area.

Except on the sandhills and on lands where hardwood species of trees were already abundant and firmly rooted, loblolly pine forests were aggressive in the regeneration that followed removal of old-growth stands. Mixed with a variety of minor, but well-established associates, loblolly pines still commonly dominate the overstory in many situations—the understory in some. Understory hardwoods increase as the second-growth pine overwood becomes older and less dense. Now loblolly pine seedlings are handicapped in many ways. A reversion of pine forests to more shade-tolerant and generally less valuable native hardwoods is underway over extensive areas. This trend stems from both man-made and natural causes.

The principal man-caused reasons for the increasing ascendancy of hardwoods are fire protection, where it succeeded without benefit of prescribed burning, and the prevailing habit of leaving hardwood associates standing everywhere pines are cut. The reversion of the pine forest to a broad-leaved type can rarely be completely reversed by any feasible action short of clearing and planting, but it must be widely arrested if pine is to be perpetuated as a commercial crop of timber. To grow pine the hardwoods must be reduced rather than eliminated. Eradication—seldom possible—is not desirable because the leaf fall from certain deciduous species improves the soil. Nevertheless pine silviculture succeeds only to the extent that it effectively retards, or masterfully arrests, the natural succession toward pure hardwood forests.

The principal natural reasons for the increasing ascendancy of hardwoods involve soils, roots, and photosynthesis. (1) Hardwoods tend to maintain the high degree of fertility needed for their best development. The litter from several species of hardwoods brings more nitrogen and calcium to the surface, favors soil fauna, and decomposes more rapidly than that from pine. (2) Hardwood roots sprout readily from residuals and develop more rapidly from seed than roots of pine, particularly where the forest floor is shaded. During drought roots of many species of hardwood have an advantage over those of pine in ramification, root hairs, and rate of early penetration. (3) For hardwoods as a class photosynthesis is not reduced as soon by drought, nor as much by shade as for pine, and hardwoods can store up more plant food in the course of a growing season.

In pine forests light and moisture together fill a fundamental need. A deficiency in moisture is the more often severely limiting to thrift and survival. Favorable moisture relations are necessary to maintain an adequate flow for transpiration and to prevent desiccation from interfering with vital processes. Poor surface drainage is associated with good quality in pine sites more often in the Coastal Plain than in the Piedmont. Loblolly pine seedlings can withstand occasional flooding remarkably well, but roots are injured by prolonged inundation. The species usually fails to reproduce itself naturally in wet bottom lands, but, once there, it thrives, and it is capable of maximum growth in alluvial silt, including tidewater sites where hardwoods are absent and the water table is under control. When in widely spaced even-aged plantations having ideal moisture relations, the growth and yield of loblolly pine is phenomenal.

Seedlings of most species, including pines, tolerate more shade than saplings or large trees, but at all ages the pines are less tolerant than most of their hardwood associates. The shade-grown loblolly pine seedlings that survive grow slowly—increasing in size directly with illumination reaching the forest floor, at least up to 20 percent of full sunlight. Even at 5 years of age, seedlings under 70 percent light may be twice as large as those under 35 percent light. The rate of increase continues for oak seedlings only until light reaches 3,300 foot-candles, whereas for pine it increases until light reaches 9,300 foot-candles, or almost full sunlight. Seedlings which start growth under a low intensity of light may die. Those that survive are delayed in attaining resistance to both drought and fire as compared to open-grown saplings whose development is more rapid.

The capacity of land to produce pine timber at a satisfactory rate varies widely. This producing power is gaged by site index—a measure which, until recently, was obtainable only from dominant pines 30-70 years old on the land in question. Site index is the average height these trees had, or will have, at 50 years of age. This remains the most convenient way to estimate site quality wherever suitable sample trees are present. When they are absent the site can sometimes be approximated from the development of other species. For example, the index for shortleaf pine, which may be obtainable, ranges from 80 to 95 percent of that for loblolly pine, often 90 percent. More frequently the estimate must be made from the soil only. In general, the unproductive soils are the ones with shallow surface soil and impervious subsoil.

Several equations to implement such estimates in various regions are under development. A simple one for the Piedmont states that site index equals 100.04 minus (75 over T) minus 1.39 IWV, where T is thickness of the surface soil in inches and IWV is the imbibitional water value of the subsoil. The IWV may be determined by laboratory measurements, field estimates of soil consistence, or from published average values for various soil series. More precise determinations of site indices depend on thorough surveys that utilize formulas appropriate to a given locality. No single method is reliable regionwide. One reason for this is that a plastic layer of subsoil tends to be beneficial if it helps to maintain a constant water supply, or it may be detrimental if located so that it restricts space available for growing roots.

Chapter 3

Protection

THE PREVIOUS CHAPTER SUGGESTS that ignorance of the forces of nature controlling the normal succession of forest types may defeat the manager who desires to perpetuate loblolly pine by natural means. Another, and equally important, prerequisite for success in keeping pine on the land is adequate protection. Timber growing should not be attempted unless the potential destructiveness of several injurious agencies is understood, and plans have been laid to prevent or control their attacks.

This chapter concerns protection for loblolly pine from logging, fire, insects, animals, disease, and climatic factors. The characteristic damage from certain of these causes, against which there is as yet no adequate or economical defense, is reported here also. It is included in the expectation that new and better ways can be devised to circumvent, alleviate, or otherwise counteract some of the presently uncontrollable damage. In any event in order to fully redeem his responsibility to protect his loblolly pine, a forester must be aware of potential damage from each of the six principal harmful agents, and should acquire a working knowledge of the ones that impair the value of his forest most often, most extensively, or most seriously.

Until very recently there could be little question but that fire was enemy number one on all three counts in the loblolly pine forest.[21] Now insects vie for recognition as champion destructive agents because of the tendency of certain insects, notably bark beetles, toward epidemics in recent dry years. Many loblolly pines first weakened by fire, lightning, or mechanical injuries are killed by insects every

[21] For many years the South held undisputed first place in any nationwide comparison of the frequency and extent of or damage from woods burning. This situation has gradually improved through education in conservation during the past 40 or 50 years. Now occurrence is less, and, except in periods of drought, the toll smaller. Prevention, detection, and suppression of fire have each improved with organization to meet the challenge, until now the place of fire as forest enemy number one is doubtful.

year. Silviculture may be helpful both in the advance removal of susceptible classes of trees and in salvage of infested ones, but epidemics call for direct attack. Progress in preventing damage will depend, as in fire protection, on improved organization for detection and prompt control. Aerial surveys of the insect situation are now beginning to implement this control.

Disease injures or kills many individual trees, but it ruins fewer whole stands of loblolly pine than do fire or insects. Loblolly pine seedlings are fortunately less susceptible to mass destruction by the brown-spot disease than are those of longleaf pine. Mortality from this disease is seldom serious. Loblolly pine in the small-pole stage is also less subject to littleleaf disease than is the shortleaf pine. Fusiform rust is controllable and heart rot tends to disappear under management with the most economic rotations. Other troubles, like root and butt rots in nurseries and plantations bear watching, but are not yet limiting.

Removal of moribund or dead trees, regardless of species or the cause of their condition, is advisable. A prompt harvest is needed both to avoid loss of timber and to make space for remaining and younger trees. The difficulty arises only in avoiding the extremely large or small losses—the former because they overtax manufacturing facilities and markets; the latter because of the high cost of locating, logging, and selling widely scattered individual dying trees. Some associated species cannot be sold. Fortunately most loblolly pine is readily accessible and in demand by local markets.

An admixture of 5 to 10 percent of intermediate and overtopped hardwood trees in pine forests makes for increased beauty, health, and quality of stems. It also brings improvement in the soil and in habitat for wildlife. Such indirect benefits of having a subordinate hardwood component, however, are directly offset by lower yields of pine where the hardwoods are dominant trees or exceed 20 to 25 percent of basal area (Paul 1952).

The relatively high susceptibility of pure stands to insect and disease troubles has long been recognized. Natural mixtures of species theoretically are both more resistant to infestation or infection and are less completely vulnerable when attacked. They are more attractive to wildlife. Fortunately, the hardwood element supplied by nature is usually ample to provide all the desired silvical and protective benefits. More often, as will be discussed later, nature contributes too much hardwood.

Artificially established mixtures of tree species are likewise easier to protect from both insects and disease than are pure stands. Unfortunately, attaining a wholesome admixture of hardwoods is more of a problem in plantations because of inequality in rates of early growth. With an equal start loblolly pine tends to crowd out its associates. Hence, it should not be set out in too intimate a mixture. An associate species should not be mixed individually by or within rows. Rather, it should be planted in pure groups limited to 9, 16, or 25 trees each. A better (and easier) practice is to locate each minor species in alternate narrow bands, though neither of these patterns for mixed stands has been adequately tested in relation to site quality.

Alternate strip planting of yellow-poplar and loblolly pine may be successful in the more moist sites on the Piedmont Plateau, and in the well-drained moist soils on stream terraces in the Coastal Plain, but in general mixed plantings have been unsatisfactory. For the sites on which loblolly pine is usually planted it is difficult to find a relatively intolerant species (other than slash pine) with an equivalent rate of growth or a tolerant species capable of developing economic value comparable to that of loblolly pine. Accordingly the introduction of resistant species, or other deliberate modifications in species composition, have as yet accomplished little in forest protection.

LOGGING

Injury from logging

Careless logging in partial cutting operations commonly injures loblolly pines in several ways. Many seedlings less than 5 feet high escape destruction after being knocked down during logging, but among trees over 5 feet the smaller ones are the more susceptible to immediate destruction. Felling some timber inevitably decapitates and splinters at least a few of the saplings and pole-sized trees. More are maimed as branches are stripped down. Careless skidding knocks bark off many of the larger trees, leaving basal wounds. Trees are injured by trucks hauling logs over temporary roadways that are too narrow. Tractors injure vital surface roots and compact wet soils. Inasmuch as, over a longer period, the loblolly pines that are thus directly injured remain more susceptible to subsequent attack from insects, fire, and disease, the indirect damage may be even greater. Salvage crews must be equipped and trained to avoid damage to young growth and reserved trees. In partial cutting operations loggers likewise must use care to prevent damage to the reserved stand.

When portable mills are set up within the loblolly pine forest, manufacturing waste should be so handled as to avoid further damage. Piles of slabs or sawdust not only usurp growing space, but also create fire hazards. Refuse burning without proper precautions may scorch nearby trees.

Careless utilization practices cause many injured trees to die of complications necessitating subsequent salvage operations. Survivors are retarded in growth, or degraded in quality, or both.

Avoiding logging damage

In large measure damage caused by logging is avoidable, but difficulty in circumventing it has increased somewhat with mechanization in the extraction of timber and some other recent developments. For example tree-length logging of loblolly pine, which facilitates better utilization of raw materials, tends to increase damage from skidding. Trucks and tractors speed woods work, but may injure more trees than horse-drawn logs and vehicles. Much depends, however, on how and when the more powerful heavy equipment is applied.

Logging can be less harmful to loblolly pine if it is timed properly. Early harvest of all pines not needed for seed results in less damage later when seed trees are removed. There is less injury to reproduction if logs from seed trees can be skidded out while seedlings are still small and flexible. Damage is less if trees are felled in the direction in which they will be skidded and if skid trails are fairly straight. This precaution is practical in the Coastal Plain, but less feasible on rolling terrain. On the Piedmont Plateau skidding along the contours causes logs to roll. This loosens and frequently breaks the taproots of loblolly pine seedlings or knocks off their bark. On the short slopes logs may be skidded across contour lines without inducing serious erosion, so long as the number moved over the same trail is not too large. Seed trees left in lines, lanes, or strips are removed with less damage than are scattered seed trees.

Where they can be used, wheel tractors are less damaging than the track-laying type, but 1- and 2-year seedlings can survive the passage of tractor treads. Soil and surface root injury to trees can be serious at landings and along skidroads when heavy logging equipment is used in wet weather. In the lower Coastal Plain many feeding roots may be destroyed in this manner. Tractors may churn saturated soil severely enough to reduce the thrift of adjacent loblolly pines and retard the growth of subsequent regeneration

(McCulley 1950a). Such trouble is avoided where stands are logged in dry weather and while the seedlings are still small. During recent years it has been found that root damage may induce bark beetle attacks. Breakage loss among the larger loblolly pines also can be reduced, if necessary, by an orderly succession of partial cuttings. This was done in one instance by taking out the small trees first, then the larger ones, and finally the isolated trees and borderline culls—thus avoiding 5 to 20 percent of the usual damage. On another job (240 acres of tractor logging near Crossett, Ark.) this was not done, and felling damage exceeded skidding damage. Among the 12 percent of the pines injured more than half were destroyed outright or found dead in the next 6 months (Worthington 1939).

Mortality of loblolly pine following harvest commonly results from a variety of causes, but decreases markedly with the degree of dominance of the trees left. The highest mortality is in understory trees with short narrow crowns. Recognition of this tendency is important in selecting seed trees. At one point near Franklin, Va., the mortality of residual trees during 19 years after harvest was as follows: Overtopped, 43 percent; intermediate, 22 percent; co-dominant, 5 percent; and dominant trees, 2 percent (Pomeroy 1949b).

There is no indication of excessive mortality in partially cut timber less than 40 years old, but as Chaiken (1941) has indicated, seed-tree cuttings in stands over 40 years old and without benefit of intermediate culture, may suffer appreciable mortality. To avoid that, certain classes of trees should be removed regardless of size. These include the ones with severe logging injury to butts or crowns, and trees that are overtopped or intermediate with short, narrow crowns. Among trees less than 10 inches in diameter, those with poor vigor (tall with small crowns) and those which might be left in isolation should be removed. Pine mortality can be anticipated and reduced by the deliberate harvest of the more susceptible individuals. In this manner some natural mortality is precluded and losses are minimized.

In young merchantable stands, commercial salvage of unthrifty and dead timber is often feasible. The value of dead trees drops rapidly if they are not utilized promptly, especially in summer. Provision should be made for prompt discovery and removal of small volumes. Many individual trees can be salvaged if all-weather access roads are provided. With dual-wheel trucks additional dead trees also can be brought in during dry weather. Where roots were injured along skid trails or elsewhere, insect-killed trees are often found in small groups that can be salvaged more economically than single trees. Crews must be organized and must use mobile equipment. A unit used by one company includes a one-man chain saw, a self-loading truck, a light tractor, and a versatile 3-man crew. Thus equipped this unit can harvest as little as 50 board feet per acre economically.

FIRE[22]

The problem of fire

The control of forest fire—its use or misuse—is a primary and perennial concern nearly everywhere in the South (plate 3). As elsewhere in the United States, the problem of fire in the South involves both prevention of destructive wildfire and the prescription of fire for specific constructive purposes. Unlike most situations in the North and West, however, these two phases of the fire problem cannot be resolved independently because they are closely interrelated in the forest and in the minds of local people. Fires, both wild and prescribed, can be somewhat unruly at times, and require effective controls. Accordingly fire behavior needs to be understood in its relation to fuel and weather and regardless of the accidental or deliberate origin of the blaze. Yet certain distinctive features in the way fires start within the loblolly pine belt need recognition. Although debris burners, hunters, and other people carelessly permit some of their fires to escape, man-caused fires are fewer per unit of area than in the longleaf-slash pine type. There is less popular demand for woods grazing privileges, less woodland forage for cattle, and more segregation of livestock in fenced and improved pastures. Hence fewer stockmen have any incentive to start fires.

On the other hand the control of fire in loblolly pine becomes more difficult north of the turpentine belt because of the diversity of forest fuels. Unlike longleaf pine, loblolly pine seedlings possess no thick-barked "grass stage" highly resistant to fire. Most seedlings under 5 feet in height are killed by prescribed burning. Shade-grown saplings, with bark and height growth both retarded, long remain susceptible to killing by light fires. Nor do they have the noteworthy ability of shortleaf pine to sprout from the base after fire deadens the tops. These features aggravate the fire problem.

The state forest services are increasingly concerned with the overall control of forest fire. Other agencies contribute within the framework of their special or local interests as follows: the U. S.

[22] Additional information on fire may be found in chapters 2, 4, 5, and 7.

PLATE 3.—Backfire in loblolly pine forest, Livingston Parish, Louisiana, 1955 (Photo 8565, courtesy Louisiana Forestry Commission).

Forest Service in or near the national forests, and on other lands
through advisory participation in interstate compacts, and as
authorized under the Clark McNary law; the Soil Conservation
Service in their conservation districts; the Defense Department on
military bases; the lumber, pulp, and paper industries on company
lands and adjacent supply areas; and protective associations on the
private holdings of members. The division of responsibility among
these groups usually rests on definite agreements that generally
work well. Together they have on hand considerable equipment for
the suppression of forest fires.

Policy toward fire

The South has long been considered provincially backward in
its prevailing attitude toward forest fire because local people have
tolerated promiscuous burning there longer than in other regions.
The South as a result of increasing appreciation and recognition of
timber values, is now definitely outgrowing its traditional apathy.
Protection from fire has been relatively effective in recent years.
Recognition of the need for a high degree of selective control generally
is replacing the earlier misplaced emphasis on rigid blanket exclusion.

Now it is realized that the extensive use of fire for silvicultural
purposes definitely reduces both the incidence and the damage from
wildfire; in this manner it mitigates effectively the overall problem
of fire protection. Some foresters have been fomenting the changed
attitude for 30 years. H. H. Chapman's pioneering exhortations
of the nineteen twenties fell on deaf ears. Experiments with fire in
the nineteen thirties seemed merely to arouse apprehension and
to forebode trouble. Not until the nineteen forties were any effective
pleas made for the recognition of controlled burning in protecting
and growing loblolly pine. Then the meaningful new term "prescribed burning" was introduced (Conarro 1942). In many sections
the need for extending the use of controlled burning became more
apparent because of the growing difficulty of maintaining adequate
protection from fire with the older methods alone.

Now as more and more forest managers are beginning to prescribe and use fire for various constructive purposes in growing
loblolly pine, they are finding that relations with the local people
are improving. In one instance the incendiary problem was reduced
75 percent. It has been found on the Francis Marion National
Forest in South Carolina that fuel reduction by prescribed burning
decreases the acreage of wildfires, and, through easier access, reduces

the cost of suppression, mopup, and cultural operations after each fire (Hills 1954). Prevention campaigns are needed elsewhere as deliberate incendiarism and careless burning of debris are each responsible in some places for a third of the fires.

To reduce the risk of fire in loblolly pine, local foresters can, first of all, improve public relations. On some forests such improvement has followed the introduction of a program of prescribed burning to lower the hazard from accumulated fuels. At the same time the introduction of silvicultural harvests, girdling or poisoning undesirable trees, and clearing to plant seedlings may be expected to increase fire hazards temporarily in some places. This is inevitable in the process of the current work to improve species composition, control the density of many stands, and reestablish others. But in operations to manipulate stand structure and to sustain yields, forest managers can materially reduce the risk of, and damage from, fire on the property as a whole as they zone or subdivide a forest— using access roads to reach, and lane barriers to restrict, fires. Because of these interrelations the extent and intensity of timber management will materially influence the overall problem of controlling fires.

Until very recently the degree of control over fire in loblolly pine forests has not been sufficient for the business world to recognize the usual forestry enterprise as an insurable risk. That situation also is changing. One company is accepting applications for limited insurance of certain forest fire risks in the South (Greene 1956). The policies are designed to cover damage to both plantations and natural stands. The basic cost of this insurance varies with the level of risk and hazard currently recognized as typical of each of the states. Then the premium is adjusted up or down according to practices or conditions that detract or add to local safety. A top credit of 20 percent now goes to certified tree farms. Various protection measures, such as firebreaks and fire fighting equipment, qualify a timber property for several lesser credits. On the other hand, lack of protection raises the premium charge 50 percent, while various abnormal hazards result in additional charges. Prescribed burning is favored, though damage that may result from loss of control of such fires is not covered. The system of making detailed appraisals of, and allowance for, the elements of risk are such that good forestry practices are encouraged. This system may well stimulate new forestry projects and lead to wider coverage where forestry is already a firmly established business.

The danger of fires—their causes, periodicity, and control

Man is primarily responsible for the frequency of forest fires in the South, whether as a result of intent or carelessness. Lightning, an important cause in some parts of the United States, caused only 1.3 percent of the southern forest fires in the decade 1945 through 1954.

The timing of fire can readily modify its adverse or favorable effects on loblolly pine. Even light or infrequent burning within 5 years of seedfall usually destroys loblolly pine reproduction. Summer fires tend to be more destructive, but fortunately wildfire is most prevalent between autumn and early spring, or in the Coastal Plain of South Carolina from January to March inclusive. In Mississippi most of the fires in the loblolly pine type of forest occur in the autumn after leaf fall. In flash fuels, such as pine straw and dead grass, fast spreading fires can start a few hours after a half-inch rain during the dormant season.

Forest managers, however, need local experience to know in which season to expect trouble with fire in loblolly pine forest. Perhaps the most important research contribution, to supplement this experience, is the development of procedures for measuring fire danger.

Daily estimates of the local situation are made at numerous fire danger stations. Two indices are used. The "build-up index," based entirely on fuel moisture, measures progressive drying of the deeper fuels, and therefore to some extent is a measure of the difficulty of control. It is most useful in deciding on the size of attack forces; it is helpful also in deciding when the use of fire may be prescribed.

The "burning index" has a broader base. The data for it include fuel moisture, wind velocity, condition of the lesser vegetation, and the build-up index. The burning index measures the severity of current burning conditions (Keetch 1954, Nelson 1955b). For example in the deep South, the readings denote fire danger as follows: 1 low, 2-5 moderate, 6-17 medium, 20-25 high, and 50-100 extreme. On the scale still used in the Northeast the corresponding readings are exactly double.

The burning index is related to size and rate of spread (table 13). A measure of the relative effectiveness of prevention programs is afforded by the number of fires experienced per thousand units of burning index. A high index can mean that fires will be more numerous, faster, larger, and more difficult to control. This index is most useful in critical periods. If, for example, it reaches 75 or if

TABLE 13.—*Behavior of surface fires in relation to burning index*[1]

Burning index[2]	All fires, average rate of spread—increase in perimeter per hour	Fastest 25 percent of fires	
		Rate of spread—increase in perimeter per hour	Size attained in first hour of free burning time
	Chains	Chains	Acres
10...............	23	55	10
20...............	27	80	23
30...............	32	104	38
40...............	37	128	58
50...............	42	152	83
60...............	46	176	110
70...............	50	200	142
80...............	55	223	178
90...............	59	247	217
100...............	63	270	260

[1] Data by John Keetch cited by Nelson (1955a) and applicable to various fuel types that are typical of extensive areas of loblolly pine forest.
[2] Burning index values based on meter number 8-100 used in the South and Southeast. Those who use meter number 8 in the Northeast need to double the above values of the burning index.

both indices exceed 50, the stage is set for an explosive type of fire.[23] Daily fire danger readings indicate when to hire extra men or to discharge or reassign them to save money. Worrell (1955c) recently reported on the economics of forest protection in Georgia where four times as many wildfires were occurring on Class 5 days as on Class 3 days. More than 20 airplanes are now available there for fire duty, but air patrol has been economical only in those periods when visibility was poor, fires were frequent, or potential damage was high. With air patrol to check smoke during the worst periods, one man can combine the jobs of tower watchman and ground checker during other periods. With a light fire load towers alone afford the cheapest detection, but if the danger is high the combination of towers and air patrol is most economical. The fire-weather stations can indicate when and where such danger exists in the loblolly pine type.

On the ground, mechanization of equipment to reach, confine, and suppress fires has increased. Appropriate machines need to be evaluated in terms of output comparable to that from crews using handtools. Well-trained crews with handtools can maintain a con-

[23] To integrate the readings from the two indices, one further step has been taken for northern forests. Preparedness classes have been charted to provide a better measure of the job load in suppression than is afforded by either index alone (Nelson 1955b). These classes provide a handy basis for adjusting the fire control force up or down to match current conditions. They are useful also in certain higher level administrative decisions. They provide advance information as to when, for reasons of safety, forests should be closed to public use. Their extension to the loblolly pine forest would be advantageous.

stant rate of fireline production for an hour or two, but thereafter under rough and difficult conditions, their rate of production drops rapidly. Human fatigue is not so great where fireline plows are used; crews can sustain their effort over a much longer period. Because of variation in soil, ground cover, sod, timber stand, and terrain, there can be no universal machine. The tractor-pulled multiple-disk fireplow has proved to be the most effective fire fighting weapon in the flatwoods and less rugged hill country of the South. A plow of suitable weight, 500 to 3,300 pounds, when adequately powered by a crawler tractor, can often build more fireline in a given time than 25 or 30 men (Hartman 1949). A design combining the rolling coulter, plow, and disks makes a wide fireline and moves a given volume of soil with the least power, but on rough or stony ground a moldboard plow is more effective and dependable.

The track laying type of tractor is widely used throughout the loblolly pine belt. In open sapling stands with light soil and sod, a plow and crawler tractor rated at 18 to 20 D.B.H.P. (drawbar horsepower) has proven satisfactory. In dense young stands, or under tough sod conditions, crawler tractors rated at 40 to 60 D.B.H.P. are needed to construct firelines at an acceptable rate. The plow units are usually moved to fires on radio-equipped trucks or trailers of appropriate capacities. Fireline plows and vehicles to transport them are under constant development. A tractor-plow unit is desirable for each 25 to 50 thousand acres to be protected in the Coastal Plain. For maximum effectiveness the basic plow-unit crew should be experienced, organized, and supplemented, during periods of high fire danger, by men trained to hold constructed lines.

Relation of fire to cutting

The passing of exploitation cutting followed closely by destructive burning has not ended the association of timber harvest and woods fires. The need to consider them jointly arises because fuel reduction is seldom the only constructive purpose in using fire. The most reliable experience in handling fire, or cutting timber, is that acquired locally. Ground cover, humus types, and forest fuels do vary significantly from hilly to flatwoods locations yet there is enough similarity within the loblolly pine type of forest in the Coastal Plain to make the empirical lore of one section helpful elsewhere. The use of fire in the rolling upper Coastal Plain and in the Piedmont is limited and the more costly because contiguous large areas in need of uniform treatment are seldom found. On some slopes burning induces the loss of valuable soil through erosion; the ultimate use of fire in the Piedmont is still questionable.

A system of light but frequent intermediate cuttings lessens fire hazard through a favorable dispersal—in both time and space—of the logging debris which contributes fuel for fires. Cutting heavily and at longer intervals concentrates logging waste on relatively small areas that may require special precautions for protection.

The timing of prescriptions for burning is of prime importance. Fire has been prescribed and used extensively in the lower Coastal Plain for preparing seedbeds. Then in young well-stocked stands the principal purpose in burning is to reduce fuel supply and fire hazard; in stands that are older or more open, the main purpose becomes suppression of hardwood underbrush. Fires kill larger hardwoods in summer than in other seasons, but the frequency with which burning is advisable or possible varies. Often fuel must be allowed to accumulate up to 3 years before an area can support the type of fire desired. Cutting can be timed accordingly. Burning is usually prescribed for an area before loblolly pine timber is marked for any kind of cutting. The tops of cut trees, always an added hazard, are less so when they rest on a freshly burned surface. A fire before each intermediate cut makes hardwood-control burning at regeneration time less difficult and more effective. Once regeneration is complete, further burning should be deferred until the dominant seedlings reach resistant size. Then the first fire in the young stand should be a light winter fire.

The Francis Marion in South Carolina and the Sam Houston in Texas are the national forests in the coastal flatwoods that led the way in such uses of fire for loblolly pine forests. Both now have intensive and successful burning programs for the benefit of loblolly pine. Burning for various purposes covers about one-seventh of the pine area in the Francis Marion Forest annually (Riebold 1955b).

The practice developed on these forests has now been extended to loblolly pine in several other districts within the national forests in most of which fire had already been introduced for the benefit of longleaf pine: The Conecuh in Alabama; the Strong River, Chickasawhay, and Leaf River in Mississippi; and the Evangeline and Catahoula in Louisiana. In the loblolly pine-shortleaf pine type, fire has been prescribed for some 100,000 acres of national forest (exclusive of the Francis Marion and the Sam Houston) since 1949. A considerably larger area is recognized as in need of this prescription as soon as trained personnel and funds for such work can be made available. Controlled burning for constructive purposes is likewise being practiced in several industrially owned forests by progressive lumber companies like the one at Crossett, Ark. A recent canvass by a state commission of forestry in South Carolina showed that about 64,000 acres, mostly in the loblolly pine type, were prescribed-burned by private interests there in the period 1952 to 1957.

All controlled fires, regardless of the specific purpose served, contribute to the ease of protecting forest property from wildfire.

Types, behavior, and handling of fire

Both the suppression of wildfire and the control of prescribed fire are easier when atmospheric and ground conditions are favorable. The common and typical surface fire is easily handled if it does not "crown" or go underground. The persistent and costly subsurface fire is fortunately infrequent in the loblolly pine type, but it may occur in very dry times in bottoms and swamps where there is a deep accumulation of partially decomposed organic matter. Such fires kill the largest as well as the smallest trees. The problem of controlling fires in organic soils will become increasingly important where loblolly pine is planted on swamp lands now being drained to control the level of ground water.

Crown fires also are fortunately becoming increasingly uncommon in the South. Carried by strong winds, they are most likely to occur on areas where there are heavy accumulations of the more flammable fuels, especially where tall understories draped with needle litter may bridge the gap between the forest floor and the crowns above. Fire travels most readily through the treetops where they form a continuous dense canopy. More destructive still is the type of fire known as a "blow-up" fire. Such fires are not so common in the loblolly pine belt as in the turpentine pine forest, perhaps because of the absence of extensive unbroken stands, but they are possible and may be catastrophic.[24]

[24] Occasionally fires develop with an intensity far out of proportion to the apparent burning conditions. Such fires form their own "chimney" or convection column. When this is well started a violent chain reaction in energy conversion takes place which may not level off until the column is several thousand feet high. Byram (1954) reports "blow-ups" most likely when the following conditions exist simultaneously: (1) Fuels are dry and plentiful. (2) The atmosphere is or was unstable for hours, possibly days before the fire. (3) Wind speed in free air is 18 miles per hour or more at a height equal to, or not much above, the fire. (4) A decrease in wind with altitude for several thousand feet above the fire, with the possible exception of the first few hundred feet.

To reduce hazards safely, to destroy sprouts effectively, or otherwise to prepare for regeneration properly, fires need skillful handling. Backfires are often used in young stands as an effective means of halting an unruly head fire, whether it be accidental or prescribed. Another way to stop the onward rush of such a fire—without generating the extra heat that develops in a collision between fires—is by control-burning with the wind on short successive strips to remove fuel from the path of the advancing head fire.

Recent work in Texas to suppress understory hardwoods (Vincent 1955) indicates that the best conditions for winter burning in blocks of 50 to several hundred acres of loblolly pine are about as follows: fuel moisture stick readings 4 to 8 percent averaging 6, wind 3-8 miles per hour in the open averaging 6, and temperature 40° to 60°F. Relative humidities below 50 percent are needed for effective burning in the light fuels of the Atlantic Coastal Plain. Backfires raise the temperature higher near the ground than do head fires, but backfires are on the whole relatively cool, slow, and erratic. They may fail to cover the area and may not kill enough of the hardwoods. When backfires are not hot enough, as is often the case in older stands of pine, head fires are used. The type of fire needed is one with flames 1 to 3 feet high progressing with an angle of 30° to 45° and advancing about 4 chains per hour.

Burning can be readily controlled when it starts with a fire that can creep against the wind at $\frac{1}{4}$ to 1 chain per hour, and is followed by head fire used in short progressive strips. In the absence of extra hazard, such as needle drape on underbrush or saplings, strip-firing can be done with a 2-chain interval. Strip number 2 is not ignited until the man firing strip number 1 has progressed about 2 chains. The two men used on plow crews average 60 to 80 chains of line per hour. The men handling the fire plan to cover 200 acres per man-day, burning mostly between noon and 4:00 p.m.

Resistance to injury and appraisal of damage

Fires may injure pine seeds, seedlings, and soils. Pine seeds are usually safe from fire unless it sweeps the forest floor after seedfall, but prior heat injury may come from a severe fire. A slash burn at Crossett, Ark., is reported (Meyer 1955) to have had the following lethal effects on seeds within cones on the scorched crowns of the pines.

Fire injury to crown	Viability of seeds (percent)
Killed	16
Upper half unscorched	50
Uninjured	70

Direct damage from fire to the forest soil is dependent on the type of humus. It is often negligible and superficial where moisture in the humus layer keeps the temperature below the kindling point. In the Piedmont the unincorporated organic matter in mor types of soil is more likely to be consumed by fire than is the organic material mixed with mineral matter in the mull types (Metz 1954).

Small loblolly pine seedlings of any age are vulnerable even to light fires; burning has often destroyed extensive stands outright. Winter or spring fires that kill none of the 3-inch or larger trees and only 4 percent of the 2-inch trees, may kill 95 percent of the smaller ones, including all below 5 feet in height (Burns 1948). In one instance three annual fires beginning the first year left only 1 percent, and a single second-year fire killed 82 percent of the 1-inch d.b.h. class. Resistance increases with diameter and bark thickness. Pine saplings up to 2 inches in d.b.h. are killed by fire of medium intensity, and by fires of high intensity up to 4 inches in d.b.h. (Anderson 1941). Free-growing seedlings become resistant to injury by winter fires in 6 to 10 years, depending on degree of dominance.

Mortality in a seedling stand after a light fire may continue for more than 6 weeks. Hence, damage appraisals are best deferred until 3 months after a fire (MacKinney 1935). This conclusion is wise also in the case of pole-size and timber trees, for many of these, weakened first by fire, succumb later to secondary complications.

The immediate and direct damage to vegetation from fire results from three primary variables: (1) intensity of the fire, (2) initial vegetal temperature, and (3) lethal temperature of plant tissue. Byram and Nelson (1952) have found that the lethal effects of a given intensity of fire vary inversely as the difference between (2) and (3) above. The lethal temperature for plant tissue is about 140°F. (60°C.). The temperature of pine foliage in bright sunlight may exceed 105°F. (40°C.). Hence, an increase of only 35°F. (19°C.) could kill the needles. At a temperature just above freezing the trees can stand a fire more than twice as intense as one on a warm day when the vegetation temperature is 95°F. (35°C). The rate of temperature rise is in inverse proportion to the size of the affected parts. The foliage and buds of pines, being relatively thin and light, are brought more quickly to lethal temperatures in a fire than is the rest of the tree. Buds often remain intact while the needles are all scorched and such trees may live if the base is not injured. Feeding roots, though considered still more sensitive than foliage, are normally well insulated within the mineral soil. If and where they emerge into the humus above they may burn.

The lethal temperature varies somewhat with exposure time. A laboratory study of heat resistance in foliage of the southern pines revealed these relationships (Nelson 1952):

Killing temperature (degrees C.)	Duration necessary for lethal effect (minutes)
52	13.3
53	9.7
54	6.4
55	4.5
56	3.5
58	1.2
60	0.5
62	0.2
64	0.1

These relations determined in water bath are a conservative basis for estimating heat resistance in dry air.

A high percentage of loblolly pines with needles consumed by flame, leaving only short stubs, have had their buds killed. Many of these trees may be expected to die, especially if the fire is in summer. If after a week or two the inner bark near the ground adheres tightly to the wood and is discolored more than halfway around, the tree probably will not recover. To judge the prospects for recuperation among trees with intermediate degrees of injury is more difficult. In one instance a fire that killed half the trees that were 100 percent scorched, killed a quarter of those scorched 90 to 100 percent, 18 percent of those 50 to 90 percent scorched, and only 11 percent of the ones less than 50 percent scorched. A recent study in Texas (Ferguson 1955) was designed to aid early evaluation of damage when relying on two of the following three avenues of injury: (1) complete crown scorch, (2) extensive basal injury, and (3) severe bark burn.[25] The primary and early secondary damages from fire were not separated. As always the smaller trees were the more susceptible to fatal injury, and summer burning was roughly twice as destructive as winter burning.

Ferguson suggests that foresters concentrate salvage operations on trees most likely to die by cutting the following classes of damaged trees, the highest risk classes being listed first:

[25] In this study "extensive basal damage" meant that half or more of the circumference was affected. "Complete crown scorch" meant that no green needles were left. Mortality data probably included insect damage as well as fire damage.

1. All foliage consumed.
2. Complete crown scorch combined with either very severe bark burn or extensive basal damage, or extensive damage by very severe bark burn alone.
3. In trees damaged by summer fires, complete crown scorch alone, extensive basal damage alone, or very severe bark burn alone.

Mortality represents only part of the damage to a stand. Injured survivors grow more slowly for a time. A light spring fire may reduce growth in basal area of a dense stand of small poles by 27 percent (Burns 1948). Barrett (1928), observing this effect in Louisiana, found that a good second-growth stand of loblolly pine of saw-log size lost about 200 board feet per acre in growth during the first 3 years following a severe fire.

Time, place, and purpose in using fire

Fire should be used only where specific benefits promise to out-weigh probable damage, both strongly controlled by local conditions. These conditions must be analyzed before a prescription to burn can make a fire safe and useful. In loblolly pine the need for protective burning at fairly regular intervals is reduced to the extent that irregular silvicultural burning lessens the hazard and risk of wild-fire. Plans for protective and cultural burns should be integrated. It is often possible to serve two or more purposes in a single series of plan-wise fires. Possible benefits, vital or incidental but worthy of some consideration in plans, are as follows (Haig 1938):

In forest protection—
1. land clearing and construction of the principal roads.
2. preparation of roadside safety strips and fire lanes.
3. disposal of slash piles of infested, infected, or waste materials.
4. backfiring in suppression of wildfire.
5. hazard reduction or range improvement by compartments.

In silviculture—
1. site preparation for planting or direct seeding.
2. site preparation for natural reproduction to expose mineral seed-beds, reduce humus, release nutrients, and foster favorable bacterial action in the soil.
3. cleaning out small hardwoods in timber stand improvement.

Although the use of fire is already widely accepted in the Coastal Plain, burning treatments for forests on the Piedmont Plateau remain experimental. Fire may find limited use in silviculture without being widely useful in protection. Larger timber can benefit from discreet burning operations, but on dry sites it is neither necessary nor desirable to prescribe fire as a protective measure for old timber (Ashe 1910).

To time the burning properly, in any location, one must be fully cognizant of fire weather, forest fuels, and variation in resistance by condition and age of stands. Where hardwoods are still small enough to be killed with fire and there are less than 300 pine seedlings per acre, burning can be done to advantage. Seedling stands that are inadequate may be sacrificed; others must be fully protected. Saplings, too, must be shielded from fire until they become reasonably resistant, i.e., after the stems reach 3 to 6 inches, with bark 0.3 to 0.4 inch thick, and height 12 feet at age 10 or more (Akerman 1926, Patterson and Weddell 1943, Rothkugel 1907). In many places in the Piedmont burning may have to be deferred until it can be integrated with intensive silvicultural operations.

The indirect loss of surface soil through erosion may or may not be serious after burning over clay soils on hilly lands in the Piedmont, depending on the type of humus. The removal of part or all of the unincorporated organic matter (L, F, and H layers) by superficially burning over an A_1 horizon has no visible effect on erosion. Until research more closely defines the probability of such losses, they should be circumvented. This may be done by excluding fire where (1) there is active sheet or gully erosion or evidence of former erosion now arrested, (2) more than 20 percent of the soil is loessial and slope exceeds 5 percent, (3) soils with slopes of over 15 percent occupy 80 percent or more of the area, and (4) soils are organic, as in pocosins.

Obviously fire is cheap, effective, and safe to use under the proper circumstances. Generally topography, weather, fuel types, and methods of management favor the use of prescribed fire in loblolly pine forests of the Coastal Plain. On flat terrain the use of fire to benefit loblolly pine forests is accepted practice.

INSECTS

Loblolly pine is attacked by a large number of insects from seed through maturity to its final use as a product.[26] In the forest, insect damage is often spotty and seldom spectacular, thus escaping attention. Periodically certain conditions favor development of epidemics and unless these are detected in early stages, they may reach cata-

[26] An annotated list of insects is contained in the appendix.

strophic proportions. In 1947 the pine sawfly caused a growth loss of 20 million board feet by its defoliation of pine (Kowal 1955b). Currently bark beetles are causing an estimated mortality of about 250 million board feet of loblolly pine annually throughout the South, while the *Ips* epidemic and the critical drought period of 1956 probably killed more than 50 million feet in Texas alone.

Detection programs, surveys by aircraft, and organized controls are gradually reducing the annual losses. Many infestations are now discovered in their incipiency and extensive outbreaks prevented. A knowledge of the location, abundance, and aggressiveness of the pests is a prime essential. It is possible that in the future, with insect surveys and control methods improved by research and with more intensive management of forests, large scale epidemics will be greatly reduced.

There is considerable undetermined loss of loblolly pine reproduction from the activity of insects, first in reducing seed crops, and later in damage to seedlings. Red spiders and tip moths may injure seedlings in nurseries. Outplanted pine and natural reproduction are killed or damaged by webworms, sawflies, tip moths, and weevils. Under certain conditions these insects, particularly the tip moth, may be a limiting factor in whether or not loblolly pine is selected for planting.

Cuttings that reduce infestations 75 percent or more are often highly beneficial in restoring normal conditions (Hopkins 1909a and 1909b). Stumps, cull logs, limbs, tops, logging slash, and debris attract bark beetles and provide for brood development of many species. Outbreaks originating in slash are sporadic, however, so that no special methods of slash disposal are justified (Beal and Massey 1945). Small localized saw-log cuttings should be made only in winter. Otherwise, a concentration of beetles may overflow, attacking adjacent healthy pines. Yearlong cutting in larger operations for saw logs is generally safe if it is continuous. With a sufficient supply of slash and cut tops the beetles will not infest live trees. The summer cutting of pines for pulpwood is not hazardous. In these operations the relatively small diameter of unutilized tops causes them to dry out too rapidly to provide suitable breeding material for the bark beetles. Beetles also attack trees weakened by fire and subsequently attack nearby groups of unscorched trees.

Southern pine beetle

This bark beetle, *Dendroctonus frontalis*, can be widely destructive. The adults are reddish-brown to black and about ⅛ inch long.

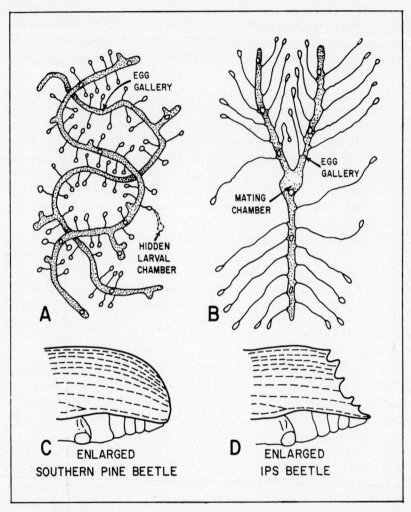

FIGURE 23.—Distinguishing features of two common species of bark beetles. Insect tunnels on inner bark: *A*, southern pine beetle, and *B*, *Ips* beetle. Side view of hind end of adult insect: *C*, southern pine beetle, and *D*, *Ips* beetle (Bennett 1956).

Except for a slight notch on the front of the head between the eyes and much smaller size, it resembles the black turpentine beetle. It can be readily distinguished from *Ips* engraver beetles, whose posterior end has a scooped out appearance. The adult galleries of the southern pine beetle alone are typically serpentine or S-shaped (fig. 23).

Records of extensive devastation of pine timber by this insect date back to the early part of the nineteenth century (Hopkins 1910). Based on present-day stumpage values well over $100,000,-000 worth of timber has been killed in the twentieth century by these beetles. An epidemic in east Texas killed 85 million board feet in 1950-51, and one in Mississippi deadened 30 million board feet in 1952. Much of the volume was harvested, but because of blue stain and degrade only a third of the original stumpage value could be salvaged (Heller, Coyne, and Bean 1955). Infestations are most likely to become epidemic in periods of drought. Any decline in the growth rate of pines, whether the result of drought, age, or overcrowding, may provide favorable conditions for a change from an endemic to an epidemic status. Beginning in 1945, and probably as a result of better methods of detection, outbreaks have been recorded with increasing frequency.

The southern pine beetle is very prolific and may produce from 3 to 6 generations a year in the southern part of its range with a possible tenfold increase per generation. Its life cycle in hot weather is 30 to 40 days, but the complex overlapping of generations makes the cycle difficult to define. Activity during the year is nearly continuous, though in winter it is retarded somewhat in the deep South and considerably in northern sections. After boring through the outer bark, the beetles mate and the female excavates tunnels in the inner bark. Eggs are laid in niches along the sides of the galleries. The larvae feed on inner bark and mine into the outer bark to pupate, emerging as adults and completing one generation in about 40 days. The adults then fly to other pines to carry on the life cycle. As indicated in figure 24, the height zone of attack is generally within that of the engraver beetle and above that of the black turpentine beetle. The southern pine beetle winters in all stages of development in or beneath the bark.

Beetles may inoculate loblolly pines with various fungi. There appears to be a close association between certain bark beetles and stain fungi, one that is possibly mutually helpful until the host tree dies. Such beetles inoculate the trees they infest with blue stain by spores carried on their bodies. Species of *Ceratocystis* have been isolated from both blue-stained wood and from bark beetles. After the insects attack a tree the stain often develops rapidly, permeating the sapwood through the ray tissues and resin ducts and growing from the galleries toward the heartwood. Consequent disruption of normal moisture relations in the tree[27] may desiccate it to a degree

[27] From base to top the moisture content increases in healthy trees, but decreases in trees with blue strain and bark beetles. The trees appear unable to

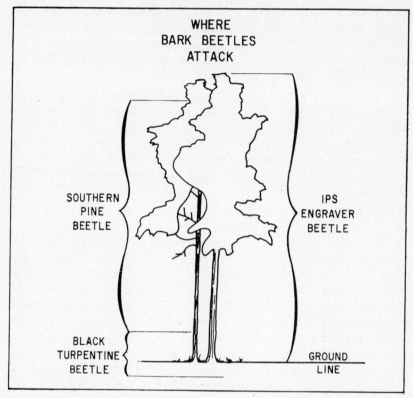

FIGURE 24.—Comparison of zones of infestation typical of three species of pine
    bark beetles.

favoring development of insect broods. Furthermore, it is possible
that the fungus may supply some element of food essential to the
insects, thus providing a truly symbiotic relationship (Craighead
1928). When moist and freshly split open, the stained wood is
steel blue or gray, and the rays and ducts are black (Rumbold 1931).
The blue stain organisms, probably by interfering with the conduc-
tion of water through the wood (Nelson and Beal 1929), appear to
hasten the death of the infested trees.

Over large areas scattered bark beetle infestations are most effectively discovered from the air and counter measures planned from
air reconnaissance. Techniques being developed for aerial survey of
infestations have been reported (Heller, Coyne, and Bean 1955). In
controlling an active outbreak 3 to 5 flights may be needed during

to draw water through the stained wood. Without uninterrupted stain-free pas-
age between roots and crown, the pine dies from lack of water (Nelson 1934).

a season to keep up with the spread of infestation. High wing monoplanes accommodating a pilot and two observers are recommended. Slow flight speeds, under 90 miles per hour, at 3,000 to 5,000 feet are used. Infested spots are plotted directly on aerial photographs (scale 1:20,000), index mosaics, or planimetric maps (1:24,000). By matching landmarks on the ground and on the pictures or maps the infestations are located. Orange or amber filters, worn as face shields or goggles by the observers, accentuate the patches of beetle-killed timber. The marked photographs or maps are used by control crews to find the dying trees. A ratio is computed to relate area or number of trees currently infested to the area or number of trees discolored as seen from the air.

Artificial controls are effective, but must be properly timed. Prompt action is necessary as soon as discoloration in a patch of timber leads to the discovery of pitch tubes on certain trees or other definite evidence of the presence of southern pine beetles. Within 6 weeks after attack during the warmer months the new broods emerge, and the foliage is yellowish to a bright reddish brown. Do not treat trees, except for salvage, if the bark shows numerous small holes, such as might be produced by a load of fine shot, indicating that the beetles have left. After a fatal infestation during the summer months, about 2 weeks elapse before the foliage fades enough for an airplane observer to spot the tree. That leaves about 3 weeks for ground crews to reach and dispose of it (Kirby 1954). In winter the foliage fades slowly. Trees attacked in the autumn may not fade until the following spring.

Salvage is recommended as the most rapid and cheapest method of control. If logs or pulpwood from infested trees cannot be promptly manufactured, they should be stored in water or chemically treated. Otherwise when infested logs are slabbed or peeled, the bark must be burned to destroy the insects.

Infested trees that are inaccessible, or without market value and cannot be used, should be felled without lopping off the branches and the dry bark of trunk and limbs to a 2-inch diameter limit sprayed with benzene hexachloride (BHC). For this purpose 1 gallon of liquid concentrate containing 1 pound of the toxic gamma isomer of benzene hexachloride is mixed with 55 gallons of No. 2 fuel oil (Coyne 1954, Bennett 1956). The trunk and larger limbs are sprayed until the bark is dripping wet. The chemical penetrates and destroys by contact, and insects that may escape are killed by the residual chemical as they emerge from the bark. Follow-up inspections to find and treat later attacks are advisable.

Natural controls destroy many bark beetles. Woodpeckers consume large numbers in the larval stage, but there are never enough of these birds to cope with epidemics. Heavy rain rarely destroys insects, but many succumb to extremes of air temperature. An epidemic of *Dendroctonus frontalis* in 1891-92 was apparently checked absolutely in West Virginia and Virginia by severely cold weather in the early months of 1893 (Blackman 1922). The overwintering broods, usually larvae, are subject to a high degree of mortality when exposed to air temperature below 10°F. for short periods (Beal 1933). Subzero weather is usually fatal to all stages except the eggs, which can withstand −5°F. High temperatures may also help to control these insects. Although standing trees do not get hot enough to limit them, a temperature of 112°F. in logs is fatal. Logs in the sun reach that temperature when the air is at 70° to 80°F. In a north and south position, three days in the sun will kill most of the insects on the upper sides of the logs; the logs must be rolled over to destroy those on the underside.

Engraver beetles

These bark beetles (*Ips* spp.) are generally distributed throughout the range of loblolly pine. They attack all Southern pines and, in the South as a whole, often cause more damage than any other bark beetle. Several species may attack loblolly pine; up to three different ones have been found on the same tree. The common ones are *I. avulsus, I. grandicollis,* and *I. calligraphus.* They are tiny, blackish, hard-shelled insects ⅛ to ¼ inch long. A distinctive feature is the distal end of their abdomen, which is concave with a terminal border of toothlike projections (fig. 23).

Although most of the infestations are secondary, when high populations develop in association with drought, storm, or fire damage to timber, *Ips* may become primary—attacking standing living pines as well as slash or damaged trees. Sometimes healthy trees are attacked for no apparent reason, but often a hidden injury is responsible. Trees injured by lightning are very susceptible to engraver beetles. Stands burned by severe surface or crown fires also, as a rule, entice these insects. *Ips* infestation is common where subsurface fire has injured the roots of trees.

Rather prolific, engraver beetles may produce 4 to 6 broods a year in overlapping generations of 30 to 68 days each. Each tree killed may breed enough beetles to kill 5 more trees (Kowal 1955a).

All stages may be found in the dormant season, but adults are the usual overwintering form. An *Ips* attack is often difficult to recognize in its early stages, as boring dust high in a tree is not easily seen. The first visible evidence may be little piles of reddish-brown boring dust on logs and fallen timber. The dust is often but not always dry and free from pitch. It may be found only in the bark crevices on weakened trees, but on vigorous trees pitch will flow from the entrance holes. Then in 2 or 3 weeks the foliage will fade—a sign of infestation and probable death of the tree—but by this time the beetles have usually emerged.

To determine if *Ips* are present, examine the inner bark for galleries that originate at a central enlarged chamber, and extend more or less parallel to the grain of the wood (fig. 23, *B*). The sapwood is to some extent engraved by these galleries. In niches along the sides of the tunnels the eggs are laid. They soon hatch into larvae that feed at right angles to the main passages without entering sapwood or dry outer bark.

The relation between engraver beetles and forest utilization practice has been observed by Hetrick (1942). He reports that pine trees injured during cutting operations are not generally attacked by *Ips* beetles unless injury is severe. The insects find breeding grounds in pulpwood storage yards, among newly felled pines, or at sawmill sites. Infestation of growing pines on the periphery of concentration yards is common. In summer enormous numbers of *Ips* beetles may develop in freshly stored pulpwood.

Unless timely action is taken beetle outbreaks may multiply. Treating trees from which the brood has already emerged is futile. Kowal (1955a) recommends these measures: (1) *cut* immediately all presently or potentially infested trees, including those badly damaged by logging, lightning, or fire if the inner bark was killed, (2) *dispose* of tops by burning or by pulling into the open where they can be lopped and scattered for quick drying; remove logs and pulpwood promptly, and (3) *spray* with BHC (as recommended for southern pine beetle) infested trees and products not handled as indicated above. Apply a medium fine spray to point of runoff. This treatment, by killing beetles already in the logs and those attempting to bore in during the next three months, retards the degrade of lumber.

Turpentine beetles

The black turpentine beetle, *Dendroctonus terebrans*, considered relatively harmless until recent years, has become a serious enemy of southern pines. It occurs throughout the range of loblolly pine and excessive damage has been reported in Georgia, 1946-47; Louisiana, 1950-51; southwest Mississippi, 1953-56; and east Texas in 1956 where it had previously, 1950-53, killed an estimated 8 million board feet of loblolly pine timber. Infestation has been rather constant during the recent drought years.[28]

Adults of the black turpentine beetle resemble those of the southern pine beetle in shape, but are about twice as large. They vary in length from $\frac{1}{5}$ to $\frac{1}{3}$ of an inch. They are hard-shelled, nearly cylindrical, reddish brown to black beetles. The larvae, creamy-white legless grubs, attain a maximum length of $\frac{3}{8}$ inch.

Turpentine beetle activity usually centers in areas where some disturbance has occurred, and the trees begin to die within a year. The first and most obvious signs of attack are masses of pitch on stumps and on the trunks of trees usually at points less than 6 feet and seldom above 12 feet from the ground (fig. 24). If the resin is free from red boring dust, the beetles may have been "pitched out" by the tree. The insects prefer weakened trees of pole size or larger, seldom molesting saplings less than 3 inches in diameter. When large populations develop pines which appear to be healthy may be attacked. With a mild winter the insects may work throughout the year, but they are most active from early spring to late autumn.

The life cycle requires 3 to 4 months. The beetles bore directly through the outer to the inner bark of the lower trunk and roots. The female deposits 70 to 200 or more eggs in broad irregular galleries which may exceed 20 inches in length. These hatch in 10 to 14 days and the larvae feed gregariously on the inner bark despoiling a few square inches to several square feet. After that, they form cells at the ends of the galleries and transform into pupae that in another 10 to 14 days become adults. Secondary injuries—other bark beetles, stain, and decay—often follow and develop rapidly. Some lightly infested trees may recover and heal their wounds; on others the foliage first turns yellow green, then reddish brown as the tree dies (Lee and Smith 1955). Burning over the forest floor does not kill insects in the trunk or roots.

Damage from turpentine beetles can often be forestalled by some modification of customary woods practice. This involves preventing injury to valuable trees, avoiding bruising or debarking trees while skidding, and promptly salvaging dead and dying trees. A

---

[28] Another species, *Dendroctonus valens*, the red turpentine beetle, occasionally kills pine trees in the northern part of the loblolly pine range.

secondary attack by ambrosia beetles is usually an indication that the tree is beyond recovery. All trees with ambrosia dust around the base should be cut, milled, and the slabs burned before the new broods emerge.

The prevalence of light attacks, a life history extending over several months, and the relative inactivity of the insects, make the turpentine beetles easier to control than other bark beetles (Smith 1955). Turpentine beetles seldom completely kill a stand; rather, each generation tends to attack about the same number of trees per acre. Without control, half the trees may be killed in 3 years. Attack is more severe in dry periods, particularly on flat, normally moist sites.

The essentials of recommended insecticidal control are (1) mark infested trees and break off pitch tubes to expose the entrance holes, improve chemical penetration, and permit detection of renewed attack; (2) without cutting deeply into firm bark, remove loose scales and debris from base of trees; (3) prepare BHC spray solution by adding 1 pound of gamma isomer of BHC to 14 gallons of No. 2 fuel oil; (4) spray the lower 10 feet of trunk during dry weather to the point of runoff. Wetting the ground at the base of a tree may reach broods in the larger roots. At the rate of 1 gallon to 45 square feet of bark surface, 2 gallons should cover twenty 18-inch stumps or the basal 10 feet on 3 trees. This should kill the beetles and prevent further attacks for 3 to 7 months. The insecticide has a residual action that helps to prevent subsequent attacks. Valuable seed trees should be watched, however, from April through July and treated whenever insect activity is in evidence (Kowal and Coyne 1951; Smith 1954b).

Tip moths

The Nantucket pine tip moth, *Rhyacionia frustrana,* occurs throughout the range of loblolly pine. Though it seldom kills pines and rarely prevents regeneration, it often injures open-grown natural reproduction and may temporarily retard plantation height growth. Many repeatedly infested seedlings become so bushy and saplings so deformed as to produce nearly worthless trees. Successive attacks may reduce height growth by half a foot annually (Wenger 1958) and may add 5 years to the rotation age of afflicted stands (Beal 1952). The work of tip moths may be discovered first by excessive resin on the pine buds and later by the dead twigs. Fortunately, the most susceptible height range is narrow: seedlings from 3 to 10 feet are most severely attacked; above 10 feet they

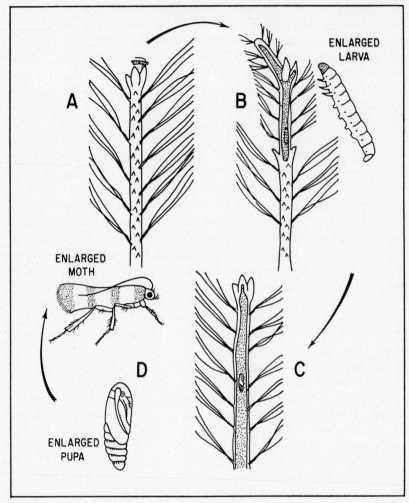

FIGURE 25.—Life cyle of the Nantucket pine tip moth: *A*, First flight in February or March; *B*, eggs on foliage hatch into larvae that tunnel in buds and twigs; *C*, pupae form within dead twigs; and *D*, emerge as moths in about 2 weeks (Bennett 1956).

are seldom affected. Accordingly, on poor sites where the seedling stage is normally longer, the infestations are the more serious. Infestations also tend to be more severe where spacing is wide, but on good sites rapid growth aids the pines in quick recovery and in getting above the susceptible size class.

The adults are delicate tan-colored moths with forewings spreading about half an inch and faintly marked with copper-colored

bands and spots. Eggs laid at intervals of 5 to 6 weeks on the succulent new growth hatch in about 2 weeks. The larvae soon spin
silken webs in the axils of needles near the terminal buds and feed
on tender cortical tissue until about 3 mm. long, then burrow into
buds and twigs. When about 7 mm. long they enter the pith of a
tender terminal and feed up into the bud. Pupation occurs in buds
and twigs hollowed out and often killed back 6 to 12 inches (fig.
25). A second brood may appear as early as the second week in
June or as late as early August. Observations indicate the number
of generations per season as follows: 3 in Virginia, the Carolinas,
and Tennessee; and 4 in Florida and Louisiana (Underhill 1943;
Mortimer 1941; Wakeley 1928, 1935a). Typical of the long gulf
coast season are the observations of four broods there following adult
flights in February-March, May, July, and August-September. In
most of its range the exact number of broods is difficult to estimate
because of the great overlapping of generations by midsummer.

Some 23 species of parasites representing 11 families have been
reared from tip moths. Though parasitism may exceed 50 percent,
it remains of minor importance (Underhill 1943).

Where other natural controls are weak and several generations
a season the rule, as in the Deep South, certain precautions may be
advisable in starting plantations. It is advantageous to avoid both
heavily infested and poor-quality sites, and to plant stock selected
for its superior growth capacity or stock treated against these insects. To avoid introduction in new areas and to provide temporary
protection for seedlings planted, mass sterilization of nursery stock
is relatively easy. Seedlings may be dipped in 1 percent white oil
emulsion or in a DDT suspension containing 1 pound of 50-percent
wettable powder to 50 gallons of water to kill the eggs or young
larvae. Pupae, as well as larvae, can be killed by fumigation with
5 ounces of sodium cyanide per 1,000 cubic feet for 1 hour. These
treatments are not recommended, however, for plantations where the
tip moths are already established.

Control under forest conditions is usually impractical as it would
require several spraying operations per season. On small or isolated
areas the prompt destruction of infested buds and twigs by pruning may help (Bennett 1955a). A spray of 1 percent water emulsion
of DDT, if very complete on foliage and buds, can kill many larvae.
Treatment against the first generation of exposed larvae—soon after
the eggs hatch—is most effective because the whole brood is then in
its larval stage. Later control is difficult because pupae are in buds
and twigs where they cannot be reached by insecticide.

Tip moths do most damage in open spots. Under shelterwood or selection methods of silviculture, the incidence of tip moth attack is less than it is under clear-cutting systems or in plantations. This is fortunate because recovery from such attack is less rapid among seedlings that grow slowly because of shelter, crowding, drought, or other causes. Hence, in spite of the advantage of having rapid growth in pine, it may be best to refrain from liberation or release cuttings until the sapling stage is reached. In one instance near Oxford, Miss., a second-year tip moth infestation affected 28 percent of unreleased seedlings and 82 percent of those released (Huckenpahler 1953b).

Rhyacionia rigidana and *R. buoliana*, the European pine shoot moth, are similar and both occasionally infest loblolly pine in the Southeast. The adults are more conspicuously marked with brownish-red spots and silver-gray stripes. By injuring flower buds tip moths may cause serious damage to pine seed orchards. The larvae of other insects reported to damage the terminal shoots of loblolly pine include *Dioryctria amatella*, one of the cone moths.

Pales weevil

Another pest that attacks young seedlings of loblolly pine is a nearly black snout beetle, *Hylobius pales*, that breeds in pine stumps and roots. It resembles the cotton boll weevil in shape and size. An insect of similar appearance, *Pachylobius picivorus*, attacks pine seedlings in the same manner as pales. Many of the seedlings up to 4 or 5 feet in height, which adults of both species attack by feeding on stems and branches, are not seriously damaged, but seedlings less than 2 years old or 24 inches high may be killed. This happens in the vicinity of freshly cut pine stumps, dying pines, logging or building operations, or piles of green lumber (fig. 26).

The pales beetle is a robust weevil up to $\frac{3}{8}$ inch long emerging first from hibernation in the litter just before the time of serviceberry flowering; others appearing 6 weeks later as the overwintering larvae develop (Beal and McClintick 1943). Most of the damage occurs from March to July but sometimes there is damage again in the autumn (Speers 1955). Apparently attracted by the odor of pitch, the weevils concentrate on areas where pines have been recently removed. New adults emerge at various times from May to October, depending on time of cutting. In one instance mortality of seedlings was 55 percent on a recently cut area as against only 1 percent where no pines had been cut (Ferguson and Duke 1954). The weevils start to feed on tender bark of the seedlings and most

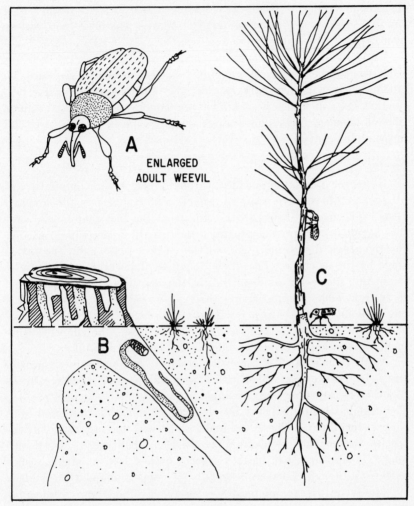

FIGURE 26.—Pales weevil: *A*, Adult insect enlarged; *B*, breeding place beneath
the bark of root of stump showing tunnel where larva makes its cocoon
and transforms into adult; *C*, weevils, attracted by fresh cut or burned
stumps, girdle and kill adjacent seedlings (Bennett 1956).

of the damage is in patches within a few inches of the ground.   In
the soil they strip the roots to a depth of 4 or 5 inches.   Bark damage, though irregular, is usually severe enough to kill seedlings in
first-year plantations on areas without natural reproduction (Sentell
1949).   This damage may be largely avoided by waiting one full
growing season before planting pine cut-over areas.   Where immediate planting is necessary, an insecticidal top dip (a BHC

suspension) for pine seedlings is recommended on areas from which the pine has recently been cut (Ferguson and Thatcher 1956, Speers 1956).

Understory advance reproduction is most vulnerable to these insects where the overwood of pine has been recently depleted by cutting, fire, wind, or bark beetles. On such areas natural reproduction has sometimes been killed completely, but in most instances in well-managed forests not enough seedlings die to warrant artificial measures of control.

Sawflies

In recent years the sawflies, through their severe defoliation of all ages of pines, have assumed economic importance as forest insect pests. The insects derive their name from the fact that female sawflies have sawlike appendages which they use to create slits in needles for their egg deposition. Actual defoliation is done by the larval stage of the sawflies. There are about 10 important or potentially important species of pine sawflies in the South, most of which seem to include loblolly pine among their preferred hosts. Some of the most common are *Neodiprion taeda linearis, N. pratti pratti, N. hetricki, N. exitans,* and *N. lecontei.* The latter, though most commonly observed, is presently one of the least important.

Adult female sawflies somewhat resemble honeybees in shape and size. The life cycle, which varies with the species, is generally as follows: Females lay eggs in single rows within slits in pine needles. The eggs hatch into hairless, slender worms, sometimes referred to as false caterpillars. These gradually take on the markings of the species and mature in about 6 weeks when they are ¾ to ⅞ inch long. It appears that most southern species have a striped color pattern, although *Neodiprion lecontei* is cream colored with a black spot pattern. Larvae of most species display the group feeding behavior habit, clustering in large numbers on needles at ends of twigs. At maturity the larvae leave the crown and pupate under bark scales or most often in the soil; they spin the characteristic capsule-shaped, chestnut-colored cocoons. After several months the pupae change into adults which emerge from the cocoons and renew the life cycle.

The effect of feeding on trees varies with the time of defoliation, its severity, and the vigor of the trees. Spring defoliation of 1-year needles, though severe, causes growth loss but no mortality. Late summer or autumn defoliation may, if severe, cause outright mortality or render trees susceptible to attack by bark beetles. Shaded seedlings, not well rooted, succumb easily. Open-grown seedlings survive well unless heavily defoliated. At one place the loss of 75 percent of foliage meant losing 84 percent of the seedlings (Beal 1942).

The larger trees usually recover without loss of twigs and often regain a full complement of needles by August. Growth losses may in some instances be significant. There appears to be a linear relation between the number of trees infested and the severity of defoliation on the individual trees. Less than 50 percent defoliation may not influence growth noticeably, but 50 to 100 percent causes increasingly greater current retardation. Summerwood production is reduced (Hetrick 1941). Trees 75 percent defoliated in 1947 were retarded in volume growth 51 percent the first year and 29 percent the second (Reynolds 1949a).

Nature assists in the control of sawflies, though usually in large epidemics the natural control comes too late to prevent damage. Many species of insect parasites have been reared from cocoons. Virus diseases sometimes control outbreaks. These are being studied for possible use in the biological control of insects. Rodents assist in control by consuming sawfly cocoons in the soil.

Silvicultural measures appear to be effective in control of some sawfly species. For example in outbreaks of *Neodiprion lecontei*, fewer open-grown seedlings are attacked and a smaller percentage of the infested ones die; therefore, release from shade is favored where not enough natural reproduction is free to grow (Beal 1942). For similar reasons, in artificial regeneration, underplanting should be avoided and pines should not be set within 25 feet of hardwood borders unless the hardwoods can be removed or girdled promptly (Benjamin 1955).

Chemical control is readily accomplished by using either ground or aerial equipment to dispense insecticides. For use with hand equipment 1-percent DDT emulsions are recommended. For aerial applications, oil solutions containing 1 pound of DDT per gallon per acre has been satisfactory in control operations conducted in Arkansas and Louisiana (Kowal 1953).

Other defoliators

The Texas leaf-cutting ant, *Atta texana*, found in Texas and Louisiana prefers deep sandy soil. Although little damage is ordinarily done to pines when other green plants are available, in winter these ants may completely destroy very young seedlings and defoliate larger ones within 300 or 400 feet of their colonies. These "towns" have conspicuous funnel-shaped mounds on the surface and a maze of underground tunnels. The larger workers cut and drop large sections of needles; the smaller ants dissect and store them. The leaf fragments are not consumed; they are material for a subterranean garden in which the ants cultivate certain fungi for food (Walter, Seaton, and Matthewson 1938).

In areas where the ant population is high it is impossible to establish pine seedlings by planting or natural means unless the ants have previously been destroyed. Satisfactory control is possible with methyl bromide to destroy the towns (Bennett 1955b, Johnston 1944). Chlordane or dieldrin may be used to destroy small isolated colonies and in mopup operations. Methyl bromide is a heavy gas applied through a tube with a valve. One-fourth pound is suggested for towns up to about 15 feet in diameter, and one pound or more for large colonies. Results are best on warm winter days when the soil is moist.

A beetle, *Colaspis pini* Barber, found along the gulf coast, chews the margins of needles, leaving a saw-tooth edge and causing them to turn partly or completely brown. Small trees acquire a fire-scorched appearance, but feeding stops in midsummer and the saplings are green again by autumn. Young pines can be successfully sprayed with lead arsenate, but the cost is not considered justifiable, as the effect of the colaspis beetle is believed to be normally slight.

A pine needle miner, *Exoteleia pinifoliella*, is a moth the larvae of which may mine the internal needle tissues of loblolly pine, browning the foliage on extensive areas. Effects are not serious and no control is suggested.

The pine webworm, *Tetralopha robustella*, defoliator of seedlings, especially where they are shaded, likewise does not require control measures except in rare instances, nor do several species of aphids sometimes found feeding on the pines.

Cone insects

Two species of moths, *Dioryctria amatella* and *Laspeyresia toreuta*, commonly feed on loblolly pine cones. The first is the more destructive, destroying seeds in the entire cone. The second destroys only a few seeds per cone. The full-grown larvae of *Dioryctria* are greenish brown or dull black, about an inch long, and the pupae ⅝ inch long. In 1946 infestation of 11 to 78 percent of the cones on 4 tracts resulted in the loss of 9 to 42 percent of the seeds (Pomeroy 1950a). Smaller and drier than the healthy cones, the infested cones commonly fail to open. After destroying the interior, the larva emerges through a ⅛-inch hole. Infestation tends to be worse in the older stands and on the better sites, perhaps because there the insects find a more continuous supply of cones for annual feeding (Knight 1951). Nothing is yet known of the possibility for control.

White grubs

The larvae of May or June beetles, *Phyllophaga* spp., may severely injure and kill pines planted on old-field sites by consuming root tissue. Eggs are laid 1 to 8 inches deep in soil in early summer. Three weeks later ⅛-inch grubs hatch to live on organic matter and roots. Some feed until autumn, then pupate and emerge in the spring. Others spend the second winter as grubs, pupate in summer, overwinter as adults, and emerge in summer of the third year.

With most of the activity underground these infestations are not readily apparent, but in time the seedlings become unthrifty and can be extracted from the soil with a gentle pull. The period of heaviest damage is usually mid-August to late October. Planting is not recommended on sites having more than one grub to each 2 square feet.

Control measures are practical in forest nurseries[29] and are being studied for use in outplanting pine. Nursery stock can be dipped in various organic insecticides. A device for spot distribution of insecticide on roots and the adjacent soil can be attached to a shoe-type planting machine (Shenefelt, Liebig, and Dosen 1955).

Wood-damaging insects

Insects damaging products of loblolly pine are numerous but detailed discussion of the subject is not attempted because of the many variables involved. In any case, loblolly pine wood is highly susceptible to attack by termites, pine powder-post beetles, carpenter ants, and other insects. Control through preventive measures is most effective; the application of remedial measure is often difficult and expensive.

Logs, veneer bolts and pulpwood when stored before milling are susceptible to severe attack by ambrosia beetles, bark beetles, and wood borers. Studies (Johnston 1952) have shown that benzene hexachloride properly applied to green logs is highly effective in preventing insect attack. A concentration of 1¾ pounds of the gamma isomer of this insecticide per 50 gallons of No. 2 fuel oil is recommended for pine logs when maximum protection from attack

[29] Discussed in the section on diseases and insects in Chapter 5, Artificial Regeneration.

by all insects is desired for about 4 months. A spray of only half
this concentration will protect pine logs and poles from bark beetles
and wood borers but not ambrosia beetles. One gallon will wet 100
square feet of bark surface. Four to six gallons of solution are needed
per cord of pulpwood. In treating decked logs the spray must be
directed from both ends into the spaces between them.

Several insects that enter injured trees or those weakened by
other agents contribute only in a minor way to mortality, but continue to degrade or destroy the value of raw wood products.

Heavy damage to recently killed or harvested pine not promptly
removed from the forest in summer is done by both the roundheaded
and flatheaded borers. Among them is a longhorned beetle, the
southern pine sawyer *Monochamus titillator*. The adults are mottled
brown and gray, $3/4$ to $1\frac{1}{4}$ inches long. In the male the antennae
may be 2 or 3 times as long as the beetle. The females deposit 6 to
12 eggs in each of their circular incisions beneath the outer bark.
Activity continues except during the coldest 3 or 4 months, resulting
in overlapping broods and at least 2 generations annually. The damage is done by the larvae before they emerge through pencil-sized holes
(Beal 1952, Webb 1911). The sculptured pine borer, *Chalcophora
virginiensis*, is a flatheaded borer. Its work is similar. Two or more
years are needed to complete its life cycle. Logs sawed into lumber
within a month after harvesting usually escape damage.

Logs not milled within 2 weeks may be damaged by several species
of Ambrosia beetles. They make tiny holes that extend deep into
the sapwood and sometimes the heartwood. They inoculate their
galleries with ambrosial fungus which is used for food. This activity causes a dark stain of the wood. Methods of chemical control of these insects in logs are given in the sections on engraver
and southern pine beetles.

Lumber having less than 50 percent moisture is not in danger of
attack. Green lumber may be protected, however, by dipping or
spraying entire stacks with emulsions of less than half the concentration of benzene hexachloride used for logs. Water suspensions
of this chemical will protect lumber and they may be combined with
the commonly used sapstain preventives such as 2-percent sodium
pentachlorophenate (Kowal 1949).

ANIMALS

Animals large or small, and domestic or wild, often damage, but
seldom prevent, the regeneration of loblolly pine.

More study of the inroads of various seed predators is needed. Seed-eating birds and rodents abound in many forest areas. Especially on cutover lands where pine reproduction is desired, the seed eaters sometimes increase tenfold in a year. They cause serious depredations of seed supplies, often taking nearly all of the crop in light and moderate seed years. As the seeds develop into seedlings, most of the birds and some of the rodents cease to feed upon them.

The larger animals that may damage loblolly pine seedlings include deer, hogs, cattle, horses, sheep, and goats. Where the range is unburned and lightly stocked, with either animals or with small seedlings, the damage to pines from livestock may be negligible. The extent of the injury to loblolly pine seedlings is related to the distribution and range habits of these animals in grazing or browsing available forage and compacting the soil by trampling. Where concentration of livestock is avoided, the trampling damage by animals is usually slight, and may be wholly offset by some reduction in fire hazard. Deer populations, however, are subject to periodic alarming natural increases that, in spite of the legal take by hunters, can preclude satisfactory reproduction of loblolly pine.

Deer

In recent years deer have been numerous enough in two southern counties of Arkansas and adjacent Louisiana to damage 1- to 4-year-old pine plantations and natural reproduction on several 50,000- to 100,000-acre tracts. The serious browsing damage is mainly confined to late winter or early spring. It occurs on overstocked range, but apparently is not related to scarcity of the better forage plants. Some seedlings are pulled up, but most of them are nipped off. Many of the mutilated ones acquire new leaders and branches, but some remain forked or otherwise deformed. The foliage of fertilized nursery stock recently planted in the forest seems to be more attractive to deer than that of natural reproduction, and this may be a serious problem even where the deer population is not excessively heavy.

Hogs

Among the southern pines, hogs prefer young starchy bark of longleaf pine; slash pine is their second choice, and loblolly pine is the species least often molested. They kill seedlings by stripping bark from around the main stem above and below the surface of the ground. A loblolly pine seedling 3 feet high has only about 25 grams of root bark, which is less than for slash pine and only a third as much as for a longleaf pine seedling one foot high. This may be why hogs usually discriminate between species of pine. Nevertheless, in LaSalle Parish, Louisiana, a loblolly pine plantation made in the spring of 1952 was damaged 4 years later when the trees were 4 feet tall. Between March and July the hogs made girdles about 6 inches wide killing 472 loblolly pines per acre and damaging 90 more. In 5 months the plantation was reduced from 747 to 195 trees (Peevy and Mann 1952). In a mixed-species plantation the hogs killed 52 percent of the slash pine and 4 percent of the loblolly pine. Protective measures using chemical repellents and electric fences failed. Feral hogs are the chief offenders; hogs that are well fed show little interest in loblolly pine.

Other domestic stock

Cattle and horses do less harm than sheep and goats, but in farm woodlands grazing by cattle may be a serious problem. Cattle seldom graze on pines if other green forage is available, but some incidental browsing and trampling damage can be expected in the first years after seeding or planting where cattle are not excluded. Plantations should not be grazed until well established. Once the seedlings are a foot or two high, cattle can be admitted in limited numbers where there is grass enough to keep them from browsing on the pines (J. E. Davis 1950a and 1950b). Brinkman and Swarthout (1942), studying reproduction of pine in Alabama, found that grazing by cattle apparently had an adverse effect on the survival and growth of the seedlings. The form and vigor of young trees was often poor because of mechanical injuries by the cattle.

Studies in central Louisiana (Cassady, Hopkins, and Whitaker 1955) have pointed out when and where to expect cattle damage. Heavy loss may occur where cattle concentrate and overgraze. Such places are watering and feeding grounds and situations in which forage is greener and fresher than in the surroundings. Hence any treatment that removes old grass and stimulates new growth is attractive. Burning, disking, scalping, and hardwood control often have this effect. In one instance 2-year-old loblolly pines were 10 inches tall on the grazed part and 17 inches tall on the nongrazed part of an area where the hardwoods were controlled. Where the hardwoods were not treated the seedlings were 22 inches tall on the grazed and 28 inches on the ungrazed parts. Fortunately, loblolly pine usually recovers readily from early retardation. When palatable forage is limited, as on the native ranges in the late winter or early spring, browsing damage by cattle is more likely.

Less damage results as the seedlings grow taller. Trampling is most injurious for seedlings less than 2 feet high and rubbing injury from 2 to 6 feet; those 6 to 8 feet tall are seldom injured. Grazing among trees of susceptible size should be regulated. In Louisiana it should not start before May 1 and not more than half the green forage should be cropped during the whole season. Range-carrying capacity for cattle indicates 1 acre per month per head on open unimproved range. More acreage is needed where the forest cover reduces the growth of grass.

Sheep, and especially goats, are inherently more destructive than deer or cattle because of close cropping and indiscriminate browsing. This kills many loblolly pines during the first year or two after planting. The animals nip the terminal buds from many of the surviving seedlings, retarding their height growth. Repetition in succeeding years deforms the trees. Both sheep and goats should be excluded until the buds and most of the foliage are out of reach. As the majority of these animals graze only within enclosed pastures in the South, range control without fencing will suffice in most instances (Stanley 1954).

Rabbits, gophers, and squirrels

Rabbits cause frequent light and occasional severe injury to loblolly pine seedlings. Wakeley (1954a) discussing plantation care describes the activity of rabbits as follows:

"They bite off the side branches, buds, upper tops, or entire seedlings, usually the winter they are planted, sometimes the winter following. They bite them off cleanly, usually at an angle of about 45 degrees, in contrast to the irregular cut or break made by cattle, sheep, or goats. They seldom injure the needles, and, unlike hogs, rats, and some insects, do not strip or chafe the bark. Often, though not always, they leave the side branch or top uneaten beside the cut stub. They are much more likely to injure small seedlings than large ones. . . .

"The seriousness of rabbit damage depends more on the mortality percent of the injured trees than on the percentage bitten. Recovery from injury during the second winter is usually good. Where the rabbits bite off the tops 1 to 4 inches above the ground during the first winter or bite only buds or side branches, recovery frequently is good. If the seedlings are large and of high quality, the site is moist, and the weather after planting is favorable, survival may be good even when seedlings are bitten off within one-fourth inch of the ground, but there may be 10 to 30 percent loss of height growth during the next 5 years, and some forking of main stems at the

ground. On dry sites and in dry years, or with small planting stock, biting off 60 to 100 percent of the seedlings during
the first winter has caused enough mortality to ruin plantations. . . .''

If there are signs of a heavy population of rabbits at planting
sites, and if planting of large nursery stock cannot be deferred until
late in February, the rabbits should be intensively hunted or the
seedlings sprayed or dipped in repellent before planting (Mann and
Derr 1954a, Stanley 1954).

For chemical repellent a mixture of asphalt emulsion and copper
carbonate is effective though somewhat phytotoxic. It is prepared
by mixing 3 pounds of asphalt emulsion with 2 quarts of water;
then add 2 pounds of copper carbonate and mix well; dilute the
mixture with 8 more quarts of water. It should be applied at the
rate of about 2 pints per 1,000 trees. When lifted stock is being
treated, the roots should be shielded from the chemical.

The eastern pocket gopher, *Geomys breviceps* Baird, also causes
frequent light and occasional heavy damage in the Coastal Plain.
In east Texas they have sometimes killed from 3 to 20 percent of
the planted trees over thousands of acres (Wakeley 1954a). These
subterranean pests measure about 7 inches with tails 3½ inches long.
Eyes and ears are small, claws are stout, food pouches open on the
sides of their faces.

Along their burrows they place soil on the surface in circular
mounds a foot or more across. Roots encountered in tunneling are
maimed or destroyed. Dying seedlings, easily pulled up, have
truncated roots. Sometimes a whole seedling is pulled underground
and devoured.

Control should start a year in advance of planting and never
later than the first winter after the presence of gophers is apparent.
The damage is best countered at nurseries and on planting sites
during the season of active burrowing between November and the
middle of May. The system of burrows is elaborate with main and
secondary tunnels, and separate storage and sleeping chambers.
Some preliminary ground probing by control crews to discover the
local pattern of tunnels can increase the effectiveness of their work
with traps or poison.

Squirrels commonly consume all immature cones found on certain
trees in off years. Damage, however, has not been extensive enough
to require control measures.

DISEASES

Loblolly pines are relatively free from disease in their native habitat, but some reduction of disease is needed for a full measure of success in forestry.[29a] Where they are reproduced naturally, pines often are less subject to disease than in plantations. No amount of silviculture can save stands planted in an unsuitable environment. For both living trees and their wood products, site is a factor that may predispose them to disease or decay. Hence, site deserves consideration not only in locating plantations, but also in utilizing wood properly where it is exposed to fluctuations in moisture.

Because, on the whole, the value of individual forest-grown loblolly pines is less than that of orchard or shade trees, foresters are necessarily limited in the use of horticultural methods of controlling tree diseases. Except in forest nurseries and sometimes in plantations it is seldom economical to resort to spraying, dusting, cultivation, or rotation of crops to reduce disease. Proper sanitation in forests depends largely on judicious cutting to remove injured and diseased pines while controlling the density and species composition of stands. Heart rots seldom damage second-growth pine seriously. In the long run silvicultural care steps up the thrift of a forest partly through elimination of the more susceptible trees and partly by progressive destruction of sources of infection.

Cronartium rusts

The southern pines are host to two species of stem cankering fungi with alternate stages on the oaks. These rusts spread from pine to oak, oak to oak, and oak to pine, but never from pine to pine. *Cronartium cerebrum*, producing spherical galls on loblolly pine, does little damage and is less prevalent than the fusiform rust, *C. fusiforme*. Fusiform rust destroys young trees after it enters the main stems. It kills large numbers of seedlings and disfigures and weakens the trunks of trees. According to Wenger (1950) working in coastal South Carolina, trees with 47 percent of the circumference cankered will last for 5 years and those with 40 percent cankered are a good 10-year risk. Pines nearly girdled by cankers may be broken down by wind (fig. 27) but very few cankered trees need to be cut in pole-size stands for fear of mechanical breakage (Klawitter 1957).

The fusiform rust has been studied intensively by Siggers (1955) who reports on its life history as follows:

[29a] An annotated list of fungus diseases is contained in the appendix.

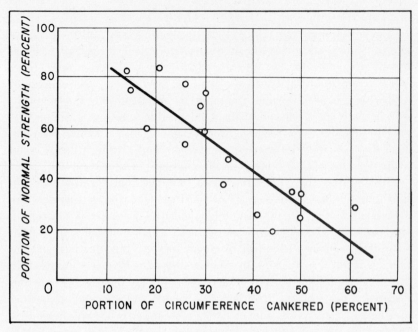

FIGURE 27.—Loblolly pine stems infected with *Cronartium fusiforme* are weakened in direct proportion to the extent of circumference cankered (Wenger 1950).

"The fusiform rust lives from year to year in the living bark of pines; on oaks it develops annually on the lower side of young leaves. The disease is not transmitted directly from pine to pine, but must first pass through a period of development on the oaks, chiefly species of the pointed-leaf or black oak group.

"The cycle of infection usually starts in March with the production of powder-like yellowish spores on pine cankers and wind dissemination of this inoculum to oak leaves. About 10 days after infection, minute yellowish spots appear on the lower leaf surfaces. In these spots spores of a different type are produced; these can infect other oaks, but not pines. This is the repeating stage of the rust and it serves to increase the amount of inoculum on the oaks.

"A few days after the repeating stage first appears numerous brownish hairlike structures, called telia, begin to develop around the margins of the older yellowish spots. ... In due course teliospore germination is followed by the formation of sporidia, the spores that can infect pine. The round of infection from pine to oak, oak to oak, and oak to pine occurs only in the spring, extending usually from about the middle of March to the middle of June."

This disease infects pine saplings through their succulent new shoots. When these are delayed, as they tend to be where the pines are reproduced under the shelterwood system, there is less damage from fusiform rust. Anything that causes an early break in dormancy seems to increase the incidence of the rust. Large variation in amount of infection occurs in different seasons in the same locality. Relatively early development of oak foliage and early seasonal activity of fusiform rust go hand in hand. A minimum of 18 hours of sustained high atmospheric humidity with temperatures between 60° and 80° F. are needed for abundant pine infection.

Infection stimulates the cambium tissue of a pine to grow 2 or 3 times as rapidly as normal. The resulting woody swelling is typically spindle shaped. These cankers, more virulent or vigorous than on overtopped branches, unfortunately grow faster toward the trunk than away from it. Vigorous growth itself, however, unless it starts prematurely in the spring, does not predispose pines to infection. A slow-growing strain of loblolly pine from Georgia suffered more at Bogalusa, La., than did the vigorous local strain.

Loblolly pine appears to be more susceptible to infection than slash pine, but a higher percentage of loblolly pine infections are limited to branches. Once infected, slash pine is more sensitive to invasion of the living bark by the fungus and hence is more easily killed.[30] The alternate hosts (*Quercus* spp.) differ in susceptibility to infection. As a group the black oaks are more susceptible than the white oaks. According to Siggers (1955) the 3 most susceptible in nature are water oak (*Q. nigra*), willow oak (*Q. phellos*), and laurel oak (*Q. laurifolia*). Other oaks in descending order of susceptibility are bluejack (*Q. incana*), blackjack (*Q. marilandica*), southern red (*Q. falcata*), turkey (*Q. laevis*), and live oak (*Q. virginiana*). An understory of these alternate hosts always favors the rust on pine, but the presence of a pine overstory has not been shown to influence the disease (Hebb 1948). Most diseased pines become infected during their first 10 years of age. Although later infections are fairly common and may be destructive at times, the stands that escape with light early infection generally reach harvest age without serious damage. Cankered bolts are usually acceptable at pulp mills. It is characteristic of loblolly pine that many of the older trees with severely cankered trunks may continue to live many years.

[30] The lower percentage of rust infection on loblolly than on slash pine in nurseries is probably due to delay in seed germination of loblolly pine. The percentage of cankered seedlings is lower in late sowings (Sleeth 1943).

The effects of fire can retard or favor this disease, depending on local conditions. Fires that kill low cankered branches in sapling stands reduce the number of diseased trees. However, a greater number of new infections may occur where fire has been used, if the burning induces an early break in winter dormancy of the trees. In that case, relatively large amounts of new shoot growth may be formed in early spring when weather conditions favorable to spore germination and pine infection prevail. Both fertilization and cultivation of pine also has the effect of stimulating early shoot growth and thus increasing the amount of rust.

In young stands the amount of damage depends on the prevalence of trunk cankers, as the expanding branch cankers that never reach the stem have little effect on growth. In dense natural stands the early formation of a canopy causes the lower branches and branch cankers to die before they reach the main stem. There is a tendency for infection to be worse in open stands (Goggans 1957). For this reason extra close spacing or the use of a resistant strain may be preferable for plantations in areas where the intensity of infection is high. The number of infections per tree decreases with age. An oak-free isolation band extending 1,500 feet from the pines is not effective (Sleeth 1943). However, a common procedure is to space the trees widely and prune cankered branches manually where they occur within 15 inches of the stem. It is unnecessary to burn the pruned branches.

When nursery seedlings are lifted for planting those with cankers should be culled;[31] cankered trees will almost invariably die if outplanted. For the first 5 years after planting, and wherever 25 to 30 percent infection is found on branches, dormant season pruning of diseased branches is desirable as a means of reducing later losses. Those trees which can attain merchantable size at the first scheduled thinning should be saved. When the main stem is not cankered during the second 5 years after planting, most pine saplings survive. In pole-size stands the first cutting may be confined to usable trees likely to die before the next thinning. Although it would be well to eliminate all stem infection before final harvest, those with half their girth healthy are often good risks for several years.

Lindgren (1948), working in the Deep South, suggests estimating the odds in favor of deferred salvage on the basis of five disease-condition classes as follows: (1) over 18 inches between canker and trunk—no problem; (2) less than 18 inches clearance—salvage with-

---

[31] Nursery spraying for rust control is discussed in chapter 5, Artificial Regeneration.

in 8 years; (3) less than half the trunk girdled—better than 50 percent chance of survival for 8 years; (4) over half girdled but no sunken area or bend at the canker—an even chance for at least 5 years; (5) same plus the bend or sunken area—an even chance for less than 5 years.

Root diseases

A condition known as "spot die-out" affects both planted and natural stands of loblolly pine in the Carolinas, Alabama, and Mississippi. It is largely in plantations over 10 years of age. Most of the spots are less than one-half acre in extent, but in the aggregate a large area is affected. The damage is closely associated with sheet erosion on soils of fine texture with poorly drained subsoils on gently sloping land. The water infiltration rates on diseased spots are only half of those on surrounding areas where trees remain healthy. Tests showing reduced oxidation in "die-out" areas indicate poor soil aeration as the primary cause. Usually, but not always, the trees die before they reach pulpwood size.

Nematodes of the genus *Xiphinema* and a group of genera reported loosely as "tylenchs" are believed to be parasites on loblolly pine seedlings. The genera *Heliocotylenchus* and *Tylenchorhynchus* particularly are suspect. They may not only attack roots directly, but also open the way to infection by fungus parasites. Control by fumigation of the soil is effective in nurseries.

On fine-textured soils in certain areas the roots of loblolly pine become black and decay as the tree dies. In this manner plantations have suffered from an unidentified black root rot in Tennessee and the Carolinas. In some sections of Oklahoma and Texas many shelterbelt species have become infected with a "cotton root rot" caused by *Phymatotrichum omnivorum* that has killed about 1 percent of the loblolly pine.[32]

Widespread, but not abundant, causes of root and butt rot in older forest-grown loblolly pine are *Polyporus schweinitzii* and *Fomes annosus*. *Fomes annosus* has been found causing root rot on several species of southern pine trees that have been uprooted. This rot is expected to become more important in pine plantations that are thinned, but there is no reason to belive it will become a major problem with loblolly pine. *Fomes annosus* on loblolly pine in the Duke Forest has been serious only in stands well beyond a reasonably economical rotation. The fungus builds up and fruits on stumps

[32] The decay of seedling roots from damping-off or other causes is discussed as a part of nursery practice in chapter 5, Artificial Regeneration.

and roots of felled trees. Eventually it enters the roots of living trees where they are in contact with the decaying roots. Once this happens there is no economic means of control other than the harvest of obviously diseased trees. In south Africa where loblolly pine has been introduced, a rot apparently caused by *Stereum sanguinolentum* (A. & S.) originates in the root system and spreads into the stems of the trees. Although damage so far has not been serious in plantations, foresters are concerned because thrifty trees are attacked for no apparent reason (Lückoff 1955).

Littleleaf disease

Loblolly pine is more resistant to littleleaf disease than shortleaf pine, its principal host. Loblolly pine usually becomes affected to a considerable degree only where shortleaf pine is severely diseased. Dominant and codominant trees are the more susceptible. Where diseased shortleaf pines suffered a 5-year mortality of 34 to 83 percent, the associated loblolly pines showed occasional symptoms and 3 percent died in 5 years. Although some individual trees may decline from healthy to severely diseased in a single year, most of them succumb only after 3 to 15 years of progressive weakening, and stands break up between 30 and 50 years of age (Hepting 1944 and 1949; Roth, Buchanan, and Hepting 1948). With this disease the average time until death is 7 years from the earliest discernible evidence, 6 years from typical symptoms, and 3 years from advanced symptoms (Campbell and Copeland 1954). The first evidence is usually a slight yellowing of the foliage. The yellowing becomes more pronounced as the disease progresses, especially in winter, and there is marked deficiency of nitrogen and calcium in the foliage (Roth, Buchanan, and Hepting 1948). Needle length and shoot growth decrease, and in the final stages diseased trees are conspicuous because of the short, scant, and chlorotic foliage confined to the ends of the branches. Affected trees may improve temporarily, but are not known to recover naturally.

A major pathogen playing an important role in the littleleaf disease is *Phytophthora cinnamomi* Rands, a fungus widely prevalent in pine soils of the Southeast, even in places remote from any recognized littleleaf disease (Campbell 1951). The incidence of this disease, however, is closely related to certain physical deficiencies in the soil. Although an Alabama survey (Boggess, Swarthout, and Toole 1941) revealed littleleaf occurring on 30 different soil series, the percentage clearly increased as the internal drainage became poorer. The disease is aggravated by root damage from soil factors such as poor aeration, low fertility, and periodic moisture stress.

Control measures devised so far are purely silvicultural—discriminating against the more susceptible shortleaf pine. In partial cutting operations on littleleaf areas where the two species are intermixed, as much loblolly pine as possible should be left in the residual stand, because this species is only about one-third as susceptible as shortleaf pine (Hepting 1949). Salvage cutting should be frequent and rotations not over 50 years (Hepting 1944).

Needle blights

Numerous native fungi cause the so-called needle blights, casts, or rusts. They occur in the South in epidemic form at irregular intervals and in years of abundant moisture (Boyce 1958). Darker (1932) has reported on 48 species, of which 23 affect the pines. Within the range of loblolly pine most of these fortunately seem to be only mildly parasitic. Hence no artificial controls have been developed. Natural control is afforded by climatic and biotic factors. For example, a large number of saprophytic fungi are known to follow these infections and prevent the primary fungus from fruiting. Darker lists 15 fungi active in checking needle cast.

The characteristic symptom is a browning of the needles over all or part of the crown. The discoloration, most conspicuous in fall, winter, and sometimes in spring gives the impression that the trees are dying. Sometimes growth is slightly retarded, but often it is not significantly reduced. These diseases are seldom fatal. Foliage is thinned by the premature shedding of the brown needles. One of the organisms associated with these troubles is *Lophodermium pinastri*. This fungus is probably not pathogenic to pines in the southeast, but it readily invades needles attacked or weakened by other causes (Boyce 1951). Needle blight produced by *Hypoderma lethale* Dearn. may be widespread in early spring from North Carolina to Texas. The infected trees develop a scorched appearance that lasts until new needles are formed and the infected needles are largely shed (Boyce 1953 and 1954a). Artificial control is not necessary.

There are several true needle rusts, sometimes abundant but seldom damaging, caused by species of *Coleosporium*, that produce similar symptoms on loblolly pine. In summer and autumn the sources of infection for pines are the herbaceous alternate hosts. *C. solidaginis* has an alternate stage on goldenrod and aster, while *C. vernoniae* infects ironweed (Hepting 1952). The main symptom is yellow to orange-colored pustules one to several millimeters in length on the needles in the spring. Usually the fungus does not extensively invade the host tissue. Only small areas of needles become yellow—apparently the result of invasion rather than of any toxic effect from the parasite (Weber 1943). Needles of blighted pines die back from their tips varying distances, and some of them are shed prematurely. Usually there is a sharp line separating the dead tip from the green base of a needle infected by a fungus. Seedlings are often more heavily diseased than saplings. Some seedlings up to 2 feet tall have been killed in Florida by this disease, but the damage is usually minor and no control is attempted.

The brown-spot fungus *Scirrhia acicola*, so damaging to grass-stage longleaf pine, is not usually serious on loblolly pine, but recently (1949-51) it appeared to blight even large loblolly pines until some stands looked as if damaged by fire. It caused extensive dieback of foliage on trees of pole size and larger, and browned the needles on sapling trees in fall and winter. Growth may be retarded but, except among very young seedlings, no mortality is expected from this disease (Boyce 1952b).

Certain foliar abnormalities affect loblolly pine outside its natural range and have been attributed to malnutrition. For example, in Australian plantations loblolly pine tops the list of species subject to fused needle disease ascribed to deficiency in phosphorus and organic matter in the soil. Affected trees did not make healthy growth until phosphatic fertilizers were added. The limiting amount of total phosphate was estimated to be close to 195 parts per million (Young 1940).

Diseased twigs

One fungus that attacks loblolly pine twigs and the smaller branches is *Atropellis tingens*. Small black irregularly cup-shaped fruiting bodies are generally associated with the cankers. The diseased twigs and branches usually die. The wood under Atropellis cankers is always deeply stained a bluish black; thus a knife cut through a canker serves to identify this disease. It is fairly common, but not severe enough to do much damage (Hepting 1942, Hepting and Lindgren 1950).

Another disease caused by *Diplodia pinea*, is capable of causing dieback of the current season's shoot growth year after year until the tree is stunted or dead. It usually starts low and spreads gradually upward killing needles and twigs. It is not known to cause any extensive injury in forest plantations (Waterman 1943).

Heart rot

Heartwood in the butt section may be decayed by *Polyporus schweinitzii* from infection entering through the roots (p. 127).

True heart-rotting fungi, such as *Fomes pini* enter most readily through exposed heartwood in dead branch stubs and only occasionally through fire scars. The fungus fruiting bodies, or conks, usually protrude at these or other points where the wood is exposed. When the fungus has been working in a tree for some years, the conks may appear in large numbers under dead branches or sometimes singly on the trunk. Other common diagnostic characteristics are exudation of resin at the branch scars and punky knots disclosed upon cutting into branch scars (Hepting 1934).

The conks are brownish black, rough on the upper surface, and sepia brown below. They vary widely in shape; some lie flat on a branch, others protrude as a shelf. Often the pores on the underside are not perfectly round. Although conks and punk knots result from infection, their absence does not indicate freedom from disease.

A representative sample of 867 loblolly pines in an old-growth stand in the middle Atlantic Coastal Plain (Nelson 1931) showed 11 percent of the trees had heart rot. It increased with age as follows:

Age class (years)	Trees with heart rot (percent)
40-90	[1]5.4
91-140	18.6
141-190	60.0
191-230	72.2

[1] One group of loblolly pines that had grown very slowly contained nearly 10 times as many trees with heart rot as indicated.

Pines less than 75 years old are usually relatively sound, but slow growth due to suppression or other causes makes them more susceptible (Gruschow and Trousdell 1958). On poor sites where the heartwood content is high, loblolly pines may acquire heart rot while they are still young and small.

Practical control is wholly silvicultural. Trees with open fire scars and those with conks should not be selected and retained as crop trees. Diseased individuals should be harvested, felled, or girdled to prevent them from spreading spores to other trees. All conks within reach on trees felled or deadened should be knocked off to reduce further the source of infection (Hepting 1934, Hepting and Roth 1950). The relatively short rotations of 60 or 80 years throughout the South will avoid most of the loss from heart rot (Roth 1949).

Stain and decay in wood products[33]

At least 7 fungi cause major stain damage to southern yellow pine logs and lumber (Verrall 1939). Stain fungi are not known to discriminate between pine species. They do not significantly weaken wood except possibly to cause a decrease in toughness (Chapman and Scheffer 1940). *Ceratocystis pilifera* works on loblolly pine wood when the moisture content is above 24 percent of oven-dry weight (Colley and Rumbold 1930).

The fungi do not infect through the bark, but may be carried into the wood by insects. Blue stain inoculum has been obtained from southern pine beetles taken from newly made tunnels devoid of stain (Nelson and Beal 1929). Effective and cheap fungicides are available, but, unless an insecticide is added, they do not repel bark and ambrosia beetles that penetrate the logs and inoculate the wood inside its exterior chemically protected shell (Verrall 1945). In a test in September 1934 at Summerville, S. C., 36 percent of the untreated loblolly pine sapwood became blue stained in the first 1½ months after felling and stacking in pens (Hepting 1945b). It is best to keep as small a supply of wood in the mill yards as possible, replacing it currently with fresh wood.

Damage from stain is most rapid in logs cut between June and October when insects spread the infection and when warm weather promotes fungous growth. Winter in the Gulf States does not arrest stain completely; some loss is likely if storage is longer than 3 or 4 months. Some blue stain on pulpwood, particularly at the ends of the bolts, is to be expected in the South because utilization cannot always be prompt enough to avoid it. In procuring pulpwood some 15 or 25 percent of stained wood may be permissible but it necessitates more bleach in making white paper.

For best protection in warm weather, chemical treatment should be applied the day the logs are cut or at the latest the following day. This can be done with an ordinary garden sprayer of the sustained pressure type. Various useful formulations, from the same type of chemical mixtures used for dip treating lumber, are reported by Verrall and Scheffer (1949). The increasing prevalence of bulk handling and package piling has also made the use of chemicals more necessary to prevent stain.

Damage from rot, caused by different fungi, may be simultaneous with stain as decay fungi work under comparable conditions. After studying 64 different decay fungi, Humphrey and Siggers (1933)

[33] See also the sections on ''Defects and Grades'' and ''Seasoning and Preservation'' in chapter 10, Properties and Uses.

estimated the optimum temperatures under which they grow to vary usually between 90° and 100°F. and not to go over 115°F. The most prevalent fungus in the decay of round products is *Pheniophora gigantea*, followed after 4 to 6 months of storage by *Polyporus abietinus,* and after 6 months by *Lenzites saepiaria* (Lindgren 1951). Of these three fungi, the first attacks both cellulose and lignin; the last one destroys mainly cellulose. Within about 2 months of summer and 5 to 6 months of fall and winter storage in the deep South pine wood may deteriorate enough to reduce the pulp yield by 3 to 5 percent. Within such periods rough bolts may lose less than peeled ones, though there is a progressive advantage for peeled wood when the storage period is longer. Although peeled wood will keep better if stored as small or split bolts in well-ventilated stacks, practices that attempt to reduce deterioration by hastening drying hold no promise for rough wood. Rough wood is best stored in close piles.

Fungicides are now commonly mixed with insecticides to control stain, decay, and insect attack in logs. A single treatment is desirable. For this purpose pentachlorophenol in a 2 percent concentration may be added to the benzene hexachloride treatment previously suggested in the section on southern pine beetles. But to be effective against fungi it should be applied within 24 hours after the trees are cut. It should never be delayed beyond 48 hours. Many sawmills store logs in water and pulp mills are beginning to do likewise. This practice makes special measures against attacks by both insects and fungi unnecessary. Another advantage is that the wood is kept continuously moist and thus in good condition for pulping.

CLIMATE

Climatic injuries often predispose trees to subsequent damage or death from the other destructive agents already discussed. Also havoc may come from joint effects of two or more storm elements, such as ice and wind together. Drought destroys many southern pines in some years, especially in the western part of the range, but normally most harm results from lightning and wind. Although the mortality caused by strong wind, logging damage, and many other causes tends to increase with the number of exposed trees per acre, this appears not to be true of lightning.

Lightning

The annual number of lightning strikes per square mile averages ten in the United States and somewhat higher in north Florida. Irrespective of the pattern of cutting operations, lightning strikes tend to be distributed rather evenly over flat topography on an area basis (Trousdell 1955b). As many trees may be hit in dense as in thin stands, though of course the odds against damage to any one tree are less in the dense stand. Isolated trees are individually vulnerable and the toll in percentage killed is naturally greater where trees are few than where they are many. This is one reason why, after attaining natural reproduction of pine and removing perhaps 80 percent of the seed source, the continued reservation of two seed trees per acre for fire insurance is not recommended. In this situation the loss from lightning is too likely to be excessive.[34]

Under good selection felling practice near Crossett, Ark., a 2-year study was made of the causes of mortality among individual trees 4 inches d.b.h. and larger (Reynolds 1940b). It indicated that although insects were the immediate cause of over half the deaths, lightning was the primary agent in fully 70 percent of the loss.

Losses from both lightning and wind continue over long periods. On the mid-Atlantic Coastal Plain it is estimated (Trousdell 1955b) that they account for over 50 percent of the losses among old-growth seed trees during regeneration and 90 percent after the seedling stands are established (table 14). Where only two trees were left per acre lightning killed twice as many trees as did wind, and together they destroyed six times as many as all other agents. With eight trees reserved lightning and wind accounted for half the total loss.

TABLE 14.—*Annual mortality of seed trees per 100 acres during average[1] periods of regeneration and development of young pine stands (Trousdell 1955b)*

Number and type of reserved pines	Lightning	Wind	All other causes	Total
	Number	Number	Number	Number
Eight trees left for seed, initial reservation:				
Old field	2.1	2.5	2.8	7.4
Forest grown	2.1	0.5	5.8	8.4
Average	2.1	1.8	3.9	7.8
Two trees left for insurance, extended reservation:				
Old field, from seed trees	2.2	2.8	0.0	5.0
Forest grown, from seed trees	2.1	3.2	0.7	6.0
Forest grown, from strips	1.9	0.0	0.6	2.5
Average	2.0	1.0	0.5	3.5

[1] The average regeneration period was 3.3 years, the development period 2.1 years additional on the Bigwoods Experimental Forest near Franklin, Va., where these data were gathered. Lightning strikes averaged 12.8 per square mile.

[34] The other reason is that two trees per acre are inadequate for seed, whereas three or more retard too much young growth while they stand and break too much of it when they fall.

Wind

Loblolly pine is usually relatively windfirm as it grows on soils conducive to the development of a deep taproot with strong laterals (Sterrett 1914).[35] Where the sands of the Coastal Plain are underlain by hardpan, and on the dry heavy upland clays of the Piedmont, the mature trees may not be very resistant to exposure. In such situations it may be advisable to leave seed trees in groups (Ashe 1910). Wind fells most trees by breakage when the soil is dry or by uprooting when it is soaked. A prolonged rainy spell at Crossett, Ark., in the spring of 1953 was followed by extensive uprooting of pines (Grano 1953b). On Caddo silt loam soils where the stands were about two-thirds loblolly and only one-third short-leaf pine, some 20 times as many of the shortleaf pines blew down as loblolly pines. On these soils loblolly pine was the more deeply rooted. In the Bigwoods Experimental Forest in North Carolina, the younger and smaller reserved trees, left for regeneration insurance only, were not damaged by wind alone for some time, and the normal rate of annual loss ranged from 1 to 2 percent. Less than 1 percent was lost during the reproduction period (Trousdell 1955b).

Wind may damage trees without destroying them. It may break branches or loosen roots exposing the trees to injury by other agents or later windfall. Ordinary high winds may permanently tilt the less firmly rooted trees. Leaning trees produce inferior products. Winds of moderate intensity usually do not harm the boles that remain upright, as loblolly pine roots seldom hold the trees firmly enough to create wind shakes (Clark 1912). In winds of high intensity, however, this may no longer be true. Then a tree whose top is uniformly strong may suffer compression failure not only in its supporting roots on the leeward side but also in the trunk near the base (Mergen 1954).

Tornadoes and hurricanes, far more erratic and devastating than ordinary storms, are less frequent but not rare in the loblolly pine territory. Timber as much as 50 miles inland may be blown down by hurricanes (Harper 1943). In Texas there were violent storms in 1865, 1873, 1883, and 1900 which overthrew old loblolly pine on many thousands of acres, affecting the whole forest region west of the Trinity River. On one occasion four days of rain were followed by four days of strong wind. Fallen timber so impeded travel that it had to be burned. These destructive fires prepared a seedbed for extensive second growth (Zon 1905). More recently there has been

[35] See section on root and shoot growth, and figure 15, in chapter 2.

lesser wind damage to pine in Texas in 3 years out of 5 (Stephenson 1956).

In 1954 hurricane "Hazel" raked loblolly pine forests on the Atlantic coast with winds up to 100 miles per hour. It hit the Bigwoods Experimental Forest when the soil was dry from 2 weeks of drought. Damage to timber was directly correlated with the size and exposure of the mature trees. About 6 percent of all pines 10 inches or larger in d.b.h. fell, most of them broken rather than uprooted. Sound trees of pole size or smaller were not damaged much. In uncut stands where defective trees had not been harvested, most of them broke at cankers, forks, heart rot infections, or fire scars. Sound trees splintered at various points from within the crown to ground level, but usually within the first two log lengths. Much internal damage to trees left standing will not become apparent until some later storm breaks them off at the weakened point or until the hidden defect is exposed in manufacture.

Damage tends to vary conspicuously with stand conditions. When hurricane "Hazel" struck Virginia it had a particularly disastrous effect on cutover areas with two seed trees per acre:

Stand condition	Area basis (acres)	Volume loss (percent)
Two seed trees per acre..........	180	59
Uncut........................	40	9
Repeated selection cuts (poor risk trees removed)..........	454	4

Much loss can be avoided by proper management. Young stands subjected to repeated crown thinnings to expose them to a liberal amount of wind will develop strengthening tissues in the lower part of the stem as well as a strong supporting root system (Mergen 1954).[36] In making clearings it would be well to avoid locating the corner of a clearcut area where the cutting edges can funnel wind into a poorly drained area. For the same reason V-shaped or egg-shaped indentations in a wall of timber should be avoided on the side exposed to destructive winds.

When wind damage occurs, wood-boring insects (pine sawyers) work to destroy windfalls. They take a toll of 25 to 33 percent of the dying trees and logs within 3 months (Hopkins 1910). Hence prompt salvage is a part of good management.

Near the coast, winds sometimes bring to pine, a different type of injury, salt water storm damage. Foliage, especially immature needles, dies in about a month from salt spray deposits that may

[36] This method of fortifying trees against wind may be in part offset by an increase in their susceptibility to ice damage. See next section.

extend a half mile inland after a storm. Of all species observed on
the shores of Chesapeake Bay, loblolly pine appears most sensitive to
such defoliation. (Little, Mohr, and Spicer 1958). Except for trees
of poor vigor this damage has seldom been fatal on the Eastern Shore
of Maryland. In plantations on the coast of North Carolina salt
spray has killed many planted trees and reduced the survivors to
dwarfed espalier forms. In places the stands of pine on lowlands
have been damaged by brackish water brought in by high storm tides.

Freezing weather

Ice in various forms may injure trees in different ways and most
often near their northern or altitudinal limits of natural distribution. Seedlings planted on badly eroded spots or other exposed sites
may be damaged by frost heaving in loam or clay soil unless they
are mulched until their roots take firm hold. A report (Wood 1936)
on the planting of loblolly pine in southern New Jersey showed that
2-0 stock suffered frost damage in June of the first year but was not
injured by a temperature of —25°F. in its third year at which time
the survival was 37 percent.

Injury may occur, however, when loblolly pines accustomed to a
long frost-free period are planted where the growing season is
shorter. After cold weather in November 1951 damaged loblolly
pine in a seed-source test in the Arkansas Ozarks, it was concluded
(Shoulders 1952) that for planting in that locality the seed source
should not be south of Maryland. Jackson (1952), measuring changes
in radial growth of loblolly pines at 2-week intervals, found stem
growth at breast height starting as the new shoots elongated and
continuing into October in the Piedmont section of Georgia.

The primary stage in the development of female flowers is often
nipped by frost. Observations by P. C. Wakeley indicate that at
Many, La., on March 25-27, 1955, low temperatures of 25° to 28°F.
killed many of these flowers on shortleaf pines. In this instance,
those of loblolly pine escaped injury because they were 2 or 3 weeks
beyond the pollen receptive stage. Only the flowers fully protected
by bud scales survived in appreciable numbers. Early fall or late
spring frost may also injure some of the youngest vegetative parts
of pines. Loblolly pine is less susceptible to frost when growing
slowly than when making rapid succulent growth. Needle droop on
terminal twigs is a symptom of such injury (Davis, Wright, and
Hartley 1942). Winter transpiration injury has been observed on
loblolly pines in South Carolina where recently planted seedlings

were desiccated by 15 windy days while night temperatures were below freezing.

Hail is comparatively rare in any one locality and usually does little damage, but it sometimes strips pine foliage severely in spots (Harper 1943). It may injure the twigs and small stems of saplings. In nurseries it occasionally kills seedlings in large numbers if it strikes them in the cotyledon stage.

Damaging glaze storms, occurring perhaps once in a decade, permanently bend, break down, or uproot slender loblolly pines after they exceed about 12 feet in height. A severe and widespread ice storm hit Texas in 1944, necessitating an extensive emergency organization for the salvage of broken trees, many of them loblolly pine. The yellow pines in plantations have often been observed to differ somewhat in their capacity to withstand an overload of ice. Damage from a glaze storm at Athens, Georgia, in January 1940 was as follows: longleaf pine 24 percent, slash pine 29 percent, and loblolly pine 4 percent (McKeller 1942). Ninety percent of all the pines straightened up after slight bending, and 20 to 30 percent of the badly bent trees recovered in part. Among the loblolly pines that were still badly bent in February, 56 percent were again erect by October. Loblolly pine was similarly found superior in northern Louisiana (Muntz 1947). There it was set out with slash pine in alternate-row or three-row mixtures. At 10 years of age the ice damage was 34 percent for slash pine and 5 percent for loblolly pine. Elsewhere at 12 years the damage was 44 percent for slash pine and 24 percent for loblolly pine. Only in Florida and in a belt 150 miles wide along the gulf coast can the superior ice resistance of loblolly pine safely be disregarded in favor of slash pine. Farther north, where ice storms occur about once in 5 years, loblolly pine can be planted with more assurance of success than the other species.

The superior resistance of loblolly pine has been attributed to the greater flexibility and resilience of its stems and branches, but never fully explained. It may excel both slash and longleaf pines partly because its shorter needles hold less ice. In mixture with other pines at Watkinsville, Ga., loblolly pine again excelled slash pine, but not shortleaf pine, in resisting ice (Hendrickson 1949). The needle length hypothesis was not supported by experience with ice damage in Texas. There the shortleaf pine suffered three times as much damage as loblolly pine (Bull, Williams, and Judson 1948) in natural stands. In this instance however, the inferiority of shortleaf pine may have been more apparent than real, because of a pre-

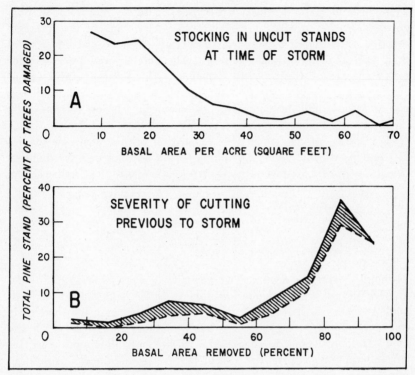

FIGURE 28.—Glaze damage in loblolly pine-shortleaf pine forest near Athens, Ga., from ice storm, December 24 to 26, 1945. The shaded band represents uprooting; the rest of the damage is from breakage. High damage is associated with stand density, *A*; and recent exposure, *B*.

ponderance of more susceptible suppressed trees and a secondary attack by beetles.

In general, natural stands appear just as susceptible to injury from ice as are planted stands properly spaced and thinned. Ice damage is found in both open-grown and dense stands, but the trees that show the effects of crowding are somewhat more susceptible. Although dense stands tend to suffer the highest percentage of loss, they are likely to emerge with the most undamaged trees. This is the situation where calm weather outlasts the ice overload.

The susceptibility of Piedmont pine stands to storm damage increases with age, but the two stand factors having the greatest effect on damage are degree and type of cutting. A detailed study[37] of the storms in December 1945 near Athens, Ga., revealed heavy

[37] Glaze damage in Piedmont pine timber—rough draft of an unpublished research report (SP-1.1) by George Stephenson, 1946.

damage from ice and wind. In stands up to 60 years old, and regardless of the density of stocking, the percentage of damage rose sharply where cutting exceeded 30 percent, then leveled off as more than half the stand was removed. The smaller and more slender stems are most susceptible to damage. Where the average size of cut trees was the same as that for the stand as a whole damage was not increased, but the larger the trees cut in relation to those left, the greater was the percentage of reserved trees lost.[38]

Regardless of age or degree of cutting within a stand, the individual position of each tree influences its resistance to ice damage. One out of four unsupported trees were lost at Athens, Ga.

Position in relation to neighboring trees	Trees damaged (percent)
No crown contact	26.6
Adjacent to recent opening	12.8
On permanent timber edge	5.2
Crown contact on all sides	0.4

Although heavy loss occurred wherever trees were exposed in any degree, relatively small damage was done to timber-edge trees. With extended exposure trees reduce their form class and improve their stability. In spite of larger crowns and more foliage to catch ice, their storm resistance is increased. Where only dominant trees are left in exposed positions the risk of loss is less imminent. Spindling suppressed trees—tall, thin, and short crowned—are especially vulnerable when loaded with ice in exposed locations. Where unmanaged stands are heavily cut storms destroy many of the spindly trees left (fig. 28). The percentage of tree height in live crown and the former stand density were observed by Nelson (1951) to be related to storm damage as follows:

Live crown length (percent)	Mortality by crown-length class (percent)	Basal area of original stand (sq. ft.)	Mortality by former density class (percent)
5-15	18.2	40-50	0.0
16-25	18.0	55-60	3.6
26-35	3.4	60-80	23.5
Over 36	0.0		

This danger from sudden exposure after thinning in overstocked stands was also noted in central Mississippi (Tyler 1952) after an ice storm in 1951:

[38] In this relationship a measure of susceptibility of cutover stands is the ratio between average diameters of trees taken and of those left. The tendency was for damage to increase directly by 15 to 20 percent as this cut-leave ratio rose from 1.0 to 1.6. This trend is the most noticeable in the older and the more severely cut stands.

Stand condition   *Loss*
Overstocked and not thinned................ Negligible
Thinned from below........................ 10-15 percent
Heavily thinned from above................ Over 50 percent

Here again is evidence that recent exposure of slender stems largely accounts for the loss sustained.

Dry and hot weather

The prime cause of first-year seedling mortality is drought. In forest openings where regeneration of pine is needed, the soil often dries out gradually from the top down between rains. Thus the moisture supply for yearling seedlings is fluctuating and uncertain. This condition is common even in localities where enough rain falls annually for the more deeply rooted saplings and trees. The deeper and more constantly moist soil is not available for seedlings in their first year or two. Transpiration cannot for long exceed absorption without serious desiccation in leaf tissues.

Closely associated with first-year drought is the possibility of heat damage to tender newly germinated seedlings. Extreme temperatures can injure them near the surface of dry mineral soil. Succulent stem tissue is more vulnerable than are the cotyledons or older leaves.[39]

After their first growing season loblolly pine seedlings can withstand ground-level temperatures of at least 149°F. without adverse effects, and are more resistant to short droughts. As they are still relatively small and superficially rooted, prolonged drought is still harmful. The effects of a 10-week drought in the autumn of 1954 were observed over the lower Piedmont in Georgia. The damage to loblolly pine was clearly related to the depth of soil. Among seedlings up to 6 years old mortality was confined to the shallow soils where the top and subsoil layers together were less than 20 inches deep. Where there were less than 16 inches of soil over impervious parent materials, pine saplings up to 15 years old died. On sites with an effective depth of 16 to 20 inches of poorly developed soil, over loose friable parent material, only the younger smaller seedlings succumbed (Brender 1955).

On many soils in Texas, Louisiana, and Arkansas, and possibly north Mississippi, repeated seedling losses from drought contribute as much as fire or over-cutting to forest depletion. Unfortunately,

[39] At 2 months of age loblolly pines tolerate higher temperatures than sweetgum seedlings. The first visible damage was observed (Thomas and Platt 1954) on open-grown loblolly pine at 131°F. and on shade-grown plants at 118°F. Similar heat injury occurred at 122°F. on open-grown sweetgum and at 102°F. on shade-grown gum (Bormann 1953).

unless hardwood and brush competition can be elminated, little can be done as yet to alleviate drought effects on seedlings. Treatments such as waxing or partially removing foliage to reduce transpiration usually interfere with vital processes. Partial shade is helpful, but difficult to provide in places where forest seedlings are otherwise free to grow.

Among loblolly pines beyond the seedling stage, mortality from drought is usually light. Growth retardation, however, may be severe among saplings or even the larger subdominant trees. In this manner unseasonable weather can modify the relation of pine to its associates favorably or otherwise, depending on intensity and timing. Untimely weather may foster or terminate insect attacks. Throughout their range, pines retarded by drought may attract bark beetles.

Severe drought may also directly and seriously retard the growth of whole stands of pine timber. An average growing-season deficit of 5.23 inches in precipitation during 5 years (1952-56) at Crossett, Ark., reduced growth of pine timber by 35 percent in cubic volume and 43 percent in board-foot volume (Reynolds 1958).

During the drought in the Georgia Piedmont in 1954, pole-size timber lost about 1 square foot of basal area per acre or 40 percent of its annual growth. Losses in volume growth alone on a sample tract of 128 acres were estimated 31 cubic feet or 84 board feet per acre. On 16 percent of this area the loss in growth plus the loss from mortality ran higher, exceeding the expected net annual growth of 82 cubic feet, and, in spots, equaling twice the normal current yearly growth (Brender and Hodges 1957a).

Where silviculture is practiced many of the weaker trees are removed from the denser parts of stands, thus anticipating and precluding much drought damage. In east Texas in 1951, a drought, assisted by bark beetles, killed 8 times as much sawtimber per acre in uncut and unimproved stands as it did on intensively managed areas (Mignery 1952). Until recent years timber stand improvement work has been concentrated largely on culling out weed species and other undesirable large trees; now many understories are being treated to make room for succeeding timber crops. As yet, in the humid South there is little evidence that, for timber on average sites in normal years, competition from a hardwood understory harms or benefits a pine overstory. However, it remains to be determined, for poor sites and dry years, the extent to which the same underbrush can retard the growth of an overwood (McClay 1955a). Soil moisture is retained at a satisfactory level for a longer period into the growing season where all underbrush has been removed (Zahner 1956). The vital reason for removal of understories is to promote the regeneration of pine; except for dry sites and in drought periods any favorable effect on growth is incidental.

SUMMARY

Seedlings are especially susceptible to outright killing by fire, but many larger trees—first injured by fire, logging, drought, or storm—succumb later to insects or disease. The smaller and weaker pines usually, but not always, are the first and most likely trees to die. Loblolly pines of all sizes often have their resistance lowered by more than one injurious agent.

Trees, both large and small, may be bruised or broken by logging, particularly during mechanized operations. Growth of timber may be retarded because soil is packed, and feeding roots of large trees injured by the use of heavy tractors on saturated ground. Mills must operate even in wet weather, but most operators can avoid such damage by the proper timing of harvests. An orderly succession in partial cutting of trees, and extraction of logs during dry weather and while seedlings are still small and flexible, will reduce damage appreciably. Mortality after partial harvest, seldom excessive in timber less than 40 years old, can be minimized further by removal of the more susceptible or "poor risk" trees in the earlier cuttings.

A mixture of species theoretically increases resistance of timber stands to insects and disease. An artificial mixture for the long-term protection of plantations and soils should provide for the dominance of loblolly pine by planting this species 3 to 1 in alternate blocks or bands with some merchantable associated species. Although many upland pine sites do not produce merchantable hardwoods the hardwood component in loblolly pine stands seldom can, and probably never should, be eliminated completely, at the lower levels. Most, if not all, of the silvicultural benefits from a hardwood component can be obtained with all hardwoods relegated to the understory. Many pure stands of pine may remain healthy throughout a rotation, but by and large the solution of the hardwood problem is to achieve adequate control, not eradication, of broadleaved shrubs and trees.

Various types of fires—surface, ground, crown, blow-up, or controlled—are distinguished. Fire kills the smaller pines and does most damage when it occurs in summer. The degree of damage can be most accurately appraised a year later. Experiments are in progress at various places to determine how fire can best be used with a minimum of damage in controlling hardwood invasions. Always where burns are scheduled the various protective and silvicultural purposes to be served should have joint consideration.

Forest protection has advanced in recent years through improved prevention, detection, and suppression of fires. A recent innovation is the prescription of controlled burning for various cultural purposes. The effect of this in the Coastal Plain has been first to reduce fire hazard and then fire risk through improvement in public relations. Where fire is used more it is abused less. Detection of fire has improved with better state organization of forces and some use of airplanes. Suppression, too, has advanced with new mechanized equipment and with the development of research to perfect the measurement and prediction of fire danger. Modern fire control becomes more economical as the suppression forces can be adjusted up or down on the basis of correctly calculated degrees of danger. All these developments are now aiding the economic objective of sustained yield in forest management by furthering the recognition of organized forestry operations as an insurable business investment.

Insects in the pine forests, as in agriculture, remain a problem. Various beetles, moths, weevils, grubs, and sawflies attack pine trees and the rough round products. In forests silvicultural cutting may reduce infestations 75 percent or more, but insects must be identified for specific control.

Infestations of the southern pine beetle or engraver beetles are most likely to become epidemic in periods of drought. Control measures must be prompt to be effective. Turpentine beetles attack the bases of pines often below ground. Their damage is usually less, but it may be cumulative and should not be ignored. Special measures to control all these beetles are suggested. Various tip moths make young trees bushy, especially in pure stands; chemical control on a limited scale may be justified. Pines planted promptly on recently cutover pine areas need chemical protection from pales weevil. Aerial chemical control of sawflies is needed only where defoliation is extensive and severe. Other defoliators and cone insects are not often controlled artificially. White grubs need control in nurseries and some field plantations. A new development in the protection of logs is to treat them simultaneously against both wood borers and sap stain.

Among domestic animals cattle and horses do least damage to pines, and hogs injure loblolly pine less than some other species.

Sheep, and especially goats, tend to be more destructive because of close cropping and indiscriminate browsing. Even properly fed and pastured farm animals should be excluded from pine plantations for the first year or two. Rodents and birds eat many pine seeds, but among wild creatures rabbits and gophers are most apt to injure plantations to an extent that calls for artificial controls.

The native fusiform rust disease has alternate stages on various oaks. It often appears on young loblolly pines in the form of spindle-shaped cankers. This rust is controllable in nurseries by fungicidal sprays. Infected small seedlings, not discarded at planting time, will die. All swollen branches within 15 inches of the main stem of saplings should be removed to prevent the fungus from reaching the main stem. Trunk infections tend gradually to weaken the larger trees, and subject them to wind breakage, though in pole sizes boles 40 percent girdled by cankers may last about 10 years. Fire may favor or retard the spread of this disease depending on local conditions.

Most of the butt and root diseases have not been extensive or serious, except the littleleaf disease, and even this injures shortleaf pine more than loblolly. This disease, aggravated by poor soil conditions, is countered so far only by the use of short rotations and by frequent sanitation or salvage cuttings favoring loblolly pine. Numerous needle blights are rather common. They retard growth, but the uncontrolled damage is temporary. Heart rots are not commercially important in second-growth forests. Stain and decay often damage stored products seriously, but effective control methods are available.

There are several sources of climatic injury to pines, but the most harmful are three storm elements: lightning, wind, and ice, alone or in combination. Some merchantable trees die; others suffer reduced radial growth. Each element produces both immediate damage and subsequent complications from insects or disease. Direct injury is mostly from uprooting, breakage, and deformation; indirect injury from bark beetles and decay. But loblolly pine is more resistant than some other species. Severe weather, drought and cold, most often interfere with natural reproduction or the survival of very young seedlings.

Climatic damage, like that from other injurious agents, cannot always be avoided, but it can be greatly reduced and adverse complications alleviated by the application of good silviculture.

Chapter 4

Natural Regeneration

THE PROBLEM

THE KEY TO INTENSIVE silviculture is the ability to bridge promptly the gap between harvest of the old and establishment of a new forest. Timeliness of measures taken is necessary to get any even-aged pine stand reproduced easily and cheaply.[40] Success with loblolly pine hinges on careful planning to bring together adequate amounts of seed and favorable seedbeds. In many places also, particularly at the western end of the range, a third requirement is the occurrence of favorable climatic conditions during the regeneration period. Where plenty of seeds reach mineral soil and escape drought in the first year or two, the "catch" is usually sufficient for a new crop of pine.

When, as often happens, these requirements are not met the year after timber is harvested, natural regeneration of pine in even-aged stands is delayed and uncertain. Good seed years and adequate moisture for seedlings often do not coincide. Recently in Texas and Louisiana dry summers have repeatedly followed good seed years, precluding regeneration even where sites were well prepared. On the Atlantic Coastal Plain failures result more often from neglecting to release seed trees or to prepare sites, or both. In the Piedmont sufficient seed is frequently not available, but on the drier sites there the hardwood sprouts encroach rather slowly, so that some delay in reproduction under shelterwood is not serious. Scarcity of seed is most likely to be the principal obstacle to natural regeneration in short-rotation cutting of even-aged pine stands for pulpwood only.

Partial failures from any of these causes not only reduce yields, but also lower their quality. Seedlings that come in late are usually too few. They either die early or remain seriously handicapped by

[40] Uneven-aged silviculture, the system wherein regeneration is permitted to extend over long periods and is scattered over large areas, is discussed in chapter 8. However, the silvical basis needed for all-aged operations is given here in chapter 4 in the section "Freedom to Grow."

competition from other vegetation. Thus when regeneration requires two or more waves of reproduction, the second surge is apt to be less effective, permitting the seedlings that started first to form a thin stand of pine. Where scattered pine saplings develop without competition on their own level, they grow into undesirable limby "wolf" trees. The prevalence of partial failure is ascribed to the fact that requirements for natural regeneration are imperfectly understood or are ignored by many who harvest pine timber. To the extent that grass, weeds, shrubs, and undesirable hardwoods take over the land, an effective remedy may need to be both drastic and expensive (Wenger and Trousdell 1958).[41]

Before hope is abandoned for natural regeneration and certain areas are designated to be planted to pine, the opportunity for successful reseeding should be appraised. For this purpose the results of an extensive survey with 445 temporary plots in east-central Alabama (Brinkman and Swarthout 1942) are useful in that state and possibly in other places with similar climate. The survey revealed a lack of satisfactory young pine stands on 80 percent of the areas where they were needed because of unsatisfactory older stands. For good regeneration the breaks in the overwood canopy had to aggregate at least 65 percent in natural stands or 50 percent in old-field stands where there was usually less underbrush.[42] Areas 30 percent covered with young hardwoods were not satisfactorily reproduced to pine. An inadequate seed supply was apparently responsible for the partial or complete failure of pine reproduction on about half the areas. To be effective in a single year, the survey indicated an average of 10 seed trees per acre was necessary in Alabama.

Combinations of conditions that were found favorable to loblolly pine reproduction after repeated seed years point to minimum standards as follows:

[41] We can confidently look forward to a third generation in pine silviculture wherein this acute problem in natural reproduction will tend to disappear. Although natural succession cannot be abolished, the source of hardwood seeds can be removed and the capacity of remaining root and stump fragments to sprout can be effectively subdued. When all woody competition has finally been overcome, the herbaceous vegetation can be easily controlled.

[42] On similar terrain, well protected from fire in the lower Piedmont of Georgia, smaller breaks in the canopy, i.e., areas aggregating about 20 percent, will suffice for regeneration under canopies that are at least 30 feet above ground. Side light under canopies is helpful, but since the amount of moisture available varies with type and depth of soil, the size of breaks in the canopy wherein pine seedlings can grow will vary tremendously from one area to another.

Good seed trees per acre, i.e., trees that can produce at
  least 250 cones in a 5-year regeneration period......number 3
Ground free from—
  Hardwood cover alone............................percent.....75
  Pine cover alone..do.......65
  Entire pine-hardwood canopy.........................do........40
Understory free from overtopping by
  hardwood reproduction or brush......................do........80
Time after seedfall without—
  Fire ....years......5
  Concentrated grazing...............................do........5

Wakeley (1944b) reports that not only has this Alabama survey withstood statistical and practical tests, but also it enables a land manager to recognize the following three stand conditions: (1) good prospects for reproduction where stands should be untouched during a crop or two of seed, (2) reproduction prospects poor and planting needed, and (3) seed source adequate, but another factor in need of correction to meet requirements.

Classification of land in some such manner is prerequisite to sound planning for auxiliary measures to favor regeneration by either artificial or natural methods. Some factors not found in the Coastal Plain complicate the problem in the lower Piedmont area. Here, in surveying the prospects for pine reproduction, recognition must be given to the effects of local topographic situation and steepness of slope. Through their influence on moisture content and depth of soils, they modify vegetal competition for prospective pine seedlings, and hence the chance for satisfactory volunteer regeneration.

The main elements in the problem of planned regeneration here considered are (1) production, dissemination, and control of seed supplies, (2) character, influence, and preparation of seedbeds, and (3) requirements for early establishment and freedom for pines to grow.

SEED CROPS

Inflorescence

Juvenile flowering is uncommon for pines. Forest grown pines must usually reach pole size before blooming profusely.[43]

The male catkins of loblolly pine are borne in crowded clusters at the base of the spring growth of twigs (plate 1). They are yellow, ¾ to 1 inch long, and surrounded at the base by 8 to 10 scales.

---

[43] Strictly speaking the pines are not flowering plants; the structures herein called flowers are technically strobili. The minimum age for flower production in open-grown loblolly pine was observed at Placerville, Calif. (Righter 1939), to be 6 years for staminate flowers and 5 years for ovulate flowers.

These flowers ripen to discharge pollen in February or March in the Deep South and in April farther north; then they are gradually shed. Some observers report that most of the ovulate flowers are borne later and higher in the crown than many of the staminate ones. This tends to discourage self-pollination of pines on small tracts wherein wind-blown pollen is most likely to land on the flowers of adjacent trees. In extensive pine forest, however, the pollination process is a random one because the atmosphere becomes heavily laden with pollen to a height of several hundred feet.

Measurements of typical loblolly pine pollen, made to facilitate identification of fossil pollens in peat deposits (Cain 1940), are as follows in microns:

Dimension	The grains		Their wings	
	Range	Average	Range	Average
Length	66-72	69	39-51	46
Depth	45-48	47	26-31	30
Breadth	50-58	53	55-62	58

Although the pollen from a given tree or stand may ripen over a period of 2 weeks in the same latitude, depending on elevation and distance from the seacoast, the pollen period is retarded on the average about a week for each additional degree of north latitude (Dorman and Barber 1956). Thus it may be 6 weeks later in North Carolina than in Florida.

Higher on the seasonal shoot the ovulate flowers are borne on short stalks, singly or 2 to 6 together easily observable. They are purplish green, erect, miniature cones, $\frac{1}{2}$ to $\frac{3}{4}$ inch long and surrounded by 15 to 20 scales. Immediately after pollination the female conelets that escape insects, disease, and frost expand rapidly, often doubling their size in 10 days. During the remainder of the season the conelets grow slowly, reaching only about $\frac{1}{7}$ the size of ripe cones, because the actual union of the male and female reproduction cells does not take place until late spring of the second year.

Recently the desire for tree improvement through artificial cross pollination has focused further attention to pine flowers. The tendency toward delayed blooming in the more northern locations is not manifest locally. For example in east Texas, with a span of 250 miles of latitude within the loblolly pine range, the trend is sometimes reversed. Only in the outlying "Lost Pine" area of Fayette County is flowering consistently early (Zobel and Goddard 1954). The period when female flowers can be pollinated in east Texas is from 9 to 34 days, averaging 19, with maximum receptivity lasting only 2 to 18 days, averaging 7, depending on the weather. Cool weather just prior to or during flower opening or cone maturity retards those processes. Female flowers may be delayed longer than the male, resulting in a scarcity of pollen by the time the flowers become receptive. Rather wide variation has been observed between trees and within trees, adjacent buds existing in all stages simultaneously, with few in the receptive stage at any one time.

Cones

Loblolly pine cones (plate 4) are from 2 to 6 inches long, averaging 3½ inches. They resemble slash pine cones, are larger than those of pitch, Virginia, pond, or shortleaf pine, and smaller than longleaf pine cones. Variation in size, shape, and other characteristics, however, within a species may exceed the typical differences between species. Loblolly pine cones are sessile and often spiney; they yield winged ¼-inch seeds that are sometimes spotted or mottled, but usually solid brown or nearly black. The size and color varies greatly from tree to tree.

The usual period of cone ripening covers late September and early October in southern coastal areas. Farther north and on the Piedmont Plateau cones ripen slightly later. Seedfall reaches a peak in the last half of October or the first half of November depending on weather conditions, and seedfall is usually 85 percent complete by the end of December. The rest of the seeds come down gradually in winter and spring. Differences in cone ripening, similar to those in flower development, extend the period of seedfall.

Yields vary widely by locality and year. A region-wide cone-crop reporting service similar to the one pioneered for the South by Wakeley (1931-41) is most useful in planning for seed collection, but some of the observation techniques developed in such effort can be used locally in the timing of site preparations for natural regeneration.

The number of cones on standing loblolly pine trees can be estimated with reasonable accuracy from observations made in a uniform manner with binoculars and corrected by some exact counts. Most unreleased trees bear less than 100 cones or less than 500 when released, but large open-grown trees can produce 1,500 cones each. There is about a month in the spring when conelets, standing out at the tips of twigs, can be easily observed and counted from the ground. Later in the spring when the immature cones are obscured by new growth and long needles, it is nearly impossible to identify them at a distance. Then counts must cease until the second summer when the enlarged new cones come into view and can be distinguished

PLATE 4.—Three age classes of loblolly pine cones as they appear in May. (U.S.F.S. Photo 476644.)

from persistent old cones. The new ones, not yet open, differ in color and are farther out on the twigs. Defective cones may turn brown early but tend to remain closed.

Counts on standing trees by ground observers are always low. They often need to be doubled or tripled and should always be adjusted by a predetermined correction factor (Wenger 1953b). In one instance estimates of yields from a 25-year-old stand were 90 percent correct after multiplying the counts by 1.4 in the closed parts and by 1.5 where the crowns had been released (Bilan 1957).

Where few cones are lost to parasites a relatively accurate estimate of a seed crop can be had 6 months in advance, but the estimates made up to a year in advance are more advantageous to users of the seed (Trousdell 1950a).

A method of cone ratios derived from sampling felled trees has proved dependable for at least a 6-month forecast; the prediction is made by counting cones on a 3-foot section taken from the tops of 50 cone-bearing trees. There are three conditions of cones on each tree: old empty cones that have shed seed the previous year, sound green cones that will produce the current crop, and small immature conelets that will not ripen till the following year. Because conelets are relatively abundant in the 3-foot top section and some loss is expected, experience has led to the use of a 45 percent reduction factor. Then a cone ratio for the current crop is obtained by dividing an estimate of the number that will ripen this autumn, i.e., 55 percent of the sample, by the number that shed seed the previous year. The divisor consists of a count of old cones found plus the missing ones indicated by stubs. The quotient shows the relative sizes of crops for the two years. A ratio greater than 1.0 indicates an increase in seed production. This technique used as much as 12 months in advance of seedfall has proved reliable in eastern Virginia and North Carolina, but forecasts for a longer period are unreliable because an undetermined number of immature conelets do not complete their development (Trousdell 1950a).

Seed production

The small brown and black seeds are borne singly or in pairs at the bases of the cone scales, and the inch-long wings facilitate their distribution by wind. A cone of average size contains 40 to 50 full seeds (Wakeley 1954a). A large-crowned tree can produce several bushels of cones and perhaps 40 thousand seeds, but the average mature tree yields only 9 to 15 thousand seeds in a good year. Seedfall typical of the Coastal Plain may be approximated in thousands of seeds per acre as follows: 18 to 37 (i.e., 1 or 2 pounds) during an average year, or 260 (about 14 pounds) in a "bumper" year (McCulley 1953e).

Loblolly pine sometimes produces good seed crops every 2 to 4 years (Jemison and Korstian 1944) but often at intervals of 3 to 10 years. In Virginia one average and five good seed crops were observed (Pomeroy 1949b) in a 13-year period, the longest time between good crops being 4 years. The phenomena that cause poor seed years include not only pollination failure in wet weather and injury to flowers by frost, but also damage to cones by insects and disease. In Texas a good seed year is expected to alternate with three failures. A larger percentage of cones is destroyed by insects on good than on poor sites. Because some cones are available for infestation even in the poorest seed years on the better sites, the insect population there seems to be maintained at a higher level than on poor sites which are without cones in poor years (Knight 1951). Wenger (1958) observed that the size of a seed crop is positively correlated with May to July rainfall of 2 years earlier and negatively correlated with the size of the seed crop 2 years earlier.

When seed supplies are plentiful they are often of better quality also. A record for one stand showed that about half the seeds were empty when a total of 200,000 per acre were produced, whereas only a quarter of the seeds were empty when the stand produced an exceptional crop of 500,000 seeds per acre. Furthermore the loss of seed to insects is proportionately much heavier in a poor than a good year.

Loblolly pine seed yields are heavier and more consistent near the coast than in the more extensive inland portion of its range. Off years tend to be complete failures and good years less frequent at inland locations. Three to five times as much seed is produced in the Coastal Plain as from similar trees in the Piedmont (Brender 1958). Cones are produced on a few pines over 6 inches in d.b.h. by the 12th to 18th year. Open-grown trees begin to bear at 20 years but under forest conditions cones cannot generally be expected before the trees are 10 inches in d.b.h. and 25 years old. Cones are not borne in appreciable quantities within unthinned stands before the 30th to 50th year or until the canopy is opened by mortality. Seed producing capacity lasts at least 150 years and is probably life-long. The yield of individuals varies widely but the average mounts steadily with increasing diameter of the trees (Grano 1957b). This trend (Barrett 1940) is as follows in open stands:

		Seeds per tree	
D.b.h. (inches)	Average annual (number)	In better than average years (number)
6	0	0
7	100	200
8	220	380
9	490	650
10	880	1,100
11	2,140	3,450
12	3,800	6,050
13	5,700	8,700
14	7,900	11,400
15	10,500	14,300
16	13,300	17,100

An 8-year record of annual per-acre yields of seed from another
stand, as recorded at the Big Woods Experimental Forest, is as
follows:

	Seeds per acre—	
Year	At 95 years (thousands)	At 145 years (thousands)
1947	830	600
1948	140	100
1949	120	65
1950	345	325
1951	545	390
1952	260	330
1953	105	140
1954	145	160

Observations on the Santee Experimental Forest near Charleston,
S. C., indicate near maximum yields of viable seed per acre from
50-year-old stands as follows: In poor years less than 100 M regardless of cutting, in average years less than 200 M on uncut areas
and more than 300 M on partially cut areas, and in ''bumper''
years less than 400 M on uncut areas, and more than 600 on partially
cut areas. Rarely are a million seeds per acre produced.

Seed requirements

There is a wide spread between the number of seeds laid down
by trees and the number of seedlings resulting therefrom. Among
the reasons for this are (1) nonviability of some seeds, (2) failure
to fall where establishment is possible, (3) consumption by birds
or rodents, and (4) early mortality after germination.

Germinative capacity ranging from 11 to 76 and averaging 60
percent (U.S.F.S. 1948a) is known to be associated with time of
ripening and level of seed yields. When annual production is high
in the Duke Forest, viability is high, but seed released early or late
is relatively unsound. The highest viability is found in good seed
years and in the seeds that drop at the peak of the seedfall (Jemison and Korstian 1944). The inferiority of seeds that fall later may
be traced to underdevelopment associated with their origin on the
atypical scales at the ends of the cones. The steady decline in viability is due, in part however, to deterioration of seed in which
insects are sometimes the cause. After the initial heavy seedfall,
release may come more and more from inferior cones that are slow
to open. Few seeds remain viable in the forest floor through the
second winter after they mature.

Seedling mortality varies widely. In one instance where some 281,000 seeds per acre fell in a Piedmont clearing beside a 70-year-old stand there were only 900 seedlings present 2 years later—one for each 312 seeds (Barrett 1940). From this it would appear that 200 to 300 thousand seeds per acre, in the absence of site preparation, are needed to get 1,000 seedlings. Elsewhere success has followed the fall of only a quarter as much seed. In fact with a favorable seedbed in the first year a mere 20 to 37 thousand seeds may be sufficient according to an intensive study (Trousdell 1950a). Wakeley (1947b) reports fair to good results from a crop of 800 to 1,500 cones per acre.

Regeneration difficulties that increase with elapsed time present a real problem. Theoretically four medium or ten poor seed years may be equivalent to one good year, but this theory breaks down in practice for two reasons: (1) birds or rodents eat nearly all the good seeds in poor years, and (2) extension of the regeneration period gives minor vegetation and hardwoods sprouting on moist sites too much opportunity to recapture the land. Grass and weeds on the drier Piedmont sites are no obstacle. Much depends upon the character and age (i.e., time since logging) of the natural seedbed. This is apparent in estimates of seed requirements in the Coastal Plain made by Trousdell (1950b). On the undisturbed portions of a good first-year seedbed he found that only a pound or two of seeds, say 25,000, were needed per acre, but if the seedbed was poorer twice as much, or if older, perhaps 5 to 7 times as much seed was needed:

Seedbed	Seed requirements	
	M seeds	Pounds
Undisturbed by logging..................	50	2-3
Two years after logging.................	250-350	10-20

Thus, in the absence of seedbed preparation, it is obvious that because of the class of timber or an inferior cone crop, years are common in which four, six or eight seed trees will not supply enough seed, and even entire stands just reaching sawtimber size will often fail to do so. Occasionally, perhaps once in 10 years, a well-managed stand may produce an enormous crop of over a million seeds per acre—more than enough to feed all the predators and reproduce the pine forest too. This occurred in the Santee Experimental Forest after three thinnings had thoroughly released the seed trees (Lotti 1956c). Obviously it is futile to specify numbers of seed trees needed without any reference to other conditions (table 38, chapter 8, Management of Mature Timber).

Much less seed is needed to regenerate pine on seedbeds prepared by partial exposure of mineral soil. This may be done in logging, particularly if, where necessary, the surface is prescribed-burned, or disked, or both. Such prescriptions are most effective when properly timed to take advantage of natural seedfall, for improved seedbeds deteriorate rapidly. In the Bigwoods Experimental Forest near Franklin, Va., the first year after cutting the catch was 1 out of 9, i.e., nine seeds fell for each one that grew where the litter had been disturbed, but over 40 were required per seedling elsewhere. Where both litter and slashings had been removed by burning, 15 seeds fell for each seedling obtained. Trousdell (1954a and 1954c), studying seedling establishment from a given quantity of seed, found that the average numbers of seeds necessary to produce one seedling in four successive years were 14, 50, 162, and 212. This rate of seedbed deterioration, indicated by progressive increases in the numbers of sound seeds needed to produce a single seedling, differs somewhat with the manner in which the site was prepared (Trousdell 1954a):

Site preparation	Seeds per seedling when time since treatment is—		
	1 year (number)	2 years (number)	3 years (number)
Disk and log...........	7	37	187
Log and burn..........	15	69	211
Log only..............	22	63	81

Because the improvements induced by either harvest or cultural treatment tend to disappear in 3 years, pine regeneration promptly attained is most complete and satisfactory.

NATURAL SEEDING

In many places timber can be harvested in a manner that permits the loblolly pine forest to reseed itself naturally without any costly special measures.

In uneven-aged management natural reseeding in small irregular openings usually extends over many unfavorable and favorable years. Usually no artificial methods are undertaken and no heavy investment is made in measures for natural reproduction. Where rotations are short, and where planting or direct seeding operations have proved to be outstandingly successful, it may be advisable under even-aged management also to avoid any heavy investment in natural reproduction.

In even-aged management effective natural regeneration is de-

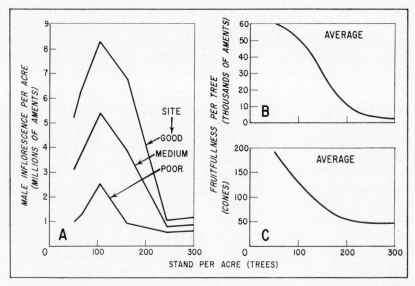

FIGURE 29.—Effect of stand per acre on fruitfulness of loblolly pine in Queensland, Australia: *A*, Male flowers per acre; *B*, male flowers per tree; and *C*, cones per tree (Florence and McWilliam 1956).

pendent on a seed source, adequate for the expected seedbed condition, either from adjacent seed trees or from trees reserved on the cutover area. Seed source can vary from as few as 3 seed trees per acre to a possible maximum of 40 trees in shelterwood cutting; maximum production requires a preparatory cutting to release 15 to 30 trees per acre to produce seed, time for them to respond in cone production, and finally enough other trees remaining to provide an operable final cut that will prepare the site for seedfall. Thus to induce well-stocked and previously unmanaged stands to reseed themselves at least two preparatory cuttings are needed. The first is to stimulate reserved pines to produce seed; the second is to scarify the forest floor to receive it. However, in less dense or managed stands one seed cutting may suffice because the trees are free from crowding. A previous series of intermediate cuttings will have prepared, for seed production, crop trees chosen for apparently good genetic qualities. Before these are marked as seed trees they merit close attention—individually to evaluate productive capacity and collectively to synchronize site preparation and seedfall. Seed cuttings are helpful, often adequate in preparing a site. The manner in which seed trees are selected, released, and removed is vital to success.

Selection of seed trees

Seed trees should be chosen from healthy 12-inch or larger pines with dominant or codominant crowns, well-formed stems, and an abundance of old cones indicating past fruitfulness. Although seed-bearing trees do not always yield their best crops in the same year, their individual capacity to produce can be fairly well estimated at any time (Grano 1957b). This is because all cones maturing in the current season plus most of the cones that matured in the past two seasons may be in the crown at the same time and remnants of the rest may be seen on the ground below.

In estimating prospective seed supplies it may be advisable to make some allowance for defective cones which are more abundant in poor seed years. For example in southeastern Virginia, the percentage of defective cones was greater on trees with small crops than on trees with large crops, and percentages defective were consistently high or low in individual trees from year to year (Wenger and Trousdell 1958):

Total current yield (cones)	Proportion of currently defective cones (percent)
100	26
300	21
500	16
700	11
900	5

Another and more controllable influence on seed yields is stand density. As stands mature and are thinned, either naturally or in cultural operations, the yield of seeds per acre increases only up to a certain point. If the stand is thinned further to less than 100 trees, inflorescence per acre is reduced (fig. 29, *A*). Meanwhile, however, the fruitfulness of individual trees continues to increase (fig. 29, *B* and *C*) indicating no serious shortage of pollen. Unless all harvest is deferred until after seedfall, to take advantage of production from all available seed bearers, trees enough should be reserved to furnish an ample supply per acre at an early date. An adequate supply of seed means reserving more trees in the Piedmont than in the Coastal Plain. For example, the yield of sound seeds per acre in the Santee Experimental Forest in the Coastal Plain (fig. 30) was, in the same period, 3 to 10 times as abundant as that in the Hitchiti Experimental Forest in the Piedmont (table 15). The seed yields in figure 30 represent stand conditions typical of a managed forest. In nearby unmanaged stands the yield of seed in the period 1952-55 was only 65 percent as great. In either region

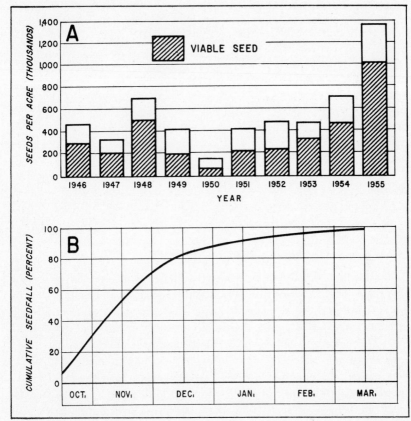

FIGURE 30.—Seedfall on the Santee Experimental Forest near Charleston, S. C.: *A*, Annual variation in yield from a stand of small sawtimber; *B*, 10-year average distribution of annual seedfall from the same stand cumulated by month (Lotti 1956c).

the number of trees left should be sufficient to comprise an operable cut when they have served their purpose. The problem of providing an adequate seed source is discussed further under silvicultural harvesting procedures.

Seed tree release[44]

Preparatory cutting to release seed trees from adjacent competition is certain in due time to increase cone production substantially.

[44] Fertilizing young trees to increase cone production is so far too expensive for forest operations with the exception of seed orchards, but ¼-inch partial girdles for this purpose may be stimulating (Lotti and McCulley 1951). Usually, however, girdling and strangulation are less effective in stimulating seed production in pulpwood-size loblolly pine trees than is full crown release. When used as a supplement to crown release, girdling and strangulation are likely to

TABLE 15.—*Production of sound seed per acre by loblolly pine in the Piedmont on two uncut and two partially cut groups of compartments, Hitchiti Experimental Forest, Georgia*

Year	Mature well-stocked	Immature open-grown	Seed tree[1]	Shelterwood[1]
	Thousands	Thousands	Thousands	Thousands
1947	24	30	7	74
1948	8	7	12	10
1949	3	1	2	2
1950	3	2	3	0
1951	11	1	13	45
1952	139	80	73	304
1953	...	2	9	7
1954	2	0	6	13
1955	214	130	184	445
1956	2	0	1	9
Total	406	253	310	909
	Percent	Percent	Percent	Percent
Relation to mature well-stocked	100	62	76	224

[1] Production three growing seasons after cutting.

Enough salable wood can be removed to pay for a seed cutting. Such liberation has doubled production on trees of cone-bearing size on the Coastal Plain in a generally poor seed year. In such years seed cuttings have failed in the Piedmont possibly because of frost damage. Disengaging the crowns of trees that previously produced only light crops may be helpful at interior locations in medium or good seed years. In one instance full crown release increased cone production sevenfold in the third year (Bilan 1957). In the coastal areas the release of seed trees, even including overmature trees, has caused 10 to 20 times normal seed production (Pomeroy 1949b, McCulley 1953e, and Wenger 1954).

Because following release in winter or spring more than 2 years are required for cones to mature, the first two cone crops succeeding the release cutting will show no response. Stands partly cut during the growing season show the effect of release in the third or fourth crop after cutting, depending on whether release came early or late in midsummer (fig. 31). It is safe to count on an increase in the third succeeding cone crop if the trees are released before the end of May (fig. 32).

In pulpwood stands seed production is less than in older timber because of the immaturity of the trees. In understocked stands this handicap of immaturity does not last long, for the crowns are rela-

do more harm than good; their beneficial effect on seed production is negligible, and the risk of losing the trees to storm breakage, insects, or root starvation is very high (Bilan 1957).

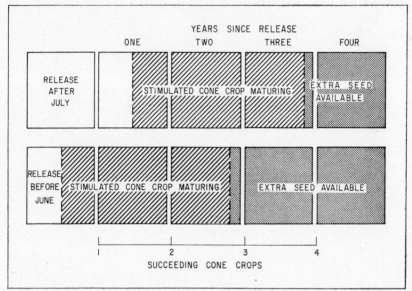

FIGURE 31.—Relation of seasonal timing of a seed cutting to formation of seed needed for regeneration of loblolly pine (McCulley 1953b).

tively large and development rapid. Hardwood competition, however, is likely to be more advanced in understocked stands at the time of cutting, thus reducing the chances for good regeneration. In well-stocked pulpwood stands brush competition is not serious at first, but seed production after release is impeded by small crowns as well as by immaturity. Then, in spite of ample initial space on the forest floor, extended delay in seeding permits hardwood development; hence on moist sites it may become serious and indicate a need to use fire. Rotations that are too short invite regeneration difficulties (Pomerening 1951).

In the liberation of seed trees it now appears that to attain full crown release it is sufficient to cut enough competitors so there is a 6- to 10-foot space for crown expansion on all sides (McCulley 1953b and 1953e), but more study of space requirements is needed. It is especially important in short-rotation management for owners of small tracts to release their crowded seed trees if heavy machinery is not available to destroy hardwood regeneration. The extra seed thus obtained at low cost when needed is often sufficient to get an adequate stand of pine seedlings started ahead of the hardwoods (McCulley 1951).

Ordinarily on the Coastal Plain, pines released for seeding should not be less than 4 nor more than 12 per acre depending on size

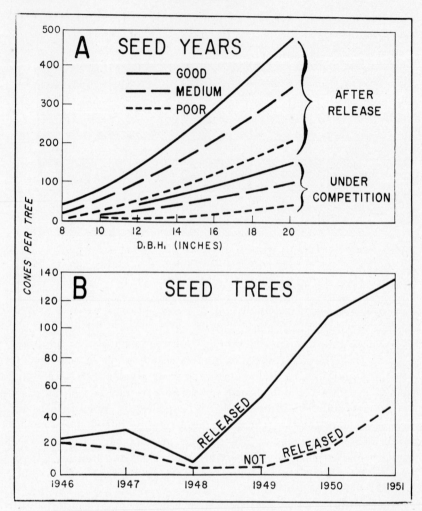

FIGURE 32.—By release of selected trees from crowding, the yield of cones is increased appreciably for the larger trees in years of generally good production. In this instance all stems within 20 feet of trees designated for release were cut in the winter of 1946-47 in stands 27 to 43 years old in Virginia (Wenger and Trousdell 1958).

(Wenger 1954). Fewer trees lead to a shortage of seed, whereas the release of more seed trees may prematurely remove so many pine competitors that the understory hardwoods may be stimulated to take over the site prior to the time of final harvest, thus making it more difficult to dispose of them at that time. This danger of complications from the release of too many seed trees applies only to the more moist one-third of the lower Piedmont area. There, the drier sites readily reproduced to pine.

Seed production on the higher level induced by release is expected to last at least 5 years (Easley 1954). How much longer it can persist—possibly 10 years—has not been determined, but Wenger (1953c) reports there is at least 3 years' leeway in the time during which harvest cutting must be done in order to benefit from an increased supply of seed on a seedbed refreshed by logging. Under both even-aged and the selection type of management frequent cyclic cuts may be expected to maintain a high level of seed production even in stands not scheduled for early regeneration.

Seed dissemination

The effective seeding distance of loblolly pine seed trees is rather short. Most seeds fall within a distance of 150 to 200 feet from the parent trees, sometimes reaching 330 feet (McQuilkin 1939, Pomeroy and Korstian 1949). It is exceptional when thickets of loblolly pine are discovered 100 yards from the nearest known source of seed. Infertile seeds, usually lighter, may possibly be windborne from greater distances, although there is evidence that this is not true (Jemison and Korstian 1944). Old fields in the Piedmont area are best reseeded naturally when the whole area is within 300 feet of an unbroken source along the windward side of the field (McQuilkin 1939).

The period of seedfall is hastened, and sometimes shortened, by dry, warm, windy autumn weather, or retarded and extended by damp, cool, calm days. Occasionally, as a result of such delay, some seeds continue to fall until spring but not enough for good regeneration. Seasonal distribution of seedfall in the Atlantic states, however, normally peaks in mid-November, is about two-thirds complete by the first of December, and at least 90 percent complete by mid-January. A few loblolly pine seeds may not fall until summer, but a smaller proportion of these are good seeds (Jemison and Korstian 1944) :

Time since beginning of seedfall (weeks)	Viability of seeds (percent)	Time since beginning of seedfall (weeks)	Viability of seeds (percent)
2	56	12	43
4	60	14	40
6	57	16	36
8	53	20	34
10	48	24	33

Siggins (1933) studied the association of seed weight and quality with rate of fall. He found that the average good loblolly pine seed fell 160 feet in 0.6567 minute, 244 feet in 1 minute, or 4.1 feet in 1 second. Another study[45] related height of cone with the distance traveled by seed as follows:

$$\text{Distance (feet)} = 18.184 + 1.2869 \text{ height (feet)}$$

When large clearings are reproduced to pine from the side, variations in dispersal distance result in conspicuous marginal gradations in the density of seedling stands. These usually thin out beginning a chain or two (66 to 132 feet) from the seed source. The stage of succession in surrounding herbaceous plants appears not to affect the zonation. Studying abandoned Piedmont fields reseeded in a good year from a wall of standing pines, McQuilkin (1939) found the seedling stands averaged good, over 1,000 per acre, out to 5 chains; fair, i.e., 500 +, to 7 chains; and erratic beyond that distance. This gradation is typical of the first 3 to 5 years when the majority of seedlings appear. In some instances 10 or more years may be needed to achieve satisfactory density.

Total production, time of ripening, and dispersal of loblolly pine seeds, and resulting stands of seedlings are shown in figure 33.

When reproduction is from seed trees on the area, the total supply of seed is more important than flight distance because of the heavy natural losses to be expected between seedfall and seedling establishment. To make the most of limited supplies the preparation of seedbeds and control of hardwoods should be scheduled before November of the third year following release cutting (Pomeroy 1949b) (fig. 31).

SITE PREPARATION

Seedbed character and possibilities for improvement

The character of pineland seedbeds depends mainly on (1) kind of soil, (2) previous use of land and fire, (3) volume of timber harvested and equipment used in its extraction, and (4) elapsed time since logging. The effect of these factors is felt first through the uncovering of mineral soil and subsequently through different rates at which the soil is again covered by debris or revegetated by competing species.

On heavily cut areas dry-weather logging with crawler tractors

[45] In southern pine the similarity of dispersal distances, regardless of differences in size by species, appears to be due to the similarity of weight-area ratios in the seeds.—Gemmer, Eugene W. The flight of longleaf, shortleaf, and loblolly pine seeds (unpublished office report, 1940).

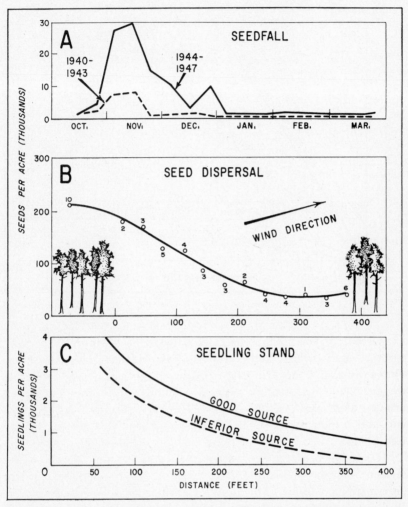

FIGURE 33.—Time and place of loblolly pine seedfall: *A*, Mid-November peaks of seedfall during two 4-year periods when yields were insufficient for regeneration. *B*, Average annual dispersal of sound seeds into a cleared strip from adjoining timber, Duke Forest, Durham, N. C. Figures on the curve are basic numbers of seed traps used (Pomeroy 1949b). *C*, Seedling stand density varies with quality of and distance from seed source (McQuilkin 1939).

disturbs about half of the soil surface, leaves a third wholly undisturbed, and deposits slashings on the rest. Such disturbance, well distributed, may lead to satisfactory regeneration. Where the cut is light and skidding is with wheel tractors or animals less surface is disturbed. When fire is prescribed to follow such logging, about

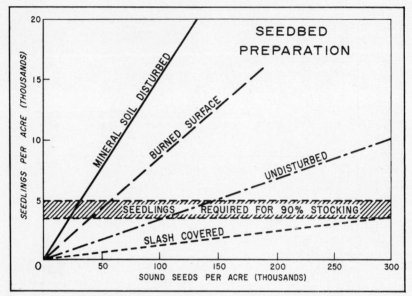

FIGURE 34.—Number of seedlings per acre resulting from various amounts of seed falling on four classes of seedbed (Trousdell 1950b).

81 percent of the surface becomes a desirable seedbed, 18 percent remains undisturbed, and only 1 percent is left under slashings (Pomeroy and Trousdell 1948). Natural regeneration is improved to the extent that freshly exposed mineral soil is well distributed over an area (fig. 34). If advance reproduction is not already present, and no burning is to be done loggers should be encouraged to use diverse skid trails to increase surface scarification.

If special measures are necessary to prepare sites, they are prescribed for one or both of two reasons: (1) to increase effective germination, and (2) to decrease injurious competition. Overstocking is seldom a problem in regenerating loblolly pine; where it occurs it usually disappears without corrective measures. Seeds require moisture to germinate and absence of obstruction to penetrate the soil. Freshly denuded mineral soil is usually superior in both respects. Although later additional moisture and free space may be needed, the original operation to expose mineral soil serves to increase both survival and growth.

Heavy advance growth of hardwood must be controlled by some means everywhere loblolly pine is to be grown. Herbaceous competition is less serious than the sprouting of well-rooted broad-leaved species. Among these the most persistent individuals can be killed economically with an application of 2,4,5-T. Drastic methods of site preparation and type conversion, to give natural succession the needed setback, are gaining in favor in the coastal flatwoods.

On the heavier soils of the Piedmont Plateau the situation is different. There burning treatments supplemented by mechanical scarification also have been successful in regenerating pine; but in the Piedmont both fire and heavy machinery have to be used with caution if at all on rolling land lest they accelerate the tendency of topsoil to move downhill, thus possibly lowering loblolly pine site quality on the sloping lands (Gabriel 1950).

On flat moist sites the risk of erosion is small and fire is needed less for seed germination than for hardwood control. On poorly drained flatwoods the use of machinery for either logging or specifically for site preparation should be avoided when the soil is saturated. The establishment of loblolly pine seedlings on surfaces churned up by heavy equipment during logging in wet weather is greatly inferior to that on ground less severely disturbed. The height growth of seedlings in these "puddled" areas, at least for the first 2 years, is less than half of that of seedlings on other surfaces (Lotti and McCulley 1951).

In the conversion of low, dense, hardwood thickets to loblolly pine the best combination of logging and burning, or spraying herbicides, with the use of heavy mechanical equipment—tractors, rollers with brush cutting blades, bulldozers, disk harrows, etc.,—is still in an experimental stage. Forceful disturbance of heavy clay soil in the Piedmont may induce erosion, but in the southeastern Coastal Plain many thousands of acres are annually being so treated, while the search for better chemicals and improved machinery continues. In fact, foresters are still in the process of learning how best to propagate a "fire-subclimax" pine type of forest with or without recourse to burning.

Timing improvements and using fire

Successful regeneration is dependent to a large extent on adequate seeding when the seedbed is favorable. Therefore, timing of improvements will often determine their effectiveness.

Disking is most effective in late summer before logging (McCulley 1953e). Autumn seedbed preparation must be done before seedfall— Lotti (1956b) suggests before November 1—lest the treatment destroy or bury the seed (Chapman 1942b, Chaiken and LeGrande 1949). Winter logging also destroys some seed on the ground, but this loss is more than made up by the extra seed that becomes available from the stand as a whole when cutting is delayed until about January 1. Logging that takes place after seed germination, however, can seriously reduce seedling establishment. Grazing animals should be excluded during winter and spring following seedfall. Open range cattle grazing at that time can reduce germination of pine seeds almost half (Gemmer 1941), though it has little effect during the growing season. Seedbed preparation may be futile in the Piedmont in years of light seedfall; areas with heavy underbrush should be cut over in years of heavy seedfall. Preparatory or partial seed cuttings can anticipate and increase the seedfall. Some landowners plan for final harvests of timber only when a heavy crop of seed is in prospect, but because industry needs a continuous flow of wood, not all cutting can be scheduled for good years. Whenever the adequacy of either seedbed or seed supply is questionable it is a good policy to improve both.

Controlled burning, as well as measures other than logging prescribed for site preparation, may not be essential when brush competition is light and seed is plentiful. But these techniques become more necessary as the supply of seed is reduced—up to the point where seed is indeed limiting, and little or none is available. Regardless of seed crop, however, supplementary measures are used under intensive practice to insure well-stocked reproduction of pine in pure stands.

Preparatory burning must not only be in season, but also timely in relation to weather and cutting operations. Weather markedly influences the handling of fire—if not indeed its failure to burn or its possible escape. Cuttings may supply too much or too little fuel, and seeds may be either burned up or fail to land on mineral soil where they can grow. These are reasons why fire even when used mainly for hazard reduction, must above all be timely. On areas burned after seedfall a few seedlings, but not enough for a crop, may be expected to develop in unburned spots or from seeds that fell later (Chaiken 1952c).

Proper planning of burning treatments involves an appraisal of the fuels needed for the desired intensity of burning. Burning immediately after logging is hard on seed trees, expensive, and difficult to control. Areas that are burned immediately after logging but before subsequent timber stand improvement operations may need a second burn (Chapman 1948). Burning that follows both these cutting operations will have additional fuel and hence can destroy larger hardwood stems. Because it is difficult to handle such fires safely, mechanical or chemical methods of site preparation may be preferred under these conditions.

Summer or early fall burns are most effective when they cover an area well. They may be superior to partial coverage by heavy machinery (Little and Mohr 1954 and 1957a), but unfortunately they are difficult to time and use safely. In Texas burning in autumn either remains hazardous until it is too late to do it extensively, or else it will not cover the area in need of treatment. Burning in spring before seedfall permits an undesirable regrowth of grass and weeds.

The extent to which fire can be utilized to good advantage is still to be determined. Certainly the frequency with which it is prescribed should vary with the local possibility of, and need for, burning either lightly or severely. Few winters are too wet for light burning, but benefits are temporary because winter fires kill very few roots.

When a tract is logged in a poor seed year, burning to kill back small hardwood stems may be advisable, if it is anticipated that enough fuel will be available for a repeat burn in the summer preceeding the next fall seed crop. The attrition of successive fires may be needed in some stands. Summer fires are needed only on areas where early regeneration cuts are planned. These commonly involve the deliberate sacrifice of some advance growth of pine seedlings. Such treatment is worthwhile in even-aged management because a full crop a few years later is preferable. This use of fire has two outstanding merits. It not only keeps many of the understory hardwood trees from becoming large and expensive to kill, but also prevents the accumulation of a mass of flammable dead material that could destroy the whole stand in a wildfire. All too often in the past the use of fire has been too little and too late. The constructive use of fire has been ignored or neglected so long now that over large areas the more expensive mechanical procedure is the only way by which another crop of pine can be started.

Mechanized site preparation

Where the danger of soil erosion is slight and when hardwood sprouts have a major role in the deterioration of seedbeds, the use of heavy machinery may be advisable to kill them back. As in tractor logging at least half the soil surface should be scarified to receive pine seeds. The improvement in seedbeds achieved by burning or from logging alone may not be sufficiently homogeneous. Following the typically variable effect of fire, machinery may be used to make regeneration more uniform. Where the competing stems are less than 6 inches in diameter a medium-sized (40 hp. or larger) crawler tractor pulling a heavy disk harrow can cover an acre per hour of operation as a double purpose preharvest treatment. A crew of two men is best, one to drive the tractor, the other to scout ahead and guide him around obstacles. The same measure may not be so effective after logging, because slash concentrations must be avoided and stumps may hang up the tractor or break disks. On small holdings or where a heavy harrow is not available, soil may be exposed and effectively loosened with a heavy drag to trail behind and help hold the disks in the ground. The drag may be a stump with the roots attached or a triangular frame of railroad iron with a few 10-inch teeth welded to it. This tears the root mat, keeping much of it from falling back into place behind the disk. Such treatment can, like burning, expose mineral soil on 80 to 90 percent of an area.

Land completely occupied by sapling hardwoods presents a problem; the felled stems may form a mat over which a light disk harrow will roll without cutting. Such land needs double treatment with machinery heavy enough to chew up the debris thoroughly and sturdy enough to withstand collisions with stumps. Where competing stems larger than 6 inches are abundant, especially on areas where reproduction has previously failed, bulldozers may be used to clear about half an acre an hour.

Where a source of pine seed is present the hardwoods are simply pushed over and left. This practice often leads to excellent regeneration except under piles of debris. When windrows of brush are kept small enough for the pine canopy to close over them they do not waste growing space. A Louisiana lumber company (Tannehill 1951) favors bulldozing as a method of site preparation for both natural reproduction and planting. It found that seedlings on such areas resisted drought better than those on adjoining areas. This treatment is normally fully justified by the pine reproduction that follows because competition from hardwoods has been reduced. Further development in mechanized site preparation may be expected from numerous ingenious tests now underway.

On land less completely covered with hardwoods a combination of disking and chemical treatment is suggested. The disk would prepare the soil and knock down small hardwoods while herbicides would kill the larger ones.

Results of seeding

The methods of preparing sites suggested above have been checked at various points against actual results of seeding (fig. 34). Unquestionably a high degree of exposure of mineral soil is typical of the best seedbeds, but a moderate amount of grass and litter does not preclude good results when the seedfall is heavy. This is especially true when rainfall is plentiful and well distributed. Many seeds lodge in the ground cover until the first rain loosens and disengages their wings, making them less conspicuous to birds, and speeding their passage to mineral soil (Wakeley 1931). Contact with mineral soil is not necessary to obtain germination but it makes it 2 or 3 times as effective (Gemmer 1939). Some seeds may sprout during any period of favorable weather but most of them germinate in March or April. Generally, but not always, germination is best on soil disturbed by logging, intermediate on burned surfaces, poor on undisturbed spots, and poorest under logging slash (Pomeroy 1949a and 1949d; Trousdell 1950b; McCulley and Elliott 1952).

The inhibiting effect of litter on regeneration increases with its depth (Grano 1949):

Depth of litter (inches)	Seedling "catch" per milacre (number)
0.5	21
1.0	13
1.5	7
2.0	4
2.5	3
3.0	2
3.5	1

Obstruction apparently varies also with the kind of litter; pine needles impede establishment less than hardwood leaves. One observation in Louisiana where loblolly pine germinated 30 percent on bare soil showed the following percentages on littered areas: Pine litter 15, grass or pine-hardwood 11, and hardwood litter 9 (Clark 1948).

Litter on the forest floor cannot be disregarded as a barrier to pine regeneration in most locations during average years. This is not true of favorable locations when seedfall is heavy. Grano (1949) reports results on an area unburned for 15 years and uncut twice as long. Without benefit of any site preparation 8 to 10 thousand seeds per acre sprouted through an inch or two of litter and survived a summer drought.[46]

[46] Unfortunately in this study no cone counts or seed-trap estimates of the seed crop were made. At the rate of 29 seeds per surviving seedling (fig. 82,

The effect of aspect of the slope on seedling catch has been noted in the Hitchiti Experimental Forest on the Piedmont Plateau in Georgia (Brender 1957b). There loblolly pine reproduces best on the ridgetops and on upper south and west slopes. On steep north and east aspects, and on lower slopes, advance hardwood reproduction is more likely to prevail to the extent that both planting and release work may be necessary.

In regenerating a forest the area stocked by seedlings is more important than their number per acre. The area stocked is the more easily estimated. It often is expressed as the percentage of area having one or more pine seedlings per unit square, usually 0.001 acre. Ker (1953), using pine seedling data from southern Arkansas, found this relationship:

$$\text{No. of seedlings per acre} = 193.3(1.0416)^x$$

where x is the milacre stocking percentage. The equation has been found useful also in the Coastal Plain area of Virginia and North Carolina.[47] The relation between seed supplies, various prepared seedbeds, and the resulting seedling stands as observed on the Bigwoods Experimental Forest near Franklin, Va., are shown in figure 34. Recently disturbed mineral soil unquestionably offers the best seedbed. For equal numbers of seedlings, the stocking that follows the typical seedbed irregularity induced by heavy harvest tends to be 5 to 10 percent less than that on a uniform surface.

A method was devised by Trousdell (1954b) to convert estimates from 0.01-acre plots to milacre stocking. He counted all pines up to ten found standing at least 2 feet apart on each 0.01-acre sample plot. He excluded trees not free to grow and entered a decimal score for each plot with less than ten potential crop trees. On this basis the result was related to the conventional stocked-quadrat procedure as follows:

$$Y = 1.1057X - 17$$

where Y is the percentage of milacres stocked and X the percentage of 0.01 acres scored as indicated above.

---

chapter 8, Management of Mature Timber) it would require about 261,000 seeds, or 14 pounds per acre, to obtain 9,000 seedlings. Where only 1 pound of seed is available, a stand of only 635 seedlings can be expected without site preparation.

[47] The formula may not apply equally well elsewhere. The tendency toward grouping of seedlings in stands over half stocked varies with locality and there is considerable doubt (Meyer 1955) that a single regression not recognizing initial catch can be used everywhere.

FREEDOM TO GROW

For intolerant species freedom to grow means freedom to survive. Limits on this freedom may or may not be serious for loblolly pine depending on intensity of competition within stands and on plans for management of forests in even- or uneven-aged compartments.[48]

Precisely how well can pine seedlings develop in the shade? How long can they withstand suppression? When release is delayed will their response be prompt and satisfactory?

Such questions are not yet answered to everyone's satisfaction. They may be resolved somewhat differently for diverse situations. But a sound solution is so vital to successful silviculture that the matter of the extent and permanence of seedling suppression warrants detailed consideration here. The problem is paramount because a poor choice of regeneration procedure can necessitate costly planting in order to sustain yields of timber and pulpwood.

Tolerance of crowding

Shade tolerance need not be regarded strictly as the capacity of a tree to endure shade. Rather it is the capacity of a tree to withstand competition and continue to develop. Room to grow means sufficient space for both roots and tops—moisture below the surface and light above it. Both are so vital for seedlings (Korstian and Coile 1938; Kramer, Oosting, and Korstian 1952; Ferrell 1953) that there is no point in deducing which is the more influential. Yearling seedlings are smallest in the forest, intermediate at the margin, and largest in the open. At 3 years the intolerance of shade is clearly manifest in the size attained by all parts above ground (table 5, p. 60).

Since the shade tolerance of any species is only partly inherent, and varies with the quality of sites where seedlings start, local estimates of it may well affect the choice of treatments. Relative shade tolerance of trees may be judged in later life by observing the following items: (1) crown density, (2) branch foliation ratio, (3) live-crown ratio, (4) recovery from suppression, (5) natural pruning, (6) persistence when associated with competitors of equal size,

---

[48] Information given previously in this chapter is supplied mainly for use in obtaining even-aged regeneration. The present section deals with the relation of seedlings to an overwood; hence it applies mainly in working toward all-aged regeneration. Some of the studies reported, as for instance the effect of an adjacent wall of uncut timber, apply in both strip cutting and group selection. The prime object of the present chapter, however, is to clarify silvical relationships without reference to any particular system of harvesting. Chapter 8 will show regeneration contrasts under recognized systems.

(7) rate of height growth in the open, and (8) degree of taper. Only the first three items lend themselves readily to numerical rating.[49]

In the spring a newly germinated pine seedling draws nourishment first from the supply stored in the seed, then from that currently elaborated by the relatively efficient juvenile foliage, and hence is less dependent on light than on moisture during its first year. Thereafter light becomes more important. Loblolly pine seedlings are sufficiently tolerant of shade to grow slowly for some time in poor light, but they often fail later as a result of their early deficiencies—poor root development, improperly hardened tissues, and inability to store enough reserve food supply.

In the presence of sufficient light low soil moisture retards growth in hardwoods more than in pine, but conversely in the presence of sufficient moisture, low light intensity retards pine more than hardwood growth. Both growth and survival of loblolly pine seedlings under a forest canopy improve not only with better illumination but also with any decrease in the hardwood component of the overstory through which the light reaches them (fig. 35).

Growing space and seedling height

At any given age beyond the first year the height of forest-grown loblolly pine seedlings is closely correlated with the extent of overwood crown cover and its species composition. Seedlings are tallest where the cover is sparse and its hardwood component minor (table 16).

One of the most convenient quantitative measures of the overwood that often obstructs pine regeneration is known as the stand density index or S.D.I. (plate 5). It represents the number of trees per acre which a given stand will (or did) have at the time when its trees average 10 inches in d.b.h.[50] The most meaningful qualitative measure of an overwood that hampers pine reproduction is its species composition, i.e., the percentage of hardwood rather than

[49] University of Michigan, School of Natural Resources, Note 4. 1954.

Loblolly pine, adaptable as it is to a wide range of soils, exhibits limited range of tolerance. It appears somewhat more tolerant in early life than at maturity. However, this apparent decrease in tolerance with age, often noted, is partly a result of the increasing shortage of growing space for many individuals unable to compete with the leading few. Loblolly pine appears to be the least tolerant of the several species with which it is usually associated (Ashe 1910).

[50] S.D.I. (Reineke 1933) is a product readily obtained from a table of factors, one for each average diameter (Mulloy 1943), multiplied by the number of trees per acre of all size classes in the stand (table 78).

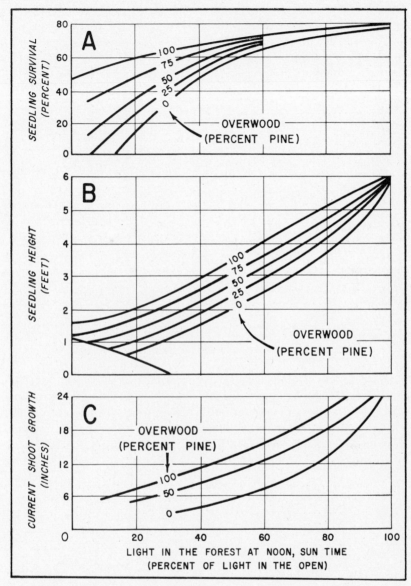

FIGURE 35.—Relation of species composition of overwood and light reaching the forest floor to the development of 5-year-old loblolly pine seedlings at Crossett, Ark. In each panel the upper curve is for seedlings under a pure stand of pine, the lowest curve for seedlings under pure hardwood. Intermediate curves are for seedlings in mixed forest. Basal areas of the overwood ranged from zero to about 150 square feet per acre.

TABLE 16.—*Average height of loblolly pine seedlings as influenced by an over-story in the upper Coastal Plain near Crossett, Ark.*[1]

Composition of overwood and age of seedlings[2]	Average seedling height when overwood crown cover in percent is—								
	10	20	30	40	50	60	70	80	90
	Ft.	Ft.	Ft.	Ft.	Ft.	Ft.	Ft.	Ft.	Ft.
Pure pine:									
2nd year	0.9	0.8	0.7	0.7	0.7	0.6	0.6	0.5	0.5
4th year	3.1	2.8	2.6	2.4	2.1	1.9	1.7	1.5	1.3
6th year	6.8	6.0	5.5	5.0	4.4	3.9	3.4	2.9	2.4
75 percent pine:									
2nd year	.8	.8	.7	.6	.6	.5	.4	.4	.3
4th year	3.0	2.5	2.3	2.1	1.9	1.7	1.5	1.3	1.1
6th year	6.1	5.3	4.8	4.3	3.9	3.4	2.9	2.5	2.0
50 percent pine:									
2nd year	.8	.7	.7	.6	.5	.5	.4	.3	.3
4th year	2.8	2.4	2.2	2.0	1.7	1.5	1.2	1.0	.8
6th year	5.5	4.7	4.2	3.8	3.3	2.9	2.5	2.1	(3)
25 percent pine:									
2nd year	.8	.7	.7	.6	.5	.4	.3	.3	.2
4th year	2.6	2.3	2.0	1.8	1.5	1.3	1.1	.8	.6
6th year	4.9	4.2	3.7	3.3	2.9	2.5	2.1	1.6	(3)
Pure hardwood:									
2nd year	.8	.7	.6	.5	.5	.4	.3	.3	.2
4th year	2.3	2.1	1.8	1.6	1.4	1.2	1.0	.7	.5
6th year	4.4	3.5	3.1	2.7	2.3	1.9	1.5	(3)	(3)

[1] Heights from ground to terminal bud as read from curves were rounded to the nearest one tenth foot. The height of dominant seedlings exceeds these averages by about 20 percent under heavy cover and about 50 percent under light cover.

[2] At 1 year seedling heights varied only between 0.2 and 0.3 feet, or 2¼ to 4 inches, regardless of cover.

[3] Average height undetermined because of mortality.

pine trees. On a given site the combined effect of these two characteristics of an overstory is closely related to both growth rate and survival of understory vegetation including pine seedlings. In a loblolly pine forest where only about one out of four or five mature trees are hardwoods, overwood density measured as S.D.I. is related to crown cover and light in summer about as follows:

Stand density index (S. D. I.)	Light on forest floor (percent)	Crown cover (percent)
25	68	3
75	55	9
125	44	23
175	36	50
225	30	69
275	25	81
325	21	89
375	17	95

The density of unmanaged forest is likely to vary over the whole range shown above, but most seedlings come in under overwoods of 225 or less. Under all-aged management the average stand density index is usually 125 or more. This average index ranges upward under even-aged management toward a maximum or "equilibrium"

PLATE 5.—Typical 5-year-old loblolly pine ranging in height from 6 for the relatively open-grown thrifty specimen at the left, down to 1½ feet for the puny one at the right, grown under the heavy canopy of an overstocked pine-hardwood stand. The overwood competition ranged from only 50 up to 400, as indicated by the stand density indices shown (Basis: 188 mil-acre samples of reproduction from seed crop of 1939 at Crossett, Ark., U.S.F.S. Photo 433813).

stocking at S.D.I. 275 on the best sites at 80 years (fig. 54, chapter 6, Growth and Yield).

The combined effect of composition and density of overwood on seedling heights at age 6 is shown in figure 36. None of these seedlings was tall enough to have yet reached the canopy above. When an overwood is low the pine seedlings can be readily injured by whipping against overhead branches. Even before that happens, however, a low overwood with closed canopy intercepts more side light than does the broken canopy typical of a high overwood. Hence, even with no variation in overwood density or composition, seedlings become more seriously suppressed under low cover (fig. 37).

The height of loblolly pine seedlings in the Piedmont is related to their age and to the density and level of the overwood (fig. 38).

The annual increase in density of overwood in second-growth loblolly pine that is protected from fire only, but otherwise unmanaged, is 4.5 ± 1.0 S.D.I. units. This rate of change in stand

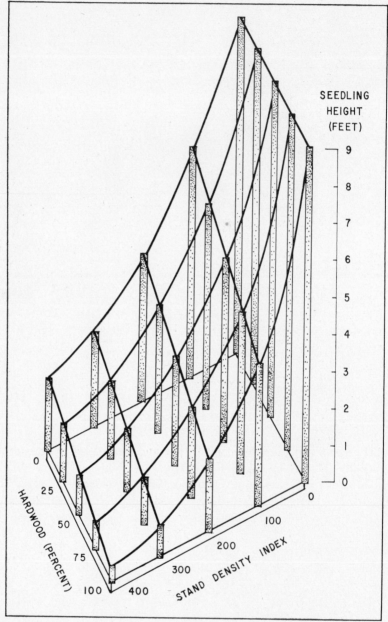

FIGURE 36.—The combined effect of overwood stand density and species composition in a mixed pine-hardwood forest on the height of 6-year-old loblolly
pine seedlings. Note height reduction from 9 feet open grown to about
half a foot for the few that survive under a dense and high hardwood
cover.

density accounts for the 6-year increase in overwood stand density index shown.

Survival of overtopped seedlings

Although loblolly pine seeds may germinate under a low canopy, the seedlings do not last long in thickets of sapling hardwoods. Under a partial canopy of hardwoods in Louisiana death occurs in an average of a little over 5 years. If pine reseeding on cutover land in that area is delayed 3 years, all pines starting under the hardwoods die (Chapman 1945).

Experience in the Hitchiti Experimental Forest in the Georgia Piedmont indicates that the pine seedlings can remain alive at least 4 years even under the complete canopy of a fully stocked pine stand, but they live less than 7 years where the shade level of the pine overwood is less than 20 feet. The persistence of loblolly pine reproduction in relation to pine overstories is as follows:

Overwood basal area (square feet)	Seedling life expectancy (years)	Overwood basal area (square feet)	Seedling life expectancy (years)
70	20	110	5
80	10	120	5
90	7	130	4
100	6	140	4

Comparable studies of longevity in understory pine seedlings in Arkansas show survival to be higher under a minimum of cover and under canopies that are largely pine rather than hardwoods (fig. 39). For example, with 90 percent cover none survived under hardwoods, but 55 percent survived 5 years under pure pine. The failure of seedlings is closely associated with the extent of reseeding in situations already occupied by the roots of established trees.

Marginal growth in forest openings

Both roots and tops of trees extend outward from the edge of timber stands into natural openings and forest clearings. This produces a transition zone in vegetation at low levels including pine reproduction. In regenerating a pine forest, border effects cannot be safely disregarded. Following perimeters, as they do, border effects vary in extent and in degree with both the size and shape of forest openings. Marginal retardation of seedling growth is measurable 30 feet out from the edge of young merchantable timber stands. It is most intense in the first 10 feet, and this heavy retardation covers a smaller proportion of large clearings than of small openings of the same conformation (table 17).

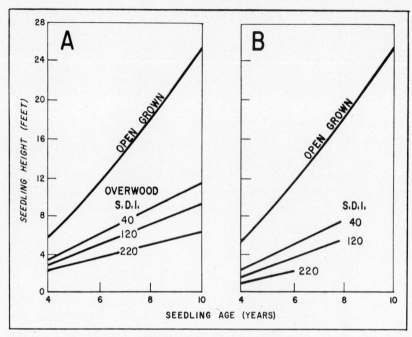

FIGURE 37.—Height of loblolly pine seedlings as affected by density of pine overwood in the Georgia Piedmont: *A*, a high (40-foot) cover, and *B*, a low (20-foot) cover (Brender and Barber 1956).

TABLE 17.—*Marginal influence of uncut timber on adjacent loblolly pine seedlings in forest openings on upper Coastal Plain and terrace soils near Crossett, Ark.*

Shape and size of opening in forest cover (acres)	Proportion of area in which degree of border retardation (by distance from timber) is—			
	Heavy (0-10 feet)	Medium (10-20 feet)	Light (20-30 feet)	None (30+ feet)
	Percent	Percent	Percent	Percent
Circular:				
¼	32	25	19	24
½	22	20	18	40
1	16	15	13	56
1½	13	13	11	63
Irregular[1]:				
¼	72	22	4	2
½	57	29	10	4
1	40	30	20	10
1½	32	30	22	16
	Feet	Feet	Feet	Feet
Seedling height at 6 years[2]	4.5	5.6	7.0	9.1

[1] These data apply to forest openings of the shape illustrated in figure 40.
[2] Equivalent heights at 6 years are attained by forest-grown seedlings when the overwood crown cover is 37, 15, 6, and 0 percent respectively.

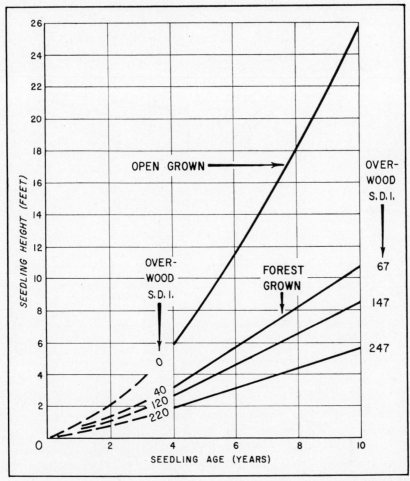

FIGURE 38.—Six-year height growth of seedlings in relation to progressive natural changes in density (S. D. I.) as shown for a 50-year overwood. The simultaneous average rise in shade level is from 36 to 42 feet (Brender and Barber 1956).

In the opposite direction the temporary stimulus from clearing is felt up to 30 feet into the woods. When a clearing is made in an overstocked timber stand (S.D.I. 400) a seedling under the closed canopy, but located within 15 feet of the clearing, will receive enough side light to grow as if the S.D.I. were 300 (fig. 36). One at the very edge of the dense timber will grow as if it were under a 15 percent canopy consisting of 75 percent pine (table 16).

A seedling in the open, but within 15 feet of the wall of uncut timber will be partially shaded and will develop as if it were under

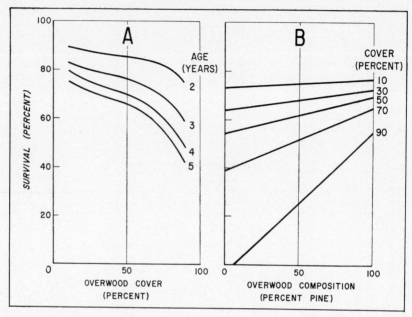

FIGURE 39.—Effect of density and composition of overwood on survival of loblolly pine seedlings near Crossett, Ark.: *A*, Two to five years old under
various degrees of cover consisting of 75 percent pine; *B*, fifth-year survival
under different admixtures of hardwood trees in the overstory.

an overwood of S.D.I. 100. Seedlings over 30 feet from the timber
are free to grow at their maximum rate unless they meet with competition on their own level (fig. 40). The extent of border retardation in regeneration that follows partial cutting may be estimated
from the part for irregular openings in table 17. The corresponding
average height and survival of seedlings at 5 years in these borders
are given in table 18.

Such inevitable border retardation may be either relieved or
tolerated, but should never be overlooked. Inasmuch as unrestricted
seedling growth may be less valuable than increment on the timber
that restricts it, full development of regeneration may be sacrificed
until the timber border reaches financial maturity.

Evaluation of regeneration

A good inventory of pine reproduction should show both where it
is and whether it is satisfactory. A choice between no action, release of existing seedlings, or a fresh start, can be made only after

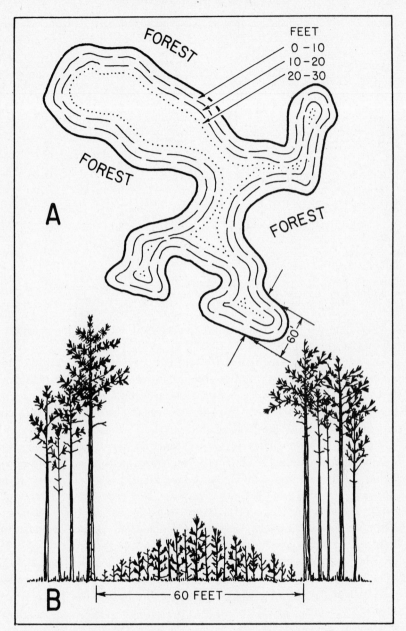

FIGURE 40.—Under group selection cutting the strip in which regeneration suffers marginal retardation varies in area, *A*, with the length of the perimeter of irregular openings (tables 17 and 18). *B*, Profile typical of even-aged pine reproduction in an opening following a harvest cutting.

TABLE 18.—*Net effect of gradations in marginal influence of timber on survival and height of regeneration*

Shape and size of opening free of overwood (acres)	Radius of circle	Five-year-old loblolly pine seedlings		Overwood coverage for equivalent forest-grown seedlings[1]
		Survival	Height	
	Feet	Percent	Feet	Percent
Circular:				
0........................	.....	66	3.2	37
.1........................	37.2	72	3.7	23
.3........................	64.5	73	4.1	14
.5........................	83.2	74	4.3	11
1.0........................	117.7	75	4.4	10
1.5........................	144.2	76	4.5	9
Irregular[2]:				
0........................	.....	66	3.2	37
.1........................	.....	69	3.3	36
.3........................	.....	70	3.4	32
.5........................	.....	71	3.5	29
1.0........................	.....	72	3.8	20
1.5........................	.....	73	3.9	18

[1] For a canopy 75 percent pine and 25 percent hardwood having the same effect as the corresponding opening on seedling development.
[2] Typically as illustrated in figure 40.

ascertaining not only what is on the ground but also its prospects for future development.[51]

Many of the prerequisites for natural regeneration of pine, described in the previous sections, must be recognized in forecasting its success. Briefly the basic essentials are abundant seed, adequate dispersal, suitable seedbed, favorable weather, about 8 years without fire, and control of hardwoods.

Commonly a deficiency in two or more of these conditions raises the question of the need for further cultural measures. As all competing hardwoods can seldom be destroyed at reasonable cost, it is essential for pine seedlings to dominate the remnants. This they usually can do, except in the more moist situations on the lower Piedmont Plateau and on true hardwood bottom lands. Because of their more rapid height growth the pines can emerge if they are not more than a year behind the competing sprouts (Chapman 1945). Then the pine component of a stand can hold its own during the first critical years and begin to dominate the hardwoods in 15 years

[51] The amount present at any time readily can be determined by a variety of sampling procedures, including random or mechanical cruises using stocked quadrats (page 172), or variable radius plots. The details of these techniques—applicable to many species—are beyond the scope of this book, but appraisal of prospects for acceptable seedling development, by saving what exists or providing replacements, depends on specific knowledge of silvical observations reported here.

(Cope 1926). Where weed species already usurp a large portion of the pine land they must be killed, at least to the ground level, before the area covered by their crowns becomes available for more pine.

The adequacy of natural regeneration may be estimated after its first year or two when survival becomes more directly related to competition from adjacent woody vegetation. Prospects are poor under large trees or dense clumps of small ones. Under high shade with intermittent sunlight loblolly pine can survive as overtopped seedlings or saplings for one or two decades, provided severe droughts do not occur and annual height growth exceeds 6 inches. With less shoot growth the seedlings die sooner or later (Chapman 1923, 1945). In a suppressed condition the survivors remain vulnerable to light surface fires at any season, by contrast to seedlings grown in open sunlight which rapidly attain sufficient size to resist winter surface fires. The prospects for survival are two out of three for 5-year-old seedlings in well-defined openings 15 to 30 feet wide (Wahlenberg 1948a) and growing little more than 6 inches annually. Where cutting cycles are more than 5 years such seedlings must be released to survive. In larger openings where the leading shoots are free at 3 years the mortality is lower.

Reproduction on cutover lands of the Coastal Plain is inconspicuous in the first few years when hardwood sprouts grow rapidly and pine seedlings slowly. Fortunately this early handicap for the pines is often more apparent than real. On many areas the height growth of pine seedlings soon tends strongly to increase while that of the competing sprouts tends to decrease each year. The sprouts remain vigorous but dissipate their growth energy in multiple stems and branches. Over much, if not all, of its range, loblolly pine stores appreciable quantities of plant food during the winter months, when the competing hardwoods are leafless and neither storing food themselves nor shading the pines. Overwinter food storage in loblolly pine apparently accounts for the relatively greater length of the first internode formed on the leading shoots of pine saplings in the spring. Thus at a given size the height growth of pines exceeds that of most hardwood associates (fig. 41).

Pine seedlings of rapid early height growth are most likely to emerge from a sea of brush. Rates of height growth in the first 3 to 5 years portend the percentage of survival and dominance to be expected, without release, and barring drought in the next few years (fig. 42).

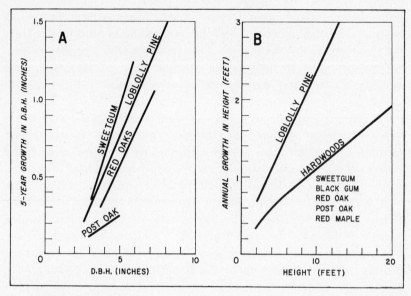

FIGURE 41.—Comparison of competitive rates of growth between loblolly pine and associated species in sapling stands 16 to 18 years old at Urania, La.: *A*, In rate of diameter growth based on d.b.h. at beginning of a period, loblolly pine was exceeded by sweetgum only. *B*, In rate of height growth loblolly pine went up about twice as rapidly as its associates (Chapman 1942b).

Wenger (1955, a,b,c) studying regeneration in the Coastal Plain, found the previous year's growth highly useful in distinguishing between the individual seedlings with good or poor prospects of survival. On undisturbed soil and excluding serious drought he found this relation: Current seedling growth (feet) = 0.35 + 1.02 (previous year's growth). The linear equation is a practical mechanism to use in estimating for several reasons. Its correlation with actual growth is high, 0.93, and it is a relationship that is measured easily, independently of seedling height or age. Furthermore it is not normally affected either by soil differences or by controlled burning.

Need of release

The need to curb undesirable vegetation and release pines varies greatly from place to place. One cutting to remove overstory competition is usually sufficient. The decision to liberate loblolly pine seedlings from competition with low-level vegetation, or let the pines languish and die, should vary both with the need for more young growth in the forest as a whole and with the locations that have

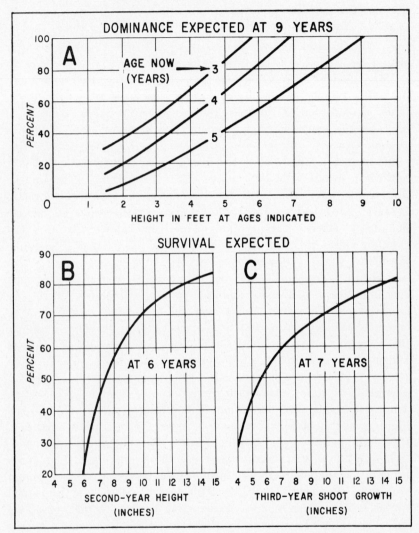

FIGURE 42.—Curves designed to aid in forecasting the success of natural reproduction of loblolly pine from its present condition. Current capacity for
height development is the best indication of the prospects for the next 4
to 6 years: A, near Franklin, Va.; B and C, near Crossett, Ark. Neither of
these apply to years of unusual moisture stress.

been designated specifically for regeneration. On reproduction areas
release should await the presence of seedlings in adequate numbers,
and should be further postponed until retardation of height growth
is evident or overtopping is imminent. Then, and especially on dry
sites, some intensive release work with chemicals may be advisable,

but release operations applied at the wrong time or place often remove more than is necessary and thus encourage hardwood sprouting. Usually release of the pine seedlings (if, where, and as needed) should be extensive rather than intensive.[52]

Misjudgment of regeneration prospects in the past commonly has led to unexpected failure or success. In many places pine seedlings, overcoming an initial handicap more apparent than real, have unexpectedly emerged unaided from a sea of brush. This is possible on some sites because normal height growth of loblolly pine tends to increase in each of the first 10 years, whereas most of the hardwood sprout growth decreases after its alarming spurt in the first year or two. Hence pine seedlings adjacent to, but not directly beneath, hardwood sprout clumps have a fair chance to become dominant. Overtopped seedlings have less opportunity to come through unless the competition is from lightly foliated species like myrtle or sumac. Release is most necessary on good sites where underbrush is low and dense, and on poor sites where the hardwood associates are of aggressive and heavily foliated species.

Even on these sites aim should be to subdue rather than to eliminate the competing vegetation. Except for unusual situations, like very dry sites, and places where aggression by honeysuckle or kudzu vines is rampant, eradication is unnecessary. The need is merely to check the competition temporarily until the pines can dominate the stand. Hence in the absence of drought it is best to avoid destroying any vegetation that will not hamper the pines—limiting treatment to the amount necessary to restrain competition. Cleaning operations in seedling stands, slashing back with hand-tools only the upper parts of weed species permits many small pines to gain dominance before multiple sprouts again menace young crop trees (Carmean 1947). Progress toward control may be judged by the lower average height of competing hardwoods and the added space for pines to grow. To shift the competition closer to the ground is worthwhile, even though in some few places the continued control of underbrush may require a series of treatments.

When and where to liberate young loblolly pines from high-level competition likewise deserves attention. If needed regeneration quotas already have been filled, additional understory seedlings should be ignored. A surplus of natural regeneration in such a

---

[52] By contrast the thoroughness in prior preparation of these areas for reproduction or planting tends to lessen the need for later release. Intensive disking before logging, or a uniform burn afterward, can postpone or eliminate the need for early release.

forest may be disregarded for several reasons. Many seedlings come in at the wrong time or place, and do not provide the current growth values that the larger trees do. The net value of saw-log trees has been known to double in 17 years, and such growth of clear-stemmed trees left in cutting is often worth more per acre as timber than is the liberation of their volunteer progeny as regeneration. Some suppression of seedlings must be tolerated, under all-aged silviculture, particularly on the less accessible and less intensively managed lands where cutting cycles are long, ages mixed, harvests are selective, and special release less feasible. More seedlings are injured where weed trees are felled than where they are girdled or poisoned (Tissue 1953), and most seedlings outgrow the sprout clusters that follow (Williston 1949a).

Under shelterwood, or other even-aged systems of cutting timber, less suppression of pine seedlings by their parents, or other larger trees, can be tolerated. Long regeneration periods are not recommended, and neglect of, or extended delay in, release operations leads to heavy loss of timber production. The extent of the forest acreage involved in this loss can be judged accurately, according to McCulley (1953a) from the potential growing space for pines beneath the crowns of inferior species. He found the percentage of area shaded by residual hardwoods near Franklin, Va., equal to 1.4 times their basal area in square feet.

Schedules for release

Site and age affect the timing of release operations to aid pine seedlings by curbing sprout competition. When pines are planted on good sites, but under open stands of oak, the seedlings usually need release at planting time or soon thereafter. In the improvement of seedling stands release is needed earlier on moist sites of high quality than elsewhere. Studies in the Piedmont region of North Carolina (Anderson 1946, Carmean 1947) indicate that where hardwood vigor is relatively low because of an impervious B horizon in the soil, no cleaning is needed in the first 4 years after logging. A single one in the 5th growing season is suggested, and this may be needed only in spots. On extremely dry sites a single cleaning between the 5th and 8th years should suffice.

On better soils, where hardwoods are more vigorous, and where herbicides are not used, cleaning, though unnecessary during the first year or two, is soon needed. In moist situations toward the bottom of the slopes in the Piedmont, cleanings in the 3rd and also in the 6th to 8th year are in order.[53] Although a single hardwood cutting or girdling operation is usually sufficient on the northern Coastal Plain, in southern Arkansas the small hardwoods also, in many places, need to be killed back to reduce the heavy competition for moisture (Reynolds 1950a). Ridgetop sites may restock with pine without artificial aid, but elsewhere neglect of cleaning may suppress or deform the pines.

The use of herbicidal sprays to aid loblolly pine seedlings needs to be timed to effect maximum damage to deciduous species and minimum injury to pines. Working in Arkansas, Ray (1957) found that foliage sprays in July and August injured the terminal buds of pine less than those applied in May and June. Spring treatments, however, were found best to subjugate broad-leaved species in tests of various treatments (McQuilkin 1955; Goddard 1955; Carvell 1955; and Grano 1955 a and b), apparently because vegetative activity was then highest. Similarly herbicides applied during the warm afternoons of bright days, when photosynthetic production exceeds foliar needs, may be most effective. Schedules to release pine seedlings should never follow general rules literally; rather they should be based on observation of vegetation in local situations.

Release of seedlings from competition with mother trees in all-aged forests is incidental to partial timber harvests and need not be formally scheduled. Under other systems, however, the release from seed trees cannot be long deferred. On areas designated for regeneration established reproduction needs prompt attention to avoid possible stagnation. Where forest protection is intensive and well organized, seed trees may not be needed to insure against fire loss, and in such places need not be long retained, usually not more than 3 years.

Mechanical injuries to seedlings from falling trees should be minimized. Removal of seed trees after the seedlings are established will result in some damage to the young stand, but where seedlings are 2 years old this can be confined to major tractor roads and loading areas. In the Bigwoods Experimental Forest six 20-inch seed trees per acre were removed with only slight damage to first- and second-year seedlings (Trousdell 1952a). Larger seedlings and saplings are more brittle and therefore more vulnerable. To spare them, the

[53] In Talladega County, Alabama, it has been shown (Westberg 1950) that it is possible to accelerate the growth of pines planted under relatively young hardwood stands through release cuttings deferred 3 or 4 years. Although it should not be so long delayed, release 8 years after planting was still helpful to loblolly pine where 52 percent of the seedlings has survived in northern Mississippi (Huckenpahler 1949b and 1952).

trees can be felled toward or away from concentration points marked
in advance, thus reducing damage to a minimum. Heavy damage
from repeated tractor trips during dry weather should not affect
more than 8 percent of a partly cut area. In dense thickets of
regeneration a moderate amount of breakage among saplings can be
tolerated, for there it represents no economic loss.

Results from release

Without release of natural reproduction many pine stands are
succeeded by nearly worthless hardwoods. Such succession can be
halted or delayed by any of several methods of release. The relative
effectiveness of these treatments varies widely with time and place.
Intensive release measures may, or may not, be justified.

What may be a good measure during a dry period may fail to
pay for itself during a wet period. Response to a given degree of
partial release from shrub-size competition in a single treatment
tends to be better on dry sites and in drought years, than on better
sites and in moist years. After the tops are killed with chemicals,
the hardwoods resprout much more vigorously in moist locations.
By lessening the competition for limited moisture, thorough release
benefits pine seedlings following drought in Texas (Ferguson 1958).
When drought occurs during the initial establishment of pines on
grassy areas, the grass offers more competition than do the hardwoods.

The effect of time of release on growth and survival of loblolly
pines planted under scrub oaks on former longleaf pine lands near
Alexandria, La. (Muntz 1950, Shoulders 1955), was as follows:

Time of release	Third Year		Seventh Year	
	Survival (percent)	Height (feet)	Survival (percent)	Height (feet)
Immediately after planting............	86	4.3	82	15.5
One year after planting..	62	3.2	61	14.5
Two years after planting.	39	2.5	38	13.0
Check—not released....	33	2.2	32	9.5

Seedlings simultaneously interplanted in small openings had survived
64 percent by the seventh year and were 10.0 feet high.

Tests in Alabama and in North Carolina have shown that in
normal years the rate of height growth of loblolly pine seedlings
may be doubled, and the rate of diameter growth quadrupled 2
years after timely liberation (Miller and Tissue 1956, Freese 1950).
Results of other similar studies in North Carolina and in Arkansas
are given in figure 43. In this work it appears that early liberation
(age 2) and a treatment of moderate intensity (number 2) were the

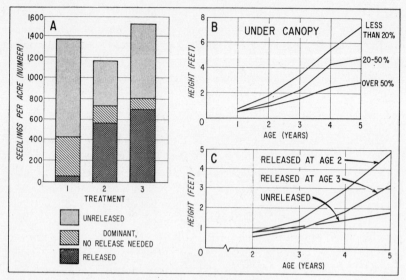

FIGURE 43.—*A*, Pine seedlings 1 inch in d.b.h. and smaller immediately after each of three liberation treatments at Crossett, Ark.: *1*, hardwoods 6 inches and larger removed, *2*, hardwoods 2 inches and larger removed, and *3*, hardwoods 5 feet tall and over removed (Mann 1951a). *B*, Height of pines growing under three degrees of overwood. *C*, Heights of pine seedlings released at 2 or 3 years of age, Bigwoods Experimental Forest (McCulley 1953a).

most effective and economical. Sometimes, when a variety of treatments all promise success, the most economical one is chosen. For instance in South Carolina manual and simple chemical methods of releasing loblolly pines already about 2 feet tall on a flatwood site of index 90 were compared as shown in table 19. The extra cost of using chemicals to deaden trees was, in this instance, unwarranted.

TABLE 19.—*Relative success of various release treatments after four growing seasons on the Santee Experimental Forest in South Carolina (Shipman 1954)*

| Treatment[1] | Herbicide | Relative cost[2] | Seedlings | |
			Free to grow	Height[3]
		Index	Percent	Feet
Untreated......................	None	0	22	4.9
Stems cut.....................	None	100	71	6.7
No cutting, base sprayed........	2,4,5-T	124	80	7.2
No cutting, stems brushed.......	2,4,5-T	188	70	7.6
Stems cut and stumps sprayed...	2,4,5-T	194	97	8.8

[1] Each treatment replicated 3 times on 1/40-acre plots.
[2] Includes labor and chemical charges, relative to each other.
[3] Based upon the best 75 seedlings for each treatment.

SUMMARY

Natural reproduction of loblolly pine is disappointing when delayed. Long periods of regeneration cannot be recommended because they allow sprouting hardwoods to recapture the land. To insure promptness certain silvicultural treatments are advocated. Measures to promote reproduction must be timely, and during the first 8 years special protection is advisable in some locations.

Short rotations invite regeneration difficulties because young seed trees normally produce little seed. Certain precautions and special measures become necessary. They concern seed trees, seed yields, seed requirements, seedbeds, overtopping by hardwood sprouts, and after the removal of seed trees the possible advisablity of further release to obviate any need to plant pine.

Seed trees ordinarily must be at least 12 inches d.b.h. and 30 to 50 years old to yield 9,000 to 15,000 seeds each. Seed bearing capacity should be evaluated, from evidence of previous fruitfulness, in selecting the trees. Not less than 4 nor more than 12 per acre should be selected depending on their distribution over the area, on their quality, on seedbed conditions, and on uncontrolled plant competition. The trees should provide an operable final cut.

Seed yields vary tremendously not only by trees, but from year to year, and place to place. Good seed crops every 3 to 10 years provide heavier yields near the coast than farther inland. Also seed in plentiful supply is of better quality. Some owners benefit by making final harvests only when a heavy crop is expected.

To facilitate regeneration in later years, the trees to be reserved for seed should have their production stimulated. This is done by harvest of adjacent trees that crowd them. These competing trees should be removed in a commercial cutting before June 1, 3 years in advance of the need for regeneration. By providing a 6- to 10-foot space between crowns of the reserved trees such a preparatory cut will certainly step-up seed production. The yield in a poor seed year may be increased several fold for released trees, making it ample in the Coastal Plain but of questionable adequacy in the Piedmont. Directions are given for making useful estimates of expected seed crops—corrected for defective cones—a year in advance of the peak of seedfall in mid-November.

Difficulty in obtaining adequate seeding is less when the viability of seeds is high and dissemination wide. Germinative capacity varies from 11 percent in some poor years to 76 percent in better years. Usually on cutover lands with an adequate source of seed, dispersal with prevailing wind is abundant beyond the parent trees for about 75 feet, good for 150 feet, acceptable perhaps for 300 feet, and insufficient farther away. Old fields recently abandoned reseed somewhat more effectively from the side. When seed trees are well scattered over an area, the total supply of seed is more important than dispersal distance. Seeds germinate profusely in March and April. The number needed is less where receptivity of the soil surface is high.

Successful regeneration is dependent to a large extent on reseeding when the seedbed is favorable. Seedling catch is usually good where the forest floor is disturbed by logging over diverse skid trails, intermediate on burned-over surfaces, poor on undisturbed soil cover, and poorest under slashings. Seed requirements may be met properly, in fact fullfilled abundantly, where sites have been freshly prepared. The improvement wrought by logging rapidly disappears in succeeding years, necessitating special measures.

Although it often cannot be firmly scheduled, preparatory burning is useful in many places. The frequency with which fires—light or severe—are prescribed must be varied with the local possibility of and need for them. With the use of fire for any constructive purpose in forestry, a deliberate sacrifice of scattered young advance reproduction is often justifiable to avoid subsequent understocking and the development of "wolf" trees. In the absence of an adequate stand of advance reproduction, a clean sweep of the forest floor is good, but the effects of even well-controlled burning may be somewhat erratic.

Machinery may be used to scarify surfaces left undisturbed by logging or fire. However, care is needed in the use of heavy equipment to prevent damage to the soil, that is, to avoid the displacement of topsoil on dry areas or its "puddling" and compaction on wet areas. Bulldozing can effectively destroy hardwood thickets on the sandy loam soils of the Coastal Plain, but is less desirable on the clay soils of the Piedmont. Where undesirable sapling stands are less dense they can be felled with a tractor and heavy disk harrow and the larger trees girdled or poisoned; if this is not done the percentage of area usurped by undesirable trees equals about 1.4 times their basal area in square feet. Such measures combine timber stand improvement with site preparation for regeneration.

The early results of pine reproduction are best judged by estimating the area stocked rather than by counting seedlings. In regenerating a forest the land recovered by pines is more important than either their numbers or distribution within the seeded area.

After the first year when the new crop of pine has become well established and relatively drought resistant, all seed trees should be removed from designated regeneration areas unless they are needed for fire insurance. In nonhazardous areas they need not be long retained.

Freedom for seedlings to grow means freedom to survive. In many situations the smaller trees have difficulty in reaching maturity. At all ages the species is less tolerant than many of its associates. In good light, dry soil impedes hardwoods more than pine, but with ample moisture dim light retards pine more than hardwoods.

One advantage on cutover lands is the early tendency for pine seedlings to increase their annual height growth while that of hardwoods at the same level tends to decrease. Low, dense hardwood cover however is fatal to pine seedlings. High and broken pine cover can be tolerated several years on good sites. Mixed pine-hardwood cover of medium height reduces growth and survival of seedlings in direct relation to its density.

In dry years, or on dry sites, release may be deferred about 4 years or until the need is clearly manifest. In wet years, or on moist sites, release should be started early and repeated if, when, and where needed. The marginal influence of a wall of standing timber affects seedlings most in the first 10 feet of a 30-foot border in which retardation is felt. Reproduction in small irregular openings is especially retarded. Seedlings growing less than about 6 inches in height annually remain vulnerable to surface fires. When more pine is needed, the neglect of, or delay in, release operations leads to heavy loss in timber production through the succession of inferior hardwoods.

Chapter 5

Artificial Regeneration

NEED FOR PLANTING

PLANTING NURSERY-GROWN SEEDLINGS is the quickest and surest means of restoring full productivity to southern pine lands that fail to restock naturally and completely to loblolly pine. So far there are relatively few examples of similar success from sowing the seeds of this species directly on forest land, but recent research is revealing the possibility of better results in the future.

These artificial methods of regeneration occupy an important place in silviculture because they bring at least three benefits. Planting (1) utilizes additional capital investments to reduce time lost in attaining natural regeneration, (2) substitutes investment in seed or seedling stock for investment in merchantable seed trees, and (3) permits regeneration of areas where natural methods are impossible—as where seed trees are absent. Even where potential seed trees of loblolly pine are present, it may be advisable to consider the costs involved in using them.[54]

Abandoned fields, pastures, or other open lands interspersed within a forest may be expected to be partially reforested through natural seeding from the side. Small parcels of such land usually restock to loblolly pine satisfactorily—the larger ones only slowly and incompletely. Wherever, because of a dearth of seed trees or other cause, adequate natural seeding is uncertain, planting not only can shorten the rotation somewhat, but also can bring three benefits in addition to the three mentioned above. It can improve on initial tree spacing and stand density, provide more positive control over species composition, and permit the introduction of new and improved strains or hybrid trees, if desired.

[54] These costs may be direct and current as well as indirect and delayed. After release of seed trees they may accelerate their individual growth enough to cover any current loss from delay in their harvest. Yet, on high-quality sites, the loss of growing stock in trees cut to liberate the seed trees simultaneously may lower the value of final per-acre yields enough to offset the alternative cost involved in artificial reproduction on completely cleared areas.

These three benefits, however, are not likely to be realized fully in planting cutover lands. Rarely is the original stand of brush and trees wholly eliminated in harvesting timber. Hence, irregular natural reproduction of mixed species seldom results in young stands stocked as uniformly as plantations on open or fully prepared sites. With a good seed source reinforcement planting alone is seldom advisable.

Nevertheless, much land suitable for loblolly pine that has been made unproductive through heavy cutting, wild fire, natural catastrophe, or abandonment of agriculture is in need of planting, because it is beyond the reach of natural seedfall. Of all land in private ownership recently cut over in the southern region (i.e., up to 1953 from Texas to North Carolina) 1 acre out of every 5 is classed as being low in productivity. The obvious way to offset low yields from depleted lands is not to acquire more acres, but to increase the per-acre yield. Where poor production has resulted from the encroachment of inferior hardwoods or from littleleaf disease among the shortleaf pine associates, planting and subsequent release may be used to reestablish pine. Loblolly pine would be the species selected to plant on much of this land, or at least it would be a close second where slash pine is desired for the next crop.

Forest planting increased in the South during the conservation programs of the nineteen thirties and again in the late forties, resulting in nearly 1½ million acres of small plantations with not less than 400 trees per acre surviving at 5 years. About 29 million more acres remain to be planted in the Southeast and Gulf coast region. Most of this open area can be reforested with reasonable assurance of success and is capable of producing loblolly pine.

On areas under active forest management the trend in recent years has been toward even-aged stands and short rotations. Then artificial methods become more important as a means of avoiding delay, if they are not actually adopted as the primary regeneration procedure.

Loblolly pine was first planted extensively in 1920-25 when the Great Southern Lumber Company reforested more than 7,000 acres near Bogalusa, La. (Hayes and Wakeley 1929). Later the Enoree and Long Cane districts of the Sumter National Forest each set out about 10,000 acres in South Carolina. Now all states and some forest industries are becoming increasingly active. Georgia produces about 40 million loblolly pine seedlings annually for planting within the state.

Loblolly pine has proved to be a superlative species for land rehabilitation and is being planted for this purpose on an enormous scale. Over 50 million trees are hand planted annually in north Mississippi for the Yazoo-Little Tallahatchie flood prevention project and elsewhere in the Tallahatchie research center area. Loblolly pine can be used to revegetate denuded soils with or without preliminary site preparation, depending on the degree of erosion. Even if the worst eroded spots fail, enough trees usually survive on the remnants of better soil and on sandbars, to reduce erosion and runoff significantly. Then a progressive healing process starts and continues as long as the area is undisturbed.

Loblolly pine planting stock is usually available from state nurseries at cost if orders are placed well in advance. Hand planting requires from 5- to 13-man hours per acre depending on the number of trees set out (table 20). Mechanized planting, faster, cheaper, and equally good, should be used wherever available machines can be operated. Tree planting machines can be leased or borrowed by many farmers having the tractors and labor to use them. Machine planting costs under contract (1954 to 1958) varied from $4.50 to $15.00 per 1,000 trees in Louisiana and South Carolina. The lower costs were for planting on old fields.[55]

Mean annual increment in volume of wood from full stands expected in the first 20 years after planting open lands is from $1\frac{1}{4}$ to 2 cords or more per acre. For example, four 18-year-old plantations on site class 80 in Virginia averaged $1\frac{1}{2}$ cords per acre.

For tracts organized for sustained yield under even-aged management the cost of the growing stock and of planting bare land may

TABLE 20.—*Cost of planting one acre by dibble*[1]

Spacing (feet)	Seedlings	Stock[2]	Labor[3]	Total cost[4]
	Number	Dollars	Dollars	Dollars
6 x 6	1,210	5.26	12.80	18.06
6 x 8	910	3.96	9.71	13.67
6 x 10	725	3.15	7.74	10.89
8 x 8	680	2.96	7.26	10.22
6 x 12	605	2.63	6.45	9.08
10 x 10	435	1.89	4.64	6.53

[1] Pine Planter's Guide, Florida Forest Service, June 1958.
[2] Based on $4.35 per thousand ($4 for seedlings and $0.35 for shipping).
[3] Two men at $8 each per 8-hour day, planting 1,500 seedlings, or $10.67 per M seedlings.
[4] Total cost, $15.02 per M seedlings.

[55] The cost for the recent planting of 17.5 million seedlings on "critical sites" on the Yazoo-Little Tallahatchie watershed in Mississippi was $9.19 per M. This figure excludes the investment in seedling stock and is based on wages of $1.06 per hour for the planters. The trees were spaced about 4 by 4 within gullies and 6 by 8 elsewhere.

be charged against current income. Without recognition of this sustained-yield status the planting costs must be carried forward at interest. The interest charges, if any, and the spacing of the trees, if close, increase the cost and lower the profits. The returns per acre from irregular natural stands of loblolly pine may be only $\frac{1}{2}$ to $\frac{3}{4}$ as much as from an equal number of planted trees. Plantations on good sites respond well to frequent light thinnings. Where continuous cover is desired, plantations on sites having a site index of 70 or more may be thinned first at 15 years and then at 3-year intervals until 30 or 35 years old and at 5-year intervals thereafter. However, where maximum rates of growth on individual stems is sought, heavier and less frequent thinning is better. Reynolds (1939b) suggests thinning about every 8 years, for instance at ages 20, 28, 36, and 44.

Finally, the financial aspect of growing pines is greatly affected by the choice of products and rotation. Consider, for example, the following three management options: (1) Clear cut for pulpwood at 20 years, (2) thin for pulpwood and clear cut for saw logs at 40 years, and (3) thin for pulpwood or sawtimber and clear cut for saw logs at 60 years. The estimated mean annual dollar returns from handling loblolly pine in this manner are (1) $3.14, (2) $10.12, and (3) $11.79 per acre (Va. For. Ser. 1954).

CHOICE OF SPECIES AND SITE

The feasibility of using loblolly pine to substitute for, or associate with, other species varies with local situations and the relative capacity of the species to survive, resist injury, and grow under competition.

On some dry but easily eroded sites, where the growth of timber trees is no object, shortleaf pine may be a satisfactory type of cover to retain the soil, though loblolly is currently the preferred species for most rehabilitation planting because of its greater vegetative vigor. Although the composition of the original forest is often acceptable as an indication of the best species to plant, some exceptions to this rule should be recognized. For example a quick-growing crop of loblolly pulpwood may be had on some abandoned hilltop fields originally in shortleaf pine. Contrary to early published reports loblolly pine is not more exacting in its site requirements than shortleaf pine. Even on dry sands, gravel outcrops, or impervious clays, loblolly pine generally outgrows shortleaf pine for at least 15 or 20 years—sometimes for 60 to 80 years. Loblolly pine excelled shortleaf in comparably spaced plantations during a 14-year test in

Georgia. Loblolly pine made 16 percent more diameter growth, 25 percent more basal area, and 46 percent more growth in merchantable volume than the shortleaf pine (Jackson 1958).

Wherever longleaf pine originally stood it can be grown again if desired. It should be the first choice in reforestation of most of the sandhills if saw logs are desired. After the soil variations there are properly classified, places may be located where slash or loblolly pines can make satisfactory growth on short rotations. It has been observed that the top 6 inches of soil consists of only 9 percent very fine sand on grass areas and 22 percent where loblolly pine stands. As the soil becomes coarser loblolly pine does less well and longleaf is superior. However, on all sites originally occupied by hardwoods and loblolly, this pine, not longleaf, should prove most profitable.

As compared (Townsend 1949, Hansbrough 1956) with slash pine in central Louisiana, loblolly pine survival is higher during its first 5 or 10 years after planting, resistance to injury by ice or disease better, and growth rate faster during the first 23 years (Muntz 1948b, Mann 1953a). Severe early infestations of loblolly pine plantations by tip moth commonly cause some retardation of height growth, but by 10 years of age little effect of the early attack remains. Loblolly pine on deep surface soil or permeable subsoil is superior to slash pine in many ways as follows:

	Ten years after planting	
	Slash pine	*Loblolly pine*
Survival, percent...............	62	76
Fusiform on trunk, percent......	17.8	5.6
Ice damage, percent............	34.3	5.2
Average d. b. h., inches.........	3.2	3.6
Average height, feet............	20.5	21.5

These initial differences, rather small but consistently in favor of loblolly, have been observed also in Georgia, Alabama (Stahelin 1946, Goggans 1949), Mississippi, and North Carolina. In fact on several different flatwoods soils the initial survival of loblolly pine is above the averages for each of three other southern yellow pines:

Soil series and topographic situation	*Survival in May after planting in January*				
	Loblolly (percent)	*Slash (percent)*	*Sand (percent)*	*Longleaf (percent)*	*Mean (percent)*
Blanton, ridge..............	92	87	89	58	81.5
Leon (hardpan), high flatwood.	93	84	82	77	84.0
Leon (soft pan), low flatwood..	89	67	59	65	70.0
Plummer, pond margin........	94	88	65	78	81.2
Mean...................	92	81.5	73.8	69.5	79.2

The high survival of loblolly pine and its outstanding superiority in early growth over these species, as well as shortleaf and Virginia pine, have likewise been demonstrated on a ridgetop in Lafayette County, Mississippi.

Despite better early survival, however, loblolly pine does not excel slash pine in its Gulf coastal "flatwoods" domain where sandy or fine sandy loam soils are underlain at 4 to 8 inches by stiff subsoils, or where the water table remains high for long periods. In such locations slash pine outgrows loblolly pine.

Regardless of soil and location at some points beyond the natural range, resulting in high or low survival, the height growth of planted loblolly pines during the first 10 years has averaged 2 to 3 feet annually (Minckler 1948, Rhodes 1953, *et al.*). At best in the Central States it has attained 17 to 19 feet of merchantable length in 5- to 6-inch stems and 32 to 38 feet in total height in 13 years. After 30 years the rate of height growth declines to 1.5 feet or less annually. When survival, growth, thrift, and resistance to damage are all considered, the superior adaptability of loblolly pine to diverse sites has been repeatedly manifest.

Loblolly pine shows versatility when introduced in afforestation or used to reforest areas where the air was poisoned or the soil devastated by the mining industry. In the denuded Copper Basin of Tennessee, although its survival was only 30 percent, loblolly pine grew better than pitch, shortleaf, or Virginia pine, adding 1.2 feet per year (Allen 1950). Loblolly pine in Alabama excels longleaf and shortleaf pines, and white ash, in the revegetation of "spoil banks" on strip-mined lands, surviving 76 percent and growing 1.9 feet annually during 10 years (Freese 1951). On the wet margins of ponds adjacent to the spoil banks, however, sycamore is a more promising species.

MIXED-SPECIES PLANTATIONS

Planting experience has disclosed pitfalls in many efforts to benefit from silvical advantages such as superior resistance to certain diseases or insects in mixed stands. Small juvenile inequalities between species, otherwise suited to a planting site, have rather promptly ruined many attempts to produce mixed stands. Other attempts have failed in later stages. A 6-acre alternate-strip mixture of loblolly pine and black locust was dominated by the pines in 17 years (Bruner 1955). By then the pines were 9.7 inches in d.b.h. and 46 feet tall, whereas the locust were 1.2 inches and 10 feet. When over half the locusts had died, pine reproduction took over the available space. Elsewhere, because of a slow start, white pines have similarly failed to compete with loblolly pine.

Mixtures that somehow survive the keen competition of early life may be difficult to manage later. Loblolly and longleaf pines in mixture are a good example. If there is to be any natural regeneration, these two species must always be grown separately, the longleaf pine pure, the loblolly pine as pure as can be attained against persistent hardwoods (Chapman 1953). The reason lies in their divergent requirements for reproduction, especially the opposite results from burning over the forest floor. Complete stocking of longleaf cannot be secured by burning without exterminating loblolly pine seedlings. And if fire is kept out, as it should be, during the first 8 or 10 years after the loblolly pine has reseeded an area, then the associated longleaf pine seedlings will in turn be eliminated by shade and the brownspot disease.

Loblolly pine and yellow-poplar have enough similarly desirable silvical characteristics to suggest that they might possibly be grown in mixture to good advantage in some places. Loblolly pine exceeds yellow-poplar on shallow and medium soils; yellow-poplar grows faster on the better sites. Height growth is equal on well-drained Piedmont bottom lands of index 90. On deep soil, with nearly equal diameter growth and stem form, they each produce two clear logs at 30 years (Hocker 1953). Such parallel development suggests that they might be compatible if planted in a checkerboard pattern of 25-tree squares. Any more intimate association on the ground is inadvisable.

Generally, species with distinctly different rates of growth should not be planted together.

SEED SOURCE

An estimated half a million dollars is lost annually through planting loblolly pine of improper geographic origin within its native range. The chance of such loss is even greater outside the range. Before pines are introduced in localities where climate and soil differ widely from those in the native habitat, the suitability of various sources of seed should be tested. Available sources must be considered by regions within the framework of existing strains.

The work of discovering and identifying existing hybrids and racial strains in southern United States as prerequisites to a program of tree improvement is just beginning. Some of the current findings may benefit seed collectors. Intermediate forms between the typical loblolly and shortleaf pines are common. It has not been determined whether these result from overlapping of the normal variations in species characteristics or whether they are natural hybrids. The usual discrepancy in time of flowering that normally prevents natural crossing may not apply in years with unusual weather, thus permitting interspecies crosses (Zobel 1953).

On the Gulf coast Wakeley (1953b) has demonstrated that the effect of geographic source of seed on net growth under intense competition in row planting may outweigh anything except catastrophic injury. At 15 years the yield from Louisiana stock was 14.2 cords whereas that from Georgia was only 6.5 cords (Wakeley 1944a). The Georgia stock suffered more from fusiform rust. At 28 years the yield from Louisiana stock has reached 50.7 cords, Georgia stock 23.2 cords, and Arkansas stock 12.7 cords (fig. 44).

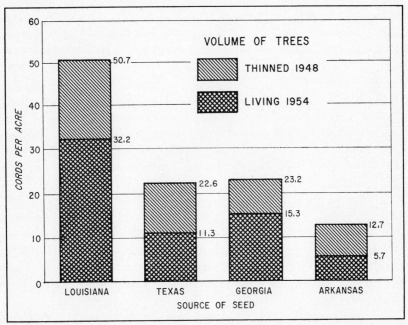

FIGURE 44.—Total wood production per acre by geographic source of seed; 28th year of measurement of loblolly pine plantations at Bogalusa, La.

Seed source influences the rate of growth and resistance to disease in loblolly pine. In Maryland seedlings from local seed survive better but grow more slowly than those from southern sources. Seedlings from northern seed may or may not survive as well as those from local seeds on the Gulf coast, but they do grow more slowly (Wakeley 1953b). From among seedlings that were half a foot high when planted at 4 locations in the Tennessee Valley, those from Alabama seed were 3.1 feet tall and the ones from Maryland only

2.3 feet tall 2 years later (Cummings 1952a). Although initial survival within the range of the species usually is little affected by geographic source (Wakeley 1952), first-year survival has been distinctly higher for certain drought-resistant strains of loblolly pine planted in Texas, and on upland old fields of southern Illinois loblolly pine seed from its more southerly sources (e.g., Mississippi) suffered serious freeze damage (Minckler 1950, 1951). Nor are Atlantic Coastal Plain sources recommended for plantings outside the natural range as for example in the Tennessee Valley (Wiesehuegel 1955).

Many striking differences among individual trees result from their immediate environment rather than from inheritance and are not necessarily lifelong. Although the greater food reserves in large seeds give seedlings an initial advantage, the benefits have not been shown to improve either survival or height growth of loblolly pine seedlings much, if any, beyond the first year. Reynolds (1952b) has shown that the logs produced by suppressed trees that trebled their diameter growth during 40 years following release are of good quality for lumber. At the other extreme the poor quality (i.e., knotty) lumber from most "wolf" trees, acquired merely because they were open grown, may not be inherited. Preference, however, should be given seed from trees of superior form whenever such seed is available.

Heritable drought resistance, caused by natural selection or possibly mutation, is most likely to be found where trees have endured drought for generations, such as in the "Lost Pine" area in Bastrop and Caldwell Counties of Texas, a western outpost of loblolly pine. On dry sandy sites seedlings from seed of that area have survived 95 percent in contrast to 8 percent from a Florida seed source (Zobel and Goddard 1955).

In Lafayette County, Mississippi, differences in height of loblolly pines from 8 geographic seed sources ranged from 29 to 49 inches 3 years after planting (Huckenpahler 1953a). Many of the scattered trials are now being succeeded by coordinated tests of seed source. In 1951 loblolly pine seeds from 15 sources were collected for systematic observation of test plantations throughout the range of the species. If 4 out of 5 of these can survive to near-merchantable size, they should do much to resolve the old question about the best sources of seed for local use (Wakeley 1953a).

Meanwhile the realization of the importance of seed source has led to recent changes in nursery practice: seedlings are being kept separate by seed source so that the planting stock can be delivered to the general area of each state from which the seed was obtained.

The policy of the U. S. Forest Service is to limit collections to places less than 100 miles away and less than 1,000 feet different in elevation from the planting site. There is an increasing tendency to gather cones locally or obtain them from a climatically similar source. The admonition to use only local seed is a sound generalization that can be made more precise as the results of current provenance tests accumulate (Wakeley 1953a).[56]

SEED PROCUREMENT

Cones are commonly obtained for forest organizations (1) by regular employees, (2) by purchase in bushel units, or (3) by contract. The first method affords by far the best control of quality of tree from which loblolly pine seeds are taken. It also assures postponement of collection until the cones are mature. The need for seed should be anticipated so that collections can be properly located and timed. A logging operation in a thrifty stand of cone-bearing trees is a favorable place; a good seed year an opportune time.

Collection from felled trees is most economical, but in a short seed year too few loblolly pines are harvested to supply the need for cones, and many trees must be climbed. Also in some poor seed years only 10 percent of the seeds may be viable; hence many more cones are needed. Good years are best for collection as there are not only more viable seeds per cone, but also more sound cones per tree. Even then, however, there is frequently a local shortage of logging operations in stands that are satisfactory for seed collection. Unless timber harvest schedules can be modified to supply the need for seed, the cones have to be picked from standing trees. It is best to avoid the possibly unfavorable heritable characteristics often associated with short scrubby trees, or limby wolf trees, whose cones are most readily accessible. To lighten the labor of using long ladders or spurless tree climbers, and to gather cones from the very best and tallest trees, further improvement in equipment is desirable. Eventually, in the absence of an aerial approach, high lift machinery may be used in valuable seed orchards. In any event benefits from selective hand picking may be realized in the form of enhanced quality in future crop trees (Wakeley 1954a).

[56] No significant differences were noted recently (Crow 1958) in seedlings from seeds collected 20 to 180 miles away from a planting site in Louisiana. The rule, however, should be followed until the validity of exceptions can be proved.

Collection of cones

Predictions of cone crop yields from loblolly pine are highly useful. Trousdell (1950c) has reported on a simple cone-ratio method of forecasting the good years and locating suitable areas and quotas for collection. A count taken in May, 6 months before seedfall, gives a convenient check on the current crop, and one in September provides an estimate for the year ahead.[57] Regardless of the method used to estimate a seed crop, collection crews must be ready to act promptly as the cones ripen.

Collectors must avoid gathering cones that are defective or too green. Despite repeated warnings this precaution is frequently violated. When some cones are opening on many individual trees the crop is ready to harvest. Because ripening time for cones varies less within trees than between them, one method of collection is to work over each stand 2 or 3 times to pick cones as they ripen. As a general rule cones are ready to gather when their specific gravity, measured within 10 minutes after they are picked from the trees, has dropped to 0.88. This point usually is reached early in October. The simplest test for maturity is to see whether freshly picked sound cones will float in a liquid having a specific gravity of 0.88, such as SAE 20 lubricating oil (Wakeley 1954a) or a 1 to 4 mixture of kerosene and raw linseed oil. When 19 out of 20 cones, one apiece from each of 20 randomly selected trees, pass this test, the crop as a whole is mature, and should be collected immediately to avoid loss of seed when cones open. Wormy cones should never be collected unless seed is very scarce because they yield only $\frac{1}{3}$ to $\frac{1}{2}$ as much seed as sound cones (Wakeley 1938).

A bushel of green cones weighs from 26 to 35 pounds, averaging 32, and contains 393 to 1,080 cones, averaging 500. This excludes the large cones of very young trees and the small ones of very old trees (Wakeley 1930 and 1938). The numbers of seeds per cone are likewise variable, averaging 110 in heavy crop years when trees average 150 cones each. In a light crop there may be only 30 seeds per cone. An over-all average would be 57 sound seeds per cone (Wenger 1958).

Extraction from cones

Correct handling in collection, extraction, dewinging, and drying of seed is essential to maintain its viability. The closed cones, however, may be handled roughly without injuring the seed. Any im-

[57] For details of making such forecasts see section on cones in chapter 4, Natural Regeneration.

pact, short of crushing them, will not affect the rate or percentage of germination of the seeds (Lyle and Gilmore 1958).

Although the specific gravity test for maturity of pine cones works well at the time of collection and should be used, collectors sometimes harvest immature cones. After green cones are picked and have been held for later delivery there is, unfortunately, no certain way to determine ripeness by field inspection. Seeds taken from green cones can be identified under magnification by the shrunken endosperm. Some usable seed can be extracted from immature cones if they are mechanically compressed by rollers. With the opening mechanism out of order from drying, sprinkling the cones with water after they have been rolled will often reactivate the mechanism (Foster 1956a).

Air drying to open cone scales and release the seed takes from 2 weeks to 3 months, and kiln drying only 6 to 48 hours (U.S.F.S. 1948a, Wakeley 1948d, 1954a). Extraction by artificial heat saves space as well as time and in large operations usually gives higher yields. A short period of partial air drying without heat is recommended for cones that have been picked prematurely, to avoid the tendency of such cones to caseharden and remain closed in the kiln. No precuring is necessary for ripe cones. Kilns should have a good circulation of air not exceeding 120°F. (Wakeley 1935b). Seed can be extracted in lumber dry kilns if suitable methods of handling the cones can be arranged. Precautions are needed to protect the kiln from fire and the seeds from rodents.

Modern kilns, equipped with forced draft high volume reversible fans, can dry a layer of cones of considerable depth provided sufficient space is allowed for expansion as the cones open. A 2- by 4-foot rack will hold half a bushel of cones. The trays need a 6-inch clearance, bottom to bottom, as green cones double or triple their volume as they open. The moisture lost by cones in drying, in percent of their dry weight, varies from 54 to 93, averaging 74.

Most seeds drop out readily when the cones are dry, but they may need to be tumbled to extract them all. There are two kinds of tumblers, the intermittent and the continuous action. Either can be revolved by hand or by machine.

The yield of clean dewinged seed per bushel of unopened sound cones ranges from 0.25 to 1.50 pounds, with an average of 1 pound (Wakeley 1954a). A hundred pounds of fresh cones yields 2 to 3 pounds of cleaned seed (U.S.F.S. 1948a). Rubbing dry seed with moistened hands is a safe way to remove the wings, but too slow.

Nurseries require machines; popcorn polishing devices may be used. The progressive type of dewinging machine, if not in proper adjustment, may fracture seed coats and lower the germination of loblolly pine seeds 37 percent (T.V.A. test).

Dewinging and cleaning usually reduce weight by 15 percent. Without wings the number of clean seeds per pound is 16,000 to 25,000, averaging 18,400. Pine needles are most readily removed before the cones open. Final cleaning requires a mill with oscillating screens to remove other impurities, and an air blast to expel light trash and empty seeds. Errors in handling seed may reduce the vitality so essential to successful storage.

Storage of seed

The problem of storage is to keep as many loblolly pine seeds alive as possible. Living seeds respire, i.e., they use stored food and oxygen and liberate carbon dioxide, water, and heat. Mortality often results from storage conditions that speed up this process. The purpose of proper storage is to hold seed in a stable state of rather low respiration and of insensitivity to minor environmental changes over relatively long indefinite periods. A reduction in seed moisture content by methods that will not injure the seed, such as air-drying before a fan in the sun, is distinctly beneficial in keeping seeds alive. Dry cold—i.e., under 20°F.—is the most effective environment in which to store loblolly pine seed. A temperature close to 5°F. in long storage, aids materially in preventing deterioration for at least 6 years (Barton 1935).

Although the drying process may safely be completed in a refrigerator, a rise or fluctuation in moisture content during cold storage should be avoided (Wakeley 1954a). Sealing the seeds against moisture is harmful unless the seed has been dried approximately to, or preferably slightly below, 10 percent moisture content, and even then is needed only when the cold storage place is humid enough to raise the moisture content above this level. Vacuum sealing is not worth while (Wakeley 1947a).

Wakeley (1954a) emphasizes that "maintaining a favorable *combination* of temperature and seed moisture content (the latter often through choosing the right container) is far more important to successful storage than is choice of temperature, initial seed moisture content, or container alone." The moisture content of seeds in equilibrium with various combinations of temperature and humidity are reported in detail by Wakeley (1954a, fig. 17, p. 46).

Germinative capacity

Prompt and complete germination aids nursery practice because fewer loblolly pine seeds need be sown, a uniformly full stand develops early, and this reduces mortality in seedbeds. Such loss is less, first because seedling shade checks heat injury at the soil surface and later because there is less room for weeds to grow (Barton 1928).

Nurserymen and foresters doing direct seeding need reports on germinative capacity before sowing their seed. Makeshift estimates of seed viability based on cutting or hammer tests show values much too high. There is no proved shortcut or substitute for a germination test for each separate lot of seed.[58]

The reason tests are needed lies in the variation in germination usually encountered. That variation is wide because it originates from diverse conditions both biological and mechanical. The ability of pine seed to sprout has been observed to increase with maturity of cones. In mature timber the viability of seed from a given stand may vary with its yield from year to year as follows (Wenger and Trousdell 1958):

Seedfall per acre (thousands)	Range in seed viability (percent)
100	44-49
200	50-54
300	56-59
400	62-64
500	69
600	74-75
700	79-81

Another source of difficulty arises from delayed germination and dormancy found in some batches of pine seed. To correct this condition before sowing probably half the loblolly pine seed collected in the South needs a stratification treatment. Unfortunately this need is undetectable as yet without actual trial, hence each lot needs to be double tested, that is both with and without stratification. Without this precaution the different degrees of dormancy are an additional source of variation in germinability. Errors in processing seed add to this variablity. Seed from the same source may be 10 percent viable as delivered by one processor and 90 percent viable if obtained from another.

Such differences are not readily detected by amateurs who at-

[58] When seeds are sliced and immersed for 24 hours in a chemical solution—1 percent tetrazolium chloride in distilled water—the embryos of the living seeds turn red. By this means an estimate of germinative capacity can be obtained in 48 hours.

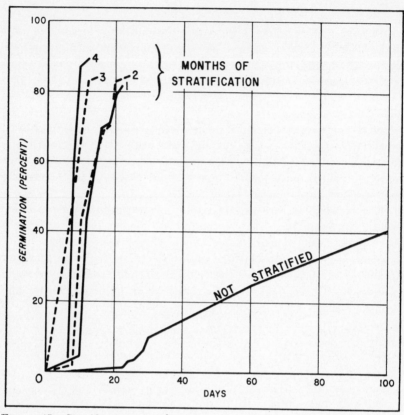

FIGURE 45.—Stratification at 39° F. as a presowing treatment both hastened
and increased germination of these loblolly pine seeds which showed 87
percent apparently sound embryos in a cutting test (Barton 1928).

tempt to test their own seeds, for they lack the control facilities
essential to accurate determinations. Hence, testing should be done
by qualified technicians at a central forest seed laboratory like the
one at Macon, Ga.

For loblolly pine 75 to 90 percent viability represents first
quality seed, 60 to 75 percent mediocre, and below 60 percent poor
capacity to germinate.

Germinative energy can be increased if necessary, and its irregularity reduced, by cool moist after-ripening. Cold stratification
for at least 30 days in wet granulated acid peat moss is an effective
presowing treatment (U.S.F.S. 1948a). The moisture content of a
medium for stratification preferably should be above 25 percent of
its moisture holding capacity and the temperature between 35° and
38°F. The object of chilling is not only to prevent heating, but also

to mobilize food reserves and induce activity of the embryo. Stratification beyond 45 days in 50- to 100-pound containers may overheat seeds within the mass. Normally, loblolly pine seed in large quantity is pretreated in smaller containers for 30 to 45 days. The usual effect is to speed and increase germination (fig. 45).

To break dormancy an alternative procedure—autumn sowing without stratification—is suitable only in the northern part of the loblolly pine range. The risk of winter mortality and of oversized survivors is too great following autumn sowing in the deep South. Autumn sowing of untreated pine seeds, however, is accepted practice in growing 2-0 or 1-1 planting stock in Kentucky, Ohio, and Indiana. In any region failure to ascertain germinative capacity leads to unsatisfactory seedling stands in nursery beds.

DIRECT SEEDING

The principal incentive for using artificial methods to reseed pine lands in the South is to avoid the cost of producing nursery stock and planting the seedlings. A minor advantage is the elmination of one of the most prevalent faults in commercial tree planting operations—the distortion of root systems forcibly crowded into planting holes or machine-made slits. Years later this planting error may lead to root defects that make the trees less windfirm. On harvest-cut areas direct seeding offers a method of reforestation that may be faster and is relatively independent of local seed years. Prompt reforestation circumvents brush problems. Time is in favor of direct seeding inasmuch as the costs of labor and seedlings continue upward, while seeding costs are decreasing as a result of recently improved techniques in this work. The direct method promises to lower plantation costs, and, if extensive current tests bring promising results, may eventually become a generally accepted practice in keeping forest lands productive.

As a method of regenerating loblolly pine, however, direct seeding is still in the experimental stage in most regions. There is some evidence that it is already beyond that phase in Louisiana, where about 35,000 acres were seeded in 1958-59. Drought is the main cause of germination failures and of mortality after germination (McQuilkin 1946). With the exception of sowing in dry years or on dry sites failures are becoming less frequent. To reduce the chance of failure, site quality should be ascertained and the most favorable situations seeded first. Badly eroded areas and very sandy soils are usually poor seeding sites. A thorough perparation of the soil and a heavy application of seed is advisable; above all some control of predators is essential.

Predators, sometimes insects or fungi but more often birds or rodents, have long been the outstanding obstacle to success with direct seeding everywhere. Studies by the U. S. Fish and Wildlife Service (Johnson *et al.* 1956) have revealed that the rodents which eat the most pine seeds are actually very beneficial creatures much of the time because they consume harmful insects. Likewise many of the seed-eating birds are desirable song or game species. For these reasons, and in order to leave the biological balance relatively undisturbed, the aim should be to repel predators rather than to kill them outright with traps or poison.

In the northern part of its range the direct seeding of loblolly pine may be in the autumn using unstratified seed. Leaves will cover and winter weather will "afterripen" the seeds for sprouting when spring temperatures reach 70°F. Where seeding is in spring, instead of autumn, the seeds need a presowing stratification treatment. If the surface is littered or overgrown the soil must first be exposed by burning, plowing, or spot clearing. Prompt sowing after such preparation of the site is essential to minimize the period of seed exposure.

Assuming that a laboratory test shows the seeds to be 90 percent viable, some 16,000 per pound should germinate under ideal conditions, perhaps 12,000 in protected nursery beds, and (again only 3 out of 4 or) 9,000 in unprotected spots prepared in open forest. If, however, the test shows only 60 percent viable, only about 6,000 can be expected in the field. The rate at which seeds of low viability are sown must be increased for a good initial catch. Such a catch is important because in their first year only about 15 percent may survive a dry summer. Disked strips can be seeded by hand at the rate of 20 gross acres per day. Aerial sowing may be economical if the right type of plane and seeding equipment are available. A single light plane operating from a crude landing strip on the seeded area can sow 1,000 acres in a day (Mann 1957).

On open areas experience with loblolly pine has shown the most common inanimate causes of injury to the seedlings are frost during the cotyledon stage, thick grass or weeds during the first year, and competition from shrubs or trees later. For open cutover land with a heavy grass sod prompt germination is essential. Apparently the best method available so far for use in Louisiana on upland areas (Mann 1954b, 1956) is to sow in February about a pound of stratified, repellent-coated seed per gross acre, on strips disked in late summer or early fall so that loose soil can wash enough to cover the seed.

Seeding upland areas under a canopy is easier and cheaper. With grass shaded out by hardwoods disking is unnecessary. Seeds can reach mineral soil immediately after a fresh burn in November and many will be masked from birds by the leaves that fall later Rodents, mostly mice, are predators that should be repelled during January and February.

If, after the heavy early mortality from drought and other causes, enough seedlings survive for a new crop of pine, the competing hardwoods should be killed back during the first summer. In Texas there is indication that deadening overtopping hardwoods and brush during April or May can save a large proportion of seedlings that would otherwise die of drought.

An ideal nontoxic repellent is yet to be discovered, but chemical formulations to simultaneously repulse birds, rodents, insects, and fungi from attacking pine seeds are being developed. Active ingredients in repellents in use include endrin against rodents and insects, Arasan (or Arasan 75) against birds and fungi, with an asphalt emulsion or preferably a latex sticker to bind the mixture to the seedcoats. About 15 pounds of Arasan (or 10 pounds of Arasan 75) are mixed with each 100 pounds of seed. Aluminum powder may be added to act like graphite in lubricating the mixture as it is dispensed from mechanical seeders. Endrin is irritating and highly toxic. The phytotoxic Arasans may reduce germination from 5 to 10 percent. Such a reduction in germination, however, may be offset by a 100 to 700 percent increase in seedling catch. When sowing from tractors or from an airplane one of the Arasans may be used, but for hand seeding and general use sublimed anthraquinone (15 pounds per 100 pounds of seed) is preferred because laborers are constantly exposed to chemical dust from the seeds. Further development in these applications is expected, and nothing can do more to make direct seeding practicable than to perfect a method of safely using some universally satisfactory all-predator repellent.

Once the critical early years are past, the pines on seeded areas face only the hazards common to all young stands and should succeed commercially. As yet the fate of field sown seeds is still fraught with much uncertainty; one reason for this is lack of control over weather conditions. If and when success can be achieved frequently through direct seeding, and improved methods become widely dependable, nursery-grown seedlings may no longer be the mainstay in artificial methods of regeneration of loblolly pine.

NURSERY PRACTICE

Until methods of direct seeding become more reliable, the demand for planting stock available at cost from tree nurseries may be expected to increase. Severe or eroding sites are more readily reforested with seedlings than with seeds. Genetically improved seeds can be more completely utilized by planting stock than by sowing seeds directly. No matter to what extent direct seeding techniques may be improved, there probably will always be a considerable demand for nursery stock. At present 1-year-old planting stock is produced annually at the rate of about a million plantable seedlings per nursery acre. In eleven southern states the forest nurseries produced nearly a billion seedlings for the 1958-59 planting season, most of them loblolly or slash pine (plate 6).

PLATE 6.—Mass production of loblolly pine planting stock in a nursery near Oberlin, Louisiana. Panoramic view of about 36 million seedlings in seedbeds (Photo 8564 by Elemore M. Morgan—courtesy Louisiana Forestry Association).

In stepping up production of loblolly pine stock to meet the demands resulting from the forestry provisions of the Agricultural Act of 1956, the nurseries have begun growing 2 or 3 successive crops of pine seedlings to each year in soil building cover crops, instead of a rotation to grow them on a given acre only in alternate years. Also research has increased the ratio of plantable seedlings to seed sown from 1 in 3 to about 1 in 2, or even 3 in 5.

Seedling culture

The amount of loblolly pine seed to sow per unit of area must be estimated closely to avoid waste of space or seeds. Useful formulas for this computation based on seeds per pound, purity, germination, and expected survival are given by Wakeley (1954a). Loblolly pine seeds are usually sown in bands, but with modern methods it is cheaper to broadcast seeds on machine-made beds and weed with chemicals. After broadcast sowing, crowns close over the beds sooner and smother some of the weeds. A desirable increase in uniformity of seedling stock within the beds is attainable by sowing seeds of uniform size. Beds are sown in February or March in the deep South, in March or April in the mid-South, and sometimes in the preceding late autumn farther north. Fall sowing may be used where winter exposure in moist soil renders presowing stratification of seeds unnecessary. Chemicals that are nontoxic, such as sublimed anthraquinone may be used to repel birds.

Seeds should be imbedded in a smooth soil surface with a roller and covered until germination is nearly complete. Some nurseries find a quarter-inch of sawdust mulch increases germination 9.3 percent above that under pine straw (Posey and May 1954). Sawdust, however, is easily washed away during heavy spring showers unless mixed with pine needles to hold it in place. An excellent mulch may be made from fresh pine straw by passing it through an ensilage cutter, or by breaking it down by rotting in piles for one year. This mulch or one made from empty pine cones from seed extraction plants stays in place better than sawdust. The cones have to be shredded by running them through a hammer mill.

For use as planting stock loblolly pine seedlings must be small enough to be handled economically in large numbers, yet large enough to survive and start growth promptly. The benefit from sturdiness appears in the following figures (Morgan 1955):

Stem thickness at root collar (inches)	Height growth February to May (inches)
Under 1/16	1.8
1/16 to 1/8	3.3
1/8 to 3/16	4.8
3/16 to 1/4	7.0
Over 1/4	7.2

The usual aim is to produce, in 95 percent of the seedlings, root collars of 1/8 inch or larger—ideally 3/16 inch. Late summer pruning of roots in nursery beds may increase field survival by 19 percent. Stems and pruned roots each should be about 8 inches long. Bud development is unspecified for loblolly pine. All seedlings should have some fascicled needles, and the injured and diseased ones should be culled.

To approximate these dimensions in 1-0 seedlings 80 percent plantable at digging time, the seedbed density must be under control. Although plantable seedlings might be produced from poor soil at a density of 10 per square foot, it would be uneconomic. Acceptable seedling quality is attainable under relatively high seedbed density where fertile nursery soils are kept in good tilth. The ideal $\frac{3}{16}$-inch stems can best be grown at 30 ± 10 seedlings per square foot (Foster 1956c). Where densities are 40 or more the stock is tall, spindly, and sometimes not well matured at lifting time. At 60 per square foot too many seedlings have to be culled out and the remainder are barely above minimum grade (May 1933).

For the first 3 months the roots develop much more rapidly than the tops. A time schedule for the seasonal development of loblolly pine in the Stewart Forest Nursery has been charted (fig. 46). There is some tendency for periods of root and shoot extension to alternate until the first frost, and then during the winter for the roots only to grow periodically (Huberman 1940a). Mycorrhizae, caused by fungi believed to be beneficial, are found in abundance on the roots of loblolly seedlings in nursery soils. Fibrous roots in large numbers are typical of the best grades of planting stock. Under favorable growing conditions most coniferous seedlings need no shade (Huberman 1940b).

Enormous savings in hand weeding costs are possible with chemical herbicides. In one nursery a seedbed weeding cost of 60 cents per thousand was reduced to 5 cents by using mineral spirits (Cossitt 1947), although at least nine species of weeds were found to be resistant. Volatile mineral weed killers injure neither the soil nor the loblolly pine seedlings. Dosages to apply and precautions to be observed in this type of weeding have been given in detail by Wakeley (1954a, p. 79).

The uncertainty and irregularity of rainfall necessitates irrigation. Water is supplied from deep wells, reservoirs, or streams. A crop of seedlings needs about 1 inch of water each 5 days. Close attention should be paid to timing in artificial watering for loblolly pine where runoff and leaching from nursery soils are high and where soil compaction from human and machine traffic is severe. Reduction of watering is vital also where excessive fertilization or

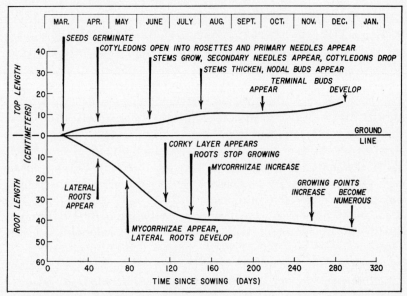

| MAR. | APR. | MAY | JUNE | JULY | AUG. | SEPT. | OCT. | NOV. | DEC. | JAN. |

FIGURE 46.—Time schedule for normal seasonal development for both tops and roots of loblolly pine seedlings from seeds sown in March at the Stuart Nursery in Louisiana (Huberman 1940a).

rainfall have produced lush late-season vegetative growth that reduces hardiness (Bryan 1954).

Soil fertility

To harvest seedling roots as well as tops repeatedly without supplementary measures is to crop with an intensity sufficient to deteriorate, if not exhaust, nursery soils. The quality of nursery stock can be impaired without conspicuous visible symptoms. To maintain the productivity of the soil and obtain healthy loblolly pine roots, both crop rotation and fertilization are desirable. Without them the drain on fertility may be 4 to 6 times that from cotton or corn.

With few exceptions the minor and trace elements in soils are adequate, but as in agriculture, nitrogen, phosphorus, and potassium are often deficient.[59] Unbalanced dosages or overdoses, ordinarily should be avoided, particularly those that may result in lush late-season growth. The addition of phosphorus alone, sometimes helpful,

[59] Complete fertilization, using all three of these ingredients is often advisable, but not always necessary. Yellow-green foliage, a symptom of nutrient deficiency, may contain only a third as much of these elements as does normal foliage. It can be corrected, and the stock improved, by prelifting growing-season fertilization. Sometimes nitrogen alone is effective (Switzer and Nelson 1956, Rosendahl and Korstian 1945).

may decrease survival, or in combination it may offset benefits expected from potassium (Andrews 1941; Lynch, Davis, Roof, and Korstian 1943; Bryan 1954). Fertilizer often fails to improve shade-grown stock (Cox 1948). Some potential benefits from fertilization can be lost in a surplus of vegetal growth, which in tops may lower survival, or in roots may have to be pruned off before planting. In connection with the use of inorganic fertilizers, there is a general need for positive steps to maintain, or increase, organic matter (Maki and Henry 1951).[60] The tremendous variation in fertilizer requirements from nursery to nursery necessitates adjusting amendments to local conditions (Wakeley 1954a, pp. 111-119). Each problem needs to be resolved on the basis of cultural trials that include field survival tests for loblolly pine.

The morphological classifications currently used to grade pine seedlings fail to distinguish certain internal conditions affecting field survival. Wakeley (1949) recognizes four fundamental causes of physiological variations: (1) differences in mineral nutrition, (2) differences in stored food reserves, (3) differences in water tension under which the seedlings were grown, and (4) possible interference with photosynthesis or transpiration from fungicides, spreaders, adhesives, rodent repellents, weed killers, or other sprays.

Nurserymen need to be alert to observe the often unexpectedly good or bad results from interactions between the ingredients in fertilizers and chemicals applied to trees or soil for other purposes. The relative promptness and vigor with which certain lots of seedlings form new roots after field planting seems to indicate some physiological superiority not manifest at lifting time. Other obscure differences in quality of seedlings may arise from lack of care in the process of lifting, packing, and shipping planting stock. Hence local tests of various cultural and handling procedures in nurseries are needed in field plantations to discover hidden, subtle, and possibly unsuspected but vital, within-grade differences in planting stocks.

Disease and insects

"Damping-off" fungi sometimes cause serious injury and loss to pines during the first month after the seeds sprout. Loblolly pine

[60] For instance at the Ashe Nursery, where the soil was deficient in both phosphorus and organic matter, the seedlings were suffering from a root rot of undetermined origin. The addition of sawdust, ammonium nitrate (at 300-600 pounds per acre), 20 percent superphosphate (at 3,000 pounds) and 50 percent muriate of potash (at 240 pounds) were needed. The solution of similar difficulties elsewhere, however, may need to be different.

seedlings wither near the ground line and fall over in a manner resembling heat killing from a hot dry surface. However, with damping-off the stem decay extends up to the ground line from the fungus in the soil, whereas heat injury starts just above the surface and the damaged tissues are lighter in color (Hartley 1929). Tall tender seedlings are susceptible when suddenly exposed to direct sunlight, as they are when excessive mulch is removed subsequent to germination. Succulent seedlings may also sunscald following a prolonged warm humid period.

Damping-off is not often destructive in southern nurseries where the soil pH is between 4.5 and 5.5, although *Rhizoctonia* may produce it even in acid soils. Sawdust or pine straw mulches help keep the pH low enough to avoid damping-off. If necessary, aluminum sulfate or ferrous sulfate can be used to lower pH. The prompt germination of stratified seeds shortens the period during which they may damp-off (Hamilton 1949). This trouble is largely prevented when methyl bromide, or certain of the other fumigants, is used to disinfect soil (Kauffman 1956).

A black root rot, discovered in soils at the Ashe nursery near Brooklyn, Miss., is locally serious in some nurseries. It causes severe root damage without clearly identifying symptoms above ground. It kills or renders unplantable large numbers of seedlings. Fumigation with ethylene dibromide, a nematocide, when soil temperatures are 55° to 72°F. has given good control, as has thorough incorporation of 1 inch of sawdust (135 cubic yards per acre) in the top 8 inches of soil, with subsequent addition of nitrogen to prevent nitrogen depression. Both have become standard practice at the Ashe Nursery. Incomplete incorporation of sawdust may cause chlorosis. No adverse effects on loblolly pine have been noted from successive annual fumigation of the soil (Henry 1953). In some nurseries having a similar-appearing root rot ethylene dibromide has failed to control the disease, but methyl bromide has been effective. While this material is more expensive it has important additional advantages in that it is a general soil fungicide, a nematocide, and a weed killer. The cost of fumigation varies greatly depending upon the material used, but has proved to be low as compared with the benefits where root rot of loblolly pine is a problem.

Control of white grubs (*Phyllophaga* spp.) in nurseries is obtained by applying the equivalent of 1 to 1½ pounds of dieldrin per acre, followed by a maintenance dosage of ¼ to ½ pound per acre every 2 or 3 years. Chlordane is also used, but the dosage is 6 to 8 pounds per acre with a maintenance dose equal to 1 to 1½ pounds per acre at 2-year intervals. Both chemicals have a residual effect strong enough to kill young larvae before they do any damage. The chemicals may be dissolved in water or added to fertilizer in order to work them into the soil to a depth of 8 inches.

Fusiform rust

In the southern part of the loblolly pine range 1 to 3 percent of the nursery stock may become infected with *Cronartium fusiforme*, in spite of control efforts, and should be culled. Incipient infection without a swelling at lifting time recently has been troublesome. Some infected seedlings always escape detection, are field planted, and usually survive less than 3 years.

Slash and loblolly pines are the principal hosts for this fungus that lives part of its life cycle on oaks. On the oak foliage it is annual and unimportant, but on pines it perennially causes stem and branch cankers that are damaging—often lethal. Aeciospores produced in the pine cankers infect oak leaves. Urediospores produced on these leaves infect other oak leaves. Finally teliospores on the oak produce sporidia which infect the pines in the spring. Periods of 18 hours or more of saturated atmosphere and temperatures between 60° and 79°F. are necessary for any major amount of pine infection by sporidia. This partly explains the variation in amount of rust infection from year to year.

Delayed sowing of loblolly pine in the nursery can reduce incidence of this disease, but satisfactory control depends on spraying with a fungicide. Control is most economical if spraying is (1) deferred until the first yellowish spots—the uredial stage—appear on the leaves of oak trees in the vicinity of the nursery, (2) deferred when the daily average temperature is not in excess of 56°F., the lower limit for germination of sporidia, and if possible (3) planned so as to precede periods of general precipitation or high humidity (Siggers 1949b, 1951). If loblolly pine beds have been sown by March 15 spraying should start as soon as sporidia are produced, because infection may occur during germination under the mulch, and the fungicide applied with high-pressure equipment (350 to 400 pounds per square inch) readily penetrates the mulch cover. Spraying at weekly intervals until the middle of June may be sufficient, but in areas where the disease is abundant or in wet years, additional applications are advisable (Siggers 1955, Verrall 1958).

Certain proprietary fungicides have given somewhat better control of the rust than that obtained from homemade 4-4-50 bordeaux mixture (Siggers 1955). An acre of pine seedlings in nursery beds should be covered with 2 pounds of ferbam, ziram, or zineb, effective fungicides against this rust, in 75 gallons of water (Verrall 1958). Distance between nozzles, tractor speed, and other factors involved in spraying for rust control are fully discussed by Foster and Henry (1956).

Preplanting treatments and storage

The possibility of applying nursery treatments to protect seedlings from pests or lessen the shock of field planting should be considered. To insure against insect damage in plantations on recently cleared areas, the tops but not the roots should be dipped into insecticide, thus eliminating most of the mortality from pales weevils (fig. 47 and the section on pales weevil in chapter 3, Protection).

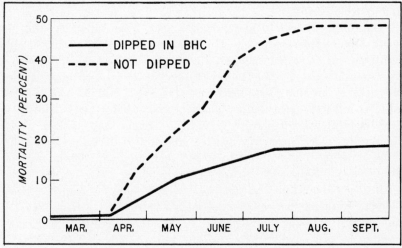

FIGURE 47.—Cumulative seasonal mortality of loblolly pine from attacks of pales weevil as affected by top dipping of nursery stock with benzene hexachloride before planting in February near Nacogdoches, Tex. (Ferguson and Thatcher 1956).

Treatments either to delay the start of spring growth or to reduce the amount of transpiration in summer are still in the experimental stage. Loblolly pine seedlings are seldom truly and completely dormant in the deep South. Roots often grow in winter and their extension immediately after planting aids establishment. It would be advantageous if the relatively inactive period for top growth could be safely extended so that the field planting season could be longer. Without cold storage it is a problem to suppress top growth even until March. Some tests with growth regulators indicate that they may inhibit emergence of new needles without retarding leader growth but they were without consistent effects on field survival (Ostrom 1945). Treatments with naphthaleneacetic acid have failed (Way and Maki 1946) as they injure pine more than hardwood seedlings.

Planting loblolly pine after April 1 in the lower South, or after May 1 north of latitude 36°, is hazardous, both because of the stage of development reached by the seedlings and because of the possibility of late spring or early summer drought. Theoretically a reduction in transpiration should benefit planted seedlings, but results from pruning, coating, or chemically retarding loblolly pine seedlings have been disappointing and largely negative. Dipping the tops of seedlings in lanolin or paraffine emulsions may reduce transpiration 60 percent without increasing drought resistance (Maki, Marshall, and Ostrom 1946).

Improvement in storage methods is more promising. A study in north Mississippi reported by Ursic (1956a) shows that loblolly pine seedlings can be stored in standard Forest Service bales at 34°F. up to 5 weeks with no ill effects. Storage in bales slightly separated on racks in an unheated warehouse was good, and in heel-in beds, with or without unfastening bundles, was satisfactory. First-year field survival was 90 percent or more following each method. Cold storage in bales, properly packed and watered, is preferred because it keeps the seedlings in prime condition with minimum handling costs. Shipment by refrigerator truck is good insurance against possible injury to the stock from delay in transit. Upon delivery watering the ends of the shaded bales twice a week makes it unnecessary to open bundles and heel-in the seedlings. The bales need to be protected from wind, sun, heat, and hard freezing.

PLANTING

Success in forest planting with any species depends on source of seed in relation to locality to be regenerated, choice and preparation of sites, quality and condition of stocks, methods of handling, planting, spacing, protecting and releasing crop trees.

Beyond the natural range

An intensive study of climatic differences between the loblolly pine belt and the adjacent territory by Hocker (1956) has provided an equation for evaluating the degree of similarity. On this basis the climate appears favorable for loblolly pine in three places beyond its present range—southeastern New Jersey, the Tennessee Valley north to Knoxville, and possibly southern Florida. Where soil is favorable and aggressive competition is under control in these areas, planted loblolly pine can reproduce itself and may be expected to thrive. How successfully it may be grown outside the natural range, however, is open to question.

Introduction far north of its native range retards growth and invites damage from sapsuckers and from ice. A good catch from direct seeding near Hoquiam, Wash., in March 1954, was damaged seriously by grazing and trampling elk. The survivors were killed by frost. Loblolly pines from Georgia seed have failed to grow at the Arnold Arboretum in Boston, Mass., and failed also at Moscow, Idaho (Parker 1955). In Moscow they came through the winter with bronze foliage and died in the spring. In the arboretum at Placerville, Calif., they have grown well, reaching 37 feet in 20 years and producing viable seed in spite of dry summers. Loblolly pines from Maryland and from Virginia have escaped winter killing in some Illinois nurseries and plantations, whereas stock from the Carolinas succumbed. In Ohio and southern Indiana also the foliage is subject to winter injury. In one half-acre plantation near Athens, Ohio, the loblolly pines reached 6 to 11 inches in diameter in about 25 years, and were then all killed in a bad freeze (26°F. below zero) in 1930. In the Missouri botanic garden the trees grew only 13 feet in 15 years (Parker 1950b).

Extension southward has been more successful. In distant countries loblolly pine has done well where winters are mild and summers moist (Boyce 1954b). In temperate parts of the southern hemisphere, devoid of native pine, it has thrived. It grows well in South Africa and in a few places in South America. Under conditions that differ considerably from its native habitat it has succeeded in Uruguay and more recently in Argentina. With competition eliminated it can make spectacular growth on alluvial bottom lands. A firm in Argentina is growing it commercially in the Parana River delta land.[61] The fluctuating water table is under control in the upper 20 inches of the soil. The pines, 807 per acre, planted 6 by 9 feet and disked one way, grow rapidly. Four-foot circles are cleared by hand in the undisturbed strips. From a growing stock estimated at over 100,000 pounds of green wood the first thinning at 8 years harvested 20 percent.

[61] Information supplied by Jorge Bolo, Vice President of Las Carabelas, S. A. Commercial and Industrial de Tierras Bosques Avenida Alen 619, Buenos Aires.

For the past 30 years the forest service in Australia has been establishing slash and loblolly pines in the summer rainfall areas in southeastern Queensland. There, with light sandy soils and climate comparable to our southern coastal plains, loblolly pine is doing exceptionally well. For the first 10 or 12 years the growth rate is superior to slash pine. They are first pruned up to 8 feet at age 7 and first thinned at age 12 years for case material and small furniture stock. The Australians have found that it pays handsomely to spend $40 an acre or more to establish pine.[62] In New Zealand, where loblolly pine has been planted since 1906, its growth is comparable to the best in its native land. It is now being planted in Japan.

In the United States in some regions adjoining its natural boundaries on the north or west, loblolly pine has been widely planted and has grown satisfactorily. For example it has done well in parts of Tennessee, southern Illinois, western Kentucky, and central New Jersey (Parker 1950b). In the absence of evidence of success in experimental trials, however, it is wise to limit the commercial planting of any species to its native range.

Suitable localities

Though loblolly pine plantations adapt themselves to a wide variety of situations they often merit more intensive care than the surrounding forest; hence they should be located where extra protection is feasible during the first 5 or 6 years when the trees are small and vulnerable. The most seriously injurious agents are fire, fusiform rust, animals, and sometimes, in certain Piedmont and upper Coastal Plain locations, ice. Each may call for special protective or remedial measures for plantations and direct seeded areas. The peak population of seed-eating rodents and shrews occurs 1 or 2 years after pine stands are cut (Trousdell 1954c). Pales weevils may also abound in the first year after cutting. In those places where certain of these risks are high, plantings should be relocated or deferred until adequate provision is made to avoid or repair probable damage (Hepting 1942).

In the rolling terrain of the Piedmont with site indices ranging from 55 to 95, the growth in loblolly pine plantations varies markedly with the slope and depth of the soil (Hamilton 1956a):

[62] Report by J. R. McWilliam of Queensland, Australia, at staff meeting of the Southeastern Forest Experiment Station, Asheville, N. C., on April 27, 1954.

Topographic position	Surface soil depth (inches)	18-year height (feet)	Approximate site index (feet)
Crest............	1.5	23	40
Upper slope......	8.0	37	60
Lower slope......	9.2	40	70
Bottom.........	18.0	46	80

In the Alabama Coastal Plain the topsoil needs to be 18 inches deep and have a silt-clay content of 20 percent for the height of planted loblolly pines at 18 years to match that shown above for the upper slopes in the Piedmont, according to Goggans and Schultz (1958).[63] Some Piedmont sites may well be found to be too poor for commercial timber growing.

But no specific topographic condition is essential to survival. Loblolly pine grows, with few exceptions, on all slopes, ridges, and upland areas. It can tolerate poor drainage with compact cloddy soil and can benefit from a top layer of dark soil, but usually it does best during the early years on the lighter, deeper, well-drained soils where hardwood competition is less intense. A light to moderate cover of broomsedge or weeds may be beneficial, but, if drought in summer can be anticipated, site preparation is essential where this type of ground cover is heavy. With normal rainfall east of the Mississippi River, planted loblolly pine survives well without site preparation, even in fields of heavy broomsedge grass. Dense over-topping briars or brush should be avoided.

Land in all stages of erosion can be planted, except possibly where only the subsoil remains (Minckler 1948). However, in 19 northern Mississippi counties thousands of acres of eroded lands have been well reforested with loblolly pine. Although success was indifferent on some of the worst sites, survival and growth on the whole was good.

A mottled or blue-gray subsoil is an indication of poor drainage and a difficult site for planting. A convenient ocular way of judging land quality is to observe the rapidity with which abandoned fields (free from hardwood rootstocks) pass from the early weed stage of vegetation to a generous cover of briars or hardwood brush. Such cover comes in promptly on the better sites whereas the first cover elsewhere is broomsedge. The old fields themselves, however, seldom need planting if pine seed trees are near.

[63] Studying the development of the tallest planted loblolly pines between 5 and 16 years of age they found this relation: $H = -14.91 + 5.96\,A + 0.00818\,DS - 0.1725\,A^2$ where H is the height (feet) of the dominant trees at age A (years), D is the depth (inches) of topsoil, and S is the silt plus clay content (percent) of the topsoil.

Site preparation

Most sites need some preparation to assure the success of seeding or planting loblolly pines. To neglect preparation may ruin a plantation; to use it unnecessarily is wasted effort; to use it effectively is clearly a self-liquidating investment. Such work aims to hold the soil, or reduce vegetative competition, or both as needed, until the pines are well established.

If erosion is currently or potentially active, some economical preplanting measures to manipulate the soil, mulch it, or introduce cover crops may be advisable in some instances. Artificial means of conserving and revegetating shifting soils are costly, however, and in most cases unnecessary.

The opposite measures are used to uncover mineral soil where erosion is not a problem and to reduce vegetation that actively competes with pine. Such preparations tend to be less costly and are more widely needed. They now employ both blanket treatments of stands, using fire or heavy machines, or selective treatments of trees using herbicides or girdling as a situation requires. These newer methods of site preparation benefit both the establishment and early development of loblolly pine plantations.

In the rehabilitation of denuded sites, and areas severely inhospitable to forest reproduction, a completely new cover of pine, though not immediately essential, is desirable and often feasible without much delay. The preliminary preparation of some of the most adverse planting sites by cultivation, furrowing, trenching, ridging, fertilizing, regrading of banks, and damming shifting soil has not improved survival and growth of loblolly pine (Gibbs 1948b, Cloud 1950), but filling planting holes with fertile topsoil may be helpful (Meginnis 1939, Hendrickson 1949).

Preplanting revegetation to hold soil temporarily on some of these severe sites may be provided by first introducing forage plants for the benefit of wildlife or domestic stock (see sections on Forage Production, and Habitat and Food Supply in chapter 9, Management for Other Purposes). The unused residue of forage cover has a favorable mulching effect. Without a mulch grown in place by such a cover crop, it is entirely possible—though seldom economical—to benefit from the artificial addition of a mulch. A mulch will lower surface soil temperatures in summer, promote early development of a favorable topsoil, hasten the natural establishment of native ground cover, and thus may benefit trees planted subsequently.

In this manner the survival and growth in a 15-year-old plantation of loblolly pine in Tennessee (Buller and Gibbs 1952) was improved as follows:

	Survival (percent)	Height (feet)	Diameter (inches)
Unmulched......	53	11	2.5
Mulched........	100	21	4.0

On no appreciable areas, however, have artificial mulches been shown to be worth what they cost. (A mulch of hay may cost $50 to $60 in place.) Where satisfactory survival can be obtained without artificial applications of mulch, needles cast from pines planted 4 to 6 feet apart will cover the ground adequately in about 8 years and afford maximum protection to the soil.

In Georgia where loblolly pines are planted on bare areas less mortality may be expected than where they are set on cutover lands with living ground cover, but the height growth is slower (Spiers 1932). The degree of slope and accompanying erosion, however, did reduce survival as well as height, volume growth, and yields in a 16-year-old plantation of loblolly pine in South Carolina (Bennett and Fletcher 1947) as follows:

Slope (percent)	Erosion	Survival (percent)	Height (feet)	Annual growth per acre (cords)	Volume per acre (cords)
3...............	slight	77	45	1.7	26.8
6...............	moderate	61	42	1.5	23.7
12..............	very severe	67	34	.8	13.0
17..............	very severe	40	28	.4	6.2

Direct reforestation of timberlands where enough soil remains to grow a cord of wood per acre annually is likewise worthwhile. An example from Tennessee is reported (Huckenpahler 1950) as follows. There the pines were planted 6 by 6 feet on Loring silt loam former cropland from which 50 to 100 percent of the topsoil had been lost to erosion. Survival was 80 percent and the crowns were nearly closed at 19 years when the following measurements of the loblolly pine were made:

	Trees per acre (number)	Basal area per acre (sq. ft.)	Average d.b.h. (inches)
Trees 4.6 inches (d.b.h.) and larger...................	504	116	6.5
Whole stand................	964	139	5.2

The dominant 19-year-old trees on this site (index 70 to 75) had 52 percent of their total 40-foot height in living crowns. The yield inside bark to a 3-inch top was 17.6 rough cords (or 1,296 fence posts) at 19 years and 43 cords at 29 years.

In the reforestation of cutover lands, where the conservation of soil and moisture is not a problem, the natural course of plant succession merely needs to be checked. Partial site preparation is adequate there if the method is wisely chosen and timed. Where soil moisture supplies are low much of the time, however, as they tend to be at the western edge of the range, rather thorough destruction of hardwood competition may be advisable before planting loblolly pine. Although in east Texas preplanting site preparation is of little benefit in normal years, it is distinctly helpful in a dry year like 1954 when there were two 30-day periods without rain (Ferguson 1956). Planted loblolly pine then responded to increasing intensity of site preparation as follows:

	First-year survival (percent)
In open fields with—	
No site preparation	10
Scalped spots	25
In the woods with—	
No preparation	18
Burned-over surface	60
Hardwoods controlled	75

The most economical method of clearing a site for planting is usually by partial cutting and burning. This is advisable where it can be done safely, but to burn broadcast in site preparation where topography is rolling and watershed values are paramount is a questionable practice. Instead limited use occasionally can be made of more costly spot treatments such as mowing brush patches too dense for access of planters, or plowing any sod or soil that is extremely dense. Scalping is seldom needed; it does not help beyond the first year, but it can be done with little extra cost by using an attachment to a mechanical planter. One such attachment consists of a disk mounted in front of the rolling coulter on a single-row planting machine. If plowing is needed to loosen severely compacted subsoil, it is best accomplished enough in advance of planting to permit weathering to soften the lumps of disturbed soil. This provides for better contact of soil and roots in planting.

In loblolly pine plantations on coastal cutover areas, especially in those on poorly drained plastic subsoil, the problem of hardwood regrowth after cutting is intense. The opportunity to use fire constructively in preparing planting sites is better there than it is on many inland areas. Evidence of this appears in the comparative rates at which hardwoods again covered the following representative cutover areas:

Region and site preparation	Hardwood cover when years since cutting are—				
	1 (percent)	2 (percent)	3 (percent)	4 (percent)	5 (percent)
Piedmont of Georgia:					
Burned-over..............	11	27	29	38	42
Unburned................	16	28	31	33	35
Coastal Plain of North Carolina:					
Burned-over..............	32	47	56	61	64
Unburned................	51	70	79	83	85

The degree of reduction of hardwood growth by fire depends on accumulation of local fuels and burning conditions. Stumps and roots preclude the use of planting machines only where dense stands have recently been cut over. Where burning is prescribed to prepare sites for planting, the fire serves mainly to increase plantable area and to make it more readily accessible for a hand planting operation, but it also leaves more of the planted trees free to grow.

Where controlled fire fails to kill many undesirable trees, especially the larger ones that sprout less profusely, they may be promptly girdled and allowed to die slowly. Planted pines often benefit from temporary shelter provided when standing dead or dying trees are left to disintegrate slowly, and the seedlings usually can outgrow weak sprouts. Herbicides applied to stumps or basal sections are useful in retarding the more prolific sprouts from medium-sized trees. There is an increasing use of chemical foliage spray applied by aircraft, especially helicopter, though within the loblolly pine belt this method remains in the experimental stage. The possibility of accidental damage from wind drift of spray is remote when the flights are well controlled. Low vegetation can be deadened by aerial spraying with $3/4$ to 2 pounds 2,4,5-T (acid equivalent in oil) per acre. Seedlings can then be safely planted the following day (Harrington 1955a), on sites prepared with scalped spots, furrows, or trenches as conditions warrant.

Another possible method of eliminating dense thickets of hardwood trees and shrubs is to use heavy machinery such as tractors and plows modified for forest use. Where erosion is no problem bulldozing is effective in site preparation. The breaking of many surface roots reduces the competitive vigor of the sprouts that follow, and makes it easier for pine to reclaim the land. Complete coverage with such machines, however, is costly and it often leaves too much debris in windrows. Hence this method supplements rather than supplants the other regeneration methods, and is most useful in changing from one type of forest to another.

State forest lands in the sandhills of South Carolina are converted from worthless scrub oak to pine as follows:[63a]

Operation	Season	Equipment
Scrub oak reduction...........	May-June	40-hp. crawler tractor and "Marden" brush cutter
Double plowing 10 inches deep..	July-August	Same tractor and Athens fire-break plow
Leveling furrowed surface......	September-October	Light farm tractor and 18-disk gang plow
Planting pine.................	January-February	Light farm tractor and planting machine

Methods of planting

Little can be said for farmers' methods and tools for planting, except that they are ever ready for small jobs at odd times. Farmers, of course, can sometimes tranplant wild pine seedlings successfully, and with full assurance of a local seed source. They can plant balled roots, too, at any season, though this is slow and more useful for horticultural than for forestry purposes (Wakeley 1945a). To establish new stands farmers should use the foresters' tools when they are available.

Slit planting either by hand or by machine is the widely used method. Though some of the lateral spread of absorbing roots is necessarily lost in slit planting, the taproot should extend straight down. Roots should be placed in close contact with mineral soil and the top of the slit should be firmly closed. Bar planting in furrows can be done at the rate of 100 trees per man-hour (Davis 1950a). By machine 11,000 to 14,000 loblolly pine seedlings per day can be planted in the sandy or loamy soils of the Coastal Plain. A reasonable goal for trained crews is 10,000 well-planted trees per machine-day. Site preparation and planting can be combined by using a crawler tractor to draw a heavy-duty fireline construction plow, to furrow strips 5 feet wide (and 8 feet apart center to center), with a tree planting machine attached. Where root treatment against white grubs is indicated, a spray attachment may be added to the planter.

Without a planting machine, the necessary hole digging can be mechanized by "spudders" mounted on the rear wheels of rubber-tired tractors. They speed the work, reduce costs, and improve the quality of the job done by inexperienced labor. The difficulty of moving over roads from one site to another is avoided by using spudders with digging points that fold back (Whalen 1956).

[63a] Lehocky and Lee "South Carolina sand-hills can grow pine timber." Jour. Forestry 52:280-281. 1954.

Several machines on the market are made expressly for forest planting. They are of two types. A "floating" planter is attached to a tractor drawbar in such a way that it can be lifted off the ground or lowered by the tractor's hydraulic mechanism. A "trailer" type planter has all or most of its weight carried on its own wheels. They function best on the more extensive flat lands that are fairly free from stumps or other obstruction. Some parts of the cutover areas in the Piedmont can also be planted by machine at variable cost, depending on soil type, percentage of slope, and degree of erosion. On favorable sites after disposal of brush, a narrow-gage crawler tractor and sturdy planting machine can do an adequate job, traversing shallow gullies.

When double-row planters are provided for large projects they should be used in conjunction with enough single units to handle miscellaneous small old fields or odd parcels of cutover lands. The single-row planters are more flexible, and, because of a slight scalping effect, are better suited to grassy areas. One foreman with an assistant can supervise the operation of 4 to 5 planting machines. To train crews and to check the condition of seedlings as well as the quality of both field work and map records, one inspector should be assigned to each 5 planting units (e.g., each two double and one single machine). Only by careful excavation of sample specimens can common errors, such as setting trees too high, flat, or "U-rooted," be detected. A deviation of 1 foot is permissible in the interval between individual trees or rows. To insure adherence to standards, followup inspections are vital.

For extensive projects advance planning is fundamental. Planting reconnaissance is essential to classify lands in need of separate treatment. Reconnaissance, together with local experience as to capacity of pines to survive on diverse sites, permits variation in prescriptions for effective spacing of planted trees (table 21). In areas of medium to heavy fusiform rust infection, 100 to 200 additional trees per acre should be prescribed. Prescription planting results in more uniformly satisfactory stands at a possible saving of 25 percent in costs. A prerequisite is that seedlings be sorted, and, if possible, baled separately by grade.

On large projects also it is advantageous to pay the workers on a differential wage scale according to the quality of their work. Contractors should be paid promptly on completion of each planting chance for only the number of seedlings acceptably planted. One favorable effect of this is to reduce the variation in costs per thousand surviving trees.

TABLE 21.—*Example of spacing guide for prescription planting by machine on the upper Coastal Plain in South Carolina*[1]

SURVIVAL EXPECTED

Soil texture and site preparation	Grade of planting stock			
	1	2	3	3[2]
	Percent	Percent	Percent	Percent
Deep sands:				
Undisturbed	60	50	30	...
Furrowed	80	70	50	65
Loamy sands:				
Undisturbed	65	55	30	...
Furrowed	85	75	60	75
Sandy loams:				
Undisturbed	70	60	45	...
Furrowed	90	80	65	80

SUGGESTED DISTANCE BETWEEN ROWS

	Feet	Feet	Feet	Feet
Deep sands:				
Undisturbed	7	6	4	...
Furrowed	9	8	6	8
Loamy sands:				
Undisturbed	8	6	4	...
Furrowed	$9\frac{1}{2}$	9	7	$8\frac{1}{2}$
Sandy loams:				
Undisturbed	8	7	5	...
Furrowed	10	9	8	9

[1] To attain about 600 trees per acre from seedlings spaced 6 feet apart within the rows; derived from 6 years of large-scale forest planting for the Atomic Energy Commission's Savannah River Project. Although based on work with slash pine, the same principles apply to loblolly pine wherever survival by grade, soil, and site can be properly evaluated.
[2] This column is for small seedlings set in furrows and planted deeply without U-rooting.

Hopkins (1949) recommends that forest managers in the Deep South (1) plan and record progress on good maps, preferably aerial photographs, (2) estimate seed and seedling requirements 2 years ahead and provide for graded stock from a suitable source, (3) hire local labor, (4) commence in the autumn as soon as there is enough moisture so as to finish before February when it may be too wet, (5) operate two or more machines close enough together to pull each other out of difficulty, (6) avoid poor planting resulting from too shallow trenches or from attempting work on cold, raw, wet days, and (7) foster local good will by keeping the community posted on the operation. However, the best time to plant is a local matter influenced by soils and the kind of planting stock available. For example, in northern Mississippi the use of stock produced in nurseries some 300 miles farther south leads to poor survival in December plantations. On soils there, loblolly pines planted from January to March, preferably in February, are more success-

ful. In other locations where frost heaving may be injurious,
planting should not start until spring.

Planting stock should be removed from the nursery in winter.
If lifted and baled after the middle of February or in early spring,
when the seedlings are breaking dormancy, the survival in the field
may be lower (fig. 48). When removed from the bales seedlings
need to be sheltered from the sun and wind. Brief exposure to air
may have no ill effects. Roots should be kept moist, but not allowed
to stand immersed in water. During a period not in excess of 2
hours they can be fortified against injurious drying by first dunking
them in puddled clay (Slocum and Maki 1956b). Regardless of pre-
treatment, however, long exposure in drying is detrimental; it lowers
survival and reduces the first-year height growth.

Within the rather narrow size limits for seedlings readily plantable with the usual tools the larger ones grow faster the first year
and tend to retain their early advantage (fig. 49).

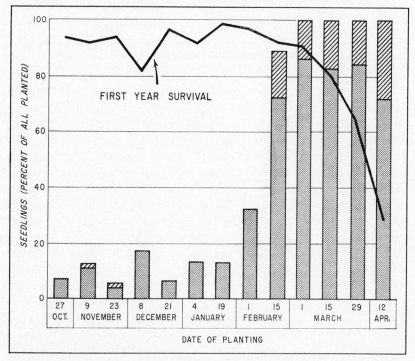

FIGURE 48.—First-year survival of loblolly pine following planting at different
times with different degrees of dormancy; stippled columns show proportion of lot with first winter bud opened; hachured part, second bud opened
(Wakeley 1954a).

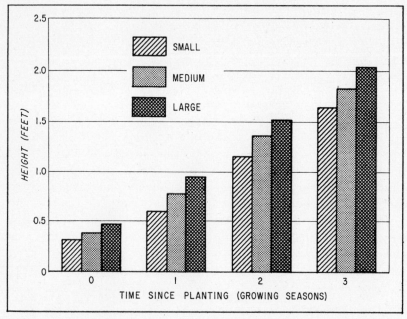

FIGURE 49.—The initial advantage from planting large stock successfully in the field may not be permanent but may last at least 3 years (Haney 1956).

Contrary to the old rule for keeping the nursery ground line at the soil surface after planting, recent evidence (Slocum 1951, Slocum and Maki 1956a) indicates that unless unusually long roots are available seedlings can benefit from deeper setting on well-drained sites. In these tests survival of 9-inch seedlings was not improved but growth was stimulated for 2 years by planting more deeply until the original stem was half buried. Shallow planting exposes roots to the air and makes the seedlings vulnerable to drouth, whereas deep planting enables them to tap moisture from beneath the dry surface layers.

Most pine plantations in the United States [64] are not managed

[64] Where a deficiency in phosphate is a major factor in poor growth, as on certain areas in Queensland, the trouble has been remedied with rock phosphate as effectively and more economically than with superphosphate. Such fertilization has been financially profitable there in hastening the production time for a needed commodity. For loblolly pine in Queensland, the optimum content of phosphorous pentoxide in the top 4 inches of soil is about 200 p.p.m. (H. E. Young 1948). Because the elements of nutrition found in needles are related to those in the soil, foliar analyses may indicate where certain top dressings are needed.

In North Carolina one study of loblolly pine (Brenneman 1953) showed the nitrogen content of needles and soil to be related, but no comparable associations were found for phosphorus or potassium. The content of these elements intensively enough to warrant fertilization. Fertilizer tests have revealed adverse effects from the stimulation of grass and weeds. Planted loblolly pines should not be fertilized in any locality in which southern fusiform rust infection is appreciable (Wakeley 1954a). Fertilizer makes the trees more susceptible to disease by inducing earlier spring growth of foliage. Until more studies are made, nitrogen especially should be used sparingly, if at all, in the Deep South, because that which is not promptly absorbed is readily lost.

Spacing in plantations

Early studies of square spacing in southern pine suggested that where thinnings can be made the distance between 3-inch trees should be about 6 feet; 4-inch trees, 7 feet; 5-inch trees, 8 feet; 6-inch trees, 10 feet; and 8-inch trees, 12 feet. One of the rules of thumb advocated by the Soil Conservation Service—the D + 6 rule (Mitchell 1952)—calls for wider spacing which is the modern trend. Although the gross volume of wood produced may be greater from close spacing, the 50-year net returns from planting 6 by 6 feet are estimated at little more than half those from planting 6 by 8 feet.

Owners interested in quick production of saw logs only may avoid spacing too closely by setting the trees 8 to 10 feet apart in plantations, particularly on the poorer sites. On the better sites the growth of the largest 100 trees per acre is retarded little if any by close spacing in the first 7 years, but is severely reduced thereafter (Ware and Stahelin 1946, Stahelin 1948b). In the first decade the formation of wide annual rings, largely of spring wood, cannot be avoided by close spacing. The former standard square spacing of 6 by 6 feet is now a minimum (Hamilton 1956a).

Ordinarily when loblolly pine seedlings are planted in squares a widely applicable general rule is to space the trees at 8 by 8 feet, i.e., 681 trees per acre. Then in the first thinning the stand will be reduced to 80 to 100 square feet of basal area per acre.[65] In special situations, however, there still may be valid reasons for planting

---

in green foliage showed seasonal variations—increasing together from March to June and decreasing from June to September. However, between September and January phosphorus increased and nitrogen remained the same, while potassium decreased.

[65] Depending on a number of factors such as the height and clear length of the pines, site quality, cutting cycle, and especially on the wishes and plans of the owner to produce certain products. More detailed guidelines to the consideration of this problem are included in chapter 7, Management of Immature Timber.

more or fewer trees per acre (Meade 1956). Pertinent considerations are as follows:

Narrow spacing, down to a minimum of 6 by 6 feet (1210 seedlings), is best to—

1. Offset the low survival to be expected on poor sites, and to fully utilize available soil;
2. Exclude grass, weeds, and shrubs through heavy needle fall instead of mulch, or to underplant groups in mixed-species forests;
3. Check active erosion promptly without artificial introduction of herbaceous cover;
4. Apply where thinnings, both noncommercial and commercial can be used to insure maximum quality and total volume of yield.

Wide spacing, up to a maximum of 10 by 10 feet (436 seedlings), is best to—

1. Limit initial costs on good sites;
2. Forestall stagnation of growth in stands;
3. Utilize short rotations for rapid turnover in invested capital;
4. Avoid all necessity for early and noncommercial thinning.

Intermediate spacing, about 8 by 8 or 7 by 9 feet (680-690 seedlings), is a compromise to obtain—

1. Reasonable first costs on medium sites;
2. Fair stem quality without any noncommercial intermediate cuttings, or
3. High quality with thinning and pruning;
4. Access for trucks after row thinning in intermediate and final harvest operations;
5. Integration of saw-log and pulpwood harvests.

When mean annual increment per acre, especially on poor sites, is expressed in cords produced by varying numbers of surviving pines per acre, the growth rate is affected by a biological version of the law of diminishing returns. Although at a given age there is more room for a large number of trees per acre on the poorer sites (because of small size), the extra stems may not add enough to the yield to justify the cost of planting them.

In actual practice what can be accomplished by planting varies with the relative availability of land, seedlings, machines, labor, and time. The supply of each of these may affect the spacing chosen for planted trees. Some adjustment in initial spacing is advisable to allow for the mortality to be expected prior to the first thinning. Actual spacing, through its effect on crown differentiation and growth rates, influences the timing of the first thinning. That operation, to be commercial, must await an operable quantity of trees above the minimum diameters merchantable for a given purpose (Lange 1952). Where the demand for certain special products from young pine can be foreseen, plantations should be spaced accordingly (table 22).

When the special product sought is pine seed for future sowing on some other land, or in a nursery, a seed orchard should be established from superior stocks. In such an orchard the trees should be spaced more widely than for any other commercial purpose— perhaps in young unthinned stands 15 by 15 feet to obtain good pollen coverage. Later when the stand has been thinned, and the reserve trees approach maturity, average spacing may reach 25 or 30 feet, i.e., 50 to 70 trees per acre.

The optimum stocking for best results in managed stands has not been precisely determined as yet, but it undoubtedly falls some- where between the biological maximum and half of that. The two- thirds maximum ("normal") in table 22 is here assumed to be a desirable operating goal in stand density.

Underplanting and release

It was discovered early (Hall 1939) that prompt regeneration of the rather small openings made where southern pine (except long- leaf) is cut commercially will pay even where planting is necessary. This measure is especially important where, as in central Alabama (Brinkman and Swarthout 1942), about half of the open areas in the forest are without pine seedlings because of a shortage of suit- able seed trees. In spite of border retardation underplanting can succeed where hardwoods are present if they are not too dense (Stahelin 1946), but it is better if the larger undesirable trees are deadened or felled before or immediately after planting the pines. In one instance where this was done the planted pines became 10 inches taller the first year. In another instance 86 percent of the loblolly pine survived at least 2 years and were then 2.3 feet high (Muntz and Derr 1949, Muntz 1951, Shoulders 1955). Delaying re- lease for a year reduced third-year survival and height of these seedlings by one-quarter. Where no release was provided, survival and growth were only about half as good as on areas released immediately.

During initial establishment of pine seedlings in years of severe drought, competition from grass may exceed that from trees, especially if no furrowing or scalping was done. Under such conditions three times as many planted seedlings may survive the first few years under oaks as in grassy openings. This happens because the surface layer of soil containing the seedling roots is dryer in open spots under grass than in shaded spots under trees. That condition is common, but not universal, and is usually temporary. Where it is found, advisable practice is to apply only partial release the first year or two, or to deaden the competition slowly (i.e., without poison). On many sites a deadened overstory provides all the shade the pines need in their first year and after that they will be rooted more deeply. Then, or on poor sites soon thereafter, they become better able to compete with grass and less able to withstand an overwood. Release from overtopping hardwoods in most situations should be immediate; it should never be long deferred (Shoulders 1955).

On average sites in years without serious drought underplanted seedlings meet with less competition from low vegetation at the start. In such cases immediate or very early and complete release is best, for the overwood cannot function as nurse trees. This was demonstrated in a loblolly pine plantation made in 1948 on Fordyce Lumber Company lands in Arkansas (Clark 1954):

Release degree and time	Survival when number of growing seasons is—			
	1 (percent)	2 (percent)	3 (percent)	4 (percent)
Complete and immediate............	100	100	100	100
Partial after 1 or 2 years............	100	90	80	80
None.............................	100	73	73	57
	Seedling height			
	(inches)	(inches)	(inches)	(inches)
Complete and immediate............	10	29	63	102
Partial after 1 or 2 years............	7	15	28	46
None.............................	7	12	15	22

In the Ozarks, farther north in Arkansas, loblolly pines planted under an overwood of 50 square feet of basal area per acre became 2.8 feet tall in 4 years while those in the open became fully twice as tall, 6.0 feet (Meade 1955).

Seedlings used in underplanting should be spaced with deliberate irregularity to take full advantage of favorable spots where the overwood is least dense. They should be grouped and spaced more closely than usual in the available openings. That is to allow for the losses which are certain to exceed mortality in the larger clearings or open

TABLE 22.—*Guide to rectangular spacing for loblolly pine plantations as affected by expected survival to time of first thinning for each of four products*

Initial product desired[1]	Operable stands— average d.b.h. of merchantable trees	Basal area per acre at maximum stocking	Stand per acre at— maximum stocking[2]	Stand per acre at— ⅔ maximum stocking	Spacing for ⅔ maximum stocking when survival is— 80 percent	Spacing for ⅔ maximum stocking when survival is— 60 percent[3]
	Inches	Sq. ft.	Trees	Trees	Feet	Feet
Local posts........	4	119	1,360	907	4 x 8	4 x 7
Commercial posts...	5	131	958	639	6 x 9	5 x 8
Pulpwood.........	6	140	712	475	8 x 9	6 x 9
Poles (No. 10).....	7	147	550	367	9 x 10	7 x 10

[1] At minimum merchantable diameters 1 inch below those in the next column (Lange 1952).
[2] For loblolly pine (after Stahelin 1949) based on normal yield tables.
[3] For planting 600 to 700 seedlings per acre without reference to specific products, spacings of 6 by 12 or 7 by 10 are appropriate except where fusiform rust is serious. There it is advisable to set out 700 to 800 seedlings spaced 6 by 10, 7 by 8, or 6 by 9 feet apart. Close planting reduces the incidence of tip moth attacks.

places, especially when release is postponed. This is indicated by the relatively high percentage of loblolly pines in acceptable condition 8 years after planting 908 seedlings in a field as compared to those planted within the forest (Boggess and Bryan 1940).

Seedling condition	Survival Old-field planting (percent)	Survival Underplanting (percent)
Fair or better quality.............	55	37
Suppressed, diseased, or defective...	36	51
Total alive.................	91	88
Dead or missing.................	9	12
Total planted...............	100	100

Although prompt, or only briefly delayed, release is clearly best, extended delay is not always a fatal error. If, because of well-distributed rainfall, enough of the neglected seedlings survive for a new crop, they merit release regardless of their age or the degree of their retardation.[66] This is due to the ability of puny loblolly pines to recover promptly and completely upon release.

[66] Some loblolly pines planted under scrub oak in north Mississippi in 1941 were not released until 1948. Branches falling from trees deadened at that time killed or damage 10 percent of the seedlings, but the response of survivors was good. On unreleased plots during the next 5 years the suppressed pines continued their relatively slow growth, increasing 7.5 feet in height, 1.2 inches in diameter, and 11.4 square feet in basal area. In the same period the released seedlings grew half again as much in height, twice as much in diameter, and nearly three times as much in basal area (Huckenpahler 1954, 1955).

TREE IMPROVEMENT

All foresters attempt to stem the trend toward forest deterioration by reserving the better loblolly pine trees for future growth and seeding, but forest trees have not yet shared in the marvelous improvement achieved for agricultural crops through selection and cross-breeding. Similar methods are now being applied to enhance the value of native loblolly pines for forestry. Inasmuch as tree generations are longer, and vegetative propagation of conifers more difficult, progress will be slower.[67] But the genus *Pinus* offers rich opportunities for improvement because of the large variety of existing species and geographic races available (Frontispiece). This will furnish the raw materials for continuing efforts to mold new forms of timber that will survive planting, grow rapidly, resist injury, make better wood pulp or otherwise excel for special purposes in different localities. Loblolly pine is destined for a major role in this development.

Hybrid vigor is a valid hope as yet seldom realized in the work with pines. When loblolly pine was crossed with pitch pine the progeny was superior in New Jersey but inferior in Maryland (Duffield and Righter 1953). Improvement in both disease and drought resistance, however, is a good prospect. Some 31 shortleaf-loblolly pine hybrids that survived planting in Louisiana in 1951 within a heavily diseased 3-year-old slash pine plantation (2 out of 3 slash pines infected) show no fusiform rust whatsoever (Henry and Bercaw 1956). A drought resistant strain of loblolly pine in Texas has been shown to transpire less water (Gilmore 1957).

As local conditions may lead to poor survival, or may obscure characteristics valuable elsewhere, all progeny tests preferably should be duplicated in distant places. This is the only practicable way to recognize that certain desired improvements are truly heritable singly or in combination. For example, when loblolly pine was exported to South Africa it was found (Sherry 1947) that stocks from

---

[67] The possibility of speeding up normal generations appears limited, but the progeny of a 21-year-old loblolly pine is reported (Reines and Greene 1958) to have produced mature cones at 4 years of age. Some inherent characters fortunately can be judged early in life. For example it has been discovered (Zobel and Rhodes 1956) that the specific gravity of the wood of a young loblolly pine—i.e., the first 8 rings—and the overall specific gravity of the mature tree are closely correlated. Also the specific gravity of the young wood of a seedling can be estimated from that of its limbs. The length of tracheids found beyond the tenth ring indicate the ultimate length to be expected in mature fibers (Kramer 1957), and the length of branch tracheids is closely related to that of stem tracheids (Jackson 1959). Together these findings make it possible to judge the wood quality to be expected from progeny in tests of inheritance.

Woodville, Fla., and from St. Tammany Parish, La., were significantly superior to most others in rate of growth, but inferior in form. Stocks from Brookhaven, Miss., and Spring, Tex., excelled in both vigor and form. Thus the current provenance tests serve not only to identify existing strains, but also as a basic prerequisite for further genetic improvements (Wakeley 1954b).

Progeny tests reveal that many of the desirable characteristics of loblolly pine are not attributes in the sense that they are inherited intact by a certain proportion of the next generation. Rather they are characters that blend into forms intermediate between those of the parents. The opportunities for worthwhile improvements are good because of the wide variation in heritable differences in individual trees now being discovered in natural stands. To develop these opportunities considerable new genetic research is now underway at various points.

Seed production areas

Ultimately special seed orchards may be expected to supply the bulk of the seeds needed for artificial methods of regeneration. They will feature so called ''plus'' trees and furnish seeds of certified superiority over native seeds. They will be permanently dedicated to and specifically managed for this purpose. All inferior genotypes will be removed, and the remaining selected or planted cone producers will be stimulated by removal of competition and perhaps also by fertilization. It may be necessary to protect flowers and cones of parent trees from insects.[68] All seeds will be collected without cutting trees and without repeatedly wounding them with climbing spurs. That means that the cones must be reached by using ladders, a Swiss ''tree bicycle,'' or other special equipment—perhaps even some expensive high-lift machinery. If only a few cones are needed as test specimens, they may be shot down by a .22 rifle with telescopic sight (McCulley 1953d).

Meanwhile seeds of acceptable quality from known sources can best be obtained in quantity only by direct collection or from reliable dealers. Stands temporarily designated for seed collection in a specific year may be thinned to stimulate the crop and later felled to collect the seed. If thinning is necessary it should be provided the first year before May in order to obtain a heavy seed crop in October of the third year. Permanent seed production areas need special

[68] A turbine mist blower mounted on, and powered by, a jeep can spray a 70-foot pine with 2 to 3 gallons (0.5 percent gamma BHC water emulsion) in 3 minutes. U. S. Forest Service, South. Forestry Notes 111, 1 p. 1957.

protection from destructive agents, and they need wide spacing with large crowns for maximum production (Easley 1954).

In Queensland, Australia, the fruitfulness of loblolly pine plantations in relation to stand density has been studied by Florence and McWilliam (1956). The maximum production of pollen seems to occur with about 100 trees per acre, i.e., about 20 feet apart in square spacing (fig. 29, *A*, chapter 4, Natural Regeneration) regardless of site quality. Average numbers of flowers and cones per tree, however, continue to increase with added growing space, at least to nearly 30 feet between trees, or 50 stems per acre (fig. 29, *B* and *C*). The spacing recommended for "plus" trees in seed orchards is a compromise. With 24 feet between planted trees—about 76 per acre—loblolly pine in Queensland is expected to produce 43 pounds of seed at 20 years. Stand density appears to reduce cone production per tree, and in poor pollen years, fruitfulness and per-acre yields as follows:

Stand— Trees per acre (number)	Yield— Cones per tree (number)	Fruitfulness— Seeds per cone (number)	Yield— Seeds per acre (thousands)
50	190	120	1,140
100	126	81	1,021
150	82	72	886
200	58	67	777
250	50	64	800
300	47	62	874

With wind pollination there is no assurance that both parents of any seed are of high quality, unless the production area is isolated from surrounding pines. Even so open-pollinated loblolly pine from good mother trees was observed in Australia to yield about twice the percentage of well-formed stems as did stock from inferior mother trees. Furthermore this percentage was again increased with stock from controlled pollination. With both parents superior, the seeds produced four times as many stems of good form as did stock resulting from general uncontrolled collection of cones (Queensland State Forest Service 1948).

Artificial measures other than thinning to increase the yield of cones on seed production areas are a distinct possibility not yet developed. Although experience so far does not indicate any probability that such measures will aid silvicultural practice, they may perhaps be applied to step up seed production on limited areas where successive crops are not desired. With fertilization to increase nutrition, and wounding to direct it to seeds rather than wood, the trees can be induced to bear more seed. Wounding alone,[69] however, is a questionable practice that may destroy seed trees (Bilan 1957). Wenger (1953a) reports fertilizer alone effective in a 25-year-old stand of loblolly pine. In the third growing season after treatment, the fertilized pines produced 98 to 123 cones each as contrasted to only 36 cones per unfertilized tree. The effect did not carry over to the next year.

Hybridization

When artificial crosses are attempted between species without close botanical relationship a high percentage of failure is expected, but the occasional success is most likely to induce radical changes—beneficial or otherwise. A certain amount of such exploratory work is needed to define the limits within which hybridization is most likely to be practical.

Attempts to crossbreed several species of yellow pines have already revealed certain interspecific compatibilities and incompatibilities and produced some desirable hybrid characteristics. Simultaneously an effort is underway to discover in nature the existence of superior strains—i.e., outstandingly good genotypes—to serve as breeding stock. The need is for a sustained program of selection and cross pollination applied to both hybrid and pure-species parent trees. Through progressive selection and rejection of progeny, it should be possible to isolate specific heritable improvements in a high percentage of the progeny. For example there is evidence that loblolly pine can be bred to produce wood having short or long tracheids (Jackson and Greene 1958). It is unlikely that in any reasonable period general improvements can be made to breed uniformly true. Hence superior stocks of the best available quality will have to come mainly from the repetition of controlled crosses between progeny-tested parent trees. Improved seed in greater quantity, but more variable in quality, should become available from the partially controlled crosses in seed orchards grown from grafted clones.

So far in the South the program of tree improvement for southern yellow pines is scarcely out of the early exploratory stages. Some second generation (F_2) crosses, however, are included among the existing loblolly pine hybrids:

[69] According to a recent report longleaf pines were stimulated by using a bark hack for partial girdling of 10- to 12-inch trees. A half circle was cut on one side, and the second half circle 4 inches higher with a slight overlap on the other side. The yield of cones was doubled (South. Forest Expt. Sta. 1955).

Successful crosses involving loblolly pine[1]

(i.e., the progeny includes at least one living seedling free from all suspicion of pollen contamination in the process)

Seed parent[2]		Pollen parent[2]	Forest Experiment Station
echinata	×	taeda	California and Southern
elliottii	×	taeda	Southern
palustris	×	taeda	Southern
rigida	×	taeda	California
sondereggeri	×	taeda	Southern
palustris	×	sondereggeri	Southern
taeda	×	echinata × taeda	Southeastern
sondereggeri	×	echinata × elliottii	Southern
echinata × taeda	×	taeda × elliottii	California
taeda	×	elliottii	California
taeda	×	elliottii densa	Southern
echinata	×	echinata × taeda	California
serotina	×	taeda	Westvaco

[1] As listed by Keith Dorman of the Southeastern and Berch Henry of the Southern Forest Experiment Stations.
[2] The list includes not only interspecies crosses but also back-crosses recognized as valid. The first seven of the above hybrids have also been produced by crossing in the opposite direction. *Pinus sondereggeri* (Chapman 1922) occurs in nature with *P. palustris* as the seed parent and *P. taeda* as the pollen parent; there are indications that the reciprocal cross also occurs in nature. An additional possibly successful cross (i.e., evidence that crosses may be made, but no surviving seedlings as yet fully accepted as genuine hybrids) under observation in California is (*taeda* × *elliottii*) × *elliottii*. References: Righter & Duffield 1951, Duffield 1953.

To ensure that new hybrids are genuine, i.e., not a result of accidental contamination in crossing, geneticists need to recognize not only gross morphological characteristics of each parent species, but also minute histological attributes as well. The basic chromosome number in the gametes of all pines is twelve (haploid) or twenty-four (diploid). Polyploidy is rare, but does occur. Increasing the number of sets of chromosomes results in decreased vigor of the trees. Multiple embryos, rarely found in loblolly pine (Nelson 1941), are more frequent in other pines than is generally known, but rarely do two embryos mature within an ovule; usually one is much larger than the other (Buckholz 1918). Cotyledon numbers range from 5 to 9 in loblolly pine, averaging $6.87 \pm .09$ (Butts and Buckholz 1940).

Vegetative propagation

Asexual methods of propagation of pines are useful in genetic research. Wood from 30- to 90-year-old trees can be grafted to seed orchard trees, but the commercial use of vegetative propagation to produce planting stock is too expensive.

Artificial methods of rooting seedlings less than 5 years old are available. Yearling seedlings root readily, but the ease of rooting falls off rapidly with increasing age. Shoots from trees over 10 years old are difficult to root (McAlpine 1957). In one set of tests (Gardner 1929) cuttings from first-year loblolly pine seedlings rooted 46 percent, those from second-year seedlings 6 percent, and older ones not at all. High humidity, though insufficient in itself, augments root initiation by juvenile material. The need is for a method that will root cuttings from older trees. The best thermal conditions for rooting cuttings in propagation benches appears to be cool air temperatures in conjunction with bottom heat of 75° to 80°F. (Cech 1958). Airlayering is now being developed as a technique useful in rooting samples of superior strains in loblolly pine (Zak 1956).

Grafting methods are also useful in these investigations. Twin grafts on a single seedling were utilized in Texas (Folweiler 1953) to isolate the heritable from the environmental influences on density of the wood. A scion from a tree of high specific gravity and another from a tree of low specific gravity were each bottle-grafted to a single seedling and allowed to develop. If the difference in density persists in future growth it will signify an inherent rather than an acquired character. In this and other ways vegetative propagation is furthering research in tree improvement.

Proper handling of scions prior to grafting is vital in practice. With control of temperature, humidity, and atmosphere successful grafts have been made with cuttings shipped to Florida from Australia and with cuttings stored for more than 4 months (Perry and Wang 1957b). The use of vegetative methods in commercial propagation of pines, however, is still to be perfected.

SUMMARY

Much planting is needed within the loblolly pine belt both to reclaim lost area and to restore understocked forests. To plant yearling trees grown in state nurseries, rather than to sow seeds, is the quickest and surest means presently available to attain full stocking in loblolly pine. It can succeed only when the source of seed is well suited to the planting site and where the seedlings are properly set out and provided with adequate growing space. With these conditions met, the resulting survival, growth, and thrift of loblolly pine is often superior to that of the other native pines. Mixed species planting commonly fails, as loblolly pine suppresses most of its associates tried so far. In pure loblolly pine plantations, however, successes greatly outnumber the failures from initial mismanagement or from neglect of subsequent care. "Prescription planting" with graded stock is the method found to be most economical per thousand surviving trees.

The adverse effect of a poor source of seed on net growth is long lasting. For generations it may outweigh anything but catastrophic injury. Many ills acquired from the immediate environment, of course, are neither inherited nor necessarily lifelong. But until more is known of the sources, seed collections should be limited to places less than 100 miles away and with less than a 1,000-foot difference in elevation. For forecasting good seed years and locating suitable areas and quotas for collection of seed a simple cone-ratio method of estimating yields is described.

Cones are ripe for collection as soon as their specific gravity has dropped enough so that they will float in SAE 20 oil immediately after being picked from the tree. The average content is about 57 sound seeds per cone. To extract the seeds requires 6 to 48 hours of kiln drying. Moisture lost in this process is about 74 percent of the weight in dry cones. A hundred pounds of fresh cones will yield 2 or 3 pounds of clean dewinged seed—with about 18,400 seeds per pound.

Mishandling in collection, extraction, dewinging, or drying may destroy vitality essential to successful storage. With moisture equal to about 8 percent of their dry weight, seed can live 1 to 3 years at air temperature, but under cold storage (at 40° down to 5°F.) they may last 6 years. To get full germination from some lots of seed it is necessary to stratify them in a cool moist medium prior to spring sowing. Seed viability increases with per-acre yields of seed, but varies so much that each lot of seed should be tested before it is used in nursery or field.

Direct seeding in the field aims to circumvent the cost of nursery stock and planting. On the basis of successful practice in Louisiana it is suggested that a pound of stratified, repellent-coated seed per gross acre be sown in February on strips disked in January. Success hinges largely on how effectively seed predators are repelled.

Stock of suitable size and quality for planting can be grown in a year at 20 to 40 seedlings per square foot of nursery seedbed, provided that the soil productivity is maintained with cover crops and fertilizer. With frequent watering in spring and summer, the seedbeds need no shade. To reduce injury and mortality of seedlings, pest controls using herbicides, fungicides, insecticides, and fumigants are suggested. Planting stock is shipped readily and may be stored temporarily in tightly packed bales.

The natural range of loblolly pine may be extended safely by artificial means only to areas not too dissimilar in climate. Parts of New Jersey, Tennessee, and Florida probably can be successfully planted. Northward it may be too cold, and westward too dry, at least in certain years. Loblolly pine has been successfully introduced, however, in New Zealand, Australia, South America, and South

Africa. Within its natural range the species can thrive on nearly all creek bottoms, slopes, and ridges in upland areas, but it does best on the lower slopes where hardwood competition is not too intense. In flatwoods where drainage is adequate, and even in bottom lands where hardwoods are controlled, its growth is excellent.

Preplanting site preparation is frequently, but not always, necessary. It is usually attained most cheaply by prescribed burning. Where hardwood stems too large to kill back with fire abound, they must be felled or deadened before or soon after planting.

Loblolly pines can be most efficiently planted by machines on large areas that are free from obstruction and without steep slopes. Special equipment has recently been developed to permit planting in brushy areas. For reinforcing fail spots or for underplanting thin places in a forest, the foresters' planting bars are best. Only the small odd jobs should be handled with farmers' standard or improvised tools.

Systematic use of fertilizers for pines is so far limited to programs to maintain the productivity of nursery soils and seed orchards. Extensive fertilization elsewhere in forestry must await evidence that the benefits are economically worth while.

Spacing of trees in plantations should be governed by numerous considerations, some silvical, others economic. Although on any acre there is room for more trees of a given age on a poor site than on a good site, the extra trees do not grow well enough to repay the cost of planting them. If the grade of planting stock is low or the risk of fusiform rust infection is high the spacing should be close. The modern trend, however, is toward rather wide spacing—about 7 by 9 feet. Spacing should vary with (1) the relative availability of land, seedlings, machines, labor, and time, and (2) the average size of trees suitable for the principal product to be grown, with or without thinning. Reinforcement planting, if any, must be prompt.

The prevalence of partially idle lands in understocked forests indicates an extensive need for underplantings. These may be spaced 6 by 6 feet in irregular patches. They can benefit from early liberation from the closely adjacent, or overtopping, competition of all undesirable trees.

As knowledge of the relative intrinsic value of existing races of loblolly pine accumulates from provenance tests, increasingly close attention must be paid to using only stock from seed gathered from the most suitable of the available sources. Tree improvement for loblolly pines is underway through both selection of superior strains and artificial crossing to combine desirable characters. Current advances in vegetative propagation will speed such investigations and help evaluate the progress in genetic work. The opportunity is great because of the large variety in related forms to work with. Although loblolly is already a leading species of pine, improvement can be expected in capacity for rapid, disease-free growth, and in superior wood from trees of better form. When inherently superior pines have been found, tested, and made available, the demand for planting stock is certain to increase.

Chapter 6

Growth and Yield

Proficiency in the constant adjustment of growing space to the needs of trees and stands is essential to good silvicultural practice. It is necessary to know how much room is needed for crop trees of different sizes and stands of various ages, not merely to retain life but also to exclude weed species, to maintain quality or increase growth, to permit regeneration only as needed, and to sustain reasonable yields of designated products. Proficiency involves deliberate compromise in so far as any of these forest objectives may be conflicting, but all costly waste of soil productivity should be avoided.

Certainly knowledge of capacity for growth and yield is prerequisite to good management of loblolly pine. Associate species, stand density, and periodic cuttings need to be well controlled in the process.

ASSOCIATED SPECIES

Survey data generally show loblolly pine producing 2 or 3 times as much volume per acre as the associated hardwoods. Miller (1954) observed this on the Hill Demonstration Forest in Durham Co., N. C., where he studied plots in the soil province known as the Carolina slate belt, with the following results:

Species	Site index (feet)	Age (years)	Mean annual increment	
			Cubic feet	Board feet
Loblolly pine......	85	31	117	488
Virginia pine.......	75	46	92	365
Upland hardwoods..	69	49	47	171

On slopes and ridges generally loblolly pine produces nearly twice as much merchantable timber in a given length of time as does sweetgum (Ralston 1955). The difference in yields in favor of loblolly pine is less pronounced on bottom lands. Where surface soil is shallow loblolly pine excels yellow-poplar in radial growth and in yield during the first 25 years, but after that the yellow-poplar is slightly superior (Hocker 1953). The yield from loblolly pine, however, less sensitive to loss of fertility than that of yellow-poplar, does not decrease so rapidly in relation to decreasing depth of the A horizon.

Hardwood species, like yellow-poplar, not only help to maintain forest soils in productive condition but also help the pines to prune themselves. In unmanaged stands of mixed species individual pines closely surrounded by hardwoods contain the most high-grade lumber. Where the basal area of hardwoods equals that of the pine at 60 years, some 22 percent of the volume per pine tree may consist of B and Better lumber whereas if there is ten times as much basal area in pine as in hardwoods at 60 years, only about 8 percent of the pine volume will be B and Better lumber (Paul 1932a). Hopkins (1957 and 1958) found no evidence that either site index or total basal area in hardwoods influenced the quality of loblolly pine lumber produced, but that the quality index of the pine increased both with age and with the percentage of basal area in subdominant hardwoods. He found the optimum amount of understory hardwoods to be about 5 percent of total basal area.

For the highest yield per acre there must not be too much volume in low-value hardwood. It was observed by Paul (1932c) that the highest net lumber values were to be found in stands where 20 percent of the timber was hardwood well distributed among the pines. A greater proportion of hardwoods resulted in a lower production of pine lumber and a smaller net value per acre because the hardwood is less valuable.

Forbes (1930), while analyzing about 700 sample plots in a south-wide study of the height of pines in relation to age, found that site indices of the four leading commercial species of southern pine averaged as follows: Shortleaf pine 69½, longleaf pine 71, slash pine 81, and loblolly pine 92. More recent extensive surveys confirm the superiority of loblolly pine sites over those occupied by shortleaf pine, but indicate that on the whole they are not better than the longleaf-slash pine sites. Site indices are the principal, but not the only criteria of timber yields to be expected.

Specific differences in susceptibility to injury, in branch habit or crown width, and in length of rotation are also involved. For example, near Woodworth, La., loblolly and slash pine were planted together 6 by 8 feet apart in alternate 3-row strips on Ruston fine sandy loam of site index 100 for the loblolly pine. At 23 years of age the loblolly supplied 56 percent of the total yield of 32.6 cords of pulpwood. Crown ratios were nearly the same and the superior performance of loblolly pine is ascribed to its slightly better resistance to both fusiform rust and ice damage. Narrow crowns in early life appear to be advantageous only in short rotations.[70]

PINE CROP TREES

Development as individuals

Loblolly, when fully developed, is the largest of the southern pines, occasionally reaching a diameter of 4 feet with the lowest limbs 50 feet from the ground and a total height of more than 100 feet (Harper 1928). The maximum d.b.h. in virgin old growth is given as 3 to 5, averaging 4 feet (Sargent 1884, Rothrock 1890, Zon 1905). On the good sites heights reached 130 or 140 feet in some places, but 90 to 110 feet was more often found with diameters of 2 to 2½ feet. Longevity was restricted by red heart. This decay in the heartwood usually was less than 5 and seldom more than 14 percent of the volume of trees 70 to 80 years of age. Old at 100, many reached 150, and exceptional ones 300 years. The longevity and the quality of the timber varied by locality. In marked contrast to the stunted trees found in the Coosa valley of Alabama were the large high-quality loblolly pine found in poorly drained swales on the Warrior tableland. Here trees 110 to 120 feet tall were clear of branches for 45 to 70 feet and averaged 2 feet in diameter (Mohr 1901).

Similarly on moist sites, within stands of bottom-land hardwoods some of the largest pines still remaining in the South are specimens of loblolly pine. The tallest known living loblolly pine in America in 1954[71] measured 54 inches in d.b.h., was 151 feet high, and had a crown spread of 59 feet (quarterly report from the Tidewater Research Center of the U. S. Forest Service at Franklin, Va., dated December 1954). The tree is located in the Bigwoods Experimental Forest, near Franklin, Va., and withstood 100 m.p.h. winds

[70] At Urania, La., on identical sites, longleaf was observed to yield 15 percent more than loblolly pine in rough cords at 36 years from seed, despite its 5-year lag in starting height growth. The explanation is that with narrower crowns the longleaf retained more trees per acre, and the excess number more than offset the slower growth of individual trees (Chapman 1953). This early advantage for longleaf pine in wood production is lost, however, as crowns widen during the longer rotations used in growing sawtimber on loblolly pine lands.

[71] A champion 63-inch tree according to the records of the American Forestry Association is located in Dinwiddie County, just below the Amelia County line, where it stands on a property corner of 3 land owners, near Petersburg, Virginia. It is 128 feet high with a crown 64 feet wide. (Virginia Forests 11 (2):16, 1956; American Forests 62 (4):33-40, April 1956, reported by R. G. Turner, Amelia.)

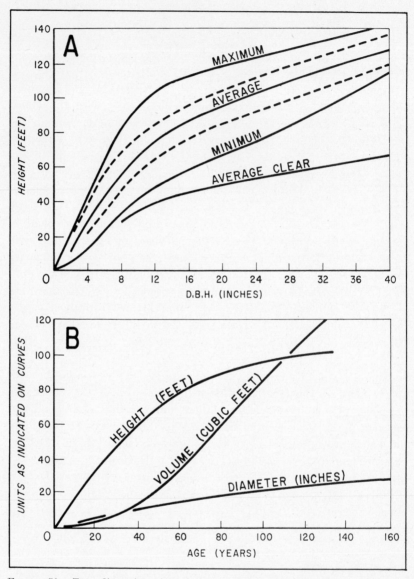

FIGURE 50.—Tree dimensions in relation to breast-high diameters and age in Arkansas: A, Dash lines delimit usual variation in height found on 2,843 sample second-growth and residual trees measured in 1938 near Crossett; B, dimensions recorded earlier on old-growth timber near Pine Bluff (Olmstead 1902).

TABLE 23.—*Dimensions of virgin loblolly pine trees on average sites in east Texas (Zon 1905)*

Stem diameter[1]		Top diameter in terms of d.b.h.	Height		Clear stem in terms of height
At breast height	At base of crown		Total	Clear	
Inches	Inches	Percent	Feet	Feet	Percent
10	....	..	85	53	63
12	6.4	53	90	60	67
14	6.9	49	93	65	70
16	7.7	48	94	66	70
18	8.5	47	96	67	70
20	9.7	49	99	67	68
22	10.9	50	102	67	65
24	13.0	54	105	67	67
26	15.2	58	...	..	..
28	17.2	61	...	..	..
30	18.5	62	...	..	..

[1] Annual burning has been observed to affect stem dimension only in the stump area; it increased butt swelling within 1 foot of the ground (Chapman 1942a).

in hurricane "Hazel" in October 1954. Its age has not been determined.

At a given age, say 100 years, heights are greater on the better sites and diameters greater where trees have long been free from crowding. Heights of saw-log trees may vary as much as 50 feet within a diameter class, but the usual range is only 20 feet (fig. 50, *A*), with slightly more than half the height clear of branches in second-growth stands or 70 percent in old growth. Typical dimensions for good old-growth timber are shown in relation to diameters in table 23 for Texas and in relation to age in figure 50, *B* for Arkansas.

Comparable records on virgin trees in South Carolina show age by size classes and volume by age classes as follows (Chapman 1905):

D.b.h. (inches)	Age (years)	Age (years)	Volume (board feet)
5	17	40	140
10	30	80	480
15	46	120	760
20	71	160	1,030
25	104	200	1,260
30	143	240	1,460

In second growth with plenty of soil moisture it is not unusual for young loblolly pines to reach 25 feet in height in 10 years. In this period diameter growth is related more closely to crown length than it is to crown ratio (Dubow 1954). During the first 40 to 45 years on the best sites the pines maintain an average rate of growth in height of 2 feet a year (Cope 1923a). For simultaneous good growth in diameter the stands may need to be thinned to prevent excessive shortening of their crowns. In relation to total height the green crown needs to cover 40 percent until the trees are 30 feet high, while taller trees need at least 30 percent crown (Lotti 1956b). The longer crowns are also broader on crop trees and growth at breast height is related to breadth of crown about as follows (Paul 1931a, 1932a and 1932b):

Crown width (feet)	Diameter growth in last 10 years (inches)
10	0.6-0.7
15	1.0-1.1
20	1.4-1.5
25	1.8-1.9
30	2.0-2.4

The trees with the larger crowns are those that have been relatively free to grow for many years. Among them the diameters at breast height increase only 2 inches in 10 years on sites of index 50, but they increase nearly twice as fast on sites of index 100 (Larson 1957):

	D.b.h.[1] when age in years is—				
Site index	20 (inches)	30 (inches)	40 (inches)	50 (inches)	60 (inches)
50	4.0	6.0	8.0	10.0	12.1
60	5.1	7.4	9.8	12.1	14.4
70	6.2	8.8	11.4	14.0	16.7
80	7.4	10.2	13.1	16.0	18.9
90	8.5	11.6	14.8	18.0	21.2
100	9.6	13.0	16.5	20.0	23.5

[1] Basis: Increment cores from dominant and codominant sample trees selected throughout North Carolina—one from each of 2,725 survey plots.

In well-stocked stands the average diameter attained at 50 years is about 27 percent less.

The yearly increase in volume and value of pulpwood trees where they grow at the rate of 1 inch in 3 years, as at Crossett, Ark., is as follows (Reynolds and Clark 1948):

D.b.h. (inches)	Volume per tree (cords)	Annual increase (percent)
4	0.009	38
5	.020	27
6	.037	23
7	.061	17
8	.092	12
9	.126	11
10	.166	9
11	.213	8
12	.264	7

On this forest the rapid high-quality growth of many trees released from suppression gives no evidence of inferiority in these trees. Their diameter growth per decade was as follows: Average of first 4 decades, 1.4 inches; decade prior to release, 1.2 inches; decade after release (about 1915), 4.2 inches. Thus release tripled diameter growth (Reynolds 1952b).

In southern yellow pine second-growth as well as old-growth saw-timber is commonly utilized up to a top stem diameter of roughly half the d.b.h. measurement (Girard 1933) (table 23). Although stem form (Form Class 59 to 82 in saw-log trees) varies widely with crown class in different stands, the usual dimensions of loblolly pine trees in North Carolina are related to their log and board-foot content about as follows:

Tree height (feet)	D.b.h. (inches)	16.3-foot saw logs (number)	Merchantable volume, International $\frac{1}{4}$-inch (board feet)
40......	10	1	19
50......	12	$1\frac{1}{2}$	53
60......	14	2	110
70......	15	$2\frac{1}{2}$	160
80......	16	3	217
90......	17	4	315
100......	18	$4\frac{1}{2}$	420
120......	19	5	535

Upper stem diameters of these trees have been tabulated in detail by height classes from 40 to 140 feet and by half-log stem sections for loblolly pine sawtimber both above and below 75 years of age (Ashe 1915). This study clearly showed that the relation of stem thickness at any given height above ground to d.b.h. is linear for all trees in a single total-height class.[72] In trees 10 to 20 inches in diameter the merchantable portion of the stem volume may vary from 75 percent in 30-foot trees up to 96 percent in 100-foot trees.

Bark volume ranges from nearly 20 percent in 6-inch trees down to about 14 percent in 14-inch trees (section on Wood Derivatives in chapter 10, Properties and Uses), but varies widely also wherever there is a wide range of ages within diameter classes. The older trees, especially the small ones, are relatively thin barked. Information on bark volume is useful mainly in approximating the solid-wood content of unpeeled wood. Rough bolts sold for pulpwood are barked by machinery at the mills.

During the past 15 years the trend has been toward purchase

[72] Formulas for these linear taper series are tabulated by half-log lengths in the appendix, table 67.

Merchantable volumes and numbers of pulpwood bolts by height classes are shown in the appendix, table 69.

of pulpwood by weight (Taras 1956, Yandle 1956).[73] Since weight decreases as wood seasons, buyers who purchase by weight place a premium on delivery of fresh wood free from blue stain.

In silvicultural operations to produce sawtimber much pulpwood is available as a byproduct, both from trees removed in thinning operations and from the formerly unused tops of saw-log trees. In the usual practice, the tree tops yield only about a quarter of a cord per M board feet cut, but this can be doubled where only high-grade material is used as saw logs.

The amount of pulpwood available increases with a decrease in merchantable (saw-log) height. Thus 3- or 4-log timber may yield only a tenth of a cord, whereas 2-log timber can yield a half cord, or 1-log timber 1½ cords per M board feet (Brender 1947). When whole trees are cut for pulpwood the yield increases with an increase in any dimension, but the amount of pulpwood available decreases somewhat with an increase in the diameter of the trees from which saw logs are taken. The volume of both products is affected by commercial utilization limits in the tops of the trees (appendix, table 70).

A host of volume tables are available and their misuse introduces a legion of errors. Special-use tables are continually needed. Samples are given in the appendix for illustration and possible use in building local tables to serve specific purposes. In general timber volumes (or weights) based on the diameters (d.b.h. or crown) and total height of loblolly pines (appendix, tables 69, 71, 72, 76) are better for research purposes than are those based on merchantable heights in feet or log lengths (table 74).

The reverse is true in commercial cruising. For that a locally chosen table (such as table 74 in the appendix or one derived from it) is preferable. The amount of lumber that can be cut from pines varies with both usable log length and form of the boles. Girard's quotient, diameter inside bark at the top of the first log in terms of d.b.h. outside bark, is a common expression of form. If the average form of the local timber, or better still, the stem quotient typical of each d.b.h. class is available, the factors shown in table 74 can be used to adjust an available table, or if necessary to construct a superior local table. For example, where the Girard quotient is 78, as it often is in southern pine, the volumes in table

---

[73] For this the cubic volume data of table 69 in the appendix are converted to pounds of freshly cut wood in table 76 in the appendix. Formulas for relating volume and weight are given in the section on Estimating Raw Materials in this chapter.

74 will apply if multiplied by 1.07. Often a determination of form permits selection of a suitable published table. To implement this problem in southern pine Mesavage and Girard (1946) have formulated 26 separate tables for form classes 65 to 90 utilizing three log rules (International ¼-inch, Scribner, and Doyle). They also provide a table of stem taper above the butt log and give instructions for correcting existing volume tables.

Where the Girard form class is 80 and where aerial photographs are available from which the height and crown diameters of trees can be determined, volume of timber may be estimated from the data in table 72 in the appendix. This works best for the dominant portion of the stand most readily visible in the pictures, but someone trained in photo interpretation and a certain amount of ground checking are essential to an acceptable cruise based on photographs. In converting pines into lumber the greatest profit per tree comes from large-crowned dominants, but the highest profit per acre comes from stands with a maximum number of trees with medium-sized crowns (Paul 1932a).

In saw-log stands only certain trees relatively free from defects can meet the exacting requirements and bring the premium prices paid for large poles.[74]

Growth of single trees

Productive sites favor rapid growth in height everywhere and rapid growth in diameter also where trees are not crowded. Where site quality is 80 to 85 feet at 50 years, trees of saw-log size growing 3 inches in diameter in 10 years, have living branches on 37 to 45 percent of their total height. The width of their crowns in feet is 1.12 times their d.b.h. in inches. Faster growing trees have longer crowns that average 1½ feet wider, and slower ones shorter crowns that are 1½ feet narrower (Guttenberg 1953). Although a live crown ratio of 40 percent of height produces the maximum volume of clear wood, one of 30 percent produces 89 percent as much (Labyak and Schumacher 1954).

Height growth and crown expansion appear to be independent of foliar density within the crown, but trees with dense crowns grow

[74] Specifications are given in the appendix, table 68, and the methods of measurement are illustrated in figure 100, chapter 10, Properties and Uses. The board-foot content of trees that qualify for various lengths and classes of poles are given (appendix, table 75), and examples of the quantity of pulpwood sticks or railroad ties contained in poles of certain dimensions are shown in table 54 in chapter 10, Properties and Uses. These data are most useful to landowners in making all-important comparisons of prices as between the differently measured products on demand in local markets.

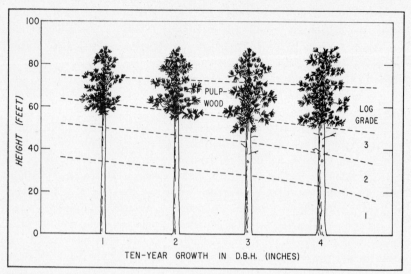

FIGURE 51.—Difference in rate of diameter growth is accompanied by differences in tree dimensions, form and quality of stems (Crossett log grades), and general appearance even among trees of the same age class.

faster in diameter (Grano 1957a). Stem-quality zones in mature loblolly pines vary with rates of growth in diameter (fig. 51). Similar differences found in another study of individual trees (Deetlefs 1954) show roughly that doubling crown-length ratio may about double basal area growth, apparently as a result of a 4-fold increase in relative crown surface (fig. 52). Such a change may be effected where severe crowding is relieved by thinning and the trees left have had time to respond. In even-aged stands the average length of living crowns is inversely related to the number of trees per acre. The relative crown-surface area of single trees of a given d.b.h. is nearly 4 times as great when basal area per acre is 60 square feet as when it is 160 square feet. Within a stand of a given basal area per acre the large trees often increase their basal area twice as fast as the small ones.

Open-grown pines that retain branches nearly to the ground have roughly conical stems. Forest-grown pines, particularly the small-crowned subdominant trees, tend to be conical within the crown and nearly cylindrical below it. Maximum diameter growth is at the base of the crown. To this the lower and weaker branches contribute little or nothing. Above them the contribution from individual limbs varies with size, abundance, and thrift of their subbranches.

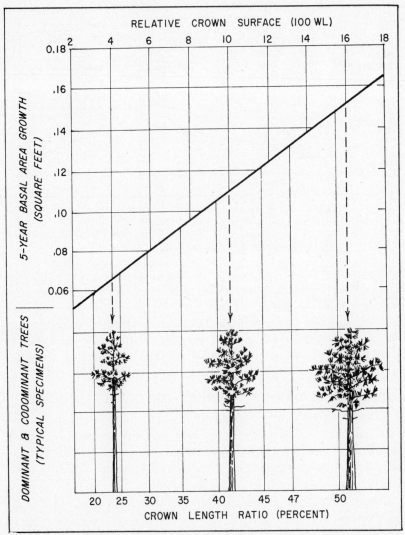

FIGURE 52.—Relation between crown surface, crown length, and the current growth of dominant and codominant loblolly pines from 20 to 60 years old. Relative crown surface was gaged by two maximum dimensions of the crown, width (W) and length (L). These two factors were each recorded in terms of percentage of total height, and used in the product ($100WL$) shown on the upper scale (Deetlefs 1954).

How stem growth varies at four heights above ground was studied in the Duke Forest using weekly measurements during two growing seasons. The maximum rate of growth was attained early in the season at all four points, but it soon decreased near the base while

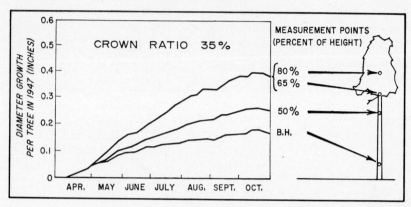

F<small>IGURE</small> 53.—Cumulative diameter increment at four points for forest-grown trees with a crown ratio of 35 percent. Growth is retarded most at breast height as crowding reduces crown ratio, and the lower bole becomes more nearly cylindrical (Young and Kramer 1952).

it continued at the same rate near the top of the trunk (fig. 53). Size of crown has a marked effect on growth below but little influence on growth within the crown. Trees with 20 percent crowns increased only one-sixth as much in diameter near the base as near the top, but the growth on trees with 50 percent crown was nearly half as large near the base as near the top. Thus in pruned trees the merchantable portion tends to become cylindrical.

EQUILIBRIUM DENSITY VERSUS DESIRABLE STOCKING[75]

When a site is fully occupied by a stand, its density tends to become constant. For example in fully stocked mature sawtimber, volume and basal area are stable except for interruptions by mortality and subsequent reaction in accelerated growth. This equilibrium density may be close to the biological maximum for a species; it always exceeds the density required for management. Nevertheless, because it is constant, it provides an efficient base for expressing degrees of stocking useful in management.

Little is known of the rate at which stands approach equilibrium, or of the factors which determine its level. The work of Chaiken

[75] Equilibrium density, for which the classical name in forest literature is ''normal'' is too high for timber growing enterprises. It represents full stocking in theory—overstocking in practice. Contrary to early conceptions it does not express the productive capacity of the soil, climate, and species; it merely shows the accumulated difference between growth and deterioration on the stump. Undisturbed stands approach this equilibrium rapidly at first, then gradually, and are eventually subject to variations above and below the level of equilibrium.

(1939) and Wellwood (1943) suggest that the approach is profoundly influenced by initial stocking, and to a lesser degree possibly by stand age and site quality.[76]

Full stocking

In undisturbed fully stocked saw-log-sized stands of loblolly pine, basal area may reach 250 square feet in some places, but it fluctuates normally around an equilibrium value between 125 and 185 square feet per acre. Analysis of Chapman's yield plots at Urania, La., (Meyer 1942) gives evidence that this fluctuation centers at 154 square feet of basal area or a stand density index (Reineke 1933) of 275 ± 15 as the 100 percent stocking "normal" for this species of pine.[77] In other words in a natural even-aged undisturbed stand of sawtimber, averaging 10 inches in diameter, the number of trees per acre will be about 275 at equilibrium stocking (Fig. 54, *A*). The density of younger or older stands can be readily expressed on this basis if the average diameter and number of trees is known. A convenient table of multipliers (Mulloy 1943) is available for computing S.D.I. (appendix, table 78). A formula similiar to Reineke's was used by MacKinney and Chaiken (1935a) to tabulate the numbers of loblolly pines needed for 100 percent stocking at each average diameter between 1 and 21.[78]

There is considerably more latitude in what may be considered normal full stocking where trees are younger and smaller (table 24), because more time is available for correction of abnormal stocking in the course of natural development. Stand density index is least significant as a measure of stands in the seedling or sapling stage, but is advantageous to use because it is independent of age and site and because of the ease with which it can be applied to widely diverse diameter distributions found in many irregular stands.

[76] The level of this equilibrium density does not appear to be reduced as site quality is lowered, though it may be reached at a later date. At a given age, of course, there would be room for more stems on a poor site than on a good one because the trees are smaller, but for a given stem size the trees on the poor site suffer the more severely from competition and hence need relatively more space if they are to make acceptable growth. Thus there is some evidence that the equilibrium level (not the time needed to reach it) is largely independent of both site and age.

[77] On this basis the early yield tables for southern pines (Misc. Pub. 50, U.S.F.S. 1929) were at least 6 percent high, i.e., above equilibrium density for loblolly pine. Figure 54, *B*, is based on these tables. See also appendix, table 79.

[78] These values were obtained from the regression equation: Logarithm of number of trees per acre = —1.707 logarithm of average D.B.H.o.b. of the stand + 4.1588; for which the correlation coefficient is .9625, and the standard error of estimate is ± .0862 in logarithmic units, or ± 17.2 percent.

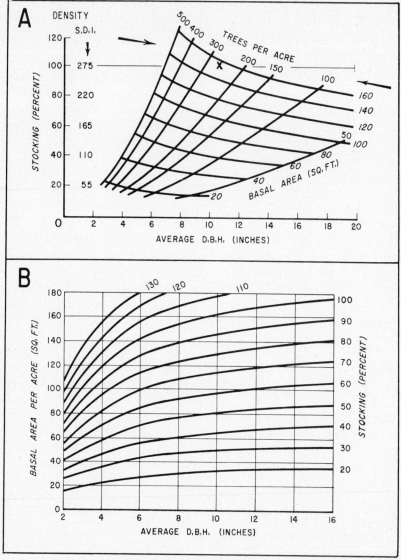

FIGURE 54.—Stand characteristics of loblolly pine in relation to degree of stocking: At *A*, 100 percent is used to represent the level of biological equilibrium. Full stocking as indicated by the southern pine yield tables is a
maximum (marked by opposing arrows) and expressed by this rule of
thumb for spacing distances 1.08 (d + 1.25) in feet. For trees 10.6
inches in d.b.h. the equilibrium observed by Meyer (1942) in Louisiana and
marked by x corresponds to an S. D. I. of 275 (Reineke 1933). At *B*, 100
percent represents full stocking according to the yield tables (Stahelin
1949).

TABLE 24.—*Fully stocked even-aged pure loblolly pine stands in relation to average diameter of trees in 2-inch d.b.h. classes[1]*

Average d.b.h. (inches)	Medium values and variation[2] in—				Area for single pine in natural stand[4]	Square spacing in planted stand[5]	Factor[6]
	Normal stand, N[3]	Basal area per acre	Stand density (S.D.I.)				
	Trees	Sq. ft.	Index	Percent	Milacres	Feet	f
4......	1350±75	117± 8	309±17	112	0.7	5.7	.379
6......	680±50	133±10	299±22	109	1.5	7.8	.445
8......	420±30	146±10	294±21	107	2.4	10.2	.499
10......	290±16	158± 9	290±16	105	3.4	12.2	.545
12......	211± 7	165± 6	282± 9	103	4.7	14.3	.586
14......	160± 3	170± 5	274± 5	100	6.2	16.5	.623
16......	127± 2	177± 3	270± 4	98	7.9	18.6	.657
18......	105± 1	186± 1	270± 3	98	9.5	20.8	.688

[1] These data are approximations from several sources including Misc. Pub. 50 (U.S.F.S. 1929), MacKinney and Chaiken 1935a, Chisman and Schumacher 1940, and the author's own studies. The densities represent the biological maxima for the species, and are not suitable for managed stands. The corresponding crown cover is usually not less than 80 percent complete—admitting not more than 25 percent of full sunlight to the forest floor.
[2] The ± signs indicate range of variation between the different authorities consulted.
[3] On "log-log" paper this trend is linear, following the formula: log N equals 4.161 − 1.708 log d.b.h. The stand ratios by 2-inch diameter classes (q values a la Liocourt) decrease here from about 2.0 to 1.2.
[4] Approximately 1000 divided by normal stand.
[5] The formula for this spacing is 1.08 (d.b.h. + 1.25).
[6] Converting factor f equals basal area divided by S.D.I. or S.D.I. equals basal area divided by f (Brender and Barber 1956).

Although normal yield tables or charts (fig. 55 and table 79 in the appendix) may be used cautiously to predict yields obtainable from well-stocked even-aged stands over long periods, they are unreliable even for short-term forecasts of yields from understocked and mixed species forests. If used for this purpose corrections for composition and for stand density are needed to allow for the rate at which each undisturbed stand will approach full stocking. With information on initial age, density, and site quality, such corrections, applicable to pure loblolly pine stands, can be based on relationships portrayed in figure 56. The report on this study (Chaiken 1939) explains the application of such information to avoid serious errors when loblolly pine yield tables are used to predict growth.

Management optimum

Forest managers who seek maximum volume production per acre need to know what stand density favors it. Correct spacing of loblolly pines unfortunately must vary not only with site and age, but also with the different objects in, and facilities for, forest management. No close agreement on this vital matter can be expected until much more research and experience are available. Under even-aged management a basal area of 90 to 95 square feet per acre is favorable (fig. 57). The mean annual increment in units of rough wood culminates at 30 to 40 years in well-stocked stands or at 40 to

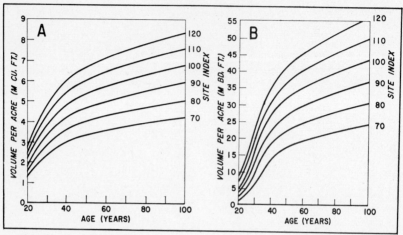

FIGURE 55.—Volume per acre of fully stocked stands varies with age and site index. The cubic measure, *A*, here is for trees 3.6 inches in d.b.h. and larger; the board measure, *B*, is by the International ¼-inch rule for trees 6.6 inches in d.b.h. and larger (Meyer 1942).

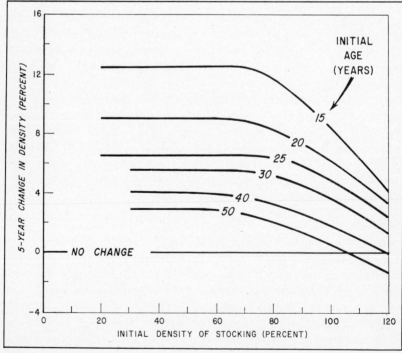

FIGURE 56.—Relation of age and initial stocking to rate of change in density (Chaiken 1939).

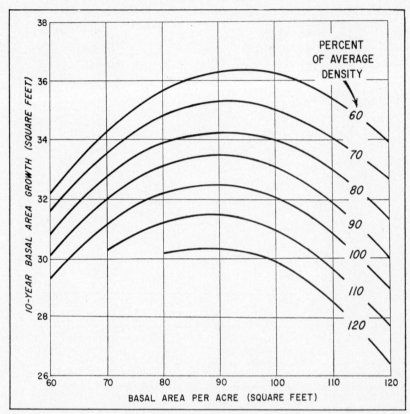

FIGURE 57.—Basal area growth of loblolly pine peaks between 90 and 95 square feet of growing stock (an adaptation by T. C. Evans of data by Simmons and Schnur 1937).

50 years in stands less than half stocked at the start (fig. 58). Under all-aged systems of silviculture the timber trees must have space enough not only for good growth but also for adequate regeneration. One thing is certain, optimum stocking for growing sawtimber under selection systems must be well below, perhaps only half or two-thirds of, the equilibrium density (Reynolds 1954b).

A study of growth in producing pulpwood (McClay 1955b) indicates most satisfactory increment where the basal area in square feet is ten below the site index in feet. Less growing stock means the soil is not being fully utilized. Ashe (1929) estimated optimum loblolly pine stocks in volume per acre by broad age classes as follows: 2,300 cubic feet at 20 to 30 years, 4,500 cubic feet at 35 to 50 years, and 6,400 cubic feet or 29,000 board feet at 50 to 70 years for maximum values.

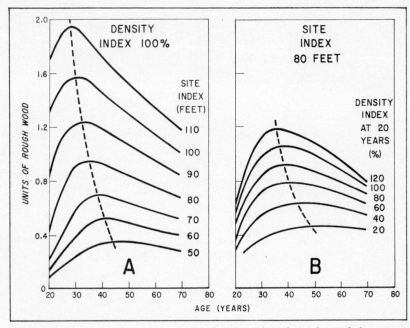

FIGURE 58.—Average yearly growth per acre in units of rough wood from trees
6 inches in diameter and larger (*A*) where density index is 100 percent
for stands of different site quality, and (*B*) on a site of index 80 and
for stands of different densities at 20 years of age. Broken lines intersect culminations of increment (MacKinney and Chaiken 1956).

Typical distribution of pines by diameter classes in undisturbed
stands is shown in figure 59.

Early plantations were closely spaced assuming that survival
would be low, thinnings would be feasible, and many stems desirable
from which to make later selection of crop trees. Ware and Stahelin
(1948) reported that 350 trees per acre are needed at 14 years to
provide enough vigorous and well-spaced trees for a maximum yield
of high-quality products. This is still true, but recently planted
pines have been spaced more widely in anticipation of better survival, to make scarce or costly planting stock cover more land, and
to obtain pulpwood on short rotations without benefit of thinnings.
Competition starts in most stands long before it is noticed.[79]

[79] This fact should be recognized—not necessarily circumvented. To avoid
early competition, loblolly pine introduced commercially in the southern hemisphere is often spaced widely. It is reported from Australia (Queensland
Forest Serv. Ann. Rpt. 1946-47) that trees 13 feet apart are already competing
at 7 years of age. The trees may become larger on good than on poor sites
by the time measurable competition starts (Pennefather 1948), but even so,
rapid growth may be expected to hasten the conflict. In South Africa loblolly

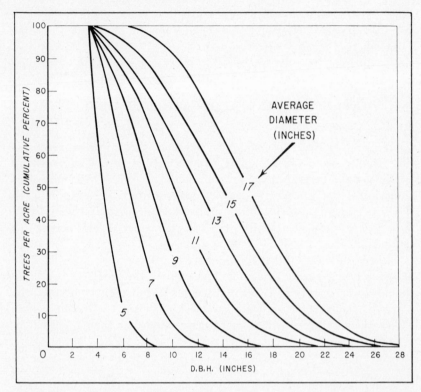

FIGURE 59.—Cumulative stand graph showing percentage of pines above the diameters given in seven well-stocked pure stands of different average diameter (Meyer 1942).

The yield of loblolly pine stands (85 to 100 percent normal) in the Coastal Plain between Chesapeake and Mobile Bays is shown in table 25 and the numbers of trees as related to age and site in figure 60.[80] For the unthinned stands in table 25 the average spacing distance varies from 8.4 feet between trees on the poorest site at 20 years to 20.8 feet between trees on the best site at 80 years. At 50 years, the range extends from 12.2 feet on site 60 to 18.8 feet on site

pines spaced 6 by 6 begin to compete in the second year, 10 by 10 in the fourth year, 14 by 14 in the sixth year, and 20 by 20 in the eighth year (Pennefather 1948).

[80] When numbers of trees are plotted over the reciprocal of age the trends are nearly linear—the curves only slightly concave upward. For saw-log stands on average sites the numbers per acre can readily be approximated from the straight line represented by the formula:

$$T = 3000R - 55$$

where T is the number of trees 0.5 inches and larger per acre, and R is the reciprocal of the average d.b.h. (Schumacher and Coile—unpublished).

120. The spacing on all site qualities less than 100 is related to average diameter (D) roughly according to rule of thumb D + 3 or 1.3D, whereas on the better sites it is only D + 2 or 1.1D. A constant multiplier may be preferred by foresters who think of spacing in terms of basal area.

EXPRESSION AND REGULATION OF DENSITY

Density of reproduction

When no attempts are made to control or localize it, pine regeneration usually occurs in irregular patches. It is then best gaged by estimating the percentage of area adequately covered. That involves observing the presence or absence of one or more living pines on each small unit-area in a series of samples. One milacre (0.001 acre) is an appropriate unit for seedlings; four milacres (0.004 acre), for saplings.[81]

Where there are 5,000 to 7,000 seedlings per acre there is little need for any accurate estimates. As soon as the seedlings are large enough to be readily visible rough ocular reconnaissance of the area covered is sufficiently accurate for most purposes. Adequate repeat observations to judge survival are more important than precision in a single survey.

Space requirements

What constitutes "room to grow and none to waste" in forest stands is ever changing as the trees become larger and less numerous. A method of allocating tree area according to d.b.h. in fully stocked stands has been developed by Chisman and Schumacher (1940). They found no perceptible effect of age or site index upon tree area ratios. According to their equation the ground area allocation of a single tree in terms of its diameter, d, is as follows:

$$Y = 0.0480 + 0.0668d + 0.0267d^2$$

where Y is in milacres and d in inches (column 6, table 24). The same formula may be applied to the summation of stand data of an understocked plot to derive its stocking in percentage of the normal.

In his study of space requirements, Stahelin (1949) used data from the southern pine yield tables (U.S.F.S. 1929) and the above

[81] The relation of milacre sampling to seedling stand per acre is reported in the section Results of Seeding in chapter 4, Natural Regeneration. A study in Arkansas showed the results from the two measures to be related essentially as follows: 1,000 seedlings restocked the land 40 percent; 3,000, 67 percent; 5,000, 80 percent; 7,000, 88 percent; and 9,000, 94 percent. The interrelationships of the two systems of measurement have been reported by Lynch and Schumacher (Jour. Forestry 39 (1):49-51. 1941).

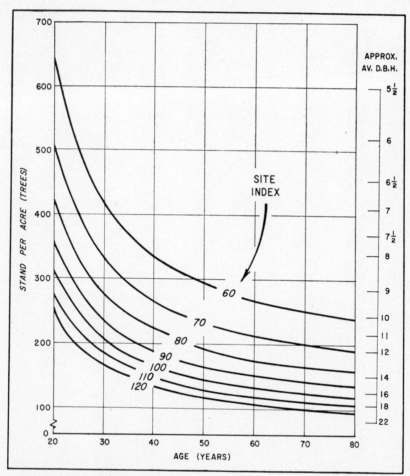

FIGURE 60.—The decrease in numbers of trees per acre and the corresponding increase in average diameter in a well-stocked stand as related to age for loblolly pine in the Coastal Plain. At a given age the trees on the better sites are fewer and larger, because, with more rapid growth, they encounter keen competition earlier and lose the smaller trees sooner (Schumacher and Coile—unpublished).

equation (Chisman-Schumacher 1940) deriving the following formula for basal area under full stocking:

$$\left.\begin{array}{c}\text{Basal area per acre} \\ \text{(square feet)}\end{array}\right\} = \left(\frac{d}{0.086936 + 0.07007d}\right)^2$$

In a study of 14-year-old plantations in Alabama (Ware and Stahelin 1946 and 1948) found the closest spacings producing the most wood, but loblolly was superior at somewhat wider spacing than slash pine.

TABLE 25.—*Yields of well-stocked stands of Coastal Plain loblolly pine (Schumacher and Coile 1954b)*[1]

Site index (feet)	Age (years)	Height of dominant stand	Basal area per acre[2]	Stand per acre[2]	Avg. d.b.h.	Entire stock[3]	Trees over 12.5 in. d.b.h.[4]	Trees over 6.5 in. d.b.h.	Pulpwood trees only[5]
		Feet	Sq. ft.	Trees	Inches	Cu. ft.	Bd. ft.	Cords	Cords
60	20	38	96	640	5.3	1,340		11	11
	30	49	114	415	7.1	2,010		20	20
	40	56	123	337	8.2	2,440	1,100	26	24
	50	60	128	292	9.0	2,740	2,300	30	26
	60	63	131	267	9.5	2,950	3,300	33	27
	70	65	133	250	9.9	3,110	4,300	35	27
	80	67	135	239	10.2	3,230	5,100	37	27
70	20	45	102	502	6.1	1,690		16	16
	30	57	121	331	8.2	2,540	1,200	27	25
	40	65	130	266	9.5	3,100	3,500	34	28
	50	70	136	233	10.3	3,460	6,000	39	27
	60	74	139	213	11.0	3,720	7,500	42	25
	70	76	141	199	11.4	3,910	9,700	45	24
	80	78	142	189	11.7	4,050	11,200	47	22
80	20	51	108	418	6.9	2,060		21	21
	30	66	129	275	9.3	3,140	3,300	35	29
	40	74	139	221	10.7	3,830	7,800	44	27
	50	80	145	193	11.7	4,280	11,900	49	23
	60	84	148	176	12.4	4,590	15,200	53	19
	70	87	150	164	12.9	4,820	17,900	56	17
	80	90	151	156	13.2	4,940	19,400	58	14
90	20	57	115	357	7.7	2,520	1,000	27	25
	30	74	138	234	10.4	3,840	7,100	43	29
	40	84	149	189	12.0	4,670	14,400	54	22
	50	90	155	165	13.1	5,210	20,200	61	16
	60	95	158	150	13.9	5,570	24,600	66	12
	70	98	159	140	14.5	5,840	28,000	69	10
	80	101	160	133	14.9	6,020	30,800	72	8
100	20	64	123	309	8.5	3,020	2,000	33	29
	30	82	149	205	11.5	4,640	12,600	53	25
	40	93	161	165	13.4	5,650	23,000	66	16
	50	100	166	144	14.6	6,280	30,900	74	10
	60	105	169	131	15.4	6,700	37,500	80	8
	70	109	170	122	16.0	7,000	40,900	84	6
	80	112	170	115	16.5	7,210	44,000	86	5
110	20	70	132	275	9.4	3,590	4,200	40	31
	30	90	162	184	12.7	5,570	20,300	65	20
	40	102	175	148	14.4	6,780	34,300	80	11
	50	110	180	129	16.0	7,520	44,100	90	7
	60	116	182	117	17.0	8,000	50,800	96	5
	70	120	183	108	17.6	8,340	55,800	100	4
	80	123	183	102	18.1	8,560	59,400	103	3
120	20	76	142	249	10.1	4,250	7,600	48	32
	30	98	177	167	14.0	6,690	30,600	79	14
	40	110	191	135	16.1	8,120	48,100	97	7
	50	120	196	117	17.5	8,970	59,700	107	4
	60	126	197	106	18.5	9,500	67,700	113	3
	70	131	198	98	19.3	9,870	71,000	119	2
	80	134	197	92	19.8	10,120	74,800	123	2

[1] By permission of the authors.
[3] Volume of entire main stem inside bark.
[5] Cords in trees between 6.5 and 12.5 inches d.b.h.

[2] Trees over 0.5 inch in d.b.h.
[4] Scribner log rule to 6-inch top d.i.b.

The recommendations for thinning young stands were conservative. It was reported that only with a spacing at least as close as 8 by 8 feet can loblolly pine with good survival properly utilize the soil 12 years after planting. To be equally good a survival of 90 percent would have to be attained in a plantation spaced 10 by 10 feet. It was concluded that the pines should be spaced 8 by 8, or, with no market for thinning, possibly 9 by 9, not wider.[82] Wider spacings were inferior because the value of speed in reaching saw-log size was offset by the low quality of lumber produced. An excessively large knotty core is formed in the butt log of widely spaced plantation trees (table 26).[83]

TABLE 26.—*Effects of plantation density on development of loblolly pine during 14 years in Alabama (Stahelin 1948a and b)*

Spacing	Avg. d.b.h.	Stand per acre	Stocking[1]	Knot surface[2]	Trees cankered[3]	Current annual increment	Wood to 2-inch top
Feet	*Inches*	*Trees*	*Percent*	*Sq. In.*	*Percent*	*Inches*	*Cords*
4 x 4..........	3.7	1,904	140	1.3	7	0.11	30.2
6 x 6..........	5.0	982	117	1.6	9	.30	30.9
8 x 8..........	6.1	566	93	12.1	11	.33	26.4
10 x 10........	6.3	418	72	7.5	10	.30	19.7
12 x 12........	7.7	260	62	15.1	16	.52	17.9
16 x 16........	8.7	154	45	20.3	12	.46	13.4

[1] In percent of (Reineke 1933) S.D.I. of 275 equal to full or equilibrium stocking of 100 percent.
[2] Cross section of all live branches, all sound dead branches, and stubs or open branch scars over $1\frac{1}{2}$ inches in diameter on the surface of the first 16-foot length of crop trees only.
[3] *Cronartium fusiforme* (A. & K.) Hedge. and Hunt.

Rules of thumb for desirable spacing

Inasmuch as many tall trees of intermediate crown development and retarded diameter growth are capable of good response to thinning, a rule of thumb based on diameters alone fails to provide them with all the space they can readily utilize. For this reason it has been proposed that height rather than diameter should be used as

[82] In understocked southern forests ''a large amount of the yearly production of dry matter is diverted to the ground flora.'' (Stahelin 1948a).

[83] To express stand density Deetlefs (1953) utilized Schumacher's approach to the problem after segregating three elements of a forest stand: (1) Dominant and codominant pines, (2) intermediate and overtopped pines and, (3) understory hardwoods. He found that the sum of the areas in milacres occupied by each of these groups expressed the density of a given plot in terms of average density for all plots in the study. His formula for density (D) is as follows:

$$D = 0.4170N + 0.1161\ n_p + 0.1161\ n_h + 4.7934\ B + 2.8620\ b_p + 2.8620 b_h$$

where the symbols designate the following stand elements: Number of dominant and codominant pines N; and their basal area B; number of intermediate and overtopped pines n_p, and their basal area b_p; and the number of hardwoods in the understory n_h, and their basal area b_h.

a guide to correct spacing.[83a] Theoretically preferable, this idea has been seldom utilized because heights are more difficult to estimate ocularly than are breast-high diameters. Where, as in the unthinned stands of table 25, the average spacing of trees at 50 years varies from 12 feet on site 60 to 19 feet on site 120, it is equal to 21 percent of dominant height on the poor site or 16 percent of that height on the good site. On sites of intermediate quality the spacing is 18 or 19 percent of the height of dominant trees.

Simple guides for spacing pines in relation to their diameters were first publicized for the South by Mitchell (1943, 1952) and critically compared by Averell (1945). The principal rules are illustrated in table 27. The most popular one among farmers in the Deep South specifies that the distance between trees in feet should approximate the average d.b.h. plus 6. For example a 10-inch and a 16-inch tree should stand 19 feet apart. It is best applied to crop trees only in the sapling and small-pole stages rather than to smaller or larger trees. It commonly brings the basal area into the range from 88 to 107 square feet per acre, but for trees larger than 11 inches in d.b.h. the D + 6 rule does not provide enough space; it may permit basal area to approach 120 square feet per acre. It permits rapid, not high-quality, growth in saplings. The D + 6 rule appears to be a good rule for pulpwood operations, but the 1.75 D rule brings more consistently good results over a wide range of sizes. The 1.75 D rule approximates 77 square feet of basal area.

TABLE 27.—*Rules of thumb as rough approximations of space requirements in relation to size of pine trees*

	Spacing for—				
	Average d.b.h. (D) in inches				
	4	6	8	10	12
Guide to spacing before and after thinning operations	Average height in feet[1]				
	30	45	57	68	75
	Feet	Feet	Feet	Feet	Feet
Before thinning:					
A full stand, 1.08 (D + 1.25) or roughly D + 2...............	6	8	10	12	14
The dominant and codominant portion, D + 4......................	8	10	12	14	16
After thinning:					
A useful common rule, D + 6.........	10	12	14	16	18
A good rough rule, 1.75 D...........	7	10½	14	17½	21

[1] In a full stand the equivalent square spacing amounts to about 1/5 of tree height, whereas after thinning it should be roughly 1/4 of tree height.

[83a] Wilson, F. G. 1946. Numerical expression of stocking in terms of height. Jour. Forestry 44:758-761.

The simplicity of additive rules[84] makes them popular, however. If they are retained, smaller constants for young stands are advisable wherever limby trees are undesirable. Tyler (1952) suggests varying the rule constant as follows:

D.b.h. class (inches)	Additive rule constant
4-5	3
5-7	4
7-9	6
9-11	8

The diameter growth of dominant loblolly pines falls off appreciably where trees are spaced at D plus a constant less than 4 (Cummings 1952b):

Additive rule constant	Years per radial inch of wood (rings)	Time required to grow 1 inch in d.b.h., o.b. (years)
6	3.7	2.8
5	3.6	2.7
4	4.0	3.0
3	4.9	3.7
2	6.6	5.0
1	7.8	5.9

GROWING STOCKS AND INCREMENT

Rates of growth of loblolly pine timber are gaged in three principal ways: (1) Diameter or height growth of trees using linear units, (2) basal area increment in square feet, and (3) volume growth in cubic or board measure. This section reports observations on growth in these terms as it is related to different independent variables. Among these the primary ones are the crown development of individual trees, and site, age, and density of timber stands. Such information leads to a consideration of how gross growth per acre may be reduced by mortality, how age is related to culmination in net growth, and similar implications for management of the timber.

Growth in diameter, height, and basal area

The usual decrease in loblolly pine diameter growth with age as noted by Chapman (1905) in unmanaged forest was as follows:

Period (years)	Periodic diameter growth (inches)
20-30	3.9
30-40	3.3
40-50	2.6
50-60	2.2
60-70	1.8
70-80	1.6

[84] Several of these rules are illustrated in their relation to numbers of trees per acre and to recommended thinning practice in figure 77,A, chapter 7, Management of Immature Timber.

In managed stands some of this deceleration can be avoided by providing adequate growing space for crop trees.

During the second 5 years after planting loblolly pines 8 by 8 feet near Woodworth, La., growth in diameter was related to crown length as follows (Mann 1954a):

Live crown ratio (percent)	Annual diameter growth (inches)
30	0.12
35	.18
40	.21
45	.23
50	.25
55	.27
60	.31

This rate of growth is 50 to 60 percent of the amount to be expected at a later stage under good management in Georgia. There the diameter growth of loblolly pine was observed to increase in direct proportion to its crown length according to this equation (Johstono 1954):

$$\text{Five-year diameter growth} = 0.3 + 0.04857 \ (CR\text{-}10)$$

where CR is live crown ratio as a percentage of total height. As related to a wide range in residual basal area in thinned plantations, Mann (1954a) found the diameter growth of the 100 largest trees per acre varied over a narrow range as follows:

Basal area left after thinning (square feet)	Yearly diameter growth of 100 largest pines (inches)
50	0.24
70	.22
90	.21
110	.19
130	.17

Diameter growth of loblolly pine over extensive areas, regardless of management, usually follows a downward trend with increased size of trees. A survey sample of 455 loblolly pines of all crown classes in the proportions in which they were found on the Coastal Plain of Georgia in 1952 showed a current average diameter growth of 3.3 inches in 10 years to be distributed by tree size classes as follows (Cruikshank 1952e):

Starting d.b.h. (inches)	Ten-year growth of wood and bark (inches)	Starting d.b.h. (inches)	Ten-year growth of wood and bark (inches)
6	3.7	14	2.9
8	4.1	16	2.4
10	4.3	18	2.4
12	3.9	20+	1.9

After saw-log size is attained, such a decline in diameter growth with increasing age and size of trees applies generally to under-stocked and unmanaged forests as a whole.

Over restricted areas of forest, particularly in well-stocked even-aged unmanaged stands, relatively slow diameter growth appears at both ends of the diameter range. The small trees have difficulty in maintaining their growth rate as the dominant ones close in and around them. The large ones also, though free from competition and continuing their growth in volume of wood, show less diameter increase because of the larger bole area over which the new wood is distributed. Thus Paul (1931a) found diameter growth of loblolly pine increasing up to the 18-inch diameter class as follows:

D.b.h. (inches)	Time required to grow 1 inch (years)	D.b.h. (inches)	Time required to grow 1 inch (years)
6	9	14	5
8	8	18	4
10	7	22	5
12	6	26	6

Maximum diameter growth was attained by medium-size dominant trees. Location of the peak in diameter growth, however, varies with the age and structure of different even-aged stands.

Height growth shows less response to stand density, but is so closely related to soil differences that dominant height at 50 years is used as an index of site quality. The distribution of loblolly pine sites is associated with topography throughout its range much as it is in North Carolina (Cruikshank 1940d and 1940e):

	Site distribution where height in feet at 50 years is—		
	Over 90 (percent)	70-80 (percent)	Under 60 (percent)
Coastal Plain:			
Rolling uplands	2	82	16
Level lowlands	6	75	19
Bays, ponds, swamps	3	81	16
River bottom lands	21	74	5
Average	6	77	17
Piedmont, rolling uplands	5	85	10

In observing the early development of loblolly pine planted in South Africa as a "medium fast growing conifer," Craib (1939) found both diameter and height related to age and site (table 28). The crown ratios in the last section are reduced to represent the actively functioning length of the living crowns—the portion needed to maintain the growth shown. This rapid growth, 31 feet at 10 years on site 90 in South Africa, is more than matched by one stand,

TABLE 28.—*Early development of loblolly pine in relation to age and site in South African plantations (adapted from Craib 1939)*

D.B.H. OF DOMINANTS

			Age		
Site index	6 years	8 years	10 years	12 years	14 years
	Inches	Inches	Inches	Inches	Inches
70.............	1.8	3.1	4.6	5.9	7.0
80.............	2.4	4.0	5.6	6.8	8.0
90.............	3.1	4.9	6.5	7.7	8.8
100.............	3.8	5.6	7.2	8.4	9.5
110.............	4.4	6.3	7.9	9.1	10.1
120.............	5.1	7.0	8.5	9.7	10.6

TOTAL HEIGHT

	Feet	Feet	Feet	Feet	Feet
70.............	16	20	24	28	31
80.............	18	23	28	32	36
90.............	21	26	31	36	40
100.............	23	29	35	40	45
110.............	26	32	38	44	49
120.............	28	35	42	48	54

FUNCTIONAL LENGTH[1]

	Percent	Percent	Percent	Percent	Percent
70.............	94	85	77	71	65
80.............	87	78	71	65	60
90.............	81	72	67	62	58
100.............	78	69	65	60	56
110.............	77	68	63	59	54
120.............	76	66	62	58	54

[1] Ratio of active crown to total height; does not include lowermost weak branches.

34 feet tall at 10 years on site 89 in an old field in east Texas, reported by Zon (1905).

After the first decade basal area is a useful measure of stand development. Increasingly evident is the fact that normal full stocking can be materially reduced with salutary effects on the growth of trees and with only relatively small sacrifices in per-acre growth. A heavy basal area of 154 square feet per acre probably can be reduced 30 to 50 percent without losing more than 10 or 15 percent of the possible growth. Where loblolly pine was planted in southern Illinois it was observed (Minckler and Deitschman 1953b) that stands thinned to 81 square feet made the same growth in basal area as did the unthinned plots with 132 square feet of basal area. From Crossett, Ark., Reynolds (1950a) has reported that apparently ideal stands have about 75 square feet of basal area, including all

trees 1 inch in d.b.h. and larger.   About 18 to 23 square feet of
this total are in trees less than 10 inches in diameter.   These are
rough approximations from many-aged stands.

Deetlefs (1954) found that for any fixed number of trees per
acre between 50 and 500, basal area growth per acre increases as
stocking in basal area decreases from 140 to 60 square feet per acre.
Only in stands of trees under saw-log size are high basal areas compatible with maximum per-acre growth.   When stocking in basal
area is fixed, growth in basal area per acre increases with each gain
in numbers of trees up to 350, but beyond that the growth in basal
area does not rise significantly where the number of trees is increased
up to 500 stems per acre.

Deetlefs' study also revealed the following relation between basal
area, increment, and age.   Between the ages of 28 and 34 years, total
basal area growth was greatest in stands periodically thinned to 80
square feet of basal area per acre.   Subsequently total basal area
growth in stands with 100 square feet of basal area exceeded that of
all other stockings.   Where stand density was held constant, current
5-year growth in basal area of loblolly pine crop trees increased with
site quality and decreased with age, indicating the need for thinning.   In a stand of 100 trees per acre averaging 12 inches in d.b.h.
(basal area per acre 79 square feet), the average tree grew about
0.15 square feet in basal area in 5 years.   This would apply to a stand
thinned to about 50 percent of its normal (or stand equilibrium)
volume.   In stands less than half stocked the increase in growth of
individual trees in Deelefs' study was offset by decrease in per-acre
growth.

Cubic volume growth and its culmination

Both the current and mean annual rates of growth, and the relation between them, are important in growing pulpwood.   Annual
growth in the first decade after cutting is clearly related to site
quality and residual basal area.[85]   There is evidence (fig. 61) that
the maximum rate of current growth in volume is reached with 60
square feet of basal area on sites of index 70, and with 70 square
feet on sites with index 80.

[85] Within the narrow limits of this 10-year period the age of stand (25 to 35
years) shows no measurable effect on the growth of timber, but a regression
analysis (McClay 1955b) produced the following equation in which each of the
independent variables was significant at the 1-percent level:

$$Y = 0.033259(BA)(SI) - 0.019459(BA)^2 - 3.429160$$

Where Y is periodic annual growth per acre in cubic feet inside bark for a 9-year
period, BA is residual basal area per acre in square feet, and SI is site index
based on average height of crop trees at 50 years of age.

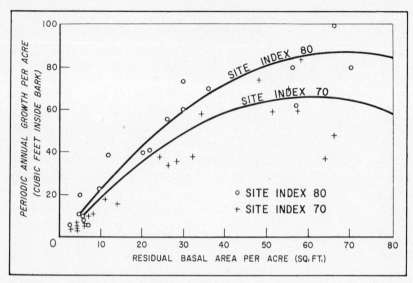

FIGURE 61.—Effect of site and residual density on annual growth for a 9-year period after cutting in even-aged loblolly pine pulpwood stands (McClay 1955b).

In the long run, however, timber yields can be maximized only where the rotation (average age of crop trees in final harvests) is selected on the basis of the age at which growth in volume or weight tends to culminate. According to the normal yield tables for southern pines (table 79) this age is about 40 years for the cubic-foot growth of loblolly pine. Maximum accretion in weight would be somewhat later. The culmination comes earlier on the better sites (fig. 58, *A*) and later where stands were poorly stocked in early life (fig. 58, *B*). This tendency for site quality to hasten culmination of growth appeared in an early study by Cope (1923a), which also showed that an additional 25 years might be needed for growth in board feet to reach its maximum (table 29). The culmination of board-foot growth may occur only 10 to 15 years later according to more recent studies by Davis (1954) (fig. 62). He has used the trend in periodic annual increment to locate a desirable rotation age. In figure 62 this is indicated by the intersection of the broken lines with the other curves. Obviously short rotations are more feasible on the sites of better quality and where no attempt is made to produce saw logs.

The continued decline of the curves of mean annual board-foot growth (fig. 62) beyond 50 years is not solely due to slower growth. Often it is largely caused by decadence—mortality (or harvest) of the

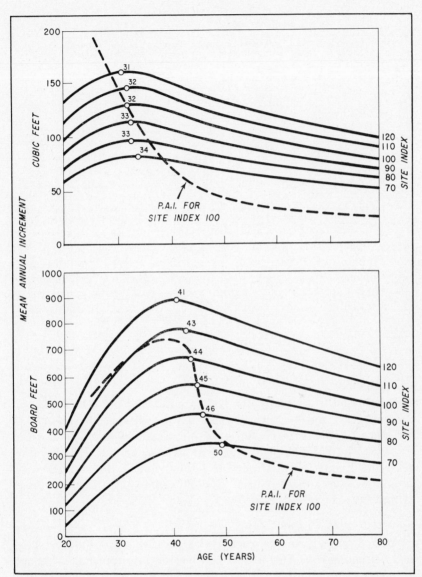

FIGURE 62.—Growth of loblolly pine in even-aged stands, including stumps and tops, but not bark, from trees 3.6 inches and larger in d.b.h. Solid lines are mean annual increments, with peaks at ages shown on the curves; dash lines are periodic annual increments for sites of index 100 (after Meyer 1942 as reported in "American Forest Management" by K. P. Davis 1954. By permission McGraw-Hill Book Co.).

TABLE 29.—*Average annual growth of loblolly pine on good, medium, and poor sites in unmanaged stands*[1]

Age (years)	Height at 50 years—site index (feet)					
	90	80	70	90	80	70
	Cubic feet	Cubic feet	Cubic feet	Board feet	Board feet	Board feet
20.........	148	120	86	134	33	...
25.........	150	125	97	255	148	60
30.........	150	126	100	374	244	143
35.........	148	126	102	490	338	223
40.........	148	125	101	595	426	285
45.........	147	124	101	673	490	333
50.........	145	123	98	711	534	368
55.........	139	118	94	706	540	382
60.........	131	111	87	676	520	383

[1] Italic growth figures indicate culmination ages. Basis: a study on the eastern shore of Maryland. Cubic-foot growth is based on stemwood with bark on trees 3 inches d.b.h. and larger. Board-foot growth is for trees 8 inches d.b.h. and larger (adapted from Cope 1923a, as revised in 1925).

larger "poor risk" trees in pine forests—a loss that is not always offset promptly by "ingrowth" of additional trees. What this mortality amounts to in numbers of trees 2 inches d.b.h. and larger on sites 70 and 80 is indicated roughly by normal yield tables as follows:

Age (years)	Mortality per decade (percent)
20	67
30	40
40	34
50	25
60	17

This holds quite generally for both natural and old-field stands on the gulf coast and northward where it was confirmed by a study of 111 plots on the Eastern Shore of Maryland (Schnur 1932). Observations in dense old-field stands at Urania, La., showed the average annual cordwood mortality to be 0.4 cord at the start between 20 and 25 years, 0.5 cord from 26 to 30 years, and 0.6 cord between 31 and 50 years (Bull 1950a).

Volume growth in board feet

Actual growth varies widely with location, site quality, stand composition, degree of depletion, and level of management. Although estimates that ignore these conditions have no precise meaning, a few samples can show the usual range in loblolly pine growth.

Old-field stands and volunteer second growth having 50 to 100 trees per acre, and having accumulated 5,000 board feet of stock by 1935 in Ashley County, Arkansas, were found to be growing 300 board feet (6 percent) annually. Some stands of comparable volume, later placed under all-aged management in that part of the upper

Coastal Plain (Crossett Experimental Forest), are now producing up to nearly twice as much—600 board feet (12 percent). Similar managed stands in Jones County of central Georgia (Hitchiti Experimental Forest) do likewise. Loblolly pine growing on the bottom lands of Washington County in West Florida, after accumulating a stock of 30,000 board feet, was found to be growing 900 board feet (or 3 percent) annually (Ziegler 1931).

Understocked stands and short rotations are not suitable for volume production in growing sawtimber, but some logs can be had earlier in understocked than in full stands. To grow logs of a size economical to mill, and to obtain high-grade lumber without artificial pruning, however, rotations of 50 or 60 years are needed. Then the current growth obtainable at rotation age corresponds closely with the degree of stocking in the stands.

Discriminate cutting first started on half-grown forests can promote satisfactory current yields without reference to any predetermined rotation age. This has been well demonstrated on the Crossett Experimental Forest. Starting with a forest wherein nearly half of the space formerly occupied by pine had been taken over by inferior hardwoods, the per-acre volume growth of small pines was increased about 30 percent in 9 years and the growth of saw-log-sized trees was increased nearly 70 percent (Reynolds 1947b). Over a period of 10 years 37 percent of the original pine timber volume of 4,807 board feet per acre on one 1,000-acre tract was removed. During the 10 years, growth restored an equivalent amount of pine plus an additional 30 percent of the original stock.

Two smaller compartments (40 acres each)—one depleted and the other fairly well stocked—in the same forest have been partly cutover annually to remove logs, pulpwood, fuel, and chemical wood, beginning in 1937. Growth in board feet, exceeding the cut in the first 14 years, increased the volume of growing stocks (table 30). In two of four 5-year periods (table 31) growth of the larger trees suffered somewhat from adverse climatic conditions, but the loss was either salvaged or offset by ingrowth of young trees.

Unless a stand is understocked it is advisable to plan for some cutting when it approaches 20 or 30 years of age. The purpose is to salvage expected mortality, and during the next 10 to 20 years to stimulate growth and concentrate it on selected trees. Such cutting also serves to improve the composition and commercial quality of reserved stocks. Improvement cutting that removes low-grade limby trees and overtopped short-crowned trees may incidentally better the

TABLE 30.—*Changes in pine stand, stock, and timber volumes per acre under annual cutting on farm forestry forties at Crossett, Ark. (Reynolds 1953b)*

Area and item	Stems over 3.5 in. d.b.h.			Stems over 11.5 in. d.b.h.	
	Trees	Basal area	Volume (inside bark)	Doyle volume	Int. ¼-inch volume
	Number	Sq. ft.	Cu. ft.	Bd. ft.	Bd. ft.
Good forty:					
Original, 1937...	132	66	1,794	5,074	5,978
14-year cut.....	52	32	900	2,597	3,059
14-year growth..	2	33	1,063	5,818	6,853
Stand in 1951...	82	67	1,957	8,295	9,772
Poor forty:					
Original, 1937...	85	38	980	2,341	2,757
14-year cut.....	32	24	700	1,866	2,199
14-year growth..	77	43	1,234	4,108	4,841
Stand in 1951...	130	57	1,514	4,583	5,399

average genetic quality of the remaining stand. Some of the clear-stemmed subdominant stems may well be left, however. Remarkable response from formerly oppressed trees often seems to refute the theory of their possible genetic inferiority. Such pines released at Crossett, Ark., tripled their rate of diameter growth and promptly started to grow about 2 cubic feet of wood or nearly 14 board feet annually (Reynolds 1952b).

Intermediate yields

When a forest is kept continuously stocked with sufficient loblolly pine trees to make full use of the capacity of the soil to produce wood, a series of intermediate harvests must be made to retrieve the maximum amount of merchantable timber grown in a rotation period. When the first thinning is made at 20 years, removing about 10 cords (or half the pulpwood volume) from old-field stands, enough of the best trees can usually be left to provide at least one more profitable pulpwood cutting before the harvest for saw logs or better products.

The current annual volume growth after thinning a loblolly pine plantation at Woodworth, La., was related to the reserved stand as follows (Mann 1954a):

Basal area per acre (square feet)	Yearly volume growth (cords)
70..........................	1.67
80..........................	1.86
90..........................	1.94
100.........................	2.01
110.........................	2.08
120.........................	2.15

TABLE 31.—*Periodic net annual growth per acre of pine on farm forestry forties at Crossett, Ark. (Reynolds 1953b)*[1]

Area and period	Cubic volume (inside bark)		Board-foot volume		
	Quantity	Growth rate	Doyle scale	Int. $\frac{1}{4}$-inch scale	Growth rate
	Cu. ft.	Percent	Bd. ft.	Bd. ft.	Percent
Good forty:					
1937-41........	81	4.5	244	287	4.8
1942-46........	52	2.8	372	439	6.5
1947-51........	98	5.6	596	702	9.2
1952-56........	50	2.5	249	293	3.0
Poor forty:					
1937-41........	86	8.8	231	272	9.8
1942-46........	57	4.7	251	295	8.0
1947-51........	118	10.0	391	461	10.6
1952-56........	75	5.0	264	310	5.7

[1] The relatively low level of growth in the second period resulted from damage suffered from a severe ice storm in 1944. Growth was again reduced in the fourth period by the drought of 1952-55. All pines 3.6 inches in d.b.h. and larger are included.

On an abandoned creek bottom that had been a cornfield, with a site index of 105 for pine, a 21-year-old stand of loblolly pine was lightly thinned in 1915 and again at 5- to 10-year intervals thereafter (Castor plots, Urania, La.). At age 56 there were 124 rough cords of pulpwood per acre or 43,500 board feet of sawtimber per acre (Mann 1951c). At age 62 the growth was as follows (Moyle 1956):

Treatment	Basal area left after thinning in 1915 (square feet)	Mean annual increment	
		Pulpwood (standard cords)	Sawtimber (board feet)[1]
Not thinned at all........	160	1.53	561
Lightly thinned..........	130	2.21	749
Heavily thinned..........	110	2.10	680

[1] International $\frac{1}{4}$-inch rule.

Many trees contained 5 or 6 merchantable logs each and the recent periodic annual growth was high—over 1,000 board feet, none of which was derived from ingrowth. Less than 23 percent of the logs were of grade No. 1, but the volume growth shows what can be produced from pure dense stands on unusually high-quality land.

When loblolly pine is planted over wider areas, which inevitably include some less fertile land, the average stocking and growth after thinning are necessarily lower. Young (1950) reported that the stand on some 1,200 acres in the vicinity of Bogalusa, La., which were planted with loblolly pine wild seedlings in 1922-23 was thinned at 18 years of age yielding 2.7 cords per acre. Eight years later the stock was 19.8 cords per acre. Thus the yield was 22.5 cords in 26 years, or 0.87 cord per acre annually.

Unthinned natural stands vary so much in density that the annual pulpwood growth over a 5-year period commonly ranges from 0.1 to 2.9 cords per acre while on thinned areas the usual yearly growth is between 1 and 2 cords (Bull 1936).

Working in the Coastal Plain of Virginia and North Carolina, MacKinney (1933) studied rates of loblolly pine growth following partial cutting for saw logs in nine stands using a flexible 10-inch diameter limit. The growth in basal area of the released trees was observed to average 130 percent greater in the 10 years following release than the growth which, according to estimates, the trees would have put on in that period had they not been released.[86]

Total yields

The total maximum yield per acre of loblolly pine from protected, but otherwise unmanaged, stands as variously estimated from 40,000 to 75,000 board feet at 50 to 80 years (Sterrett 1914, Ashe 1915, Cope 1923a, U.S.F.S. 1929) is solely of waning academic interest for several reasons. These maximum volumes, attainable only on certain individual acres of the best quality sites, are not possible over extensive tracts. Nor are they desirable because they involve slow growth, heavy loss from mortality, and long rotations without intermediate yields.

It is more realistic to utilize the data in table 25, which indicate, for example, that on site 80 at 50 years a yield of about 11,900 board feet, or 4,280 cubic feet of timber is a reasonable expectation from stands stocked well above most forests under present-day management (plate 7). As management experience accumulates, present estimates of volumes obtainable from intermediate cutting can be made more precise.

Loblolly pine yields well all the way from the Eastern Shore of Maryland to Texas, particularly where the growing season is long and rainfall is high (Chapman 1921). This indicates up to a 25 percent possible advantage for the Deep South, but in unusually dry periods such as the early nineteen fifties in east Texas, timber

[86] The response of individual trees was related to their characteristics in MacKinney's regression equation as follows: Basal area (square feet) of wood and bark 10 years after release equals 0.8681 basal area outside bark at time of release + 0.2914 crown length ratio + 0.0065 crown width (feet) + 1.6332 basal-area growth in prior 5 years +0.0017 total height − 0.1212. A simpler approximation of tree basal area o.b. expected 10 years after release may be computed from the following expression: 1.0332 basal area (o.b.) at time of release + 0.3116 crown ratio + 0.0088 crown width − 0.0602.

PLATE 7.—An even-aged 60-year-old stand of loblolly pine containing about 25,000 board feet per acre, on a site of index 90, Crossett, Ark. (courtesy R. R. Reynolds, U.S.F.S.).

growth may be restricted by droughts and mortality may offset up to one-third of the growth that does occur (Stephenson 1956). Nevertheless the mid-Atlantic data in table 25 may be widely applicable.

ESTIMATING RAW MATERIALS

The use of local forest lands and timber supplies available through ownership or purchase are a vital concern for each unit of the wood-using industry. Growth and drain on these supplies creates a recurrent need to estimate them. How much is actually or potentially usable today? And for tomorrow how much will be added by growth, lost in mortality, or recognized as waste that must be sacrificed or might be salvaged? Such questions must be resolved separately for each situation.[87]

Present supplies

To estimate merchantable trees, logs, and pulpwood bolts readily requires certain information on cutting practice and on the inter-relationships of wood weight and volume in cubic or board feet. Highly useful converting factors are available for loblolly pine by diameter classes to translate the contents of logs or trees from one common scale or unit of measure to another (Reynolds 1937a, Minor 1953c, U.S.F.S. 1951, Mesavage 1947a).

Pulpwood sticks are now commonly cut 5 feet, 3 inches long from pines up to a 4-inch top. Working in the southern Piedmont Mc-Clay (1952) found the following numbers in trees of average height:

D.b.h. (inches)	$5\frac{1}{4}$-foot bolts per tree (number)
8	6
9	7
10	7
11	8
12	9
13	9
14	10

Working with $5\frac{1}{4}$-foot bolts of loblolly pine pulpwood in southern Virginia, Schumacher (1946a) derived the following useful formulas:

$C = 0.00195\ N + 0.00932V$ wherein symbols designate —

$$C = \text{stacked volume (cu. ft.)}$$

$$V = \frac{C - 0.2502N}{1.1929V}$$

$V = \text{solid wood (cu. ft.)}$

$D = \text{av. bolt diameter (inches)}$

[87] This book makes no pretense of covering standard methods of cruising timber described in texts on forest mensuration. Instead it presents numerical or graphic aids based specifically on, or useful for, work with loblolly pine. Many of these are in chapter 10 Properties and Uses, or in the tables of this chapter; others appear in the appendix.

$$U = 0.00195N + 0.00932V \qquad N = \text{no. bolts per cord}$$
$$= 0.00195 + 0.000267D^2 \qquad N' = \text{av. no. bolts per sq. ft.}$$
$$\text{of stack face}$$

$$U = \text{volume in stacked cords } (C \div 128)$$

$$\frac{V}{C} = 0.838 - 0.04N' \qquad \frac{V}{C} = \text{percentage of solid}$$
$$\text{wood in stack}$$

Diameters of the 5¼-foot loblolly pine bolts are related to cords as follows:

D	U	N
4	0.0062	161.0
6	.0116	86.5
8	.0190	52.5
10	.0288	34.7
12	.0404	24.8
14	.0543	18.4
16	.0703	14.2
18	.0884	11.3

A cord of freshly piled round, smooth, 8-inch, unpeeled loblolly pine wood averages 64.1 percent solid wood, 19.2 percent bark, and 16.7 percent air space (MacKinney and Chaiken 1956). On this basis solid wood is overestimated if the sticks are smaller or underestimated if they are larger. For a mixture of stick sizes a better determination of volume can be had by ascertaining the average number of bolts per square foot of side-face area and referring to figure 63. The volumes shown are for 128-cubic-foot cords and 160-cubic-foot units.

If only number and average size of trees to be harvested for pulpwood are available, the volumes and weights (appendix, table 77) may be helpful in estimating the yield. Roughly, bark constitutes 14 to 20 percent of the volume and only 10 or 12 percent of the weight, and there are 30 to 31 cubic feet in a ton of green wood with bark.

Measurement of pulpwood on the basis of solid volume or weight, rather than in cords or other units of stacked wood, is equitable. This suggestion (Cuno 1939) has been rapidly gaining in favor during recent years in the procurement of green wood for pulpmills. Human errors in measuring are largely eliminated when wood is sold by weight. Buying by weight puts a premium on the prompt movement of good fresh wood and discourages delivery of both poorly

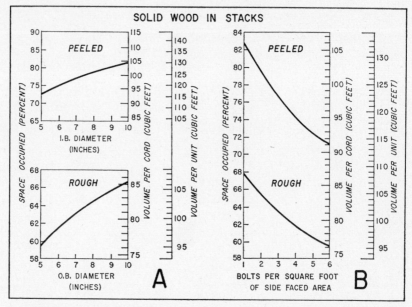

FIGURE 63.—Converting factors for loblolly pine pulpwood showing the percentage of stacked space occupied by solid wood, exclusive of bark, in piles (*A*) having different average bolt diameters, and (*B*) containing different numbers of bolts per square foot of side-face area (MacKinney and Chaiken 1956).

trimmed and old wood (Jeffords 1956, Taras 1956). Prices can logically vary by species groups, but for a given kind of wood, buying by weight can serve as an interim method of recognizing quality, at least until some grade standards have been adopted (see section on Defects and Grades in chapter 10, Properties and Uses).

According to a recent survey of wood density from loblolly pines in Mississippi (Mitchell and Wheeler 1959) the dry weight of the wood was related to age as follows:

| Age (years) | Specific gravity— | | Weight per cubic foot (pounds) |
	of cores at breast height	of merchantable tree volume	
10	0.44	0.43	27
20	.48	.45	28
30	.51	.47	29
40	.53	.48	30
50	.55	.48	30

Except for the rapid early growth of sapling trees and of some old-field stands, age may be safely disregarded in these estimates and tree specific gravity (*Y*) computed from breast-high core specific gravity (*X*) by formula (Wahlgren and Fassnacht 1959):

$$Y = 0.69798 - \frac{0.116701}{X}$$

Where pulpwood has been harvested and the average size and weight of bolts are known, the volume of wood per ton may be estimated by formula (Miller 1941).[88]

A study of 200,000 acres of loblolly pine forest made by Barron and Osborn for one large company furnished the volume-weight ratios and weight tables (appendix, tables 76 and 77) useful in cruising standing timber by weight. It also furnished the following averages with 95 percent confidence limits attached:

Volume of green wood per 100 pounds of wood and bark is 1.525 ± 0.0206 cu. ft.

Weight of green wood and bark per cu. ft. of wood is 65.6 ± 0.88 lbs.

Volume of green wood per 100 pounds of green wood is 1.708 ± 0.0204 cu. ft.

Weight of green wood per cubic foot is 58.6 ± 0.84 pounds.

The percentage of bark weight to the weight of green wood and bark was found to be $10.79 - 0.0143D^2$ for wet or medium sites, and $9.41 - 0.0143D^2$ for dry sites. The confidence limits on these percentages vary with diameter from ± 0.84 for 5-inch trees to ± 1.58 for 20-inch trees.

If only the number and size of weathered stumps of loblolly pines cut in trespass are known, the breast-high diameters can be approximated by timber cruisers from the following relationships:

Stump d.i.b. (inches)	Piedmont average d.b.h. (inches)	Southwide average d.b.h. (inches)
4	4.6	3.7
6	6.6	5.6
8	8.4	7.6
10	10.4	9.6
12	12.3	11.5
14	14.2	13.4
16	16.1	15.6
18	17.9	17.6
20	19.5	19.8
22	20.9	21.9

Piedmont data (Fields 1947); Southwide data (U.S.F.S. 1929); stumps average 1 foot high.

[88] Yt equals $5.51 D + 0.46 NT - 17.14$, wherein Yt is cubic feet in a ton of green wood with bark, D is average diameter of bolts in inches, and NT is the number of 5.3-foot bolts in a ton. (If the bolts are 4 feet long the coefficient of NT would be 0.35.) Or if the number of 5.3-foot bolts per cord (Nc) is known, the number of cubic feet of solid wood in a cord of green unbarked bolts (Yc) equals $18.27 + 0.52 Nc - 68.18$. (If the bolts are 4 feet long the coefficient of Nc becomes 0.39.) In this study 70 percent of the actual values were within ± 1.1 cu.ft. of the estimated values of Yt, or ± 2.9 cu.ft. of the Yc estimates.

If the bark still adheres and the stumps are of various heights, the figures given by McCormack (1953) are useful in such estimates.

Future supplies

Time and resources available for reconnaissance influence the methods generally used in the appraisal of forests. The accuracy with which the present condition can be determined and future yield can be forecast specifically for a loblolly pine forest is no exception. It depends on the intensity of the chosen inventory. A few loblolly pine data are given here to implement, in part, the following three intensities in such examinations: (1) Casual and superficial inspections, (2) systematic ground cruising to predict volume growth, and (3) extensive aerial surveying to determine composition and density of stands.

Superficial inspections roughly gage stocking and growth by number, size, and appearance of trees. Loblolly pine bark changes in color and character as growth decelerates with advancing age and maturity of trees:

Progressive changes in appearance of loblolly pine bark[1]

Age (years)	Color	Character
0-10	Light to dark brown	Smooth, continuous, and papery to touch
10-20	Dark ridges with orange cleavage	Vertical ridges appear between papery clefts
20-30	Black with orange fissures turning gray and fading into faint lines	Ridges gradually become more prominent
30-40	Steel gray as a whole	As cross breaks develop the ridges become less prominent
40-50	Gray reverting to orange	Bark loses roughness as ridges disappear leaving a pattern of small blocks
After 50	Orange again changing into light gray	Blocks gradually become large plates; whole surface is smoother on slow-growing trees.

[1] Based on trees free from suppression or release, and adapted from U.S.F.S. descriptions made near Rome, Ga. (Hubbard 1955).

Crown-length ratios and current rates of diameter growth, also, are useful in estimating vigor classes in forest-grown trees.

Current growth can be readily inspected on cores taken with an increment hammer or measured over longer periods with an increment borer. Radial growth measurement or ring counts can be used as a base to quickly approximate volume growth in cords or percentage (table 32) over short periods wherein both additions from ingrowth or loss from mortality are disregarded.

TABLE 32.—*Data for short-cut volume growth estimates of loblolly pine trees from increases in diameter alone*

EFFECT ON PERIODIC GROWTH OF SPECIFIED RADIAL INCREASES (MINOR 1952)

(rough cords)[1]

D.b.h. (inches)	Radial growth (inches)									
	0.2	0.4	0.6	0.8	1.0	1.2	1.4	1.6	1.8	2.0
5	0.01	0.02	0.03	0.04	0.05	0.06	0.08	0.09	0.11	0.12
6	.01	.02	.03	.05	.06	.07	.09	.10	.12	.14
7	.01	.02	.04	.05	.07	.08	.10	.11	.13	.15
8	.01	.03	.04	.06	.08	.10	.11	.13	.15	.17
9	.02	.03	.05	.07	.09	.10	.12	.14	.16	.19
10	.02	.04	.05	.07	.09	.11	.13	.17	.18	.21
11	.02	.04	.06	.08	.10	.12	.15	.17	.20	.22
12	.02	.04	.07	.09	.11	.14	.16	.19	.21	.23

EFFECT ON ANNUAL GROWTH PERCENT WHEN THE NEXT TWO INCHES OF DIAMETER ARE ADDED AT THE RATE INDICATED[2]

(percent)

D.b.h. (inches)	Logs per tree	Growth per inch (rings)							
		3	4	5	6	8	10	12	14
10	1	48	36	29	24	18	14	12	10
12	1½	37	28	22	18	14	11	9	8
14	2	25	19	15	12	9	7	6	5
16	2½	21	16	13	11	8	6	5	(3)
18	3	16	12	10	8	6	5	(3)	
20	3½	14	11	9	7	5	(3)		
22	4	9	7	5	5	(3)			
24	4	9	6	5	(3)				
26	4	7	5	(3)					

[1] Figures based on trees of a form typical of average sites.
[2] Mississippi Forest Commission, Tech. Note 5, 1956. If the possibility of accelerated growth after cutting be ignored, it may be deduced from these data that in order to avoid reserving trees now growing less than 5 percent, only trees larger than $27 - 1.27$ (R-3) inches should be cut where R is the number of rings per inch.
[3] Less than 5 percent.

To ignore bark thickness introduces error in growth studies. Bark thickness at breast height is closely associated with diameter and growth rate, and varies slightly with height. Within a diameter class the bark is somewhat thinner on the older trees, but because of the usual narrow range in age within each diameter class, bark can be estimated in the Deep South to the nearest 0.17 inch from diameter alone.[89] Because the outer bark sloughs off as it weathers with age, total bark thickness increases more slowly than its inner growth

[89] This can be done using the following formulas:
Single bark thickness = $0.241 + 0.037D$
where D is outside bark diameter (inches).
Similarly d.b.h. inside bark = $0.93D - 0.48$
Bark thickness can vary with geographic location because of differences in racial strain, weathering, or both, but these Louisiana formulas (Minor 1953b) corroborate results from early studies in Maryland (Sterrett 1914).

would indicate. Hence within a diameter class the bark is thinner on the older trees (fig. 64). Bark corrections are needed where growth estimates are based directly on ring measurements and age is not determined.[90]

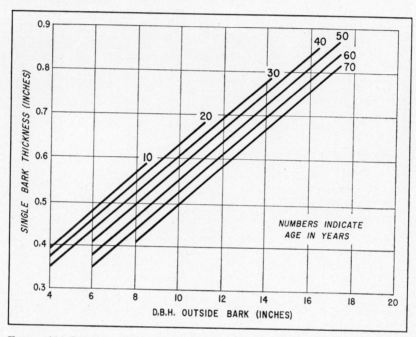

FIGURE 64.—Relation of bark thickness to age and diameter of loblolly pine at breast height in Louisiana (Minor 1953b).

Prediction of volume growth expected from specific loblolly pine holdings necessitates inventories—single or recurring, on the ground or from the air. These involve a choice between two main approaches.

Rather extensive long-term forecasts of growth from even-aged stands can be made from estimates based on normal yield tables. These are useful only when adjusted to allow for the tendency in all loblolly pine stands to approach the normal stocking at different rates (fig. 56). Yields from well-stocked stands of loblolly pine are given in table 25. Methods of constructing yield tables for non-

[90] For example, the current growth of loblolly pine, expressed as years needed to add 1 inch in diameter, equals the number of rings produced in a given period (e.g., 5 or 10 years) divided by the product of 1.095 and twice the i.b. radial growth during the period. The radial increase of wood and bark is 1.095 inches for each increase of 1 inch in wood only as measured on cores (McCormack 1955b); that is for measurements at breast height. At the top of the first log at 17.3 feet the factor is 1.077 (Posey 1957).

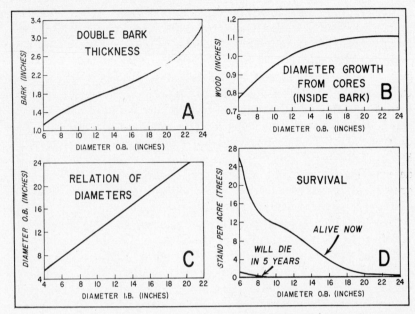

FIGURE 65.—Four graphic steps used in projecting loblolly pine stand data
from timber cruises into the future for estimates of allowable cut: *A*, Twice
bark thickness averaged by diameter classes to obtain present d.i.b.; *B*,
average wood growth in diameter in past 5 years to obtain past d.i.b.; *C*,
ratios of d.b.h. o.b. to d.b.h. i.b. to obtain past d.o.b.; and *D*, present stand
and mortality expected, to estimate future stand. Only local data are
useful in predictions; these curves merely illustrate a widely applicable
method.

normal loblolly pine stands are reported by MacKinney, Schumacher,
and Chaiken (1937).

More intensive short-term forecasts of growth in many-aged, or
otherwise irregular, forests are usually based on inventories from detailed ground cruising of timber. Methods of using a single timber
cruise to project loblolly pine stands 5 or 10 years into the future
are available (Wahlenberg 1941). The computations involve some
17 steps of which four are graphic (fig. 65). The weakness in single
forecasts of this kind stems from somewhat inadequate means of
gaging the effects of cutting on ingrowth, the changes in rates of
growth, and the mortality allowance. Because of these sources of
error, recurring cruises (i.e., the method of "continuous inventory")
are a more useful means of controlling the cut in forests under active
management.

The approach to a knowledge of growth used in the method of
stand-table projection is reversed in the method of recurring in-

ventories. Periodic changes in stands and in mortality are the items that are measured directly, and from summaries of these tallies the growth behavior of individual diameter classes may be deduced if desired (Wahlenberg 1941, pp. 39-41). The basic concept on which growth determinations rest in this inventory system is very simple. Covering a given period, e.g., 5 or 10 years, trees that died are added to a stand table of living trees harvested, and both are added to the stand of living trees inventoried at the close of the period. The difference between this total and the stand at the first inventory is the gross periodic growth. This method is a convenient means of determining actual past growth, and estimating expected future growth, of forests that are managed silviculturally under a system of regular partial cuttings for harvesting timber.

Aerial photographic surveys are the quickest and, for large tracts, the cheapest means of completing an overall picture of forest density and composition as these influence the yield of timber. Color tones and shade patterns in the picture serve to indicate forest types and conditions on an area basis. One of the chief advantages, however, in using aerial photographs is in reconnaissance to indicate where ground cruises are necessary.

Detailed explanation of how to gather cruise data directly from photographs is beyond the scope of this book. Suffice it to say that much work requires special viewing apparatus, area grids, crown closure scales, and other highly specialized measuring devices. The height of trees can be approximated with parallax measuring devices and the stem diameters directly from crown images. Width of crowns among loblolly pines of saw-log size varies directly with stem diameter:

$$S = 4.66 + 0.55C \text{ (Minor 1951)}$$

where S is d.b.h. in inches and C is crown width in feet. Crowns, however, are smaller where trees are crowded (fig. 66). For example, in the 15-foot crown class stem diameters vary with stand density roughly as follows:

D.b.h. (inches) $= 14.28 - 0.011$ trees per acre (Minor 1951).

Of course a smaller proportion of total numbers of trees per acre are visible in aerial photographs of dense stands than in those of thin stands. Because of the difficulty in making correct allowance for this and other sources of systematic error, estimates of timber volumes from photographs alone are seldom accurate. The data from the pictures need to be supplemented by, and tied to, ground-control plots. Even so, 3 to 4 times as many photo plots as ground-cruise plots are needed for equal accuracy. Sometimes small tracts can be cruised from the ground with fewer plots than are needed properly to supplement an aerial cruise (Meyer and Worley 1957). Some of the ground checks may be made quickly, however, using the variable-plot radius and angle-gauge or wedge-prism methods of one-man cruising (Grosenbaugh 1952a, 1952b, 1955, and 1958, Bruce 1955, Avery 1955).

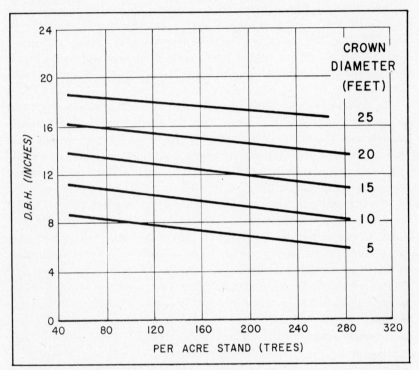

FIGURE 66.—Effect of stand density on relation between average crown width and tree diameter (Minor 1951).

SUMMARY

"Room to grow and none to waste" is, for timber growers, a worthy admonition, but a difficult one to follow because research has not yet developed all the necessary information. Part of it is reported here, or in the appendix, as a material background for, or guide to, actual practice. These data concern merchantable volume (or weight) of loblolly pine and its rate of increase, as associated with the size, age, or crown development of trees. They deal also with the degree to which all trees are influenced by soil quality, and how certain ones may have suffered from crowding or benefited by release. The data on stands concern net gains in volume (survivor growth minus drain from mortality or harvest) and rates at which full stocking is approached. Although these problems are not peculiar to any one species, specific data for loblolly pine are needed to implement the plans to grow it.

There are diverse ways to measure or predict growth and yield, but they involve subtle ways in which mortality or other waste can be overlooked. Unless thinning is possible in cordwood stands, an average annual mortality of 0.4 cord may be expected between 20 and 25 years, 0.5 cord from 26 to 30 years, and 0.6 cord between 31 and 50 years. Space released by mortality seldom remains blank, but to allow it to be reclaimed by inferior vegetation is, in itself, wasteful.

Loblolly pine commonly produces 2 or 3 times as much volume per acre as do its broad-leaved associate species, but all hardwoods cannot, and should not, be wholly eliminated. The highest net lumber values per acre are grown where not more than 20 percent of the trees are certain soil-building hardwoods well scattered among the pines.

On the best sites the dominant pines can average 2 feet of height growth annually for 40 years. To do this the live crown needs to cover 40 percent of the height until they are 30 feet tall and at least 30 percent thereafter. With crown ratios of 37 to 45 percent on sites of index 80 to 85, diameters can increase 3 inches in 10 years. Although a live crown ratio of 40 percent of height produces the maximum volume of clear wood, one of 30 percent produces 89 percent as much. In even-aged stands the average length of living crowns is inversely related to the number of trees per acre. Silvicultural cutting or pruning, or both, deliberately to change crown length in reserved trees are effective means of controlling the volume and quality of timber grown.

Well-stocked stands that remain uncut increase in basal area at a diminishing rate as they approach full stocking. When they are protected, but otherwise unmanaged, they eventually fluctuate around an equilibrium density of 155 ± 30—i.e., somewhere between 125 and 185 square feet—with a stand density index of 275 ± 15 for stands of saw-log size trees. One-half to two-thirds of this stocking is a suitable density for growing timber at economic rates. The somewhat greater taper and limbiness of merchantable stems is more than offset by the values from accelerated growth of individual trees. The sacrifice in per-acre yield is small. For production of saw logs 90 to 95 square feet of basal area is a favorable stocking, but for production of pulpwood alone a lower density, a figure 10 below the site index, appears more suitable. Mean annual increment in volume of rough wood culminates at 30 to 40 years in well-stocked stands or at 40 to 50 years in stands less than half stocked at the start. In board feet annual rates of growth culminate 10 or 15 years later.

On site 90 a well-stocked stand may be expected to yield about 3,800 cubic feet per acre at 30 years, 5,000 cubic feet at 50 years, or 28,000 board feet at 70 years, which represents a mean annual growth of 400 board feet per acre annually. Decay in heartwood does not exceed 1 percent of the volume of trees 70 to 80 years of age. The approximate spacing in feet of the merchantable or crop trees may well be about 1.75 D.

Stands of sawtimber that are not only well stocked, but also well managed, respond in current growth rates. Basal-area growth has been increased 130 percent following release cutting in previously neglected saw-log stands. Second-growth loblolly pine can readily grow 300 board feet per acre annually with the benefit of protection only. The 400 board feet, mentioned above, assumes only non-intensive management. Some 600 board feet can be had with more intensive silviculture. And, on good sites, either heavily stocked with tall (5- or 6-log) trees, or else with the benefit of frequent light thinning, the current growth of loblolly pine may be 900 to 1,000 board feet annually.

Stands of pulpwood now vary so much in density that the current (i.e., 5-year) annual growth commonly ranges from 0.1 to 2.9 cords per acre. Properly stocked and thinned the yearly per-acre growth is usually between 1 and 2 cords. A yield of about 70 cords, for example, is to be expected on site 100 at 40 years.

The section on estimating raw materials, in present and future supply, enumerates several interrelationships useful to implement the estimates for loblolly pine. Progressive changes in the appearance of bark with advancing age are listed. Weight and volume of trees in cubic feet, bolts, or board feet, as related to diameter or height classes, are given by formula or tabulation. Some converting factors applicable to loblolly pine in both short- and long-term forecasting are presented.

The information in this chapter facilitates providing desirable trees with "room to grow and none to waste."

Chapter 7

Management of Immature Timber

SILVICULTURE OF SOUTHERN PINE forests,[91] with special measures to favor loblolly pine, is warranted where suitable land and an active market for products exists. This is true over most of the range of the species. In general pines are least profitable to landowners where first costs are high, where early growth is retarded either by sterile soil on poor sites or by hardwood sprouts on good sites, where rotations are too short, and where harvests are restricted to a single low-priced product. These handicaps become less prevalent with the increasing application of silviculture.

The midrotation care of timber stands requires less precise timing than does harvest and regeneration, but deserves careful planning. Especially is this true of mixed pine-hardwood stands. The primary need in extensive stands of poor composition and low density is for timber stand improvement operations. Land heavily stocked with pure pine is more readily kept productive. The care of pine forests that have reproduced least successfully is more complex later because of irregularities and mixed composition. Often the stands are crowded in patches but understocked as a whole, and both desirable and undesirable trees may be present in a wide range of sizes. If the forest has been badly neglected it may even support an overburden of undesirable relics of the exploitation that took place in previous stands. Serious depletion of stocks calls for liquidation and a fresh start, but elsewhere a variety of rehabilitation measures may be feasible. A series of them tailored to fit local conditions may

---

[91] In loblolly pine, as in other types of forest, silvicultural management seeks to (1) protect soil and forest, (2) restock open areas, (3) improve species composition and timber quality, (4) control stand density, (5) harvest the forest crop systematically, and (6) provide certain supplementary benefits. Measures to achieve objects (1) and (2) are covered in the preceding chapters, (3) and (4) in this chapter, and (5) and (6) in the following two chapters. With the exception of one section in chapter 8, the financial aspects of forestry are not discussed in this book, but it is assumed that the business of growing loblolly pine will be confined to lands that are favorably situated.

be necessary. The section on timber stand improvement describes appropriate measures. At best the process of restoring badly depleted forests to productivity without planting is a gradual one.

The principal measures needed in the denser stands of relatively pure pine are for thinning and stem improvement. Sapling thickets of loblolly pine, however, usually need some "cleaning" to better their species composition together with light thinning to relieve severe congestion. There is a continuing need, even in the most thrifty stands, to remove certain trees, identity of which becomes increasingly clear with further development of the stand. Dominance is well expressed when the small pole stage is reached—sometimes earlier. As crowns differentiate within a closed canopy, the selection and reservation of the best crop trees is relatively easy. Guide lines to indicate when, where, and how much thinning and pruning of loblolly pine is needed are given in the last two sections of this chapter.

STAND IMPROVEMENT

Removal of competition from undesirable trees by cutting, burning, chemical treatment, or heavy machinery is widely necessary in growing loblolly pine timber. Stand improvement is needed where advanced reproduction of loblolly pine is present and desired but is retarded, where the competing brush is dense or aggressive or both, and where potential values are worthy of the expected costs. Choice of blanket or selective measures of disposing of weed trees must rest on an appraisal of local stand conditions. The problem deserves increased attention.

Need for treatments

Loblolly pine predominates in many immature stands of mixed pine and hardwood.[92] Because of early mismanagement, most of the inferior trees are weed hardwoods. It has been estimated (Reynolds 1949b) that nearly half the pine land in southern Arkansas and northern Louisiana is occupied by low-grade hardwoods. Excessive

---

[92] In places where nearly pure loblolly pine forests emerge rapidly from the regeneration stage, the need for further care of young timber is minimized. In other places where the pine seedlings, in mixture with undesirable species, emerge slowly the young stand of saplings and poles requires earlier and continuing attention. In many intermediate situations, where the local need for improvement measures is less obvious, an appraisal of the chance for good crop trees to become dominant without release is useful.

An estimate of the percentage of area that will remain shaded by hardwood weed species, if an immature forest remains unimproved, may be obtained by multiplying basal area in undesirable stems in square feet by 1.4 (McCulley 1953c).

underbrush has appeared on only about 10 percent of the upland in that territory, but a major problem is recognized in the disposal of sapling and pole-sized hardwoods 10 to 40 years old.

Eastward from Mississippi to Florida nearly half of the upland loblolly pine forest area is being taken over by little-used hardwoods. In South Carolina there are 2 to 3 cords of wood per acre in such trees (Chaiken 1952a and 1955). A few can be pulped, but the value is low. Some individual "wolf trees" monopolize a tenth acre. Intermediate cuttings, through the harvest of inferior pines and the felling or girdling of the worthless hardwoods, are highly worth while.[93]

The most profitable mixed pine-hardwood stands are those in which the hardwood trees occupy only intermediate or subordinate positions in the crown canopy. Where these hardwoods are codominant they do increase the quality of lumber in pine crop trees, but they do so only with some sacrifice in pine volume per acre. Where hardwoods form a considerable admixture in pine stands, the value of the increase in "B and Better" lumber is more than offset by the decreased pine volume resulting in lower net per-acre values.

Improvement cuttings are generally profitable. In one forest the initial large-scale operations removed 3 to 5 cords per acre from natural stands and 5 to 10 cords per acre from old-field stands (Reynolds 1937c). The sawtimber cut for improvement consisted of 40 percent grade 1 logs, 34 percent grade 2, and the rest of low grade. Thus many of these operations to remove the least desirable trees are immediately profitable. There is evidence from Georgia (Worrell 1956) that it pays to practice intensive silviculture on good sites to produce full crops of loblolly pine.

Type of stand improvement

Recent developments have provided a variety of new methods for stand improvement. Mainly they help to do three things—kill nonmerchantable material, reduce its sprouting, and lower the cost of disposal by older methods. To accomplish this they employ fire, chemicals, and manual or mechanized tools, or combinations of these as situations indicate. A thorough treatment often should employ more than one agent to dispose of inferior trees (Bull 1934). This is true especially where a variety of sizes and species of unmerchant-

---

[93] A moderate investment in timber stand improvement may be doubled in the value it adds to a crop in the form of increased subsequent growth of pine saw logs. In many places on average sites an investment of $10 per acre can probably be recovered in the next 3 years, and on the best sites an investment of $30 to $40 may pay handsomely (Stoltenberg 1956).

able trees must be treated, for they differ in resistance to mortality
from girdling, chemicals, or burning.

A wise choice of methods and tools must be based also on the
degree of control needed or desired. Uncut forest is best for soil
conservation. Cutting is destructive or constructive according to the
way it is done. Young growth of pine needs enough release to permit it to gain dominance, but not so much as to induce an excessive
upsurge of new multiple-stem low-level competition. In most difficult situations the plan to achieve a certain degree of control must
be a compromise between effective kill and reasonable cost (Chaiken
1952a). In game management cutting should not destroy vegetation
useful to wildlife for food, cover, or dens. In timber management
cutting should neither overdraw loblolly pine wood capital nor overstimulate the inferior species associated with it, if yields are to be
sustained.

The five principal measures for improvement and release are related to specific aims as follows: *Fell* to harvest minor products, re-
movable without excessive damage, and locally usable or salable;
girdle to avoid damage to advance reproduction from felling, and
to deaden tops of nonmerchantable cull and weed trees; *poison* to
kill both tops and later roots of all sizes of undesirable trees and
sprouts as quickly as possible; *burn* to deaden saplings less than 2
inches in d.b.h. back to ground and destroy all small sprouts; *machine*
with heavy equipment to break down large saplings and small poles
without potential value. These measures are prescribed singly and
separately, or repeatedly and in combination, where they are feasible
and as local conditions indicate the need.

Vegetal competition, varying greatly both in lateral extent and in
height above ground, must be evaluated before a measure of control
is prescribed. A suitable treatment often needs to reduce competition
only in the spots and at the canopy levels where it is currently intense and hampering the crop trees. After an initial deadening of
small trees such a treatment does not necessarily accomplish any
prompt reduction in the total numbers of hardwood stems, for they
sprout from the stumps or bases where the tops—not the roots—are
killed. Thus uncovered, the density of the understory tends to increase during the first years, in some degree, whether the lethal agent
be a machine, fire, or chemicals. In liberating sapling pines from
overtopping trees, sprouts from the stumps of pole-sized hardwoods
seldom reoccupy—during the period required for pine to gain ascendancy—more than 10 percent of the area formerly covered by the cut

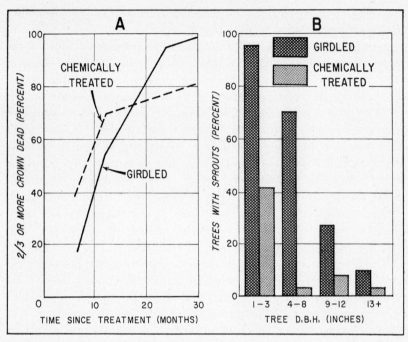

FIGURE 67.—Degree of liberation achieved in northern Mississippi by girdling or by applying Ammate in notches 6 inches apart on oak, gum, and hickory trees, as indicated by (A) dying of crowns with elapsed time and (B) resprouting after treatment (Huckenpahler 1952).

trees. The principal silvical gain, however, consists in shifting to a low level the space covered by undesirable species.

The choice of a lethal agent and a specific method to achieve these ends affects initial cost, incidental damage, or both. Costs, the number of treatments needed, and the results obtained vary widely by locality. Undesirable trees may be girdled, poisoned, felled, burned, or bulldozed.

Aerial spraying of foliage is fast. First cost is low, control of herbicide is somewhat difficult, and results are variable. Supplemental ground work is needed first to mark strips to be treated, and later to mop up the remaining vegetation to be deadened. Usually (in this work or when they do the whole job) the ground crews cut down undesirable trees if they are small and girdle or fell the larger ones, whichever is the easier.

Trees deadened with Ammate or 2,4,5-T tend to die sooner and sprout less than do girdled trees (fig. 67). Where it is unnecessary to kill both roots and tops quickly, as on game management areas, simple girdling is useful in silviculture. Many girdled trees sprout promptly and then die slowly. Thus they remain temporarily useful for browse production during the period when their competition is being removed from the overwood.

Scheduling treatments

Where they may be needed, timber stand improvement operations of a blanket type, prescribing the use of fire or heavy machines, are most effective early in a rotation. Intermediate cutting, and the application of herbicides, are useful over a longer period. Late in a rotation it may be advisable to defer, for the benefit of a habitat favorable for wildlife, all further timber stand improvement until the time of final harvest.

The proper season for stand improvement in young immature timber deserves minor consideration. Summer work is effective, after the period of most active growth but while the trees are still in full leaf, facilitating identification (Carmean 1947). Another advantage of summer treatments may be less vigorous sprouts. Buell (1940) found that sprout clumps were 2½ feet shorter and 1½ feet narrower after cutting in July or August than they were following winter work. The best season to apply herbicides in preharvest improvement work in older stands may be somewhat earlier, though satisfactory results are obtainable throughout the year.

Estimates of working time required to eliminate undesirable trees are useful in choosing the method to use. Girdling work proceeds most rapidly if it can be mechanized, where slopes, if any, are gentle and the trees soft textured, and while the pole-sized stems to be treated are still relatively small (fig. 68). Disposal time for trees less than 4 inches in d.b.h. was less than 1 man-minute each regardless of method in one test, but for the larger trees felling with saws was most time consuming, girdling intermediate, and poisoning most expeditious (MacKinney and Korstian 1932).[94]

[94] By each method the per-acre time requirement varies mainly with the size and number of trees treated. For example, when axes were used to notch-girdle the sapwood in mixed hardwoods on 83 acres in Alabama the time requirements were as follows (Yocum 1952, Muntz 1952):

$$T = 0.006005 \text{ (sum } D) - 0.010066 \text{ } N$$

where N is the number of trees, "sum D" is the total of their d.b.h. measurements in inches, and T is man-hours. As rough approximations of this we have the formula 0.005 (sum D), which may be accurate to ± 5 percent for 8-inch trees (Walker 1956), and the formula 0.0056 (sum D) + 0.25 (Harrington 1955c).

Man-hours needed to girdle and treat trees with 2,4,5-T in frills (Wenger and Trousdell 1958) are 0.00584 (sum D). When Ammate crystals are used in

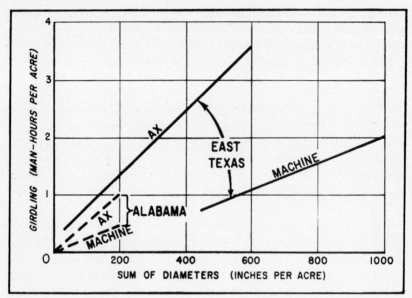

FIGURE 68.—Comparative tests in the gulf states show that girdling weed trees with a machine takes less time than girdling with an ax. With either tool hickory requires more time—especially on the steeper slopes—and more sharpening of blades (Harrington 1955c).

Commercial cuttings

The primary reason for improvement cuttings in pole-sized loblolly pine is to transfer wood production from the poorer trees of inferior species to the better stems among the pines. Although intermediate cuttings[95] may, in crowded spots, reduce stand density enough to step up rates of growth, that is incidental to improvement in stand composition and stem quality. Like the other measures here discussed, commercial cuttings can be used to effect such improvement in growing stocks. They may well dispose of as much undesirable, but salable, material as local markets currently per-

---

notches to kill trees, the time requirement has been reported as follows (McClay 1953d):

$$T = 0.009 \ (\text{sum } D) - 0.005 \ N$$

An approximation for treating stems under 6 inches in d.b.h. by this method is simply one-third of the basal area in square feet (McClay 1953b).

When the trees are girdled with back-pack machine the time requirement (Yocum 1954) in man-hours is reduced to:

$$T = 0.003641 \ (\text{sum } D) - 0.008017 \ N$$

The simpler but less accurate formulas for this type of work are 0.0025 (sum D) or 0.0023 (sum D) — 0.27 (Harrington 1955c).

[95] That is all cuttings between periods devoted to harvest and regeneration, except thinnings in young dense stands of pure pine, discussed in the following section, Thinning.

mit. Hence they may follow or be combined with other improvement measures, though usually it is advantageous to have the commercial cut precede the others. It is also desirable for hardwood removal to precede chemical treatment of weed species by at least one full year.

The discriminating judgment needed for effective improvement cuttings rests on practical knowledge of two things: (1) The relative capacity of desirable trees to survive and dominate with or without release, and (2) the present worth or disposal value of undesirable trees, and the future worth or potential value of the desirable ones. Those that can be used or sold at a price at least equal to the cost of their removal, and with little or no investment in slash disposal, should be harvested (Smith 1947, Reynolds 1952a). If the inferior trees can be sold to better advantage later they can well be kept in stands under even-aged management to avoid breaks in the crown cover (Hopkins 1948).

The general principles of tree selection are useful throughout the range of loblolly pine, although skill in such selection is best developed locally. The different types or forms of pines are found in varying proportions in different stands (fig. 69). Nearly everywhere the "wolf trees," Nos. 5 and 6, should be removed early be-

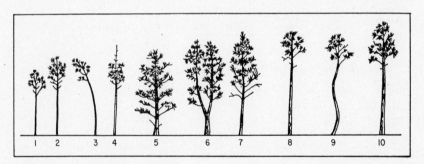

FIGURE 69.—Typical remnants of old growth found in second-growth stands. The prevalent mixture of such remnants aggravates the problem of harvesting the least promising trees early. Classes 2, 8, and some of 10 should be reserved as growing stock. Nos. 3 to 7 and 9 are trees for early use or disposal to free the area for better trees to be grown (Heyward 1939).

cause they occupy too much space and will not produce better than No. 2 logs or grade 2C lumber (Reynolds 1939a). The other types may be held longer provided they are good survival risks and not retarding better trees. Many loblolly pines cankered with fusiform rust are good risks and grow at satisfactory rates (Klawitter 1957).

Normally the slower growing and defective trees are removed first if they are merchantable.

The almost regionwide market for pulpwood and more localized markets for crossties are usually the best outlet for all pines and some hardwoods removed in improvement cutting. The relative values of the wood content by size classes and the growth potential of trees, if reserved, have been determined (table 33). Such differences deserve consideration when choosing between trees to remove in improvement cuttings.

TABLE 33.—*Volume of loblolly pine pulpwood and its value per inch of increase in the diameter of typical trees*

D.b.h. (inches)	Volume per tree[1]	Stand per cord[2]	Pulpwood value per tree[3]	Value of 1 inch of growth in diameter[4]	Increase in value for 1 inch increase in diameter[5]
	Cu. ft.	Trees	Dollars	Dollars	Percent
6..............	2.8	27.8	0.18	0.12	67
7..............	4.7	16.7	.30	.15	50
8..............	7.2	11.1	.45	.18	40
9..............	10.3	7.9	.63	.21	32
10..............	14.3	5.8	.84	.24	27
11..............	18.4	4.6	1.08	.26	24
12..............	22.6	3.7	1.34	.31	22
13..............	28.1	3.0	1.65	.33	20
14..............	34.1	2.5	1.98	.36	19

[1] Heights from figure 50A, chapter 6, Growth and Yield.
[2] Cu. ft. per cord equal 77 for 6-inch trees up to 86 for 14-inch trees (MacKinney and Chaiken, 1956).
[3] Pulpwood values at $5 per cord smoothed by curving.
[4] Differences in preceding column.
[5] Ratios between data in preceding two columns.

For improvement cuttings on a 5-year cycle in pole-size single-storied stands in the loblolly pine-hardwood type of forest the following approximate guide to desirable spacing is useful (U.S.F.S. 1933):

Average d.b.h. (inches)	Distance between trees[1] (feet)	Stand per 1/10 acre (trees)
4................	8	68
6................	10	44
8................	12	30
10................	15	20

[1] Estimated average space to be provided between a crop tree and each of its nearest three neighbor trees.

The cutting may be heavier if a 10-year cycle is used.

A complete canopy helps to keep the forest floor clear and receptive of subsequent measures to obtain reproduction. Large breaks in the crown canopy from stand improvement operations may result in premature reproduction. In this situation the opportunity for secondary benefits (i.e., seedling release) through further removal of trees from the overstory is sharply limited, if plans for a regulated forest are to be followed. That is, under intensive even-aged management, scattered volunteer seedlings have nothing to gain from early cuttings in the overwood because all adequate regeneration is, or should be, segregated on separately designated areas. Hence premature reproduction in response to improvement operations need not be liberated. Under uneven-aged management such seedlings need not be regarded as premature. Within the larger openings, and on the still larger regeneration areas used in even-aged management, especially along the borders of each, the pine seedlings may, or may not, need deliberate release depending on soil moisture supplies. Elsewhere it is appropriate that seedling advances, if any, be ignored and sacrificed to the system in use.

Herbicides

A marked increase in the use of chemicals to kill weed trees in loblolly pine forests has followed the development of several new compounds, including two synthetic plant hormones in recent years (plate 8). The three principal chemicals are Ammate, 2,4-D, and 2,4,5-T.[96] Their utility is well established but the prescriptions for applying them are still under development. Ammate and 2,4,5-T are now used most extensively. The latter appears to function as a hormone by depressing photosynthesis while stimulating excessive respiration. Sold in concentrated form, they can be used in water solution, though light oil carriers are usually preferred, for oil is in itself toxic and is better able to penetrate bark. Amounts of 2,4,5-T to use in preparing solutions or emulsions are as follows:

		Acid equivalent per 100 gallons of spray material (pounds)
Used for—	Carried in—	
Foliage.........	Water.............	2
Frills.........	Water or oil.......	8
Basal or stump sprays.......	Oil...............	20

[96] These are abbreviated designations. Ammate is 80 to 95 percent ammonium sulfamate. 2,4-D is derived from 2,4-dichlorophenoxyacetic acid, and 2,4,5-T from trichlorophenoxyacetic acid. Another chemical, 2,4,5-TP or 2(2,4, 5-trichlorophenoxyproprionic acid), has been formulated but not extensively tested (Walker 1956). The most useful forms of the hormones are the salts or esters. As effective as the high volatile esters are the low volatile ones like the propylene glycol butyl ether esters. The esters may contain 40 to 50 percent of the commercial product sold in concentrated form containing 2 to 4 pounds of acid equivalent per gallon.

PLATE 8.—In managing immature forest to grow loblolly pine, inferior hardwoods should be deadened, *A,* to liberate planted or volunteer pine seedlings from suppression by the overwood, and later all dense stands of young pine timber, *B,* should be thinned periodically to release the better trees from crowding and to confine all hardwood sprout growth to the understory (Photos courtesy U.S.F.S. and Louisiana Forestry Commission).

Aerial and other blanket methods of killing undesirable vegetation by foliar spraying with herbicide so far have had limited aplication for several reasons. The pattern of variation in value of species associated with loblolly pine does not match their relative susceptibility to chemicals. Thus lack of selectivity (horizontal control of lethal effects) is a disadvantage in blanket treatments of mixed stands. There is also some danger of accidental damage elsewhere when wind may shift the spray and injure adjacent crops. Repeated spraying of a forest may be needed for successive reduction in levels of shade. A spray that kills the overstory may not penetrate to the understory; a second spraying to eliminate shrubs may, in turn, overstimulate grass and weeds that compete with pine seedlings. Thus differences in penetration from above (i.e., lack of vertical control) is also a disadvantage. The cost of repeat treatments may be prohibitive. Another difficulty, where a thorough killing job is sought, is that downward translocation of herbicides within defoliated plants is apparently negligible.

Aerial spraying is helpful in extensive clearing operations prior to planting, or on open areas where sprouts are competing actively with the seedlings. The application of 1½ to 2½ pounds of acid per acre from aircraft can economically defoliate hardwoods 90 percent in the first year. One or more applications can reduce sprout coverage nearly 70 percent (Martin and Clark 1954) and may be effective in releasing about 20 percent of suppressed seedlings. Followup treatments by interplanting and other measures are often essential (Ray 1957).

Ground work permits effective placement of chemicals in low level incisions where they can most readily travel upward to girdle the main stem, and thus kill the whole tree promptly. Roots transmit certain chemicals readily (Moreland 1950a), even through natural grafts (Grano 1951b), but resist ingress of them from the stems. Also the aboveground horizontal translocation of herbicides in sapwood is sharply restricted. To counter these limitations current practice uses heavy applications on the large trees, or on stumps of small ones (Grano 1952a, Peevy 1953 and 1954). All trees larger than 4 inches in d.b.h. may be girdled with single-hack "frills" (Chaiken 1951b, Carvell 1956). These frills can then be treated with a mixture of 2,4,5-T in oil. The identical formulation can be applied by the same crew as a basal spray to saturate the lower 4 inches of stem and the root collar of saplings down to a quarter inch in d.b.h. if desired. A 6- or 7-man crew can operate efficiently in this manner if the ratio of ax men to spray men is adjusted to local variations. Under normal conditions using 8 gallons of spray and covering strips about 50 feet wide, such a crew can treat 12 to 17 acres in 8 hours. All herbicides used in incisions must be applied to freshly cut surfaces before the conductive cells of the wood become clogged.

Another way to deaden the larger trees is to deposit ammonium sulfamate (Ammate) in freshly chopped basal notches. This substance, being hygroscopic, is absorbed by moist sapwood usually within 24 hours. (In storage it deteriorates rapidly unless sealed against moist air.) Two chopped notches are sufficient for all trees up to 6 inches in d.b.h. Larger trees need an additional notch for about every additional 2 inches of diameter (Peevy 1949, Peevy and Campbell 1949). A heaping tablespoonful of Ammate is used per notch or twice as much for refractory species. Resistance to Ammate poisoning is tentatively listed for upland weed trees in the Deep South as follows:

Easy to kill	Intermediate	Hard to kill
Sweetgum	Blackjack oak	Hickory
Blackgum	Elm	Beech
	Ash	Persimmon
	Hornbeam	White oak

Numerous other associates of loblolly pine have been listed as relatively easy or hard to kill (Walker 1956).

Requiring less time and less herbicide, frills tend to be effective because they actually incise the entire perimeter of a tree. Trees may survive treated frills if any of the cambium remains uncut. Two-hack girdles, or girdles machined at a convenient height, are commonly used without chemicals where quick release is not essential (Grano 1952a). Time requirements vary considerably for the different methods of treating cull hardwoods (fig. 70). The chemical solution may be carried to frilled trees in a 5-gallon back-pack can with flexible hose and trigger shutoff, or a 1-gallon jug fitted with a spout for pouring.

One gallon of 2,4,5-T in diesel oil may be used to treat the following numbers of frilled trees (Chaiken 1951 a & c, Cassady and Peevy 1948):

D.b.h. (inches)	Frills 1 gallon will treat (number)
6	38
8	29
10	23
12	19
14	16
16	14

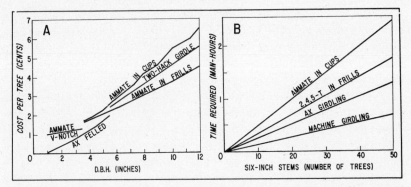

FIGURE 70.—Various methods of killing cull hardwoods and retarding sprouting, by size of tree in relation to cost, *A*, in Louisiana; and by time required to treat specified numbers of 6-inch stems, *B*, in North Carolina. (Mann 1950a and 1950b, Wenger and Trousdell 1958).

It may act more slowly than Ammate, but foliage may discolor in 2 days and the trees die in from 2 to 12 months. At least, after spring treatment many trees will be dead by the following winter. There is a general tendency for both crown kill and basal sprouting to increase slightly during the first 2 years after treatment (Bull and Campbell 1949). When the unthrifty trees are cut the first year, the stumps are more likely to sprout than if they are permitted to die slowly (Peevy and Campbell 1947). Most of the sprouts induced by herbicide in frills die within 3 years.

Sometimes a dense thicket of hardwood sprouts can be held down effectively with a single chemical treatment at less cost than that of two weedings with cutting tools (Lotti and McCulley 1951). Among twenty hardwood species commonly associated with loblolly pine, only one, *Ilex opaca* Ait., has been observed to be appreciably resistant to early growing-season frill treatment with 2,4,5-T in oil (Lotti 1957).

Seldom is eradication possible with any single treatment. Where chemical eradication was attempted on a test plot in Arkansas, some 250 living sprouts per acre were found 4 years later. To cope with sprout thickets of 2- to 3-inch trees chemicals can be applied to the base of stems or tops of fresh stumps in two principal ways: (1) Automatic injection with each thrust of a special chisellike instrument such as the "Cornell tool" or the "Little Tree Injector," and (2) basal sprays to get 2,4,5-T to penetrate bark and kill the vital cambium tissue.

The pipe reservoir that forms the handle of the Cornell tool may be filled with a mixture of 1 gallon of 2,4,5-T in 20 gallons of diesel oil. The basal perimeter of each tree is struck at ground level with one downward jab for each inch of diameter. Although resistance varies by species, about 3 out of 4 of the sprouts will be dead a year or two later (Brasington 1950, Grano 1952a, Shipman 1953, Goddard 1954).[97]

Where stumps alone are to be treated to reduce sprouting the simplest treatment is to spread Ammate crystals on the freshly cut cross section of sapwood and bark. A less costly alternative is simply to wet tops and sides of the stumps with the same diesel oil-herbicide basal spray used on uncut saplings.

Basal spraying is a good selective way to dispose of the small undesirable trees of various species, or larger individuals of thin-barked species. The amount of emulsion needed to treat trees of different diameters is about as follows (Chaiken 1951c, Goddard 1955):

D.b.h. (inches)	Tree bases 1 gallon will spray (number)
6	13
8	9
10	7
12	5
14	4
16	3

The reaction is slow but satisfactory on most species at any time of year—sometimes all the trees die—provided enough liquid herbicide has been used to thoroughly saturate the bark at the root collar where dormant buds are most numerous (Bramble, Worley, and Brynes 1953).

Four principal procedures now used to eliminate undesirable trees with or without herbicides are shown in figure 71. The fifth method, not illustrated but rapidly gaining in favor, utilizes special injectors to put the herbicide into the sap stream.

With the exception of sodium arsenite, rarely used in the South, the hazards of applying modern herbicides are low. Some of them may irritate the skin after long exposure. Ammate and 2,4,5-T are nontoxic to both animals and human beings. Some poisonous plants, ordinarily shunned by domestic stock, may be browsed after being wilted by chemicals, but this seldom happens in the selective use of hormone sprays. Any possible sterilization of soil from the over-

---

[97] When a 16-pound modification of this tool called the "Little Tree Injector" was tested on trees 7 inches or less in diameter (D) in Texas the following formulas were derived (Davis and Duke 1955):

Solution needed in gallons = 0.0015 (sum D) + 0.147

Injection time in man-hours = 0.124 + 0.0042 (sum D)

FIGURE 71.—Sapwood chips are removed with an ax or machine from the notch girdle, *A*, to kill the top slowly and let the smaller trees sprout. At *B* the base is drenched with 2,4,5-T to deaden the tree slowly without any incision. At *C* notches are closely spaced near the root collar and filled with Ammate to kill the tree promptly and discourage sprouting. *D* shows a frill wherein no chips are removed, but the perimeter, completely girdled, is soaked with a liquid herbicide, usually 2,4,5-T in oil.

flow of herbicides is temporary and insignificant for these compounds disintegrate rapidly in the warm moist soil of the loblolly pine region.

A herbicidal treatment that kills trees slowly but surely is often preferable to one that injures them quickly but indecisively. Where a prompt kill is desirable, however, the most favorable season for the use of herbicides deserves attention. For example it has been shown (Shipman 1958) that although 50 percent destruction of sweetgum (i.e., without sprouting) may be achieved 3 years after plain girdling at any season, the same results can be had in 2 years from late dormant-season treatments (December to February) with 2,4,5-T in oil applied in frills. Furthermore the herbicide treatment in the early dormant season (September to November) brought like results in 1 year, and during the growing season was equally effective in 6 or 7 months. Hormone herbicides work most rapidly in warm weather, but at the end of 3 years after treatment not much difference is attributable to season of treatment.

Manual and mechanized measures

Mechanical treatments are used largely for type conversion, or to prepare sites for regeneration, rather than for stand improvement. However, in changing over from mixed to relatively pure stands of pine, through the reproduction process, mechanized treatments reduce the ensuing need for cleaning operations.

Manual methods are often used in stand improvement, but seldom is a single procedure wholly adequate to recondition neglected forest stands on any extensive area. Most often mechanical methods are best applied in conjunction with a preliminary controlled burn, or a final chemical "mopup" treatment, or both. The fact that chemically treated trees die sooner and sprout less is not in itself sufficient reason to rely solely on herbicides. Furthermore prescribed burning alone may not do a complete control job. Logging may inadvertently release weed species. Then if the desired seedlings fail to come in promptly, the sprouting of old hardwood roots can aggravate the subsequent measures needed to liberate the next crop of pine.

In some situations the conventional manual methods of releasing pine from cull hardwoods are economical and satisfactory. This is particularly true where most of the hardwoods are at least 10 inches in d.b.h. and less likely to sprout vigorously. It is best to cut rather than girdle trees under 4 inches in d.b.h. The problem size-class of hardwoods consists of trees 10 to 30 years old that are too small to sell but too large to kill by control burning (Clark 1947b). There is some evidence that among these trees the smaller ones can be killed by injections of 2,4,5-T at costs not exceeding those for felling them. During dry cycles, at least, there is considerable merit in rather complete removal of the understory vegetation, but ordinarily there is no need to eliminate all coppice growth, the aim being to lower its level until established pine can overtop the sprouts.

The intermediate cutting and girdling used to subordinate the hardwoods, and otherwise improve pine stands, can cause incidental felling damage to regeneration in irregular stands, or to crop trees in even-aged stands, but usually this damage is not excessive. In improvement cuttings, as much as half the growing stock can be removed from many stands, if necessary, without excessive damage to the remainder. The damage inflicted on loblolly pine saplings and pole-sized trees need not exceed 12 percent in natural second growth or 20 percent in old-field stands of loblolly pine (Smith 1947, MacKinney 1934a). Snags from deadened trees that break and fall early do little damage; the ones that disintegrate gradually cause even less. Damage can be avoided in skidding timber out with animals, even when it is handled as tree-length logs (Williston 1949b). Benefits from disposal of culls and weed hardwoods far outweigh the damage incident to their careful removal.

Heavy power-driven machinery promises to be most useful in type conversion where pine forests are seriously depleted and the land largely taken over by inferior hardwoods. If the prime need is to reduce the existing competition, power must be applied to destroy hardwood growth perhaps by bulldozing or chaining;[98] undercutting or root raking; chopping or shredding. Both scarification and soil mixing operations may damage pine sites where soils are erodible, land is sloping, and rainfall heavy. Elsewhere plowing may injure the site less than excessive scraping that displaces too much productive topsoil. Small bits of root stocks left in the ground sprout vigorously. Nevertheless, bulldozing is most effective in controlling thickets of hardwood trees up to about 6 inches in d.b.h. Near Crossett, Ark., Grano found it reduced the numbers of stems present 2 years later to about 8,000 per acre whereas after various other mechanized treatments 13,000 to 15,000 stems were still present. Fortunately the surge toward hardwood need only be subdued in order to grow pine, for eradication at any reasonable cost is seldom possible.

The use of heavy machinery in stand improvement, however, is sharply limited by its lack of selectivity, together with the necessity of keeping fire hazards low and avoiding damage to the soil. Particularly is this true in using it deliberately to minimize later cleaning and weeding, or incidentally to accomplish such work in existing stands. By contrast the use of the new light portable machines for power girdling of trees does permit selectivity in stand improvement. Such machines may double or triple the rate of disposing of undesirable trees, provided they are not badly scattered, are not on rough terrain, and do not have hard abrasive bark like that of hickory (Harrington 1955c, Doolittle 1955).

---

[98] Chaining is a relatively new idea. An anchor type chain weighing about 50 pounds per foot is drawn from each end by two tractors operating 100 to 120 feet apart. One pass is made to knock trees down and a return trip to uproot them. The material may later be pushed into windrows 100 feet apart or deposited in depressions that are not good pine sites. (Experiment by Brunswick Paper Co. in Georgia.)

Use of fire[99]

Foresters who desire to use fire in stand improvement are cognizant of many limitations in its proper application. There are situations where it is impracticable to burn, and times when, because of fuel conditions, it is impossible or inadvisable to burn (Chaiken 1950b). Frequent rainfall limits the number of good burning days. Usually burning can safely be prescribed in cured fuels 2 to 5 days after a rain of one-half inch or more (Walker, L. W. 1956). In summer 2 weeks of drought may be needed before fires will carry in a light "rough," and then only with considerable breeze. Yet hardwood underbrush in loblolly pine forests that remain long untouched by fire becomes dense enough to impede any work in stand improvement by other methods (Golden 1951).

The relative size of stems to be killed or saved largely controls the possibility of using fire effectively. An ideal burning for hardwood control, i.e., one that kills a high percentage of hardwoods while damaging few pines, seems unattainable where trees of both species groups are of equal size (Ferguson 1957b). Periodic winter burning alone can readily be used to control underbrush only where nearly all hardwood stems are less than 2 inches in d.b.h. and the pines appreciably larger (Chaiken 1949, Silker 1955a). It is best not to burn until the loblolly pines are at least 10 or 15 years old and 15 to 20 feet tall and until their crowns are high enough to escape scorching. In the management of immature stands this first burn, to remove accumulated fuels and underbrush draped with flammable litter, is difficult to execute. In the Southeast it is done in cool weather a few days after a rain by backing a fire into a steady wind to dissipate the hot gases.

Purposeful burning under a prepared plan is often done in winter when the cured vegetation and weather conditions provide a fairly long burning season. It should be repeated at intervals of 4 to 10 years to keep the hardwoods small enough for continued control by fire. Winter fires do not burn deeply into the litter and have little effect on mull or duff-mull soils. Daytime burning is preferable to night burning, because cleaner, more continous burns are attainable. Fortunately labor for standby duty and for emergency suppression is more readily available in daytime. Backfires—used espe-

[99] Prescribed burning in relation to the exclusion of wildfires is discussed in chapter 3, Protection; in relation to forest succession in chapter 2, The Species and Its Environment; in relation to preparing sites for reproduction in chapter 4, Natural Regeneration; in relation to direct seeding or planting, in chapter 5, Artificial Regeneration; and in relation to improvement in stand composition here in this chapter.

cially in young stands—may be set when the wind is between 3 and 10 miles per hour near the ground in the open areas. When and where fuel is scarce on the ground it will be necessary to use head fires, but they should seldom be used in sapling stands when the wind exceeds 5 miles per hour.

Large areas of level ground or gently rolling slopes should be burned progressively. The strip burning method is appropriate for large pole or sawtimber stands with a light soil cover of flat fuels. Rows of spot fires or parallel lines of fire are set at right angles to the wind beginning on the leeward side of the tract rather closely in front of a prepared barrier and then firing each succeeding strip to burn with the wind toward the previously burned-over land. Strips 1 to 4 chains wide, depending on burning conditions, are ignited in succession in order to take advantage of the wind to carry fire and yet not have an uncontrolled head fire going. The burning intensity can be controlled deliberately according to fuel supply and the stems to be killed (Hills 1957).

Progressive burning with spring fires in the "Big Thicket" area of east Texas has been successful. The burns were repeated at short intervals over a period of 5 years. Here the underwood consists of oaks, gums, yaupon, haws, arrowwood, candleberry, and huckleberry. The stand of these species was reduced at the rate of about 731 stems per acre by each additional spring fire (Harrington and Stephenson 1955):

	Stems per acre after—			
Stem size-class	No fire (number)	One fire (number)	Two fires (number)	Three fires (number)
1-inch.............	1,708	1,354	1,104	333
2-inch.............	708	708	271	104
3-inch.............	396	396	104	83
Total.........	2,812	1,916	1,479	520

Rootstocks may not have been much affected, but the reduction represents ingrowth of new stems minus the mortality among all stems. The damage to pines was negligible.

Summer fires may be needed to destroy hardwoods that are too large to kill at other seasons. Experience in dormant season burning is desirable before any attempt is made to use fire in summer. In any case the excess hazard caused by a heavy accumulation of fuel should be reduced by a winter fire a year or two in advance of summer burning. Then a series of summer fires can be used to improve stand composition. Summer fires can deaden trees up to 4 inches in d.b.h., but in hot weather they may burn severely enough to kill much larger trees, and great skill is required to avoid excessive damage to young pine stands (Lotti and McCulley 1951). In the Francis Marion National Forest the preliminary winter burning sometimes fails to remove damp fuel accumulated at the base of valuable pines; summer burning of such areas is avoided. Because of the need for extra precautions, summer burning in strips 25 to 100 feet wide is likely to cost one-third more than winter burning. The few surviving 4-inch hardwoods are likely to be nearly encircled by basal scars. The disposal of these and larger cull trees is deferred until it is time to regenerate the pine stand (Riebold 1955a).

In the Coastal Plain of South Carolina four consecutive June fires in 40- to 50-year-old loblolly pine stands eliminated about half of the small hardwoods, but resistance varied widely with species (Chaiken 1952b). The cumulative mortality percentage after the fifth fire was 45 for the oaks, 52 for blackgum, 78 for sweetgum, and 94 for myrtle (fig. 72). Some 69 percent of the understory was eliminated (Lotti 1956a). Mortality expected from successive summer burning on the Francis Marion National Forest includes 75 to 90 percent of all undesirable trees less than 6 inches in d.b.h. (Hills 1954).

In other locations, where the more common hardwood weeds may be more resistant, the results may be less satisfactory. Less effective initial control also results when, because of poor scheduling or bad weather, the summer burning becomes biennial rather than annual (Lotti 1955); but after about the third biennial fire mortality is at the same level as for annual fires. A prerequisite for extensive use of fire in summer is adequate local experience with it.

A practical, though not everywhere necessary, 3-phase program for utilizing fire in producing an even-aged crop of loblolly pine can be briefly stated. This program calls for one or more fires at each of at least three occasions as follows: (1) Early—i.e., at about 15 years—in stands of pine saplings, (2) later, when the thicker bark and higher crowns of pole-sized trees make the pines more resistant, and (3) finally, just prior to seedfall and final harvest of mature timber. The primary reasons for this burning are respectively three: (1) To reduce hazard and protect the stand from wildfire, (2) to destroy or suppress underbrush and hardwood trees with small stems (less than 2 inches) so as to develop relatively pure stands of pine, and (3) to kill recent sprouts and prepare the ground for reproduction of pine. To these ends the prescriptions for burning vary mainly as follows: (1) Burn against a gentle, but steady,

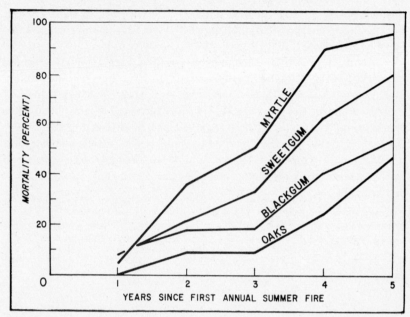

FIGURE 72.—Cumulative lethal effects on understory hardwoods from successive summer fires in 40- to 50-year-old loblolly pine stands on the Santee Experimental Forest (Lotti 1956a).

wind, (2) burn with a light wind when and where control is assured, and (3) burn over strips progressively with controlled headfires.

The use of fire in midrotation stand improvement is most effective, and less necessary, where its applications for the other purposes (phases 1 and 3 above) have been most successful. Indeed in those situations where, in response to a burn at harvest time, pine reproduction is prompt, highly satisfactory, and readily protected, the use of fire in immature timber (i.e., during its sapling and pole stages of development) is not necessary.

Response to release

Sale of poor pines from well-stocked spots in immature timber stands serves to release the better ones for more rapid growth and to increase the value of the final harvest. Also the capacity of loblolly pine of all sizes to respond to release usually, though not always, makes even the noncommercial early removal of competing hardwoods a profitable operation. The release of chosen crop trees, and the improvement of species composition can be a combined measure, but it need not be so precisely timed in immature timber as in seedling stands. The need for crop-tree release extends over a much longer period; several light cuttings are better than a single heavy one, if the possibility of a reduced volume in the final harvest is to be avoided.

Loblolly pine rarely succumbs to sudden exposure; all reserved trees that survive tend to benefit from release. For instance, diameter classes 5 to 8 inches inclusive can make over 100 percent improvement in growth (fig. 73) (Bull 1939b). Where little trees are abundant, a smaller percentage of them may live through the release operation, but the survivors among them often respond best of all to improvement measures, and then, through ingrowth, swell the ranks of sapling stands (table 34).

TABLE 34.—*Pine sapling stand near Crossett, Ark., before and 7 years after liberation by three different degrees of release (Mann 1949)*

Degree of release and d.b.h. class of pines (inches)	Pines per acre before removal of hardwoods	Pines per acre 7 years after hardwoods were cut
	Number	Number
Hardwoods 6 inches d.b.h. and larger removed:		
2	9	113
3	15	47
4	12	4
5	13	16
6+	47	69
Hardwoods 2 inches d.b.h. and larger removed:		
2	17	129
3	13	74
4	9	59
5	11	8
6+	41	77
Hardwood 5 feet high and over removed:		
2	28	242
3	21	94
4	15	78
5	15	55
6+	46	74

In the first 5 years an improved stand may be expected to grow in diameter at a faster rate, but add less wood, than a comparable untreated stand. In the second 5 years, however, the improved stand should not only increase its lead in rate of diameter growth, but also attain superiority in volume growth per acre (Bull 1944). In one instance the yield per acre was increased by 1¼ cords per man-hour invested in girdling the undesirable trees. In most localities this extra volume would be worth from 2 to 5 times the cost of the girdling that made it possible (Bull 1945).

Inordinate delay readily may cancel out these benefits, however. Both improvement cutting that is started late (after 40 years of age)

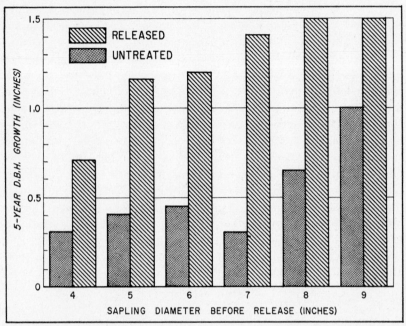

FIGURE 73.—Loblolly pine response to liberation by removal of high level competition in Louisiana (Bull 1939b).

and partial harvests that are not an integral part of silviculture can be rather unsatisfactory (Chaiken 1941). Where stands of immature loblolly pine are dense thinning should be started early.

THINNING

Is thinning necessary?

Obviously, by natural or artificial means, thinnings are inescapable because large loblolly pines occupy more space exclusively than do small ones. However, dense stands thin themselves naturally only after suffering considerable retardation of growth.

Silvicultural thinnings are designed to reduce density and increase rates of growth in overstocked portions of pure, even-aged, young stands of pine. They are less necessary in all-aged stands and in mixed stands that have been reduced in density by means of improvement cuttings. In rough stands on poor sites and where only small products are to be grown under nonintensive practice for a limited market, artificial thinning may be inadvisable. Up to 30 or 35 years unthinned stands of loblolly pine almost invariably produce more wood than do thinned stands (Wheeler 1952).

In young, even-aged, and closely spaced pure stands of loblolly pine (table 25, chapter 6, Growth and Yield), or mixed loblolly and shortleaf pines, some silvicultural reduction of the stand is essential to proper development of crop trees. Very heavy thinning induces much less epicormic sprouting—i.e., "feathering out" on the upper bole—in loblolly than in the shortleaf pine. Without artificial thinning, natural thinning is inevitable but unsatisfactory. Among pole-sized trees it starts late, progresses slowly and irregularly, and wastes much raw material. In longleaf pine marked crown differentiation results in an early expression of dominance in sapling stands, and less need for thinning in pole-sized stands. Even-age stands of loblolly pine are more uniform and therefore more subject to reduction in diameter (not necessarily volume) growth before the natural thinning process can relieve the congestion. In pure heavily stocked loblolly pine stands, many of which are plantations, thinning is a cultural operation of prime importance (Muntz 1948a, Williston 1950, Mann 1952d and e, Chapman 1953, and Guttenberg 1954).

Benefits from thinning

Silvicultural thinnings increase yields of loblolly pine products not by any increase in gross production of wood per acre, but through additions to the net merchantable volumes that can be harvested in any rotation period. Or if an earlier, rather than a larger, harvest is desired, accelerated growth on selected trees can provide for it. Rotation periods can, in this manner, be shortened somewhat without reducing the volume of the harvest. An adverse side effect from this procedure may be some reduction in the quality of the harvest where short-rotation products other than pulpwood and rough saw logs are desired. The final yield from a short rotation may, of course, also be lowered if the thinnings are heavy or frequent enough to prevent using the soil to its full capacity.

When stands are thinned the surplus trees are cut or destroyed in order to transfer their growth to a limited number of crop trees of greater potential value. This operation is usually deferred until the trees removed can be used or sold. In that way thinnings recover existing values in trees which would not be salvaged if they were permitted to die naturally. Thinnings serve best not only to preclude mortality, but also to anticipate rather than to relieve serious competition. The opposite is true only where trees with long clear boles are to be produced for poles or piling without artificial pruning. In any event thinnings are more likely to prove successful if made from the standpoint of the trees to be left rather than of the trees to be cut.

Noncommercial and nonselective thinning is appropriate only where extremely dense even-aged thickets of loblolly pine saplings may fail to express dominance if left untreated, and where the operation may well be made mechanical or economically mechanized. One company has utilized road-grader blades, veneer knives, or giant stalk cutters pulled by a tractor to clear swaths through stagnant stands of overcrowded seedlings (Ryan 1952). Normally this is unnecessary, and thinning is deferred until the inherent superiority of certain trees is manifest, and enough of the others are sufficiently large to be sold to cover the cost of removing them.

Commercial thinnings provide early returns, and, by speeding growth, hasten subsequent returns, thus helping to defray interest charges, if any, on the cost of establishing a stand of pure loblolly pine (Livingston 1956). They do this through providing salvage of, and income from, the poorer trees, and selection of, and additional space for, the better trees (Bruner 1938). Single thinnings are seldom advisable unless currently profitable. A series of several thinnings can be effective to enhance the quality of the crop when growing sawtimber, or other large products, on relatively long rotations.

Time and intensity of thinning

Thinnings usually can commence as soon as the inferior trees can be used or sold, and repeated whenever the better trees can again benefit. The exact time to begin, and the intervals between thinning, however, are dependent on how local marketing opportunities can be used to further the wishes and plans of the owner in producing specific products. In uniform stands on good sites where wood products, especially those of large size, are to be grown under intensive practice for an active market, thinning is needed sooner or later to anticipate stand congestion. For high-quality saw logs it may commence late, but once started it should enter the canopy lightly from below at rather frequent intervals. In moderate thinning there is much latitude in choosing a program to fit local needs and take advantage of current prices.

The earliest time for a first thinning is at the age of 12 to 15 years on reasonably good sites with 1,800 or more trees per acre. The first thinning is needed to keep green crowns from getting too short and to permit early removal of the more heavily branched

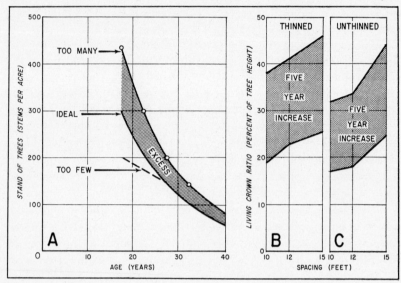

FIGURE 74.—For maximum volume growth, the dense stand, upper curve in *A*, should have been thinned at ages indicated by circles, that is, at 17, 22, 27, and 32 years, reducing it each time to approximately the stand indicated on the curve marked ideal. In both the thinned stands, *B*, and the unthinned stands, *C*, crown ratios increased in 5 years as shown by the interval between upper and lower curves (Chapman 1942b, table 15).

trees. Such thinning allows surrounding codominant and subdominant trees to take over the openings created.

The latest time for a first thinning is when merchantable trees begin to die in volumes worth salvaging—as for example where there is a prospective loss of 2 or 3 cords of pulpwood per acre during the next 5 years (Bull 1950b). This time may come sooner on good sites than on poor ones, and possibly sooner in the gulf states than on the Atlantic seaboard. Likewise where growth is rapid for any reason the interval between thinnings can be shorter and the results better (Simmons and Schnur 1937).

To keep the rate of growth in basal area from declining too rapidly it is suggested (Morriss 1958) that thinnings should keep stand density below 80 percent of normal. On this assumption, and if the annual rate of approach toward normal can be estimated (fig. 56, chapter 6, Growth and Yield), the proper time to start thinning may be approximated on that basis. For example, if an 18-year-old stand is 74 percent stocked, and is approaching 80 percent at the rate of 2 percent annually, then thinning should start in 3 years. Loblolly pines in well-stocked stands may be thinned 4 to 10 times at

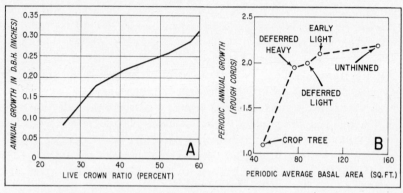

FIGURE 75.—Periodic annual growth of loblolly pine in Louisiana, as measured in current 5-year periods, in relation to live crown ratio (*A*) at Wood-worth (Mann 1954a), and basal areas (*B*) left after four methods of thinning (Mann 1952d and 1952e).

intervals of 3 to 7 (often 5) years without too much reduction in the number of saw-log trees needed for an effective final series of regeneration cuttings.

In a series of thinnings frequent cuttings should be light; infrequent ones heavy. If too light, little is accomplished for a stand, but the error is readily corrected in subsequent cutting. If too heavy, individual trees respond well, and the stand is restored in time. Moderate thinning maintains or increases net yield through salvage and improves quality of product through selection (fig. 74). Stands should be thinned early if necessary to keep crowns from becoming too short for good individual tree growth, yet moderately to retain enough trees and basal area for good per-acre growth (fig. 75).

Overcutting in immature timber stands tends to reduce quantity of yield when it comes late, and it commonly reduces quality of the yield when it occurs early in the rotation. It is now realized that, within certain rather wide limits of growing stock, satisfactory yields of pine can be obtained from most sites. Without planting and with only 50 percent of full stocking at the start it may be possible to produce 95 percent of the maximum possible current annual increment.[100] Working with loblolly pine, McClay (1953d) found that in thinning from below the heavier cuts returned greater total yields, in a decade during which both pulpwood and saw logs were taken,

[100] This has been the experience in the Crossett Experimental Forest and has been reported also from extensive experience with thinning in Denmark (Moller 1954) where the initial volume of a stand may be completely removed, and its equivalent fully restored, in a period of 20 years of good management. The concept of "full stocking" is explained in the section "Equilibrium density versus desirable stocking" in chapter 6, Growth and Yield.

than did moderate thinning. However, where uniformly high-quality wood is a consideration, early crown closure should be followed by only enough thinning to keep about one-third of tree length in live crown (Paul 1952).

While thinning ordinarily is used only in even-aged stands, it may also be needed in group selection or other uneven-aged systems where overdense groups of pines occur. In using the selection system (Reynolds 1950a) loblolly pine saplings may be left in crowded groups 20 to 30 years, or until pruned naturally to the desired length. One 16-foot log length may be clear by the time the trees are 3 or 4 inches in d.b.h. (Paul 1932b). As soon as merchantable trees are available the stand can be thinned to reserve the best clear-stemmed codominant trees and to permit them to expand their crowns for rapid growth.

Products from thinning

Loblolly pine thinnings supply raw material for three principal commercial products: posts, pulpwood, and saw logs. They can be made available in that order as developing young stands are thinned.

Good fence posts can be made from trees too small for pulpwood, if they can be treated against decay (Cummings 1952b). A tenfold increase in preservative treatment for fence posts in the past 30 years has enlarged the market for pine thinnings (Osborne 1955). As many as 1,000 posts per acre have been thinned out of some 10- to 20-year-old stands (Barker 1953). More often 400 to 600 posts are obtained from stands averaging 4 inches in diameter when first thinned. The remaining trees should average 6 inches in d.b.h. 5 years later. Then they can be thinned again to yield 3 to 6 cords of pulpwood per acre (Cummings and Thurmand 1952). In one instance where planted loblolly pines had been spaced 4 by 7 feet on claypan soil they were thinned at 13 years to yield 296 fence posts per acre, 180 mine props, and 3.9 cords of wood, and to leave 81 square feet of basal area, or 362 cubic feet, of growing stock (Minckler and Deitschman 1949 and 1953b). With or without thinning the net volume growth per acre annually in the next 4 years was the same (161 cubic feet), but less of this growth could be harvested from the unthinned stand where it was placed on many inferior stems not expected to live (Minckler 1953b). Largely pulpwood, poles, and some saw logs are the products from later thinnings.[101]

[101] In the past most of our pine poles were harvested from slow-growing subdominant remnants from earlier stands, but now thinning operations in 20- to 35-year-old timber are beginning to supply them. Over twice the stumpage return now available from pulpwood can be had from trees that will make 20-

Thinning extends the financial maturity of many intermediate trees by increasing their rate of growth and their potential value for some higher priced product. A pulp tree that, because of poor form or low capacity for growth, will not make saw logs in the next cycle is more nearly mature than one that will.[102]

Recommendations for thinning[103]

Where stems are fairly well distributed on the ground young loblolly pine stands develop much more rapidly when half stocked than when stocked to full equilibrium density. Simple approximations may be useful in deciding where and how much to thin crowded stands. Number of stems of a given size or age on a sample area (0.1 or 0.01 acre) may be counted as a guide. For example 6 saplings per 21-foot square indicates about 600 per acre. Another rule applicable to somewhat larger trees indicates that the space to be left between crowns of any two crop trees should equal one-half the sum of their crown width. Stands fully stocked at about 20 years of age may be thinned using certain rules of thumb that place them in condition to grow rapidly on the poorer sites with about three-quarters of the growing stock shown in table 25 (chapter 6), or on good sites with about half of the stock shown in table 25. These most popular rules are based on stem diameters merely because they are so easily seen and estimated.

Because d.b.h. and crown width themselves reflect the crowding of trees, they are theoretically inferior to height as an indication of how much additional ground space a tree can use (fig. 76, *B*). As a criterion of space needed, height has the advantage of reflecting differences in both age and site quality, but it has the disadvantage of being difficult to see and to approximate in marking trees for thinning.

The need for thinning (fig. 76, *A* or *B*) may be checked against the rules of thumb (fig. 77). Although no single one of the rules is best for all conditions, they are in fair agreement for the size of

---

to 30-foot poles, while those larger trees that qualify yield about 35 percent more stumpage as poles than as saw logs. The use of artificial pruning to grow such trees more rapidly in thinned stands still has to be developed.

[102] A tree or stand is financially mature when it will no longer increase in value fast enough to earn a satisfactory rate of interest. The application of this concept in thinning is limited because in dense stands the capacity for growth is so readily shifted from the cut to the reserved trees. It becomes useful mainly in later selections between the larger crop trees under uneven-aged management, and in judging the maturity of entire even-aged stands.

[103] Space requirements for loblolly pines are discussed in the section ''Rules of thumb for desirable spacing'' in chapter 6, Growth and Yield. For full stocking see table 25 in chapter 6.

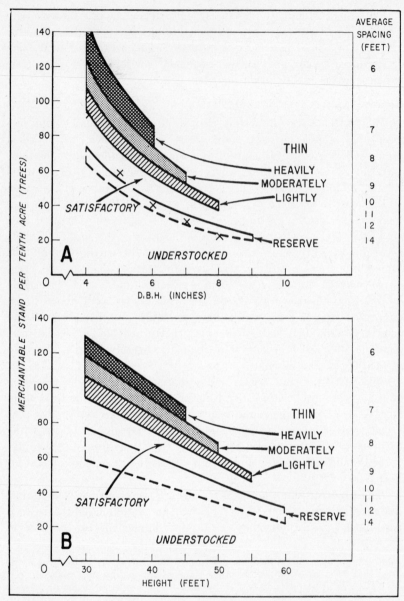

FIGURE 76.—The need for and severity of the first commercial thinning from below in pine plantations may be judged (on tenth-acre samples) by stand density in relation to (A) tree diameter or (B) height of crop trees.

trees usually reserved in thinning. For instance, neighboring 7- and 9-inch trees should be 14 feet apart according to either the $D + 6$ or $1.75\ D$ rule, and if the average d.b.h. is 8, some 229 trees per acre (spacing 13.8 feet) will have the 80 square feet of basal area commonly desired. Where the constants in these rules are additive, the slope of the parallel curves resembles that of the normal (fig. 77, upper curve) approximating the biological maximum, whereas with the multiplier 1.75 the slope is steeper, providing for relatively more of the smaller trees. Early freedom from crowding is advantageous in growing pulpwood, fence posts, or rough low-grade saw logs. For high-grade veneer or saw logs, or for poles and piling, the small trees can benefit from more crowding. Note that the 20-year-old well-stocked stands of 5- to 10-inch saplings and ''poles'' in table 25 (chapter 6, Growth and Yield) are spaced at more nearly $1.45\ D$ or $D + 3$, instead of $1.75\ D$ or $D + 6$.

All such rules are merely roughly suggestive guides to thinning practice. While they serve field men well in gaging the proper degree of thinning, they do not help in designating the trees (Averell 1945). No mechanical method of selection is appropriate beyond the sapling stage. When differences in rates of growth and in stem quality appear they deserve recognition in choosing trees to retain. In natural stands, when thinning clusters of trees with no others within about 30 feet, 8 or 10 of them may well stand closer together than any rule specifies. Current thinning practice commonly leaves the basal area about 57 percent normal (Morriss 1958). In closely spaced plantations it has been suggested (Muntz 1948a) that the first thinning cut one row of trees clear every 2 chains to serve as an access road for subsequent cultural measures.

A true thinning, however, should have better coverage and its type can be as important as its degree. The release of all dominant trees by cutting all interfering codominants regardless of quality may result in maximum volume growth, but not in maximum profit, for the codominants commonly make superior saw-log trees. In growing valuable products particularly, space arrangement should seldom interfere with quality selection. Recommendations for thinning loblolly pine (Bull 1934a) are shown in table 35.

PRUNING

Veneer bolts or saw logs from pines artificially pruned in the small-pole stage are definitely of superior quality. When saw logs from pruned trees are abundant enough to demonstrate their supe-

TABLE 35.—*Recommended thinning practice for first thinnings (Bull 1934a)*

Assumed market condition and wishes and plans of owner	Stands in which dominant trees are clear or have dead branches only for an average length of 34 feet or more (i.e., at least two logs)[1]	Stands in which dominant trees are clear or have dead branches only for an average length of about 17 feet (i.e., one log)[1]
A.—Assuming there is a market for pulpwood or other small material, or the trees can be used to advantage for firewood, etc.:		
Sawtimber alone is desired and as soon as possible.	Leave best 30-80 trees per acre (average spacing 23-38 feet); cut nearly everything else, except small trees in openings. In general, leave all trees 5 inches d.b.h. or less when they are not directly interfering with the crown development of the best or crop trees.	Leave best 100-140 trees per acre (average spacing 18-21 feet); cut nearly everything else, except small trees in openings. In general, leave all trees 5 inches d.b.h. or less when they are not directly interfering with the crown development of the best or crop trees.
Sawtimber alone is desired, but maximum volume and highest quality are preferred to an early return.	Leave best 80-120 trees per acre (average spacing 19-23 feet); cut nearly everything else, except small trees in openings. In general, leave all trees 5 inches d.b.h. or less when not directly interfering with crown development of the best or crop trees.	Leave best 160-200 trees per acre (average spacing 15-17 feet); cut nearly everything else, except small trees in openings. In general, leave all trees 5 inches d.b.h. or less when not directly interfering with crown development of the best or crop trees.
Both sawtimber and pulpwood are desired, and even relatively small quantities of each are salable.	Leave best 30-80 trees per acre (average spacing 23-38 feet) for sawtimber. These trees should be clean, straight, sound, and give promise of producing at least one No. 1 saw log. Leave all sound trees less than 6 inches d.b.h. that are likely to live until the next cutting. Cut all trees 6 inches d.b.h. and larger that will never produce at least one No. 1 saw log.	Confine thinning to removing trees directly interfering with the best 150-200 trees per acre (average spacing 15-17 feet) or do not thin.
Pulpwood alone is desired and a more or less continuous sustained yield is to be achieved.	(1) In stands averaging 11 inches or more in d.b.h., leave all sound trees under 9 inches in d.b.h. and also leave one 10-inch or better tree per quarter acre as a seed tree (average spacing 105 feet). (2) In stands averaging about 8 inches in d.b.h., leave about 200 sound 6- to 9-inch trees per acre (average spacing 15 feet) and all sound trees 5 inches in d.b.h. or less that are likely to remain alive until the next cutting. (3) In stands averaging 5 inches in d.b.h. or less no thinning is recommended. Wait until pulpwood can be removed. If, however, there are a number of trees 6 inches and more in d.b.h., these should be thinned out.	

Assumed market condition and wishes and plans of owner	*Stands in which dominant trees are clear or have dead branches only for an average length of 34 feet or more (i.e., at least two logs)*[1]	*Stands in which dominant trees are clear or have dead branches only for an average length of about 17 feet (i.e., one log)*[1]
B.—Assuming there is no market or use at all for the thinned material, but a reasonable hope for a future market for small material within about 10 years.	No immediate thinnings are recommended. Wait for a market or use for the cut material to develop, and then thin according to part A above.	
C.—Assuming no market or use for the thinned material and no hope for a market within about 10 years:		
Sawtimber alone is desired and as soon as possible.	Leave only best 30-80 trees per acre (average spacing 23-38 feet) or make no thinning at all.	Leave only best 100-140 trees per acre (average spacing 18-21 feet) or make no thinning at all.
Sawtimber alone is desired, but maximum volume and highest quality are preferred to an early return.	Leave only best 80-120 trees per acre (average spacing 19-23 feet) or make no thinning at all.	Leave only best 160-200 trees per acre (average spacing 15-17 feet) or make no thinning at all.
Pulpwood alone is desired, and a more or less continuous sustained yield is to be achieved.	No thinning is recommended. Wait for market to develop.	No thinning is recommended. Wait for market to develop.

[1] For intermediate conditions, assume intermediate or compromise recommendations.

rior quality they will undoubtedly command a commensurate price.[104] So far few loblolly pines have been artificially pruned in deliberate attempts to grow poles.

The abundance of clear wood in virgin forests was due largely to early suppression and to the advanced age and large size of the trees. In second-growth loblolly pine certain insects, *Pityophthorus* spp., occasionally breed in the lower branches dying slowly from shading and thus hasten the process of natural pruning (Blackman 1922). Such pruning may be furthered or retarded by fires. The death of the lower limbs of saplings may be hastened by the heat killing of foliage and buds, but fires that kill trees may open stands so that the survivors become unusually limby. In old-field pine timber and in some plantations the trees are often knotty even when the stand is fairly dense. Pine stands with a rather uniform, though

[104] There is unfortunately no visible external evidence of the depth of the outer shell of clear wood. If it is not more than 2 inches deep, or the thickness of slabs, it is probably not worth what it cost. The relatively small number of timberland owners who operate a sawmill can obviously benefit from early artificial pruning of pines, but for a purchaser their superiority must be certified or conclusively demonstrated before the owner can expect to sell logs at premium prices.

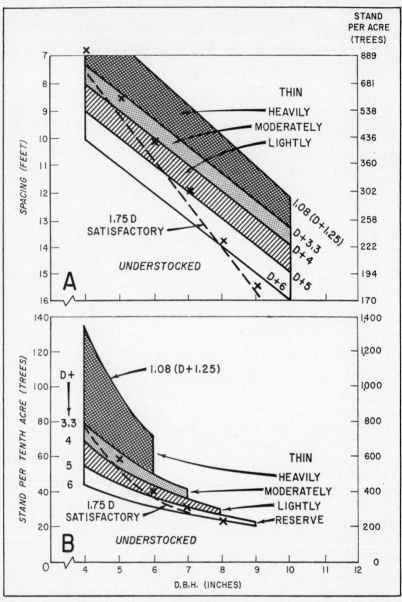

FIGURE 77.—Comparison of various spacing rules of thumb based on average
diameter of crop trees. The zone between the lines for $D + 5$ and $D + 6$,
or the 1.75 D rule for 6- to 8-inch trees, is considered satisfactory stocking. The X's represent a stand of 80 square feet of basal area.

subordinate, hardwood component shed their lower limbs more quickly and get an earlier start in forming clear wood. In a mixed forest the heavy shade of broad-leaved species maintains a relatively high moisture content in the air and in dead limbs, and thus promotes decay and early shedding of the branches of associated pines.

In brief, mixed stands, dense stands, and possibly judicious use of fire, favor natural pruning in loblolly as in other pine species. Artificial pruning attempts to get the same or increased benefits without the disadvantages—growth on undesirable stand components, and retarded diameter growth—inherent wherever the main reliance is upon natural pruning.

Reduction of branches and branch knots

The value of pine lumber is determined primarily by the number, size, and character of the knots. Lumber of the highest grade may be worth 2 to 5 times as much as that from the lowest grade (Mann 1951d). The average number of knots found in the first 20 feet above the stump in loblolly pine is 70 as against 110 in shortleaf pine. However, the loblolly pine knots are a little larger, ranging up to 2.0 inches and averaging 0.4 inch in diameter; shortleaf pine knots range up to 1.7 and average 0.3 inch. The number of years that dead branches or stubs persist to produce encased or loose knots has been placed at 7 or 8 for loblolly and 12 for shortleaf (Paul 1938a and 1938c), but preliminary results from current studies indicate a somewhat longer average period. The innermost knots in a well-pruned tree are small, tight knots formed from branches that were living at the time they were severed. In unpruned trees such knots join short loose or "black" knots formed from dead wood close to, or under, the bark where the limbs died (fig. 78, A). Mann (1951d) estimates retrievable board-foot volumes from artificially pruned pines as in table 36.

Methods, tools, and time requirements

Artificial pruning should be started early, that is, at 15 years or when the trees become about 4 inches in d.b.h. If pruning starts on 4-inch trees, two operations are needed to clear the first log (Mann 1953b), but nearly twice as much clear lumber is available from 16-inch trees as when pruning starts at 9 inches (Mann 1951d, 1953b) (table 37). When pruning is delayed too long, costs increase, probable benefits decrease, and fungi may attack the trees after limbs containing heartwood are removed. For these reasons, slow-growing trees with branches more than 2 inches thick usually should not

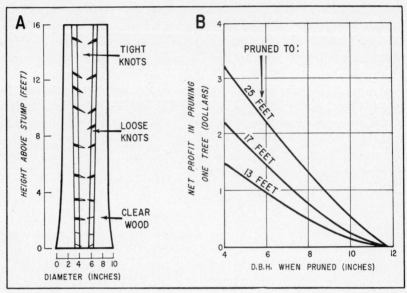

FIGURE 78.—Pruning loblolly pine: *A*, Quality zones in the wood of the butt log of a 52-year-old tree (Paul 1938a); *B*, net estimated profits from stem pruning to different heights on old-field trees of various sizes that were cut later when the trees were 16 inches in d.b.h. (Bull 1942).

TABLE 36.—*Estimated lumber-grade yields from short logs pruned at various sizes and later harvested from 16-inch trees*[1]

D.b.h. when pruned (inches)	Volume of 12-foot butt logs cut when tree reaches 16-inches d.b.h.		Proportion clear
	Clear	Knotty	
	Board feet	Board feet	Percent
4......................	94	12	89
5......................	90	16	85
6......................	86	20	81
7......................	68	36	65
8......................	56	48	54
9......................	48	56	46
10.....................	40	64	38

[1] Assuming that 1 inch of diameter growth will heal over all knots.

be pruned. Fast-growing young trees produce no heartwood even in 2-inch limbs. However, pruning limbs less than 1 inch in diameter from about 125 selected crop trees per acre is good practice.

Axes are not suitable for the flush cuts that bring maximum reduction of knots and promote prompt healing without infection. Saws are better than shears because they cut more closely. A 14-inch, pistol grip, cross-cut, handsaw with 5 to 8 incurved teeth per inch works well up to 7 or 8 feet. A light 12-foot ladder facilitates pruning up to 17 feet with such a saw, but in experienced hands a pole saw is faster. A preferred pole saw has a similar blade 16 to 18 inches long with 7 teeth per inch cutting on the pull stroke only. Light wood handles need to be of different lengths from 7 to 13 feet, or longer according to the height of pruning. How these items are related to size of trees and pruning methods is shown in table 37.

The cost for labor to prune to a given height varies with the diameter of a tree and number of branches. Pruning the first 10 feet of 4- to 7-inch loblolly pines cost about 4 cents in 1957 (Williston 1958a and 1959).[105] The study indicated that 10 cents per tree invested in pruning at age 20 can increase stumpage values at age 60 by $10 per tree. This work may be done at any time of year, although winter is best, especially for small operations. Pruning at other seasons or during severe drought may induce insect attacks (Mann 1953b).

Rates of growth, healing of wounds, and form of stem

Moderate pruning improves the quality of stems without retarding their rate of growth. Wounds from severed branches must heal before perfectly straight-grained wood can be grown. Wood needed to cover over pruned knots is as follows (Mann 1952a and 1953b):

Knot size class	Knot diameter (inches)	Radial growth (inches)
Small	0-1	0.60
Medium	1-1½	.76
Large	1½-2	.92

Thus on trees growing 3 inches in 10 years clear wood will start to form 4 years after the small knots were pruned, and 6 years after the large ones were pruned.

It has been observed in South Africa that the removal of 25 percent of a vigorous crown from a loblolly pine has no effect on either diameter or height growth. Removal of 50 percent slightly retards increases in diameter but not in height. The removal of 75 percent significantly affects both diameter and height growth

[105] For each tree pruned to 10 feet in one forest the gross working time varied as follows:

$$T = 3.7 - 0.73D + 0.06D^2 + 0.06N$$

where T is time in minutes, D is d.b.h., and N is number of branches removed. To prune the first 17 feet cost 2 or 3 times as much with the time requirement as follows:

$$T = 6.4 - 1.4D + 0.16D^2 + 0.09N$$

TABLE 37.—*Choice of pole saws to prune loblolly pine of various sizes to specified heights by each of two methods (Garin 1955)*

Pruning method	Pruning height	Length of saw handle	Size of best trees	
			Height	D.b.h.
	Feet	Feet	Feet	Inches
3 step...............	1- 7	$\frac{1}{2}$[1]	15-20	3-4
	7-12	7	25-30	4-5
	12-17	13	35-40	5-8
2 step...............	1-9$\frac{1}{2}$	2$\frac{1}{2}$[2]	20-25	3-5
	9$\frac{1}{2}$-17	13	35-40	5-8

[1] Hand-grip saw type.
[2] "Meylan" saw.

(Lückoff 1949). Forty percent of the height of an open-grown tree may be pruned without loss, but pruning two thirds of tree height in summer, or half of total height in winter, reduces diameter growth somewhat for several years (McClay 1953e). Although severe crown reduction seldom alters height growth, it changes both the rate and the distribution of subsequent diameter growth. The stem section below the crown loses some of its taper. The smaller the living crown, the more nearly cylindrical the lower bole becomes (Young 1948a).

Recommendations for pruning

Pruning is most likely to be profitable if it is first applied to small trees making (or capable of) satisfactory growth (fig. 79, *B*). That may mean pruning only 6- to 8-foot lengths on dominant, co-dominant, or selected crop trees, on good sites only, or on medium sites where diameter growth can be maintained by thinning. However, if only one pruning of the butt-log section is contemplated, it should be deferred until the trees are about 35 feet high. When trees are 5 or more inches in diameter pruning may sometimes be combined advantageously with commercial thinnings and limited to 100 or 150 selected trees per acre (fig. 79, *A*). At this stage, final crop trees 20 to 30 feet apart can be selected with enough certainty to avoid the expense of pruning many trees that will be removed in preharvest cuttings.

In a second operation 5 or 10 years later, when the stand is 45 or more feet high, pruning can be extended upward at least another half-log length if desired. If the trees are to be cut at 16 inches, pruning above 17 feet is not justified, but if 20- or 22-inch trees are to be grown, pruning the more promising trees to 33 feet might be profitable (Mann 1951d).

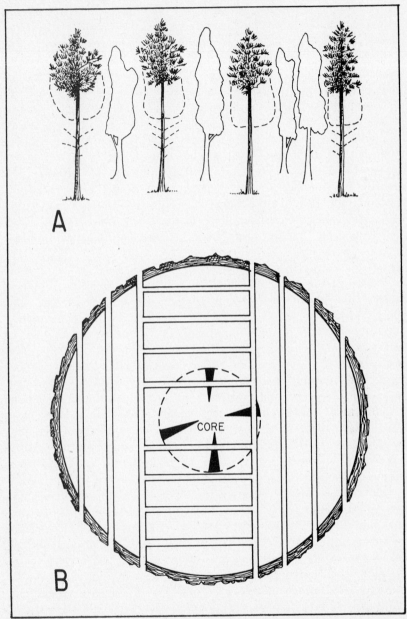

FIGURE 79.—*A*, Crop trees should be pruned not over two-thirds of total height, nor over one-third of live-crown length; for best growth of the pines, inferior intervening trees should be killed if they can be cut or deadened at reasonable cost. *B*, Top end of a 12-inch butt log pruned when the tree was 6 inches in diameter at breast height, showing clear lumber around a 4-inch knotty core (Mattoon 1942).

Briefly the essentials of good practice (Mattoon 1942) are to prune (1) young or small selected trees, sound, straight, thrifty, and evenly spaced; (2) close to the trunk so as to leave no protruding stub; (3) not much more than half the total height of the tree, or more than the lower one-third of the live crown; and (4) a second time if necessary, perhaps 5 years later, to produce at least one clear 16-foot log, and, from high-quality tall timber, to get two clear 16-foot logs.

Under this practice, and about 40 years after the first pruning operation, 40 to 90 percent of the butt log should be lumber of the highest value (fig. 78, *B*), and an increase of 8 to 33 percent in "B and Better" lumber, and over 50 percent in net per-acre values, can be anticipated (Paul 1931b). As the scarcity of high-value timber in the midst of an abundance of low-grade wood becomes more acute, the need for—and profit from—artificial pruning will increase.

SUMMARY

In the management of immature timber the handling of mixed loblolly pine-hardwood forest presents many problems. The most effective mixtures are those in which the broad-leaved trees occupy only intermediate or lower positions in the crown canopy. The eradication of deciduous species is seldom possible at any reasonable cost, but hardwoods need to be confined to subordinate positions. Those that sprout vigorously and profusely need harsh treatment just prior to regenerating the pine. Where enough pines have started in pure stands there is little need for later release measures on moist sites. On dry sites or on shallow soils release may become necessary. It is best to avoid making large openings in the canopy by destroying vegetation which, if left, would not immediately hamper prospective crop trees.

Nevertheless, early disposal is best for all trees without high prospective value. Inferior trees should be harvested, and the useless ones killed. In addition to weed species this often includes some open-grown pine trees that are growing fast but are rough and branchy and other pines that grow slowly or are defective. In the disposal of miscellaneous undesirable trees, felling is most time consuming, girdling intermediate, and poisoning most expeditious. Chemically treated trees show some tendency to die sooner, and sprout less, than the ones killed by some other means. The extent of oppression of crop trees or the degree of release from it are the principal factors that influence growth and survival of the loblolly pines in a reserved stand. Although in improvement cutting the primary purpose is to better species composition and to release promising pines, the operation need not remove unmerchantable material exclusively.

The disposal of surplus and inferior forest trees and shrubs calls for intelligent selection of the best time, place, and method of treatment. Blanket treatments utilizing severe summer fires, heavy machinery, or both, rather than chemicals are most useful just prior to the regeneration of pine in even-aged stands. Light burning is properly selective only where the hardwoods to be killed back are less than 2 inches in diameter and the pines considerably larger. With other stand conditions, particularly under all-aged management, the blanket treatments have limited application. Where advance reproduction has started, the need is for a highly selective treatment. To deaden slowly and let the trees sprout, the ax is still effective for notch-girdling large trees and felling small ones. To deaden slowly without cutting, a basal spray of 2,4,5-T in oil is effective on smooth-barked large trees and clusters of sprouts or saplings. To kill rough-barked large trees more quickly and discourage sprouting, use ammonium sulfamate crystals in low notches on large trees and on the fresh stumps of the small ones, or substitute 2,4,5-T in oil for trees freshly girdled by ax-cut frills or by machine. In accessible stands power girdling may double or triple the rate of progress in this work on all but hard-textured trees.

The benefits from the disposal of undesirable trees, where pines are released, far outweigh the cost of, and the damage incident to, this work. Formulas are given for estimating the per-acre time requirements in deadening weed and cull trees by various methods. In normal years the rate of height growth may be doubled and the rate of diameter growth quadrupled in pine seedlings 2 years after their release. In the first 5 years an improved stand of pines of pulpwood size may be expected to grow at a faster rate, but add less wood, than a comparable untreated stand. In the second 5 years, however, the improved stand should not only increase its superiority in rate of growth, but also attain superiority in volume growth per acre. In most localities the increased per-acre yield is worth from 2 to 5 times the cost of the girdling that made it possible.

To insure promptness in converting a hardwood forest to loblolly pine drastic blanket measures against deciduous species may be used. Aerial foliar spraying has somewhat limited application in this work because of lack of positive control in placement. Control burning in progressive strips may be prescribed where numerous small 3- to 6-inch stems need to be killed back to ground level, and heavy machinery is useful where roots as well as tops need to be destroyed. These measures, used primarily for regeneration, are mentioned here only because they reduce the need for subsequent highly selective cultural operations. To the extent that the blanket measures succeed, the ensuing chemical "mopup" or other selective improvement and liberation measures are minimized.

In even-aged management of loblolly pine fire is normally useful at least three times, each in a different way, for a specific purpose, as follows: (1) in the sapling stage—against a gentle wind—to reduce the hazard, (2) in the pole stage—with a light wind—to improve stand composition, and (3) prior to harvest and seedfall—progressively in strips—to prepare the site for regeneration. Normally it will be advantageous to burn more than three times in a rotation.

Once loblolly pine is well established in pure closely spaced stands it needs thinning. Thinning, usually avoided until the material to be removed can be sold, is most successful if timed and executed largely for the benefit of reserved trees. Where long clear boles for poles or piling are desired, without artificial pruning, thinning measures, if any, should be late in the rotation. But an early improvement cutting is needed to remove crooked and defective pines. For the other more customary products, it is best to thin early, as early as 12 or not later than 20 years, in order to anticipate rather than to relieve serious crowding. Then the benefits are salvage of, or income from poor trees, as well as selection of, and additional growing space for the better trees. Very light thinning does nothing but salvage imminent mortality—which can amount to 2 or 3 cords of pulpwood in 5 years.

In growing both pulpwood and saw logs it is advisable to thin heavily from above and below to speed the growth and shorten the rotation somewhat. If the rotation is not too short, stands only half stocked at the start may produce 95 percent of their maximum possible current annual increment. For final yields primarily of large high-grade products it is best to thin only moderately throughout the canopy, to avoid any extreme in stand density, and to maintain growth at a fairly constant rate. For intermediate yields of lesser products, posts, poles, and rough saw logs, loblolly pine may well be thinned at an average interval of about 7 years. A program for thinning must depend on how local markets can be utilized to further the wishes of the owner in producing specific products from available stands.

Loblolly pine wood from young stands that are pure, or widely spaced, is knotty unless the artificial pruning of dominant trees was started early. For lumber, or other clear wood products, the lower limbs should be severed with special saws before the trees reach about 4 inches in d.b.h. Branches can be cleared from some 25 to 33 percent of the crown, or 40 to 50 percent of the height of vigorous trees without significantly retarding their growth. The limbs should be removed close to the trunk, and taken from only sound, straight, evenly spaced trees, to obtain, in one or two operations, a clear log or two from each final crop tree. Formulas for estimating the time requirements in such work are given. The practice should add about 50 percent to the values recoverable when mature trees are harvested.

Chapter 8

Management of Mature Timber

SILVICULTURAL HARVESTING PROCEDURES

Aᴛᴛᴇᴍᴩᴛs ᴡᴇʀᴇ ᴍᴀᴅᴇ ᴅᴜʀɪɴɢ ᴛʜᴇ first quarter of the present century to prolong the cut from old growth, but most foresters have concentrated their attention on second growth. Some deliberate planning is needed to keep it in balance. In places there is a temporary need for reduction of harvests, for planting, or both. Proper management of immature timber may be the principal need until it is time to reproduce the pine, but the regeneration period is a critical time under management at any level of intensity.

Form of forest and methods of cutting

Loblolly pine timber grows well in many forms of stands, if the trees are free from excessive crowding. This is less true of regeneration. Where the species requirements for reproduction have been met, production can continue without adhering strictly to any one of the classical methods of silviculture. Yet a conception of differences between the principal systems is presently useful. It will be essential ultimately, perhaps in the next few years, when a choice must be made between "even-aged" and other methods of reproducing the forest (fig. 80).

The four main harvesting systems are:

(1) Clear cutting—with regeneration from adjacent timber or by artificial means.
(2) Seed-tree cutting—with seeding from a minimum of pines left temporarily for that purpose.
(3) Shelterwood cutting—where a partial stand is retained for re-seeding and incidental growth.
(4) Selection cutting—resulting in relatively continuous recruitment of young trees in small openings.

Overwood remaining during the regeneration period thus is absent or negligible in (1), tolerated briefly in (2), kept longer in (3), and

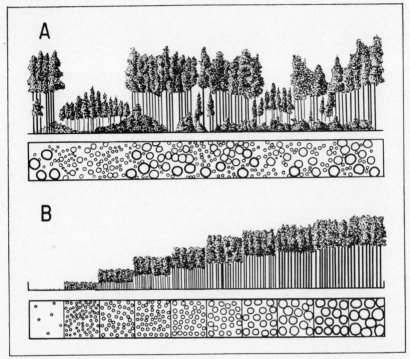

FIGURE 80.—Characteristic structure in plan and profile of two distinctly different forms of loblolly pine forest organized for sustained yields of timber: *A*, Distribution of tree sizes balanced through natural and silvicultural control of growing stock; *B*, distribution of stands balanced through allotment of equal areas to each one of a complete series of age classes.

accepted over many years in (4). The first three methods concentrate reproduction in stands for even-aged culture, whereas the fourth gradually disperses it extensively for subsequent culture in many-aged stands (Reynolds 1941b). Even-aged stands, reproduced under the first three systems, are 15 to 20 years old before they yield trees of merchantable size, whereas selection stands perpetuated under the fourth system yield a continuous supply of older trees in a variety of commercial sizes.

These distinctions between stands differently reproduced do not apply to whole forests after they develop a balanced distribution of sawtimber. Such balance is not practicable on many small woodlands, and may be attained on large holdings only gradually as they remain organized to sustain yields. Meanwhile the above distinctions, related to stand origin, do apply to separately managed forest compartments.

In the past the choice of a silvicultural system has frequently been a temporary expedient dictated on the basis of the existing form of forest to be placed under management. The wisdom of continuing to operate a loblolly pine forest indefinitely under a system so chosen is open to question. In fact whether the even-aged systems (1 to 3 above) or the all-aged system (4) are preferable has been sharply controversial (Bond 1953, McCulley 1953f). Where the suppression of broad-leaved competition is well in hand, it has been amply demonstrated that the loblolly pine type of forest is amenable to management through either an even-aged or all-aged type of silvi-culture. However, where the problem of hardwood weed species is acute, where storm damage may be severe, and where an attempt is made to utilize the soil at its maximum capacity, it is not yet evident that loblolly pine can be reproduced and grown with equal facility under each of the two principal systems.

On good Coastal Plain and lower Piedmont sites, forests operated for purely commercial purposes can readily produce sawtimber in many-aged stands. But, regardless of sites and locations, certain other considerations involving incidental benefits from irregular stands should be recognized. For example, where "high grading" is deliberately avoided, there is opportunity to retain inherently superior parent trees longer, while keeping the ground cover intact.

The continuous forest cover provided under the selection system may especially benefit forests managed primarily for their water-shed or outdoor recreation values. In all-aged form, stands become more resistant to wind because of the partial vertical closure of their crowns. Some pines near the most recent openings may be damaged by ice or felled in storms, but most of them will have developed windfirmness on at least one side, and the larger ones will be well fortified. During dry periods a selection forest also retains moisture enough in the forest floor to reduce the danger from fire below that found on recently clear-cut areas. Furthermore when rainfall is heavy, the selection forest affords better protection to steep slopes and erosive soils than do even-aged forests.

An admixture of hardwoods likewise adds to these indirect values regardless of the structure of forest,[106] but the form of forest is

[106] Several of these indirect but desirable "side effects," now attributed to systems of silviculture, may be found more closely associated with site quality, and with the density and composition of stands, than with form of forest and method of management. The intensity of application of any system that pro-vides trees with room to grow, but none to waste, should in some degree result in many such benefits.

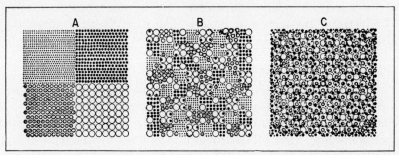

FIGURE 81.—Bird's-eye diagrams of idealized space arrangement of tree size classes, resulting from long-term application of different silvicultural systems of timber harvest and replacement: *A*, even-aged; *B*, group selection; and *C*, single tree selection (Bourne 1951).

necessarily linked to method of management. In a many-aged forest relatively inexpensive and periodic stemwise control of weed trees permits retention of certain individually desirable hardwood specimens.

In any region where full use is to be made of controlled burning, or any other blanket cultural measure, the need is for intensive even-aged silviculture (McCulley 1953f). The trend toward greater use of mechanical labor saving devices or heavy machinery, both to extract timber and to prepare seedbeds or control hardwoods, is increasing under even-aged methods of growing loblolly pine. The use of machines in logging injures a smaller percentage of trees in final than in partial harvests. Delayed or heavy thinning in even-aged young stands, or partial cutting, in certain Piedmont locations, may lead to serious damage from ice storms. Similarly under any system the creation of large openings in an overwood canopy can favor natural succession towards hardwoods. After clear cutting a previously unmanaged stand of pine, artificial control of species composition needs to be more positive to counter the sudden and complete release of competing natural vegetation. Overall site preparation that can be used early in even-aged management permits such control, and facilitates a high degree of success in attaining it.

Blanket treatments, less feasible in all-aged stands, are becoming increasingly less necessary in managing them. However, in either form of forest, any serious difficulty with regeneration indicates a need to change or intensify the silvicultural system.

The choice of a system and its successful operation over a rotation period will produce both characteristic space arrangement of stands and definite structural differences within the stands, owing to the separation or intermingling of the size classes of trees. Figure 81 illustrates the structure typical of each of three idealized silvicultural systems.

Contrasts in silvicultural systems

The general methods of handling various stands in loblolly pine forests are essentially similar except during regeneration periods. The manner of obtaining reproduction is distinctly different for even-aged and many-aged silviculture. This is true because according to plan the even-aged regeneration is both localized and concentrated in a short period, whereas many-aged regeneration is scattered and covers a long unspecified period. The resulting dissimilarity in cultural polices, schedules, and procedures influences five phases of forest management about as follows:

A. Immature stand management

UNDER EVEN-AGED CULTURE

In well-stocked immature stands, thinnings and other partial cutting at regular intervals are usually for purposes other than regeneration. Hence partial pine reproduction incidental to such cuttings may be disregarded. Its survival is then less important than satisfactory growth and value in the remaining trees. In fact, advance reproduction may interfere with uniform regeneration later, and may be sacrificed for this reason.

UNDER MANY-AGED CULTURE

Because a many-aged form of stand is desired, advance pine regeneration may at any time be allowed to replace trees removed in partial cutting. Where seedlings have room to grow, reproduction is never premature. If it is insufficient for the forest as a whole, reproduction may be periodically released, incidentally by cutting crop trees, or deliberately by deadening undesirable trees, but a surplus is avoided by letting the weakest seedlings die.

B. Preharvest measures

As thinned stands approach maturity partial cutting for stand improvement is no longer needed, and basal area is allowed to increase. The cutting cycle should be adjusted to regeneration needs, not growth. The final partial cut should be a preparatory or seed cutting; its purpose is to release potential seed trees for increased seed production.

Regular short-cycle cuts combine stand improvement with partial harvest by mature groups or single trees. Basal area per acre is held fairly constant at a relatively low level. This usually keeps the upper canopy sufficiently open for adequate seed production in good years. Seedbed preparation, if any is needed, is spotty, not uniform.

C. Harvest procedures

When released seed trees start producing cones, and before their production is again reduced by crowding, all timber should be removed from spots or strips to be seeded from the side, and all but the seed trees from other regeneration areas. Blanket seedbed preparation is desirable.

Volume growth of timber is harvested periodically. Guiding diameter limits in partial harvests should be selected with due regard to both the current demand for products and the need for replacement of timber stocks in stands of desirable density. Seedbeds and seedlings are ignored except as is necessary to minimize incidental damage.

D. Special measures

In thin stands of young trees a preparatory cutting may be useless and seed supplies may be short. In those situations, and where ground cover is heavy, deliberate seedbed preparation is essential if planting is to be avoided. The ground should be prepared for seedfall only in good seed years. Subsequent weeding should continue until the pine canopy closes.

In thin two-storied or selection types of stands crop trees are chosen on their own merits to be cut or left with little regard for reproduction. Advance growth, commonly present, emerges without liberation, except that which is incidental to cyclic cuts and measures to better species composition by reduction of hardwoods. In place of site preparation at harvest time, subsequent weeding is usually needed only in relatively open spots.

E. Removal of seed source

Seed trees and uncut strips should be harvested when the new seedlings are well established but before they are large enough to break easily and suffer heavy damage from logging.

Seed trees should be removed only when they reach financial maturity. No attempt need be made to liberate seedlings directly overtopped by crop trees until logging releases them automatically.

Clear cutting systems

Clear cutting timber on intermittent strips or patches is a recognized silvicultural method for the even-aged reproduction of loblolly pine forests. Reseeding from the side, however, may be inadequate if the parent stand was too light to produce enough seed or if it was so heavy that excessive logging slash reduces the catch of seedlings. Stands of medium density may be regenerated from 60- to 70-foot strips of uncut seed-bearing timber by alternating them with 150- or 200-foot clear-cut strips (Pomeroy 1949b and 1949c). The clearing should be thorough—that is, it should remove timber, pulpwood trees,

and merchantable tops.[107]   Or parallel 150-foot strips can be cleared
toward the prevailing winds to progressively enlarge the regenerated
area.   Where scattered single-acre or smaller patches are used in
lieu of strips they can be similarly extended as seedlings become
established within them.   The pattern formed by these cleared
patches is immaterial provided that cutting cycles are short enough
to constantly release marginal seedlings from retardation imposed
by the adjacent uncut timber.

Usually a fairly definite program of strip cuttings is necessary.
If the first strip has not restocked by the time the second strip should
be cut, artificial regeneration is needed to avoid leaving a strip beyond the reach of seed, or disrupting the schedule, or both.
Because of droughts, seed crop failures, and sometimes damage from
fire or insects, artificial methods are frequently necessary to supplement natural ones.   Reinforcement measures must be prompt to be
effective.   Where pine regeneration and the simultaneous control of
undesirable species are uncertain or costly, direct seeding or planting, and subsequent weeding, may well be adopted as standard
procedure in reproducing loblolly pine in even-aged stands.

Seed-tree methods

It is best to leave enough saw-log volume in seed trees to provide
an operable cut later, as well as assure enough seed for adequate restocking (plate 9).   Loss from windfall should not exceed 1 percent.
Sometimes 8 scattered seed trees will produce more seed per acre
than one-quarter of the stand left in strips.   During the period in
which timber remains on the land to supply seed, the trees may
grow enough to more than repay all costs of reserving them (Lotti
1953).   Favorable reseeding can be confidently expected only when
the cone bearers are selected from dominant trees, for the power of
recuperation in trees long subdominant decreases with age of stand
and with the length of the period of overcrowding.   Suppressed
trees can seldom recover enough in a reasonable period to be satisfactory as a source of seed.

The best number of seed trees to leave per acre is an important
question for which no simple unqualified answer is reliable.[108]   A

[107] Favorable response to thorough clearing was demonstrated in early experimental cutting of loblolly pine in east Texas.   In a 45-year-old stand 10
years after heavy cutting on 1-acre plots reseeded from the side, stocking with
pine saplings $7\frac{1}{2}$ feet tall was 35 to 43 percent complete, whereas on comparable
plots lightly cut the restocking was only 0 to 5 percent (Bull, Williams, and
Judson 1948).

[108] In the past seed trees have often failed because landowners were re-
luctant to invest in good ones.   All too often owners left no merchantable trees

PLATE 9.—An average of four well-formed trees per acre were left for seed
in harvesting saw logs and pulpwood from this even-aged stand. Note
that close utilization leaves only a moderate amount of slash. View of
loblolly pine in Able Chance, 1950, Francis Marion National Forest, South
Carolina (U.S.F.S. Photo 465161).

wide variation in the yield of seed and the catch of seedlings results
from numerous factors—mainly the year, the size and inherent fruitfulness of individual trees, the prior release provided, and the
receptivity of natural or prepared seedbeds.[109]   How to consider
these matters separately has been suggested in the chapter on natural
regeneration.   Forest managers, however, need some way to integrate
the various factors that jointly determine the adequacy of seed supplies.   Basic data in table 38 offer the best means so far available

or only trees too small, too few, or too defective to get results. Minimum practice rules were adopted early by several states in a more or less vain attempt
to halt needless devastation and keep pine forests reasonably productive.
Differences in fruitfulness and in seedbeds were often ignored by the cutting
guides. Such rules, without legal status, uniform compliance, or the will to
succeed, could not be effective.

[109] Receptivity of seedbeds was compared in one study (Pomeroy and Trousdell 1948) on the basis of first-year per-acre catch in hundreds of seedlings as
follows: Undisturbed surface or slash piles 2-4, light burn 6, disturbed surface
or medium burn 21-26, and a severely burned area 31-37.

TABLE 38.—*Approximate number of unreleased seed trees needed per acre to attain desired stocking of seedlings the first year after tractor logging (Wenger and Trousdell 1958)*[1]

Kind of seed year and desired reproduction by milacres stocked (percent)	Diameter breast high (inches)					
	10	12	14	16	18	20
Good seed year:	Number	Number	Number	Number	Number	Number
40	17	9	5	4	3	3
60	37	19	11	7	5	3
75	..	35	20	13	9	6
90	..	..	41	25	17	12
Mediocre seed year:						
40	38	18	10	6	4	3
60	..	38	21	13	9	6
75	..	..	39	24	16	11
90	..	..	..	49	33	23
Poor seed year:						
40	..	..	32	19	12	8
60	..	..	..	40	25	18
75	..	..	..	..	47	32

[1] Selection of seed trees to take advantage of fruitfulness and release to increase it is advisable. It is not feasible in practice to leave either less than 3 or more than 13 seed trees per acre. All of the above estimates greater than 13 are hypothetical; the numbers of suitable seed trees shown below the stair-step dividing lines are seldom available to be left and may restrict the growth of their progeny.

Seed-tree estimates between 6 and 13 may be reduced by a tree or two if the seedbed has been improved by burning or disking, or reduced possibly by one-third or one-half if definitely fruitful trees are chosen. Seed production may normally be increased by relieving seed trees from crowding, but on the Piedmont Plateau no amount of release will provide seed in adequate quantities during poor seed years.

to implement good judgment as to the number of ordinary unreleased seed trees needed on unprepared sites.

From unreleased seed trees on an area burned over in late summer before seedfall and within 1 year after logging, about one-third less seed is needed for a given stocking of reproduction. The relative efficiency of four types of seedbed under average conditions is shown in figure 82. The ratios change with soil quality and adequacy of spring rainfall. Because of differences both in seed trees and in seedbeds, there are optional ways of obtaining a desired degree of stocking. For example, 60 percent restocking may be achieved during an average year, where enough trees are available, by leaving pines as follows: 21 unselected 14-inch trees (table 38), or 14 fruitful 14-inch trees, or about 10 such trees on a burned or disked area. If the available seed bearers are larger than 14 inches, or if their productivity has been increased by prior release, still fewer trees will suffice, but it is not advisable to leave less than three per acre. Rates of mortality among seed trees from lightning, wind, and other causes in the Virginia Coastal Plain are given in the section on "Lightning" in chapter 3, Protection.

Where the danger of wildfire escaping control is slight, the early removal of seed trees that have served their purpose on regenerated areas is advisable to permit free growth of the seedlings.

Shelterwood methods

The practice of leaving a relatively large number of seed trees and then, as reproduction proceeds, harvesting them gradually, is called shelterwood cutting. This system usually supplies an abundance of seed and the site is more fully occupied during the regeneration period. In the shelterwood method mature timber is removed in a series of cuts extending over one-tenth to one-quarter of the rotation period (Heeren 1956). In the case of loblolly pine the seedlings have no direct need for shelter, but an overwood helps to keep the forest floor clear of vegetation until the pines can claim it. To this end shelterwood cuttings in mixed stands should not only liberate pine trees to be reserved for seed production, but also retain enough hardwood or other noncrop trees to prevent an upsurge of understory hardwoods.[110]

Leaving too many trees will result in the pine progeny having too much competition from the mother trees, but this is a minor and temporary difficulty for which correction is provided through progressive continuation of the harvest. Thus the seed source is removed in what is, in effect, a series of thinnings that serve briefly to stimulate not only better seedling height growth but also better reserve tree diameter growth. The latter benefit, however, appears to be limited to selected trees in thrifty stands of young pine.[111] Shelterwood cuttings in the Hitchiti Experimental Forest in Georgia have left 25 to 30 square feet of basal area per acre, lost only 4 board feet annually in mortality, grown 200 to 300 board feet each year,

[110] This is difficult to manage in some situations. Duke forest shelterwood operations have not been as successful as seed-tree or strip methods with loblolly pine, except where supplementary measures were taken. This has been particularly true of areas of high site index where there is a hardwood problem. On such areas shelterwood is not recommended (Heeren 1956). By contrast in the lower Piedmont, and where all seed yields are low, the shelterwood method has been most successful in regenerating loblolly pine.

[111] It has been observed on the Eastern Shore of Maryland that after partial cutting in mature loblolly pine sawtimber of old-field origin the growth on residual timber—i.e., pines capable of adding 3 inches in 10 years—was more than offset by the mortality of other trees. Basal area growth decreased 18 percent and volume growth 14 percent in the first 4 years (Little and Mohr 1957b). In such situations also the shelterwood system cannot be recommended.

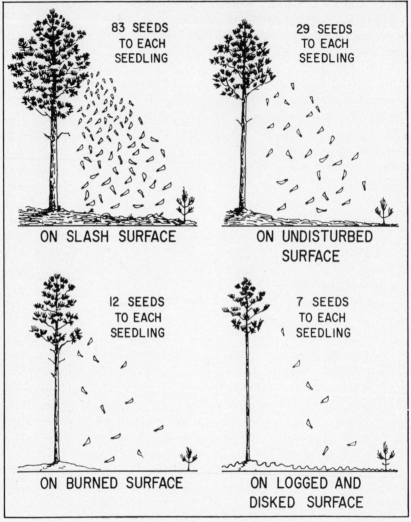

83 SEEDS
TO EACH
SEEDLING

ON SLASH SURFACE

29 SEEDS
TO EACH
SEEDLING

ON UNDISTURBED
SURFACE

12 SEEDS
TO EACH
SEEDLING

ON BURNED SURFACE

7 SEEDS
TO EACH
SEEDLING

ON LOGGED AND
DISKED SURFACE

FIGURE 82.—Numbers of loblolly pine seeds needed to establish one seedling on each of four classes of seedbed (Trousdell 1950b).

and provided satisfactory regeneration of loblolly pine even in mixed pine-hardwood types of stands.

Selection cutting

The selection system of cutting provides certain benefits in addition to the protective value of a continuous cover. An outstanding initial advantage is that many small potentially valuable trees need not be sacrificed by removing them while still financially immature

(Bond 1953). With some refinements, economic selection is being applied successfully in the management of many large and some small tracts of loblolly pine. Even on small properties, for example, group selection can provide some income from timber cutting every few years. With good markets loblolly pines can be selectively harvested on cycles short enough so that the incidental stimulus to seed production from the reserved trees remains still effective at the time of each succeeding cut.

Loblolly pine seedlings start sometimes beneath an overwood canopy, and often in openings 25 to 50 feet wide where mature trees have been removed. There, on good sites and with the benefit of frequent light cutting in adjacent timber, they can grow sufficiently well to permit satisfactory regeneration under the single-tree selection system. Grass and weeds—less thrifty than in large openings—retard them less seriously than under even-aged systems, but success hinges more on survival than on rapid initial response. On the clay soils in the lower Piedmont overtopped seedlings persist for a long time and quickly respond to release when the canopy is opened. Fortunately, badly suppressed seedlings respond to liberation rather promptly everywhere, and vigorously where moisture is adequate. In dry situations even the dominant seedlings may be expected to benefit from release. A mixture of several ages or sizes of trees can be handled under this system on the best sites.

Wherever unaided pine reproduction is poor, the single-tree selection method designed for all-aged forests needs modification for effective production of pine timber in relatively pure stands. In some places selection methods are less satisfactory on light sandy soils than on clay soils. Fortunately, because of the usual dispersion of tree diameters within broad age classes of timber, a forest need not be "all-aged" to have the structure, and share in the benefits, of a selection forest. It may well be many-aged by small even-aged groups of trees.

Group selection (fig. 81, *B*) is a method of cutting that readily creates such a forest in situations where the single-tree method fails. It is a practical compromise between two sharply contrasting systems (fig. 81, *A* and *C*). It is flexible enough to apply well to the existing variations in many understocked stands; there need be no uniformity in size or shape of the tree groups. Clusters of two or more neighboring trees can be harvested from 0.01- to 0.25-acre spots to be reseeded from the side. Such seeding may extend even over an acre or two, provided that the openings are kept sufficiently irregular in shape to retain a good source of seed within 200 feet (figs. 33 and

40 in chapter 4, Natural Regeneration). Openings of a quarter acre or less reseed best, but, if more reproduction is needed, they must be enlarged later to relieve 3 out of 4 seedlings from the competition of parent trees. The larger openings (1-2 acres) reseed less well from the side. Therein only about 1 out of 3 seedlings suffer marginal retardation, but they may need early relief from low-level competition stimulated by the clearing. Despite these procedures the forest as a whole retains the advantage of its essential group-selection form unless the scattered even-aged new stands become large enough (3 acres or more) to be recognized in mapping forest condition classes.

Under the selection system there is no need to have the cut and and growth correspond closely within individual stands, though the severity of local intermediate cuts may well be related to the growing stock and the scheduled cycle. The degree of partial cutting suitable for a loblolly pine forest with a post-release growth rate of about 6 percent (compound rate) has been reported (Reynolds *et al.* 1944) as follows:

Present growing stock per acre (M board feet)	Suggested 5-year cyclic cut (percent)	Suggested 10-year cyclic cut (percent)
2	13	22
4	15	27
6	17	33
8	21	38
10	25	44

With the above volumes roughly restorable in the time allowed, the harvest can be so limited, but where the trees that can be left are not of acceptable quality for further growth it may be advisable to reserve less volume. Although it is obvious that local stands require different treatments, the general instructions for cultural work can be so worded as to provide appropriate treatments by subunits without specific plans or separate records for the subordinate units (Grosenbaugh 1955).

Regulation of the cut

Midway between the silvical and financial aspects of forestry, and related to both, is a need for some sort of voluntary control of the business to relate the allowable cut to the overall growth. In growing timber the most immediately available benefits come from protective and silvicultural measures rather than from regulation, but other measures based on local experience and forest data are essential. Without suitable rotations, cutting cycles, and planwise regulation of long-term production of timber, there can be no real assurance of sustained yield.[112]

The rotation represents average felling age. Under uneven-aged management it is a superfluous concept; under even-aged systems a rotation should be selected, but need not be precisely specified. The choice is influenced by size specification for wood products, by land quality, and by certain financial considerations. For instance, where heavy initial investments and high interest charges must be met they discourage long rotations. Relatively small wood products may be grown profitably on good land under short rotations. The demand for pulpwood has resulted in short-rotation management throughout much of the range of loblolly pine. West of the Mississippi River there is some indication of an opposite trend. Even pulp companies are interested in growing some pine trees to sell as saw logs or to trade for pulpwood. For instance some companies will barter 1,000 board feet of saw logs for four cords of pulpwood.

Pulpwood volume growth in unmanaged loblolly pine culminates at about 40 years and pulpwood rotations vary from 30 to 40 years. For larger products like saw logs longer rotations are needed (page 278 of chapter 6). Increment in unmanaged loblolly pine sawtimber culminates at about 45 years on good sites and 5 or 10 years later on the poorer ones; hence for medium-sized timber on sites of index 80 or more, rotations up to 60 years may be suitable. Sites of index 50 or less are better suited to pulpwood production, but if sawtimber is desired rotations of 60 to 80 years are needed. These are not waiting periods because good management avoids rotations that mature concurrently. Further improvements in management may also be expected to extend the above mentioned culmination periods.

The interval between major felling operations in a given stand tends to become shorter as the management of uneven-aged forest is intensified. In understocked loblolly pine forests a cutting cycle of 8 years is suitable, but the period should be reduced to 5, or even 4 years, in well-stocked compartments. Because regulation of selection forests is based on timber volume and volume growth, rather than area covered, the record of progress in cyclic cuts must be kept current.

[112] *Sustained-yield management* has been explicitly defined as follows: Management of specific forest lands under single ownership or cooperative control within an economic unit, under a definite management plan which limits timber cutting to the capacity of such forest lands under existing methods of management, as determined from existing growing stock and growth, to provide without interruption or substantial reduction raw material for industry or community support—*Lumber Code Authority Bul. 95, Sec. 2(9) of schedule C, page 4.* Chapman and Meyer 1947, Forest Valuation, page 243.

To this end timber marking crews may not only designate each saw-log tree to be removed but may tally separately all timber to to be cut or left. This procedure provides the forester a convenient means of keeping currently informed (Bond *et al.* 1937). Modern plotless cruising with wedge prisms is a less expensive means of checking and regulating timber harvests. Net growth is readily determined from the records of partial harvests and recurring inventories. The results of such work can be totaled by compartments and may be used in allocating cutting budgets by means of a skyline chart (Wackerman 1934, Barron 1951). By this method graphic averages serve to replace laborious computations, and provide a visual method of adjusting the cut, block by block, to the overall estimates of growth.[113]

Under even-aged systems of silviculture good regulation of yields is most readily achieved simply by allocating an approximately equal area to each age class of timber. Some adjustment of these areas is needed to allow for differences in average site quality.

Regulation of the cut to sustain yields of loblolly pine timber need not be an involved process, but it entails careful consideration of both the silvical and financial aspects of the business.

FINANCIAL ASPECTS OF HANDLING LOBLOLLY PINE TIMBER

The value of a forest property as an investment in timber growing depends on numerous local considerations beyond the scope of this book. Although no reliance can be placed on absolute prices or values, continually shifting as they do with place and time, some examples to show labor and cost requirements as related to various phases of the work may be helpful in planning operations.

[113] Similarly under close control, the distribution of the overall cut can be regulated if necessary, by diameter groups, to correct any apparent abnormalities in tree-size representation that account for a loss in uniformity of growth. Structual differences in forests, arising from contrasts in age within some stands and in stem growth in all stands, are difficult to study except by graphic methods. Herrick (1945) proposes a numerical expression of stand structure— a single factor to characterize the arrangement of size classes—just as site index integrates the complex influences which determine the capacity of land to yield timber.

A highly technical evaluation is involved. To illustrate the computation the author uses data from a productive uneven-aged loblolly pine forest at Crossett, Ark. He introduces the concept of a ''maximum-product d.b.h. point.'' This point in terms of percentage of the entire diameter range is his stand structure factor. Its significance is only slightly different in even-aged stands, with their bell-shaped distribution curves, from that in many-aged stands where the trend is J-shaped. However, a simple way to check the adequacy of an existing distribution of diameters in a many-aged forest is to compare it directly with Liocourt's geometrical progression using a q value of 1.5 for loblolly pine. See also table 24, of chapter 6, Growth and Yield.

In the face of continuous change in woods and mill technologies and product markets, the forester must be prepared to make periodic economic analysis. Interest rate is important to a forest manager in his long-range planning. The rate consists of four main elements: (1) the pure or risk-free rate, (2) the risk rate to insure against loss of income or principal, (3) the profit rate to induce investment capital to shift from low risk to higher risk in anticipation of greater profit, and (4) the time-preference rate which indicates the relative importance attached to present versus future cash funds. Separate estimates of these elements lead to selection of a rate appropriate for a given forestry undertaking (Guttenberg 1950).

Cost and returns in growing loblolly pine

The general trend in the price paid for stumpage continues upward as the years go by. Stumpage price bid for national-forest timber tends to increase with the total volume offered in a sale and with its concentration in terms of cut per acre, and to decrease with increases in the ratio of hardwood included with the pine (Guttenberg 1956). In private transactions stumpage prices increase less with the cut per acre than with the size of the trees sold (Cruikshank and Anderson 1955). Working time requirements per unit of product, either saw logs or pulpwood, increase with a decrease in the average size of trees handled.

In the first 8 years of managing a typical loblolly pine-hardwood forest at Crossett, Ark., the timber cut had an average market value of $14.55 per acre per year (Reynolds 1947a). There the man-hours required per acre annually averaged 5.30 to fell and buck the pines, and as much again to skid, load, and deliver timber to the mill. Another 0.9 man-hour—for supervision, inventory, marking trees, scaling logs, and fire protection—brought the total to 11.5 man-hours per acre annually (Reynolds 1942). For that forest it was estimated that, if labor were employed 45 weeks of the year, 8 hours per day, 5 days per week, then the average size of crew needed full time per 1,000 acres of managed woodland would be 6.4 men. The use of chain saws and other mechanized equipment in recent years has reduced this estimate somewhat.

The need for access roads and competent supervision in silvicultural operations should not be overlooked. The cost of these items is sometimes relatively large. The annual per-acre costs of selective timber management on the Crossett demonstration forest in 1956 totaled about one dollar itemized in descending order as follows (Reynolds 1951c):

	Cents
Road depreciation and maintenance.............	32.0
Timber marking and sales......................	15.0
Taxes..	15.0
Timber stand improvement.....................	13.3
General supervision...........................	9.4
Fire protection...............................	8.0
Automobile depreciation and maintenance........	4.2
Cruise and management plan...................	3.0
Total.................................	99.9

The time requirements for some of the common cost items in silviculture have been collected and median estimates given for a wide area by Worrell (table 39). Fortunately the most time consuming item, planting, can usually be avoided. Note that hand planting requires 4 or 5 times as much labor as machine planting. Marking trees individually for harvest requires little time, costs less than a dollar per thousand board feet, and should not be neglected. The median cost per mile of boundary line was reported at $40 to establish and $6 to remark. Access roads are often a major item of expense. The median cost per mile for them was $750 to construct, and $90 annually to maintain them.

To plan and supervise all of this work there should be at least one technical forester per 25,000 acres. He should have a non-technical assistant—both men provided with a car or truck (Reynolds 1943a, 1952a).

After the timber has been grown considerable labor is needed to harvest, manufacture, and deliver lumber to a building site. Broad averages to cover this in the southern pine belt are as follows (Lowther and Murray 1946):

Woods to building site	Labor per thousand board feet (man-hours)	Woods to building site	Labor per thousand board feet (man-hours)
Conversion:		Additional handling:	
Logging.......	14.6	Rail transport..	5.7
Milling........	9.5	Hauling to the	
Seasoning.....	6.7	building site	1.5
Planing.......	6.4		
Shipping......	2.3	Total......	48.4
Selling........	1.7		

Intensity of forestry measures

No economic appraisal of benefits from silviculture can be wholly valid without more long-term experience with successive cuts than is so far available. Even so, the income that now can reasonably be expected from a forest when yields are sustained is an inducement to increase yields through intensified practice.

TABLE 39.—*Median labor time and median total costs per treated acre of certain forestry operations in eleven southern states in 1952 as reported to the school of forestry at Athens, Ga. (Worrell 1953a)*[1]

	Labor requirements			Total costs		
Operation	Sample No. 1 Reports	Range in time	Median time	Sample No. 2 Reports	Labor, material, & equipment	Median cost
	Number	Man-hours	Man-hours	Number	Dollars	Dollars
Control burning........	13	0.1- 1.0	0.3	12	0.09- 0.46	0.21
Site preparation for natural reseeding by—						
Heavy disking......	6	0.8- 4.0	2.3	6	4.00- 6.50	5.25
Light disking.......	..	..	....	3	0.40- 1.84	0.50
Planting open land by—						
Hand.............	26	3.8-20.0	10.0	13	7.50-19.45	9.12
Machine..........	24	1.1- 5.3	2.0	21	5.00-10.58	6.65
Planting cutover land by—						
Hand.............	20	2.0-24.0	11.0	10	6.01-11.91	8.66
Machine..........	12	1.1- 6.0	2.8	8	6.16- 9.00	7.25
Control of composition through release by— Cutting undesirable						
trees............	9	2.2-10.6	4.0	5	3.25- 5.55	4.17
Poisoning large trees.	17	0.1- 7.5	2.4	8	3.30-10.00	5.25
Poisoning small trees.	19	0.8-12.0	4.0	11	3.70- 8.00	4.77
Girdling large trees..	17	0.3-12.0	3.0	15	0.88- 8.00	3.00
Girdling small trees..	14	1.7-16.0	4.0	11	1.98- 6.22	4.50
Marking trees for—						
Thinning...........	25	0.3- 2.6	0.5	5	0.20- 1.73	0.45
Improvement cut....	27	0.2- 2.7	0.4	2	0.20- 0.42	0.31
Seed-tree cut........	17	0.1- 1.5	0.3	1	..	0.66
Selection cut........	21	0.2- 3.0	0.5	2	0.42- 1.50	0.96

[1] Based on information from 85 returned questionnaires. In each instance half the reports were higher and half were lower than the "median" estimate shown above. The rate for labor in the estimates of total costs ranged from 75 cents to $1.00 per hour.

In managing a given tract where pine reproduction free to grow is abundant, heavy investments in silviculture well may be avoided during early years only. Net returns from fairly well stocked loblolly pine lands of site index 50 to 80 increase both with land quality and with the intensity with which immature timber is managed (fig. 83 and table 40). The incentive to apply intensive practice first to good sites and eventually to all of the managed lands is manifest.[114]

As to the scale of operation, the revenue-cost ratios indicate some advantage for the larger forest holdings. To utilize capital with equal efficiency small woodland owners apparently need propor-

[114] This study in Georgia (Worrell 1956) assumed (1) capital and labor both available in adequate quantities at prevailing prices, (2) a 3 percent interest and discount rate, (3) fire protection for all managed lands, (4) yields from well-stocked stands at 80 percent of normal and from understocked stands at 70 percent normal.

tionately more good land than do the larger ones (table 41). Much depends, however, on managerial skill available. For various reasons many owners of small woodlands are not yet interested in forestry. A forest farmer who knows how, can manage a small woodland efficiently, and a large owner can hire professional assistance. In between are holdings too complex for family-type operation but too small to justify hiring staff specialists. On these holdings part time assistance from extension, industrial, or consulting foresters is becoming increasingly available.

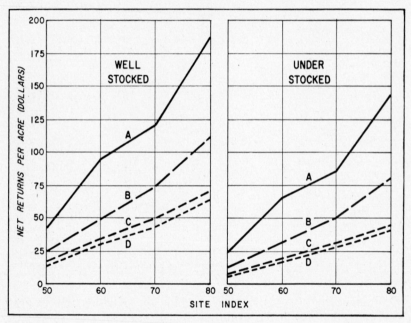

FIGURE 83.—Discounted economic rent (''soil rent'') from present pine stands resulting from four levels of management: *A*, intensive silviculture; *B*, minimum to retain pine; *C*, protection and seed trees; and *D*, fire protection only (Worrell 1956).

According to Wheeler (1952) it is unlikely that the average annual value received per acre for pulpwood alone, in a rotation as short as 35 years, can approach even half the annual value that can be grown in somewhat longer rotations producing saw logs and using intermediate thinnings and tops for pulpwood. According to Cloud pulpwood returns from loblolly pine are highest during 35 years in a pulpwood rotation and a sawtimber rotation should not be less than 60 years with money at 3 or 4 percent invested in the

TABLE 40.—*Present net values of future returns per dollar invested, and per acre managed, as influenced by the intensity of practice in growing loblolly pine in Georgia (Worrell 1956)[1]*

RETURNS PER DOLLAR INVESTED DURING A ROTATION

Level of management intensity	Land productivity class (pine site index)			
	80	70	60	50
	Dollars	Dollars	Dollars	Dollars
Intensive silviculture............	2.17	1.76	1.58	1.18
Minimum to retain pine.........	1.88	1.57	1.37	1.12
Protection and seed trees........	1.50	1.25	1.06	0.85
Fire protection only............	1.66	1.17	0.84	0.49

AVERAGE ANNUAL RETURN PER ACRE MANAGED

Intensive silviculture............	13.12	10.23	9.26	4.73
Minimum to retain pine.........	9.19	7.01	5.74	3.84
Protection and seed trees........	1.90	1.26	0.99	0.69
Fire protection only............	1.24	0.74	0.58	0.28
	Years	Years	Years	Years
Basis: Efficient rotation periods..	45 - 50	55 - 60	60 - 65	60 - 70

[1] These estimates evaluate gains expected from both investment and entrepreneurship on holdings of average size using a discount rate of 3 percent.

TABLE 41.—*Return per dollar invested (revenue-cost ratios) for well-stocked (i.e., class A) pine lands managed intensively(Worrell 1956)*

Size class of farm ownership[1]	Land productivity class (pine site index)			
	80	70	60	50
	Dollars	Dollars	Dollars	Dollars
Very large....................	3.63	2.98	2.69	1.71
Large........................	3.55	2.89	2.60	1.65
Medium......................	3.38	2.72	2.45	1.54
Small........................	2.85	2.24	1.98	1.24

[1] These data are from farms varying in size from less than 100 to more than 500 acres. The average forest land area per farm was as follows: Very large, 720 acres; large, 135 acres; medium, 60 acres; and small, 19 acres.

operation. With money at 5 percent it should not be more than 60 years (fig. 84).[114a] Obviously a financial rotation—the age of greatest returns from an investment—does not always coincide with the age of maximum annual growth of timber.

Preliminary theoretical analysis of existing information, assuming reasonable silvicultural treatments, indicates how the forest rental values are related to rotation periods for loblolly pine. The

[114a] Based on information in a term paper prepared in 1949 at the School of Forestry, University of Georgia, by M. C. Cloud, Jr., entitled "A financial comparison between pulpwood and sawtimber rotations for planted loblolly pine in the Georgia Piedmont."

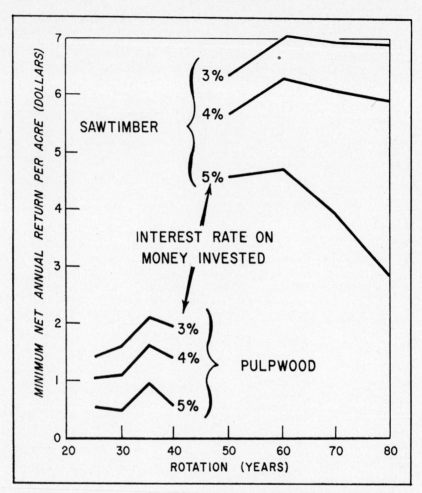

FIGURE 84.—Minimum profits expected in growing loblolly pine sawtimber or pulpwood under three rates of interest on invested money and each of four rotation periods.

so-called forest rent (fig. 85) shows dollar values placed on the mean annual growth in volume reported (fig. 62) in chapter 6, Growth and Yield. These yearly increments in dollars represent the net returns expected from continuous successful management of loblolly pine in full stands.[115] The peaks of these curves indicate

[115] In these computations Davis (1954, page 234) assumed establishment and early development costs at $14 per acre and administration at $1.03 per acre annually. In computing "forest rent" no interest on invested capital is charged where a going concern pays current expenses out of current receipts. "Soil rent" (fig. 85) is a different concept, in which the expense of re-stocking bare land has to be carried at compound interest rates. Stumpage

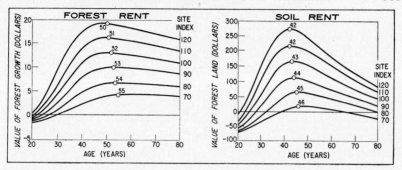

FIGURE 85.—Variation by site and age in "forest rent," the mean value of annual growth obtainable from an acre of loblolly pine forest; and "soil rent," the mean yield in dollars expected from the management of an acre of loblolly pine soils (from "American Forest Management" by K. P. Davis 1954. By permission McGraw-Hill Book Co.).

that the best mean annual growth and yield in value accrue on good sites during rotations of 42 to 51 years, and on poor sites during 45 to 54 years for loblolly pine.

Economic log and tree size, and the concept of financial maturity

Wherever 8- to 10-inch trees or logs are used in place of 16- to 20-inch ones in obtaining a given volume of pine lumber, more pieces, volume, and weight of wood are handled. The time and cost of each operation on the raw material is increased from 2 to 4 times in producing the same amount of lumber. The values realized at the larger grade-lumber mills from saw-log stumpage are usually negative for pines less than 13 inches in d.b.h. Small portable mills apparently can process rather small logs profitably, but maximum profits at large mills come from harvesting sawtimber over 18 inches in d.b.h. or 21 inches outside bark on the stump (Ashe 1916, 1925, 1926b, 1928, 1930a, 1930b; Garver et al. 1931; Reynolds et al. 1944; Rawls 1952).

The average size of saw logs may be increased by making more pulpwood from small trees and the top portion of large ones. The upper limits of utilization for logs or pulpwood normally shift according to the relative demand for these products in local markets. A typical 3-log tree has only 21 percent of its board-foot volume in the top log, 33 percent in the middle log, and 46 percent in the butt log. Making lumber from top logs tends to be uneconomic when the market for low grade structural material is slow.

values used are averages weighted by the full stand tree-diameter distributions expected by Meyer (1942, table 13). The basic stumpage values used ranged from $1.20 per M board feet for 7-inch trees, through $12 for 12-inch trees, $25.60 for 17-inch trees, and $33 for 22-inch trees.

It may be best to postpone final harvest of saw logs in locations where the merchantable volume of trees 14 inches and larger in d.b.h. is less than 2,000 board feet per acre. This does not apply to thinning in small patches of timber, where the better 13-inch or smaller trees are released by removing the poor ones for pulpwood. Good pole-sized pines, with space to develop, then grow rapidly in percentage—because they are small; in absolute volume—because height and diameter both increase; and in value—because of increased grade and size (fig. 86).

A study in east Texas (Clark 1952) indicates that the average volume cut per acre, and the average size of log, account for all but 4 percent of the variation in logging costs. Logging costs (per MBM Doyle) were as follows:

$$\text{Cost (dollars)} = 10.70 + \frac{1{,}100}{\text{Cut (bd. ft.)}} - \frac{\text{Av. log (bd. ft.)}}{10} \text{ [116]}$$

A small increase in log size reduced logging cost far more than a small increase in the volume cut per acre. At any given cut per acre, an increase of 10 board feet in the average log reduced costs $1 per M board feet. Cutting less than 1,100 board feet per acre was relatively costly, but a sixfold increase in the cut, i.e., 1,100 to 6,600 board feet, decreased costs per M by only 83 cents.

Well-stocked even-aged stands may mature financially for pulpwood only at about 30 years with from 170 trees on the best sites up to about 400 (including all pines down to ½ inch in d.b.h.) on the poorest sites, or mature for saw logs at about 50 years with 120 trees on good sites up to about 300 on poor sites (table 25 in chapter 6, Growth and Yield).

Sale value in timber trees varies, of course, with local markets and current prices, but despite these fluctuations, it has been shown to correspond rather closely to the current value of "No. 2 Common" lumber.[117] A readily useful concept is the excess in value of lumber content over the cost of logging and milling, called "conversion surplus." The aim in partial cutting operations may well be to maintain on each acre the greatest possible conversion surplus value

---

[116] Felling and bucking cost $1.08 per man-hour and the skidding, swamping and loading $1.71 per man-hour. The standard error of estimate is 15 cents.

[117] Thus the relative commercial value of the trees remains fairly constant and may be appraised on the basis of their lumber-grade contents in terms of the current price per M for No. 2C lumber. Index numbers to be used in these appraisals have been computed from records of lumber price per M board feet for the 5 years 1947-51. These indices were: 185 for B and Better, 140 for No. 1 Common including C finish, 100 for No. 2 Common, and 85 for No. 3 Common, including 3-inch and thicker timbers.

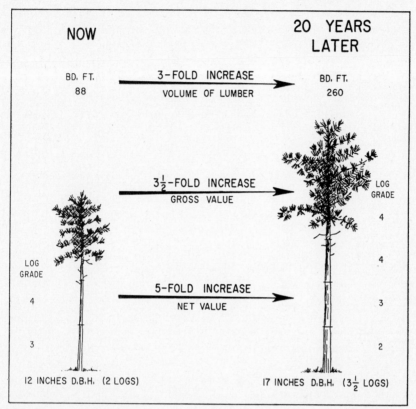

NOW

20 YEARS LATER

BD. FT.
88

3-FOLD INCREASE
VOLUME OF LUMBER

BD. FT.
260

$3\frac{1}{2}$-FOLD INCREASE
GROSS VALUE

LOG GRADE

4

LOG GRADE

4

4

5-FOLD INCREASE
NET VALUE

3

3

2

12 INCHES D.B.H. (2 LOGS)

17 INCHES D.B.H. ($3\frac{1}{2}$ LOGS)

FIGURE 86.—Estimated 20-year increase in volume and value of a typical loblolly pine free to grow on an average site.

in trees not yet financially mature. This will result in securing for that area the highest income that the desired rate of return will afford (Guttenberg and Reynolds 1953).

How to utilize tree size, vigor, and grade in appraising the financial maturity of individual loblolly pine deserves consideration when sawtimber is marked for partial harvests. Fixed overhead costs need play no part in the choice between alternative uses for trees or parts of trees (Guttenberg and Duerr 1949). The most profitable use for any part of a tree is that which yields the highest conversion surplus. The rate at which conversion surplus is expected to increase as trees grow can indicate maturity. A tree is financially mature when its expected rate of increase in conversion surplus during the coming cutting cycle falls below the prospective rate of return from alternative uses of the capital (Duerr and Vaux 1953).

TABLE 42.—*Volumes per tree by size class, indices of their "conversion surplus" values, and percentage increment in these values (Duerr, Fedkiw, and Guttenberg 1956)*[1]

D.b.h. (inches)	Lumber per tree	Present conversion surplus per tree	Annual rate of increase in conversion surplus during the next 5 years		
			High vigor	Medium vigor	Low vigor
	Board feet	Index	Percent	Percent	Percent
14...............	186	12.9	6.8	5.2	3.5
15...............	221	15.3	6.3	4.8	3.2
16...............	256	17.9	6.0	4.6	3.1
17...............	296	20.8	5.7	4.3	2.9
18...............	336	24.0	5.4	4.1	2.8
19...............	382	27.5	5.1	3.8	2.6
20...............	427	31.2	4.9	3.7	2.5
21...............	478	35.3	4.7	3.6	2.4
22...............	528	39.7	4.5	3.4	2.3
23...............	586	44.5	4.2	3.2	2.1
24...............	644	49.5	3.9	3.0	2.0
25...............	706	54.7	3.6	2.8	1.8
26...............	767	59.9	3.4	2.6	1.7
27...............	836	65.3	3.2	2.4	1.6
28...............	904	70.8	3.0	2.3	1.5

[1] These data assume no change in vigor class, log height, or grade during 5 years. Vigor is classed as high for trees growing 2 inches in d.b.h. in 5 years, low for those growing 1 inch, and medium for those growing about 1½ inches. The table is for pines composed of logs graded 1-2-3, which is typical of young unmanaged stands where the site index is not above 80.

Without a close study of growth, table 42 may be used as a rough guide to the economic maturity of loblolly pine trees, if it be assumed that over 45 percent crown means high vigor, under 37 percent crown low vigor, and intermediate crowns medium vigor. For example, if the rate of return from alternative nontimber investments is 4 percent, the data indicate that pines of high vigor are mature at 23 inches, and those of medium vigor are mature at 18 inches in d.b.h. It will just pay 4 percent interest to hold typical managed trees of these sizes for one more cutting cycle before harvesting them. At this interest rate the low-vigor trees do not qualify as sawtimber; if 3 percent were satisfactory they would mature for saw logs when 16 inches in d.b.h. Slow growth obviously brings maturity at a lower diameter than fast growth. The data are conservative because they assume no increases in merchantable height and quality of trees; and because trees of medium vigor, still capable of height growth, can extend their crowns upward and grow at the rate of the next higher vigor class when released. A premium is still paid for the quality found in large trees.

On good sites certain young well-formed loblolly pine crop trees less than 13 inches in d.b.h. tend to increase in log length and grade. A third log usually develops at about 14 inches and a fourth at 18 inches d.b.h. on dominant trees in uncut stands and on many sub-dominants after release through cutting. On sites of index 85 or more 4-log trees, graded 1-2-3-3 or 1-1-2-3, become common. Thus certain timber trees progressively improve in quality as they add logs while growing from 12 to 24 inches in d.b.h. The accompanying 40-year increases in the expected value of such trees steps up the annual rate of increase in conversion surplus, somewhat above that indicated in the last 2 columns of table 42, as follows:

D.b.h. (inches)	Tree quality by grade and position of logs				Annual rate of increase in conversion surplus	
					With increase in height and grade (percent)	Without increase in height and grade (percent)
	Butt	2nd	3rd	Top		
12	2	3	—	—	11.2	5.6
14	2	2	3	—	7.9	5.1
16	1	2	3	—	7.1	4.6
18	1	2	3	3	5.2	4.1
20	1	1	3	3	4.9	3.9
22	1	1	2	3	4.3	3.6
24	1	1	1	3	—	3.3

Usually the ultimate merchantable length of a tree is apparent by the time it reaches 15 to 17 inches d.b.h. and the period of rapid grade change is over when it reaches 22 to 24 inches.

In separate sections of a tree the surplus in conversion value decreases upward. This decrease in the surplus is sharp for saw logs and less pronounced for pulpwood. Hence the top sections, often unprofitable for saw logs, are best utilized for pulp.

In designating trees to be cut for saw logs under 5-year cutting cycles, a simplified guide (Duerr et al. 1956) to the diameter groups with which loblolly pines mature may be useful:

Vigor class	D.b.h. range at financial maturity when alternative rate of return is—		
	3 percent (inches)	4 percent (inches)	5 percent (inches)
High............	25-29	21-25	18-21
Medium.........	21-25	16-20	14-16
Low............	14-18	—	—

In each instance the range is to cover the spread in value which accompanies the usual variations in log-height and tree grade.

These economic concepts—conversion surplus in trees and financial maturity in stands of timber—have their limitations. They are best utilized only within the requirements of the silvicultural system and program of regulation adopted for a forest. They must be applied with considerable flexibility, especially to individual trees, if the welfare of stands as a whole is given due consideration, and if the forest is to be molded in definite form to sustain yields. Young released trees have a strong capacity for recuperation that is difficult to forecast accurately. Hence contrasts in the expected rate of change in conversion surplus are most useful to timber markers only when choosing between adjacent trees that appear to be otherwise silvically comparable.

Optimum stocking for profitable operation

A question that arises inevitably in long-term management is how far to build up stocks before starting to harvest the full amount of annual timber growth. As in other businesses maximum net return is a common objective.

A "marginal growth" method for computing the most economical stocking to use in growing loblolly pine under the selection system is useful. It is based on the principle that profit will be maximized by building up growing stocks to the point where the last addition just pays for itself in added value growth. A decision to retain or liquidate any recent additions to stock may, in this manner, be based on the rate the additional volume alone can earn currently. The method may be employed where certain information on aims, rates of growth, cost of production, and value of timber can be made available.

As a prerequisite for application of the marginal growth method, the policy adopted by a forest owner should first: (1) Specify the maximum size, quality, and use to be made of crop trees, (2) decide on a favorable distribution of sizes needed to attain the desired production, (3) determine the marginal values and, if possible, growth in values obtainable in relation to degree of stocking, and (4) recognize a guiding alternative rate of return—the so called marginal cost (MC).

To illustrate this method Duerr and Bond (1952) present an example with these assumptions: (1) Product—saw-log trees of reasonably good quality from 10 to 24 inches in d.b.h., (2) a J-shaped distribution of diameters with a stand factor ("q value") of about 1.2, (3) diameter growth of 2.0 inches in 5 years at 5,000 board-foot stocking and growth reduced 0.1 inch for each additional 1,000 board feet of stock, (4) unsalvagable mortality insignificant, and (5) alternative rate of return 4 percent.

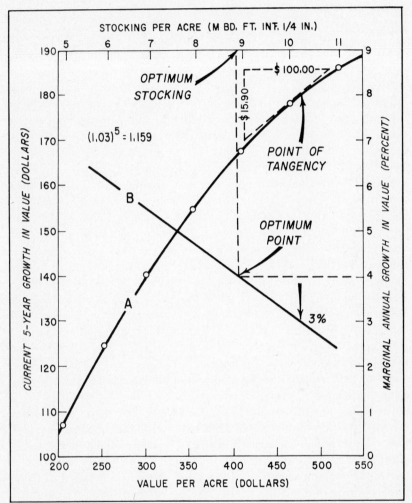

FIGURE 87.—Duerr's method of determination of economic optimum stocking. It is a graphic procedure to utilize first a curve of current value growth, *A*, from local valuations (table 43, last column) to construct, as explained in the text, a second curve, *B*, of marginal value growth. The predetermined alternative rate of return is then located on the right-hand scale, thus indicating the optimum point on curve *B*. Directly above this point the optimum stocking may be read from the upper scale.

Two monetary values are basic to a determination of marginal revenue: (1) The per-acre increase in total net value obtainable from current stock—through an anticipated unit addition to the volume of that growing stock—is called "marginal value" (*MV*), and (2) the per acre increase in current annual value-growth that will accompany such an increase in stock value, called "marginal value growth" (MVG). Then the marginal revenue (MR) or ratio between these two values in terms of simple interest would be:

$$\frac{100 \ (MVG)}{(MV)} = (MR)$$

When this percentage (MR) is converted to its equivalent compound interest rate it is directly comparable to the alternative business rate (MC) mentioned above. If (MR) is greater than (MC) it indicates that still further additions to stock are desirable before removing the full volume of growth annually.

The hypothetical data in table 43, together with the graphic procedure in figure 87, illustrate this economic "marginal-growth" method of solving the moot question of the most favorable stocking in growing loblolly pine timber. The seven estimates of current value growth define curve A. From curve A curve B is derived as follows: The slope of the hypotenuse of the test triangle shows the rate of value increase represented by curve A at an arbitrarily selected sample point. The point of tangency in this instance designates a stand of 10,200 board feet (upper scale) worth $475 per acre (lower scale). The vertical leg of this right triangle bears a value read as an intercept (from the left-hand scale). Note that the hypotenuse slopes at the rate of 0.159 per unit of value (lower scale). This equals the interest accumulated on $1 at 3 percent compounded for 5 years. Thus determined the 3 percent point is plotted on the ordinate for $475 to fix the first point in locating curve B. Other points plotted in like manner determine the position of curve B as a straight line. Then opposite 4 percent, the alternative rate for this enterprise, is the point which indicates on the upper scale a desirable stocking of about 9,000 board feet for the beginning of a cutting cycle. By this method the optimum growing stock is that whose marginal value growth percent equals the alternative rate of return.

OTHER MANAGEMENT CONSIDERATIONS

Tools and mechanized equipment

Progress in mechanization in producing loblolly pine pulpwood, accelerated by labor shortage during World War II, has continued as a result of the higher wages paid for lighter work by other industries. Small powerful direct-drive chain saws are widely used in the forest to fell, buck, and limb trees. The shift to power to save labor and to increase production per man-hour is extensive.

TABLE 43.—*Illustrative per-acre volume, value, and growth data for local determination of optimum stocking of loblolly pine (Duerr and Bond 1952)*

| Volume | | Value[1] | | Current value growth |
Now	After 5 years	Now	After 5 years	
Bd. ft.[2]	Bd. ft.[2]	Dollars	Dollars	Dollars
5,000	7,340	210.00	317.30	107.30
6,000	8,670	257.30	382.30	125.00
7,000	9,960	306.50	447.50	141.00
8,000	11,190	357.40	512.70	155.30
9,000	12,380	410.10	577.80	167.70
10,000	13,520	464.70	642.80	178.10
11,000	14,610	521.00	707.30	186.30

[1] Lumber sales values minus the direct costs of production, termed "conversion surplus."
[2] International ⅛-inch rule.

When the costs of cross-cut and chain saw operations were compared in the eastern Piedmont (Goodwin 1947), the totals were nearly the same, but the chain saws were faster. The time requirement per cord was 1.21 man-hours less. A five-man crew with chain saws was most efficient—making a cord of pulpwood in 51.4 percent of the time it took with cross-cut saws. The mechanization of felling and bucking operations is here to stay, but many farmers cutting less than 100 cords annually may rent chain saws because they do not handle enough wood to cover depreciation on such equipment.

Skidding also is increasingly mechanized. Although horses are still used on rolling terrain and in farming districts where woods work is a part-time operation, full-time producers prefer tractors. The tractors are commonly used in bunching the wood with sleds, skids, wagons, and trailers at points convenient for loading on trucks. The sleds are used in wet places and times where no other conveyance will work. In using crawler tractors, track maintenance is high on sandy soils, and wheel tractors with "bombardier" tracks (an attachment of half-track type to increase traction) may be preferred. The wheel tractor entered the logging field in competition with the crawler because of its low initial cost, higher speeds, and favorable maneuverability. However, unless they are designed specifically for logging duty, maintenance is high and the life of wheel tractors short in woods operations. Steel wheels or tracks damage more timber than do rubber tires. To withstand unavoidable snagging, the tires need to be 10-ply or more. Wheels with lugs have not been surpassed for maximum traction, but a combination of pneumatic tires and spade lugs permits faster operation (Knapp 1946). The wheel tractor seems to be at its best in medium-sized timber, or down-grade slopes of 10 to 20 percent. Down slopes over 40 percent and skid loads over 700 board feet are beyond the limits of wheel tractors (Cobb 1957).

Crawler tractors are available for skidding in a wide range of horsepower and weight. Some logging crawler tractors are heavy and equipped with a bulldozer blade, but lighter ones are usually preferred in pulpwood harvest. A log-carrying tractor on a raised frame with a 4-foot clearance for attaching logs between rear wheels 8 feet apart is an indication that this equipment is undergoing specialized development (Smedberg 1947). Worthington (1939) found that, in moving loblolly pine logs over distances of 1,000 feet or more, ground skidding is less efficient than pan or arch skidding with crawler tractors. In each such case the costs were lowest where a modified relay system was used, and a team and teamster helped to concentrate the load prior to tractor transportation to a landing. An outstanding feature of the operating cost with tractor equipment is the fact that only about one-fourth is for labor. An equal amount is needed to cover ownership costs of depreciation, interest, taxes, and insurance. The remaining half is for fuel, maintenance, supplies, and transportation of the crew (Worthington 1939).

Skidding prior to bucking has come into practice largely because it reduces costly maneuvering for a truck in the woods. A considerable saving is possible by skidding pulpwood in tree lengths. Where items other than pulpwood can be used or sold, the concentration of bucking at the loading deck has another outstanding advantage. It can, if an experienced operator is available, facilitate more advantageous sectioning of tree lengths by recognizing all grades of material and diverting each to its best use.

A loader mounted on a truck may be used to advantage where the cut is light. The transfer of short-length wood from sled or wagon to truck remains largely a hand operation in the Piedmont, but special machines have recently been installed successfully at railroad sidings to shift wood from trucks to cars. Mills and wood dealers are making increased use of concentration yards where individual truck loads are received, paid for, and reloaded mechanically (Jeffords 1956). In handling material skidded in tree lengths, both the mobile pulpwood harvesters in the forest and the multiple saw slashers in mill yards save labor where a supply of wood is continuously available to them (Jones 1947).

The loading of logs by crosshaul on a stationary trailer truck represents a loss in transportation time if it can be avoided. Where the hauling distance is not over 10 miles, the time spent in loading an idle truck may be sufficient for a round trip to deliver wood. The remedy may be found in an iron standard to support an extra detached trailer while it is being loaded (Reynolds 1939c). For similar reasons multiple pallet loading now is being used more and more to speed the delivery of pulpwood (Wright 1955, Guttenberg and Perry 1957).

Roads

Quality and spacing of forest roads, like the selection of logging equipment, materially affect production costs. On many loblolly pine sites in the Coastal Plain, truck logging is essentially a dry weather operation unless the timber is adjacent to gravel, pavement, or other hard surface roads. During years of average rainfall in Arkansas, truck logging ceases from about December 15 to April 15 except over all-weather or especially constructed hauling routes. Hauling logs over gravel or hard surface roads costs roughly 20 percent less than over graded dirt roads. Hauling them costs at least twice as much over woods roads as over graded dirt roads (Reynolds 1951b). The cost of hauling 1,000 board feet is greater for small than for large logs. Likewise in delivering pulpwood, the loading, hauling, and total costs per cord are somewhat greater for small than for large loads, and for light than for heavy trucks. Consequently an investment in good roads is essential to any operation designed to perpetuate timber yields.

How to space logging roads in a loblolly pine forest so that the investment in them will be repaid during a reasonable period through economy in logging costs may be computed with the following formula (Matthews 1942, page 227):

$$S = \sqrt{\frac{0.33\,R}{VC}} \qquad \text{Where:}$$

$S =$ road spacing in hundreds of linear feet
$R =$ road cost of construction per mile (dollars)
$V =$ volume of timber in M board feet to be removed per acre.
$C =$ cost of moving 1,000 board feet from stump to road (dollars per 100 feet of distance)

In using the formula for pulpwood, substitute 2 cords for 1 M board feet (Reynolds 1941c).[118]

[118] Reynolds' original article tabulates the solution of this formula for road building costs from $50 to $300 per mile, three average log sizes between 60 and 100 board feet, and seven degrees of cutting between 1,000 and 10,000 board feet per acre, under each of two woods-hauling conditions, good and poor.

A typical example of how this problem may be resolved follows. Extracting logs averaging 60 board feet each, from consolidated forest holdings under poor woods-hauling conditions, and over roads that cost $140 per mile to build, the routes should be spaced about ¾ mile apart if 3,000 board feet per acre is to be removed, or every ½ mile if twice as much is to be harvested. This spacing assumes ownership of all lands through which the roads pass. If, owing to interspersed farms or other adverse ownerships, a forest holding covers only half the area, the distance between roads is increased about 40 percent. This necessitates longer hauls and about doubles the cost of hauling.

The formula must be modified when applied to perpetual forestry operations. Where yields can be sustained while cutting each 10 years a given volume, V, beginning 1 year hence, the formula should be:

$$S = \sqrt{\frac{0.33R}{2.466VC}}$$

Conversion to lumber and other products

Sound decisions as to which loblolly pine trees or parts of trees should be cut for saw logs or converted into pulpwood depend upon relative "conversion surplus" values (see preceding section "Economic log and tree size, and the concept of financial maturity") as affected primarily by the upper limits of utilization in trees (fig. 99 in chapter 10, Properties and Uses).

For the smallest pulpwood trees it has been shown (Chapman 1942b) that reduction of the upper limit from 4 to 3 inches saves much wood otherwise left in the forest. For example, this reduction increases the volume extracted from 9-inch trees only 3.4 percent, but it increases it over 10 percent from 6-inch trees and nearly 21 percent from 5-inch trees.

In harvesting mature trees, however, the highest net values often can be realized as readily by saving labor as by saving wood. Close supervision to develop skill in cutting logs can augment both the volume and quality of lumber recovered. Without power saws less of the stump and less of the top can be utilized from large trees. When the tops of saw-log trees are used for pulp, heavy limbs and knotty wood add greatly to the work unless the level of the top cut is lowered and its diameter increased from 3 or 4 to 6 or more inches (appendix, table 70).

Sawmills produce additional waste from defect, slabs, edgings, and kerf seldom effectively utilized (table 49, chapter 10, Properties and Uses). This is reduced for the larger 16-foot logs as follows:

| Saw-log scaling diameter (inches) | Volume of wood (cu. ft.) | Log scale | | | Utili- zation (percent) |
		Doyle (bd. ft.)	Int. ¼-in. (bd. ft.)	Rough lumber (bd. ft.)	
10	10.1	36	65	63	52
14	18.4	100	135	130	59
18	32.8	196	230	240	61

Success in reduction of waste in lumber manufacture depends largely on experience of the sawyer and the efficiency of his mill.[119] Sawing small logs is relatively expensive everywhere. In the conversion of 16-inch trees, two-thirds of the total labor required from stump to railroad cars is incurred after the sawing has been completed. It is for handling, finishing, and disposal. An example of conversion time requirements in the forest of the Coastal Plain and at two types of mills is shown in figure 88. It is well to realize that while direct costs of manufacture are somewhat more at small mills, the fixed and overhead costs are greater at the large mills.

Conversion time studies at several mills in South Carolina and Texas have related log size to time and cost of sawing loblolly pine. For example in the Piedmont, if the most common size of log handled has scaling dimensions of 7 inches by 12 feet, 1,000 board feet can be sawn in 64 minutes. The same time is required for logs 10 inches by 8 feet; or half that time for logs that are 16 inches by 16 feet (table 44, center section).

For a medium-sized mill in east Texas cutting somewhat larger random length logs, similar relations are shown in table 45. There, for example, in 1945 with an approximate average log diameter of 11 inches, 1,000 board feet were sawn from 14-inch logs for $5.86, or 90.2 percent of the $6.50 it cost to saw an equal volume from 11-inch logs. When cut from 18-inch logs, 1,000 board feet cost $5.27, or only 81 percent as much as from the 11-inch logs. Because costs change markedly with time and place, the average current costs and log size should be determined separately for each sawmill. Then the ratios in tables 44 and 45 can be widely applied to show local costs by log size.

[119] A handbook useful to operators of small sawmills is available (Telford 1952). It deals with types of equipment available and how to install and use them. It applies especially to mills of the circular head-saw type cutting up to 20,000 board feet per day. It portrays mechanical principles controlling the function of various parts.

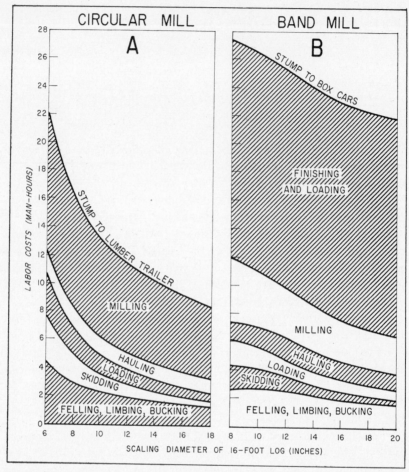

FIGURE 88.—Direct costs in man-hours for producing 1,000 board feet of southern pine lumber from logs of different sizes—based on (*A*) green lumber tally at a circular mill and (*B*) finished lumber at a band mill (Guttenberg and Duerr 1949).

Marketing wood products

To dispose of loblolly pine products effectively and profitably woodland owners should give careful consideration to four primary factors: (1) Their methods of measurement, (2) their choice of product, (3) their market situation, and (4) their procedure in sales.

A reliable estimate of both amount and value should be had by both parties to any timber deal. In measuring logs the use of an inaccurate scale rule may not be serious if buyer and seller are equally aware of its limitations. Otherwise certain rules shortchange

TABLE 44.—*Relation of log size to sawing time and volume of mill-run pine lumber produced in small Piedmont mills (Anderson 1954)*

SAWING TIME PER THOUSAND BOARD FEET (MINUTES)

Log length (feet)	Log scaling diameter (inches)											
	5	6	7	8	9	10	11	12	13	14	15	16
8..............	107	88	76	70	67	64	63	62	61	60	59	59
10..............	84	80	70	62	58	56	54	51	50	49	49	48
12..............	71	72	¹64	57	52	49	47	45	44	42	42	41
14..............	63	65	58	52	48	45	42	40	39	37	37	36
16..............	62	64	55	49	45	41	39	37	35	34	33	32

SAWING TIME RATIO[2] PER M

Log length (feet)	5	6	7	8	9	10	11	12	13	14	15	16
8..............	167	138	119	109	105	100	98	97	95	94	92	92
10..............	131	125	109	97	91	88	84	80	78	77	77	75
12..............	111	112	*100*	89	81	77	73	70	69	66	66	64
14..............	98	102	91	81	75	70	66	62	61	58	58	56
16..............	97	100	86	77	70	64	61	58	55	53	52	50

OUTTURN PER LOG (BOARD FEET)

Log length (feet)	5	6	7	8	9	10	11	12	13	14	15	16
8..............	6	9	13	17	22	29	36	44	52	62	72	83
10..............	10	12	16	22	29	37	46	56	67	79	92	107
12..............	13	15	21	28	36	46	56	68	82	97	113	130
14..............	16	19	26	34	43	54	67	82	98	116	134	154
16..............	19	22	30	40	51	64	79	96	114	135	155	179

[1] Modal size of log.
[2] i.e., percentage of time for log of modal size.

the man who sells small saw logs (fig. 89).[120] What this amounts to in percentage of board-foot volume recovery from trees of different diameters is shown in table 46.

The final choice of products should be adjusted to available prices. To wholesale timber for a single product is convenient, but in quantity it is less profitable than to sort out the stems, or parts of stems, when they can be sold separately at better prices. In most locations pines are seldom used for lumber if less than 8 inches, or for pulpwood if more than 14 inches in d.b.h. But between these sizes they are bought and sold in lively competition between sawmills and pulpmills. As in other crops, the domestic use or other disposal of the low-grade products may facilitate profitable commercial sale of the higher grades. Nevertheless owners often forego extra profit because they neglect proper comparison of basic prices.

[120] In the work on which figure 89 is based log diameters were scaled inside the bark, except in the use of the Doyle rule which followed the Texas practice of measuring to the nearest inch outside bark above 8 inches, while the 8-inch and smaller logs were given their length as their scale (Gregory and Person 1949).

TABLE 45.—*Percent of average log-sawing cost per M board feet Doyle scale or mill tally for sawing pine logs of different average size[1] (Gregory and Person 1949)*

Log diam. (inches)	Mill tally by size of average log (inches)				Doyle log scale by size of average log (inches)			
	9	10	11	12	9	10	11	12
	Percent	Percent	Percent	Percent	Percent	Percent	Percent	Percent
6	132.5	141.0	147.9	154.1	111.1	131.4	150.4	169.3
7	120.4	128.1	134.4	140.0	137.9	163.1	186.6	210.0
8	108.9	115.9	121.6	126.7	129.4	153.0	175.1	197.1
9	100.0	106.4	111.7	116.3	100.0	118.3	135.3	152.3
10	93.9	100.0	104.9	109.3	84.5	100.0	114.4	128.8
11	89.5	95.3	100.0	104.2	73.9	87.4	100.0	112.6
12	86.0	91.5	96.0	100.0	65.6	77.6	88.8	100.0
13	83.2	88.6	92.9	96.8	59.9	70.8	81.0	91.2
14	80.7	85.9	90.2	93.9	55.6	65.7	75.2	84.6
15	78.4	83.4	87.6	91.2	52.2	61.7	70.6	79.5
16	76.3	81.2	85.2	88.8	49.4	58.4	66.8	75.2
17	74.3	79.1	82.9	86.4	47.2	55.8	63.8	71.8
18	72.5	77.2	81.0	84.3	45.2	53.4	61.1	68.8

[1] To use this table an operator must ascertain his average sawing cost per M board feet and the approximate average diameter of the logs. He can estimate cost by log-size class by multiplying his average by the factor in this table representing the log size in question.

TABLE 46.—*Approximate overrun of lumber from sound straight 16-foot logs, i.e., excess of mill tally over log scale from trees of different sizes[1]*

D.b.h. (inches)	Log rule			D.b.h. (inches)	Log rule		
	Doyle	Int. $\frac{1}{4}$-inch	Scribner		Doyle	Int. $\frac{1}{4}$-inch	Scribner
	Percent	Percent	Percent		Percent	Percent	Percent
6	366	5	50	22	9	2	4
8	150	4	21	24	7	2	4
10	80	4	14	26	5	1	4
12	50	3	9	28	3	1	3
14	30	3	3	30	0	1	3
16	25	3	6	32	−1	1	3
18	17	2	5	34	−2	0	4
20	13	2	4				

[1] Selling Timber Wisely. Ga. Agr. Ext. Serv. Cir. 348. 1955.

Data to implement such comparisons in single-product sales (McClay 1952, Jiles 1957) may be applied in the following manner. One thousand board feet equals nearly 3 cords (including 0.2 cord in tops) when cut from 12-inch trees, or 4 cords when taken from 8-inch trees (table 47). Where these ratios are observed to hold, figure 90 is useful in price comparisons. For example, if the price offered for saw logs alone is $15 per M board feet, any alternative price per cord (including top wood) less than $5 for 12-inch trees should

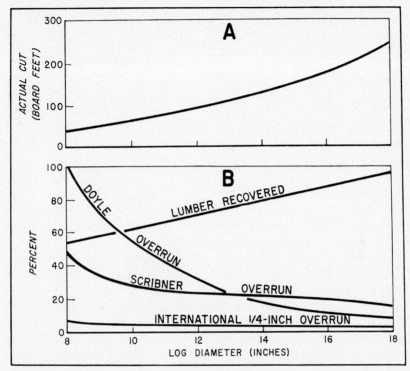

FIGURE 89.—Lumber production by log diameter from a typical medium-sized circular-saw mill in east Texas: *A*, Rough lumber cut from pine logs; *B*, three log rules compared on the basis of the sawmill overrun and portion of the cubic-foot volume retained in the lumber (Gregory and Person 1949).

be rejected. Similarly when $5 per cord is offered, any alternative price per M board feet less than $20 for 8-inch trees should be rejected. Furthermore any manager who can withhold his extremely knotty top logs from saw-log sales, and reserve his high-grade butt logs from pulpwood sales usually will be in a position to demand above average prices. The price of pulpwood may be expected to rise, but not above that of high-grade lumber. High-grade lumber, becoming scarce, is likely to command increasingly good future prices, while poor lumber may become a drug on the market (Worrell 1957). The trend now is toward chemical conversion of cheap wood into forms more usable than low-grade lumber.

In preparing loblolly pine products for sale they must be sectioned differently to take advantage of commercial grades or to serve various uses. For sawtimber the minimum log lengths are usually 12 feet, standard 16 feet, and maximum 22 feet or more—plus a 4-inch trim

TABLE 47.—*Number of cords per M board feet for loblolly pine trees, by diameter breast high and log rule (McClay 1952)*[1]

D.b.h. (inches)	International ¼-inch	Scribner	Doyle
	Cords	Cords	Cords
8...............	4.0	4.4	6.8
9...............	3.7	4.1	6.8
10...............	3.4	3.8	6.8
11...............	3.2	3.6	6.3
12...............	2.9	3.4	6.2
13...............	2.7	3.2	5.2
14...............	2.5	3.0	4.5

[1] Basic utilization limits in upper-stem diameter inside bark were 4 inches for pulpwood and 7 inches for saw logs.

allowance on each log. Besides sawtimber and pulpwood, some small trees may be suitable for fence posts, and larger ones for crossties or specialty products, such as package veneer, excelsior, or possibly handle stock. Poles and piles bring high prices if certain specifications can be met.[121] However, buyers revise their specifications occasionally. Most plants manufacturing loblolly pine products will, upon request, furnish a set of their current specifications to people who can supply them with needed raw material.

The market situation is a prime consideration. A grower should ascertain seasonal requirements for timber in his neighborhood. Saving in hauling costs may increase the returns from local sales. The seller should remember, however, that thrifty timber can wait over a period of low prices without deterioration. Large forest-products plants now gather wood from widely scattered locations. Thus many owners of loblolly pine timber have gained an open market that will accept small sales (Wackerman 1945). More and more farmers and small operators plan to cut, and hope to sell, their timber only in the dormant season to avoid insect damage. Hence the big companies—who can avoid such damage by cutting throughout a growing season—can advantageously harvest from their own lands in spring and summer if labor is available (Jeffords 1956). Such operation helps to assure farmers an adequate autumn and winter market. The price of saw logs tends to rise in autumn to a peak value in October (Anderson 1957). Forestry organizations that issue advice on timber management may, in some instances, also act as clearing houses for marketing information.

Supply, demand, and accessibility of loblolly pine timber affect the movement of saw logs as they do other raw materials. Additional

[121] The number of crossties, pulpwood units, or 5-foot sticks usually found in trees that will make poles or piles are shown in table 54 (section on "Poles and Piles" of chapter 10, Properties and Uses).

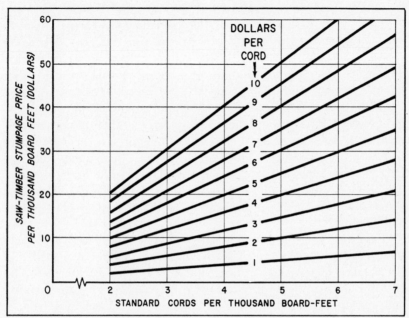

FIGURE 90.—Comparative stumpage prices for pulpwood and sawtimber based on number of standard cords of pulpwood per M board feet of sawtimber. Average number of cords per M board feet for different tree sizes and log scales can be read from table 47.

factors and people influence the way pulpwood moves toward its expanding markets. In increasing numbers, tree farmers are growing it to sell, middlemen are procuring it to handle, and manufacturers are buying it to process. Far flung procurement operations are being organized to meet competition and keep mills supplied.

Many mills have adopted a dealership system to regulate their current supply of pulpwood. Dealers are independent contractors who procure wood for companies on a commission basis. After it is cut, an oversupply of a moderately perishable commodity like pulpwood may lead to serious loss. Hence the contractor's quotas are specific by periods rather than by areas. These dealers often subdivide their assigned quotas to give business to various local semi-dependent wood buyers, and help them to find available stumpage and to finance its purchase. These local buyers then cut, extract, load, and haul or ship the wood to a pulp company or to a regional woodyard where they may receive direct payment for these services. Obviously, owners who are skilled loggers and can sell, harvest, and deliver their own wood will find such an arrangement profitable.

Sales procedure is vital to all growers of loblolly pine (Todd and Zirkle 1949). Results from a study of numerous transactions in north central South Carolina (Fairfield County) are instructive (Parker and Aull 1953). Although volume of sale appeared to have no consistent effect on the unit price received for sawtimber, the larger sales of pulpwood brought somewhat greater returns. Prices received in the sale of both sawtimber and pulpwood were shown to have been influenced by the basis of sale, its initiator, and the number of bids received. Thus sales brought more per M board feet or per cord if based on these units rather than lump sum, and if they were seller initiated and preceded by two or more bids (fig. 91). It behooves a seller to provide these favorable conditions and then follow through by exercising his right of control over cutting and hauling.

Payments may be based on piece products or logs scaled prior to removal, pulpwood weighed in transit, or tallies at a mill. In the absence of a timber cruise, lumber tally may be accepted as a base for payment. With full mutual information on both quantity and quality a lump-sum sale may be used.

To assure a satisfactory transaction in selling his loblolly pine timber an owner should—

1. Know the volume and value of timber offered—based on current unit prices of various products as affected by volume available per tree and per acre.
2. Mark trees to realize highest total value.
3. Obtain three or more competitive bids.
4. Select a responsible purchaser.
5. Sell when prices are highest.
6. Use a written timber sale agreement.

SMALL WOODLANDS

The small woodlands in the loblolly pine belt now supply a large share of the industrial needs for timber in the region, but under good management they could supply much more. As it is, several generations of destructive cutting have depleted many small holdings more than the larger ones. Actually two-thirds of the recently cut land on small holdings fails to meet reasonably obtainable productivity standards. Most of the present owners are unaware of both the potential capacity of their woodlands and the measures necessary to make them again moderately productive of timber. These owners are a very diverse group of people—farmers, profes-

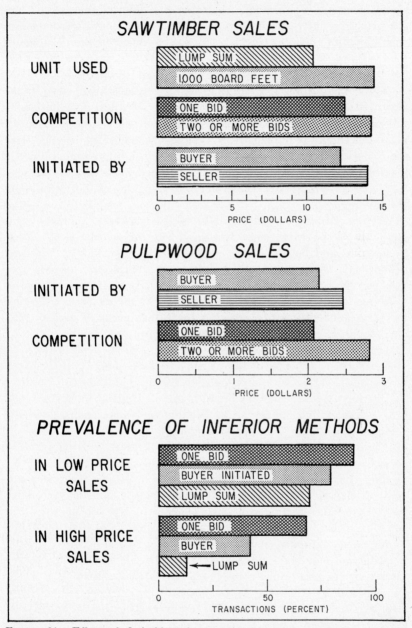

FIGURE 91.—Effect of desirable sales practice on prices received for timber and pulpwood and the relative prevalence of dependence on inferior methods in a sample area of South Carolina (Parker and Aull 1953).

sional men, and many others—but they are alike in one way. They are primarily interested in activities other than timber growing and wood manufacturing (U.S.D.A. Forest Service 1958). Not more than a third of the nonindustrial owners have a well-developed interest in better forest practice (Folweiler and Vaux 1944).

These small forests, averaging about 70 acres each, need to be improved in species composition, degree of stocking, distribution of age classes, and freedom from defects. What can be done to remedy these deficiencies is influenced by type of ownership, its location, and the outlets for commercial products. These conditions that influence the intensity of forest management practiced make the average returns per dollar invested somewhat less from the smaller woodlands (table 41).

Within the limits of available soils, resources, markets, and public interests, each small woodland enterprise should be suited to the aims and desires of the resident or absentee owner. His attitude may be sentimental or mercenary, long- or short-sighted, visionary or practical, wasteful or conservative. His prerogative is to act as, or to select, a forest manager. At the owner's discretion the farm woodland can be reserved for future needs or used to produce products currently needed, such as pulpwood, posts, poles, or timber. In either case the woodland may contribute a place for local recreation and wildlife if conditions are favorable. Treatment of forest cover varies with management for any of these purposes.

Cutting cycle, the period between regular partial harvests, tends to be relatively long under heavy cutting, on remote tracts, or under absentee ownership. The period should be shortened with accessibility, light cutting, and intensive practice. Annual cutting is often possible and frequently advocated for farm woodlands to place forest products on a par with row crops. Under a 1-year cycle each annual cut may be taken actually from only the half, quarter, or smaller part of the forest where the need currently is most urgent. An annual harvest, however, is not always advisable. The need for funds is not equal annually, nor is the need for regeneration. Periodic reproduction may make the control of hardwoods easier. The longer cutting cycles can promote reserve or investment values in a woodlot, thus making it a better source of funds for emergency use (Chapman 1951). The owner's difficulty, however, stems not so much from low cut per acre as from low volume per sale. If his supply of high-value special products is limited, he must often decide whether to dispose of a small volume at a high unit price or a large amount at a lower price.

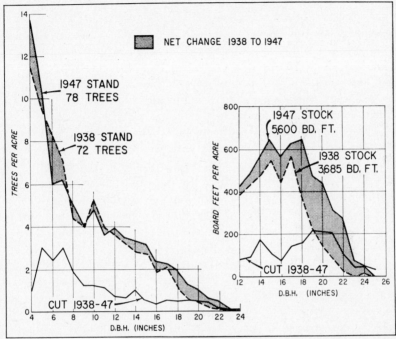

FIGURE 92.—Original second-growth stand and stock per acre, amounts cut from various size classes in 10 years, and the distribution of stock resulting from selection management of compartment 55 at Crossett, Ark. (Reynolds 1950a).

FARM FORESTRY DEMONSTRATIONS

Unmanaged, but protected, forest lands are moderately productive in favorable locations. Two 40-acre compartments near Crossett, Ark., have been maintained in natural condition since the old-growth loblolly pine timber was removed in 1915. In 1942 these tracts averaged nearly 9,000 board feet (International 1/4-inch rule) per acre, 78 percent pine. In the next 10 years, on sites of index 85 or higher, the annual growth was 443 board feet per acre, 88 percent pine. Comparable figures on an adjacent 1,000 acres of managed forest are 5,000 board feet of stock which grew 551 board feet, all pine, in the same period. The simple-interest percentage rate of production was nearly doubled on the managed tract of forest (Reynolds 1954a).

Two other compartments of the same forest provide an outstanding demonstration of 15-year results from management of small woodlands. Only the equipment and methods available to most farmers were used. One well-stocked compartment is called the "good forty"; the other, lightly stocked at the start, is called the "poor forty." Each was a mixed stand at the start with 25 to 35 percent of the volume in deciduous trees. These hardwoods were greatly reduced in numbers through fuel and chemical wood harvests. Labor requirements for fire protection were 0.4 man-hour per acre, and half as much for each of three other measures—timber stand improvement, timber marking, scaling and supervision— a total of 1 man-hour per acre annually.

These operations materially increased the growth of pine (table 31). On both forties the change in numbers of large trees was slight, but the volume increase in such trees was substantial, enabling the good forty to maintain its lead in timber. With more growing space on the poor forty, a net increase there in small trees is evident in both numbers and volume. This initially poor forty has become superior in young-growth trees and in percentage rates of increment, but not in gross or net returns.

One typical 40-acre compartment (No. 55) within the 1,000-acre "sustained-yield" study at Crossett, Ark., is a good example of a commercial type of small woodland management using a 3-year cutting cycle. A preliminary 20 percent cruise indicated that of the cubic volume present in 1935 about half was contained in small trees and tops[122] and about a fifth was in hardwoods. However only 6½ percent of the board-foot volume was in hardwoods.

Growing stock per acre in 1937 was 3,685 board feet (Reynolds 1949b). Of this, 45 percent was removed during 10 years. Yet the volume present in 1949 was 5,600 board feet per acre or 52 percent more than in 1937. Apparently now the cut can be doubled in the second 10 years without interrupting the progress toward good stocking. Figure 92 shows both the superior growth of crop trees above 17 inches in d.b.h. and the abundance of recruits below 7 inches. Because of good site and the elevation of the main canopy, and in spite of accumulating overwood, reproduction is adequate.

Here silviculture has curbed natural succession toward hardwoods. The success in selective management of loblolly pine at Crossett is manifest in that the increased current yield of mature timber has been attained on individual compartments simultaneously with the development of sufficient recruits to maintain the supply in future years. It is a good demonstration of the art of sustaining commercial yields of timber.

---

[122] Small trees were pines 6 to 9 inches in d.b.h. or hardwoods 6 to 13 inches in d.b.h. The tops were from saw-log trees, i.e., pines 10 inches or larger, and hardwoods 14 inches or larger in d.b.h.

SUMMARY

Profitable harvests of mature loblolly pine timber without jeopardy to future yields of the same species have two aspects: silvicultural and financial.

Although loblolly pine cannot be produced everywhere with equal facility, there are four principal procedures in reproducing it naturally: (1) Clear cutting, (2) seed trees, (3) shelterwood, and (4) selection. Under the first three methods, age classes are segregated as in plantations; under the fourth they are intermingled. Preharvest partial cuttings are similar for all systems, except that in (4) they may be heavy enough to let many seedlings come in, whereas in the first three they should be light enough to keep most of them out. In both time and place, reproduction following harvest is concentrated in the first three, but dispersed in (4). The first three methods result in even-aged stands, the fourth in many-aged stands, although in each case the forest as a whole must be in all-aged form to sustain yields. Even-aged and many-aged silviculture for loblolly pine each have advantages and disadvantages.

The outstanding *objections* to the conversion of irregular forest to a regulated even-aged form are economic—the sacrifice involved in the harvest of many small trees and the investment needed to prepare sites for uniform regeneration. Any attempt to avoid either this initial sacrifice or this investment, while harvesting mature trees only, will destroy the even-aged uniformity needed for the adopted system. The *advantages* of even-aged methods are that less skill and generally less cost is involved in harvesting relatively heavy cuts per acre, and broadcast treatments utilizing fire, machines, or chemicals can be used in preparing sites for natural reseeding. Such site preparation incidentally delays revegetation by weed species enough to reduce the need for subsequent release of seedlings. Where such regeneration methods fail, the prescription for even-aged culture is to clear cut and plant loblolly pine.

The outstanding *objection* to the many-aged method of reproduction is that, in the less favorable locations, a well-stocked forest may fail to renew itself in the absence of artificial aids that are relatively expensive to apply without blanket measures incompatible with many-aged silviculture. In these less favorable locations understocked stands may readily acquire an all-aged structure sufficient to sustain yields, but only at a relatively low level. In timber management an *advantage* to be had in favorable locations from the many-aged method is that more of the productive capacity of the soil can be skillfully used for long sustained growth in value on, and reproduction from, the very best trees. Hence it is good for producing large products, and for sustaining timber yields on small tracts. Where timber production is not the primary purpose, another advantage of many-aged management is that at all times an irregular, but continuous, forest cover protects the soil against erosion, and favors recreation, wildlife, and watershed values.

Where the single-tree form of selection fails, the prescription for many-aged culture of loblolly pine is to utilize group selection, and produce many-aged forests consisting of irregular even-aged patches. Natural regeneration is often best in heavily cut spots small enough to reseed from the side, yet large enough to permit relatively free growth.

Where the reproduction must come from the forest on the area itself, enough trees should be left under any system for an ample supply of both seed for reproduction and of timber for an operable later cut. The number of trees needed depends on the seed year, tree diameter, crown size, individual fruitfulness, desired restocking, and character of site preparation. Data to integrate these several factors in a single estimate of trees required—never less than three per acre—under even-aged systems are presented. The trees must remain at least until a seedling stand is attained, and may be temporarily retained thereafter only if and where needed for insurance against excessive seedling losses from drought or fire. Accelerated growth of seed trees can readily repay all costs of their retention up to the time when their removal is advisable to completely free their established progeny for rapid development.

When regenerating loblolly pine on progressive or alternating strips or patches, using either shelterwood or seeding from the side, the number of seed-bearing trees is a less exacting requirement. Width of the seed cuttings, preparation of the ground below, and subsequent release of seedlings remain important. On burned-over clearings 150 to 200 feet wide reproduction can thrive if later released at least one time.

Once silvicultural measures have placed a loblolly pine forest in reasonably good productive, and reproductive, condition, some regulation is needed to determine an allowable, and ensure a readily maintainable, level of production. If sustained yields of timber are desired, a cutting budget should be based on special forestwide study of actual net timber increment, or on the existing records from regular partial harvests and recurring inventories. Methods of reg-

ulation reported here were devised for use in loblolly pine, but may
be applied also to other types of forest.

Highlights of economic production of loblolly pine include intensity of operation, and if even-aged silviculture is used, the length
of the rotation. The financial aspects of growing loblolly pine concern many items that vary widely with both time and place, so that
dollar estimates have only temporary local application.

If land is the principal limiting factor in production, it is best
in the long run to manage the forest with increasing intensity. Because of a somewhat less favorable revenue-cost ratio, small owners
need proportionately more good land than do large owners in order
to utilize their capital with equal efficiency.

Loblolly pines are profitable to grow on short rotations where the
first costs are low, and where the development of crop trees is not
retarded by poor soil, crowding, or competition with weed species.
They are profitable also on long rotations where protective measures
are adequate, regeneration successful, and low-priced raw materials
can be harvested early to provide growing space for products of
higher value.

In the Carolinas a crop of loblolly pine pulpwood may mature
financially at about 30 years. Under even-aged management at
Urania, La., there is evidence that the best mean annual growth
and yield in the value of a crop of loblolly pine sawtimber accrues
on good sites during rotations of 42 to 51 years, and on poor sites
during 45 to 54 years.

If uneven-aged systems of regeneration are to be used in silvicultural harvests, the rotation age becomes of no importance, but skill
is necessary to select properly all trees to be reserved, to recognize
financial maturity in trees, and to log them economically.

When the rate of increase in net returns to be expected from an
even-aged stand falls below the rate expected from comparable alternative capital investments, such a stand is financially mature and
should be cut. Because changes in unit sales value of timber correspond rather closely with changes in current prices for No. 2
Common lumber, index numbers so based are useful in timber appraisals. A method of computing marginal value growth is presented as a means of estimating optimum growing stock in stands
of loblolly pine.

This concept of financial maturity applies to a lesser degree to
individual trees. Estimates of conversion surplus values for individual trees may assist timber markers in choosing between other-

wise comparable trees to cut or leave. In growing from 12 to 17 inches in d.b.h. the gross value of a loblolly pine may increase 3½ times and its net value fivefold. Maximum profits usually come from the retention of an adequate stand of well-formed pines that can grow rapidly.

To properly select mature loblolly pines in partial cutting operations, timber markers must have accurate ocular judgment not only of present but also prospective value of the trees. They should be able to recognize the point beyond which most of the promising trees cease to increase in log length and grade. On good sites a third log usually develops when 14 inches in d.b.h. is reached, and a fourth at 18 inches d.b.h. The ultimate merchantable length of a tree is apparent by the time it reaches 15 to 17 inches in d.b.h. and its period of rapid grade improvement is reached at 22 to 24 inches. Low-vigor trees often mature at 16 inches, if indeed they can ever qualify at all for sawtimber growing stock. Trees of medium vigor mature for saw logs at 18 inches and those of high vigor at 23 inches.

Some recent outstanding mechanical developments implement the economical extraction of loblolly pine timber. Chain saws, faster than the cross-cut type and safer than the wheel type, are increasingly being used to fell and buck timber. In skidding logs only a small fraction of the cost is for labor when tractors are used, but both size of timber and character of terrain affect choice of machines. Skidding in tree lengths appears to be practical for distances up to about 900 feet, and advisable where expert separation of timber by product and grade can be provided at a concentration point. In east Texas it was found that an increase of only 10 board feet in average log size reduced logging costs $1 per thousand board feet— a greater reduction than from any moderate increase in the volume cut per acre. The multiple pallet system of handling wood speeds the process of loading it.

Economy in hauling logs or pulpwood varies with the quality and spacing of forest roads. They may be constructed three-quarters of a mile apart to extract 3,000 board feet per acre, or half a mile apart to extract 6,000 board feet per acre in a single harvest. Somewhat closer spacing of roads is advisable under intensive operations to sustain yields. Extraction and conversion time requirements per unit of product decrease with increases in the size of logs handled, and in size of the sawmill that cuts the rough lumber.

Labor requirements in the intensive application of selective timber management to grow loblolly pine, harvest it, and sustain its yield (estimated on the basis of 8 hours per day, 5 days per week, and 45 weeks per year at Crossett, Ark.) amount to an annual crew of 32 men for each 5,000 acres of forest.

In marketing loblolly pine from any woodland, attention should be paid to these four factors: Method of measurement, choice of product, market situation, and sales procedure. Log scale bias introduced in using rules other than the International ¼-inch rule should be understood. The spread in price of the same tree for different products should be realized. If as much as a carload of each product is available, segregation may pay. Perhaps all butt logs should go to a sawmill, all top logs to a pulpmill, and all poles to a treating plant. The local market situation should be ascertained, and all outlets investigated. To dispose of a quantity of loblolly pine timber satisfactorily on an open market a seller should benefit from experience of neighbors, advertise his available timber, get local prices, preferably secure bids, select a reliable purchaser, and use a written agreement.

Chapter 9

Management for Other Purposes

THE GROWING OF TIMBER IS THE most obvious function of loblolly pine forests. Another function of the forest is to supply water from protected watersheds. Still another is to produce forage in the form of grasses, weeds, and shrubs under trees and in openings. The rural South has depended in part on the utilization of its forest range by cattle—and hogs. Wildlife and recreation are also linked closely with the forest.

The manager of loblolly pine lands may well consider the values of water, forage, wildlife, and recreation as well as timber in determining the use of the land. He should attempt to achieve a reasonable balance between the net values obtainable from the different products or through various services.

Soil and water together are basic resources in growing and using forests. Cotta, the early 19th century German publisher and scientific agriculturist, observed this: "Without any utilization the forest soil improves constantly; if utilized properly, the soil retains its natural balance; if utilized improperly, however, the soil deteriorates." In the loblolly pine belt nearly all the land has been used in some way. There are scattered samples of good usage and an abundance of improperly treated land where much of the original soil has deteriorated or washed away.

WATER, LITTER, AND SOIL

The quality of the soil, and adequacy of water supplies within it, influence what crop can be produced, whether it be timber, domestic stock, wildlife, or other forest products. The abuse of land has caused less impairment and loss of soil in the lower Coastal Plain than it has farther inland. The present condition of the abandoned agricultural land in the Piedmont, now occupied by loblolly pine stands, has been profoundly affected by past use. Some sections of the upper Coastal Plain, such as the loessal bluffs from Natchez,

Miss., to Memphis, Tenn., similarly portray the results of misuse. On the upper Coastal Plain and Piedmont Plateau since about 1800 the principal row crops, cotton and corn, were grown on cleanly cultivated fields, even on steep slopes. Often immature old-field pine was harvested to farm the land a second or third time. Under repeated abandonment and recultivation, fertility naturally declined until about 1880 when commercial fertilizers became popular. This encouraged continued tillage and many slopes were cultivated until a large part of the subsoil was washed away.

In spite of abuse by man, the loblolly pine forest lands are usually covered rather completely by vegetation, though not adequately for all uses. In managing these lands for either their watershed or crop producing values, an understanding of topography, vegetative cover, and physical soil properties as related to water is important.[123] In these respects the higher Piedmont hills and the flat sandy seaboard locations represent two extremes. Between them, in the upper Coastal Plain of northern Alabama, southern Arkansas, and eastern Texas the topography and soil cover are intermediate in character. But soil is less stable in all the dissected interior part of the range of loblolly pine, because the velocity and silt carrying capacity of runoff is greater than it is along the seaboard.[124]

The permeable surface layers of the soil in the loblolly pine forest have been stripped from many hilly inland acres exposing stiff subsoil. Differences in the organic portion of the other rolling upland soils affect their water relations to some extent. The mull types of soil, with their greater porosity can store more water than the mor types. When fully saturated the surface 6 inches of the mor types will hold 2.77 inches of rain water, the duff-mull types 3.36 inches, and the mulls 3.54 inches (Metz 1954).[125]

Forest litter makes a major contribution to subterranean storage of rainfall by increasing the rate of absorption of water while it blocks surface movement of many erodible soils. In fully stocked 30- to 40-year-old loblolly pine stands, unburned for 20 years, the litter may become 3 inches deep. Some 11 or 12 tons per acre may

[123] Methods and equipment appropriate for measuring pore space and percolation rates for water in forest soils have been reported (Hoover, Metz, and Olson 1954).

[124] Streams wholly within the southeastern Coastal Plain have clear slow moving water, whereas those that rise inland from the fall line have rapid flowing muddy water. However in the Upper Coastal Plain of Mississippi, and in the West Gulf region generally, turbid streams are commonplace.

[125] These three humus types of soil are described by M. D. Hoover and H. A. Lunt in ''A key for the classification of forest humus types.'' Soil Sci. Soc. Amer. Proc. 16:368-370. 1952.

accumulate in 60 years in places where the annual fall of about 1 ton is offset by decomposition losses. Accumulated leaf fall is related to the age of well-stocked loblolly pine stands about as follows (McGough 1947):

Age of pine stand (years)	Dry weight per acre of surface litter (pounds)
10	6,300
20	12,700
30	17,400
40	20,700
50	22,600
60	22,700
70	21,000
80	18,000

On soils composed of coarse sand, pine straw may have only insignificant effects on water absorption and soil movement. However, on clay, sandy clay, or sandy loam soils the effects are important. When such soils are burned over, runoff and erosion tend to increase. Where erosion has removed the sandy (formerly plowed) horizon from Piedmont soils, little rain water is detained—nearly all that falls runs off. This shifting of a large portion of runoff from subsurface to surface flow has caused much disastrous sheet and gully erosion. The flow becomes flashy, rising rapidly to flood stage after rain and receding nearly as fast. Hence vegetation is subjected to more vicissitudes of moisture deficiency and excess. Roots located above the relatively impermeable layers of soil may suffer as much from prolonged flooding and deficient aeration as from drought.

Loblolly pine is an excellent tree species to use in flood control planting because it produces considerable litter in even a short period of time (section on "Organic matter" in chapter 2, The Species and Its Environment). Thus Broadfoot (1951) observed that the surface 2 inches of soil under old-field loblolly pine absorbed water faster than did an adjacent old field in native grass cover.

Improvement in soil properties proceeds slowly beneath pure stands of loblolly pine. In newly established stands a superficial accumulation of needles tends to ferment and decompose gradually in place without becoming a part of the mineral soil. Without benefit of a hardwood component in the litter, the formation of an A_1 horizon[126] is delayed, and the stand may become 30 years old before even a thin layer of humus is manifest. Thus a full rotation for medium-sized pure-pine timber stands may elapse without much

[126] The surface mineral-soil horizon containing incorporated or infiltrated organic matter.

noticeable improvement in the soil. With further increase in the age of timber grown on longer rotations there is usually an increase in the hardwood understory and the broad-leaved component of litter. The decomposition of such litter—particularly that which is relatively rich in calcium (section on ''Soils influence'' in chapter 2)—accelerates soil improvement through incorporation of organic matter within the surface layers of soil.

Erosion losses

Much of the timberland in the Piedmont has suffered greatly from erosion in the past. It has left the surface soils thin—often less than 2 inches—and in places has left stiff subsoil exposed.[127] Most of the upland terrain has at sometime been subjected to varying degrees of erosion. Nearly all the surface soil has already disappeared from 47 percent of the rolling land (Brender 1952a). About 25 percent of the land slopes more than 7 percent and thus is susceptible to erosion through mismanagement, though erosion is currently active on less than 4 percent of forest land.[128]

In south central Georgia, one study (Bond and Spillers 1935) showed that 80 percent of the old fields with slopes of 12 percent or more had once been gullied or seriously depleted by sheet erosion, whereas only 3 percent of the gently sloping land was so damaged. Of the loblolly pine old-field area as a whole, however, some 90 to 99 percent, depending on stand conditions, was either unaffected or the scars had healed through natural revegetation as follows:

Age and density of pine timber	Status of erosion	
	Active (percent)	Absent or arrested (percent)
Sawtimber, well stocked.............	1.3	98.7
Sawtimber, poorly stocked...........	1.7	98.3
Young timber, well stocked..........	5.9	94.1
Young timber, poorly stocked........	10.0	90.0

Basis: 542 quarter-acre land-use survey plots (Bond and Spillers 1935).

Erosion control

Loblolly pine, with its rapid growth and abundant litter, has proved its value in rehabilitation of eroded sites and is considered

[127] Chemical amendments for these inhospitable soils show no promise as yet. One proprietary compound (''Krilium''), when tested in Mississippi on hard-packed kaolinitic subsoils typical of gully bottoms and scald areas, failed to improve the early growth or survival of loblolly pine seedlings (King 1955).

[128] A minor or temporary benefit from the loss of surface litter may accrue to loblolly pine in the form of increased natural reproduction on exposed mineral soil, but a complete loss of topsoil reverses this effect (Brinkman and Swarthout 1942).

one of the finest gully stabilizers (MacNaughton 1953) (plate 10). Loblolly pine may be planted directly in the less deeply cut gullies or washes which have not completely severed deposits of silt loam or loess. Pines may even be planted in rapidly eroding gullies after they have been partially stabilized with soil binding vines or grass so that they may support the trees (Meginnis 1933b).

Grass and legume mixtures are being used increasingly as a vegetal cover to prevent wind or water from moving soil, or to heal the scars left by erosion, particularly on steep lands retired from cultivation but not yet reclaimed by loblolly pine. The cost of re-vegetating severely eroded sites, however, tends to be exorbitant. Cover could be more readily established if a mulch of straw or other suitable material could be added at reasonable cost. If available, Lespedeza sericea hay, cut when enough ripe seeds are attached to the plants to produce a stand, is effective in the Southeast (Graham 1941). Crotalaria is another promising species. Premulching with pine boughs in the autumn preceding spring sowing is effective but costly. The branches not only retard erosion during winter, but also retain enough moisture and catch enough soil, to eliminate the need for preparation of the surface. On relatively clear and flat areas of denuded or depleted soil, seeds can be broadcast on a pre-pared surface that has been plowed, disked, or raked, and then rolled or settled. On eroding areas of rolling terrain small inexpensive brush dams may be used to trap sediment. Spots that silt in can be sown with love grass (*Eragrostis* spp.) which retards movement of soil until planted trees can anchor it. The more aggressive vines like kudzu or honeysuckle, if used at all, may not require this prep-aration. Though these vines are browsed by deer and cattle, they are not recommended, except possibly where they are unlikely to smother more desirable vegetation (Brender and Hodges 1957b).

Planting winter cover crops on ''galled'' spots, or other barren areas, may be unnecessary as a means of reducing high soil tempera-tures before such sites are planted to trees. Only a very thin sur-face layer of clay soils exposed to the sun becomes too hot for satis-factory root growth. A dense living cover, similar to that of an old-field stand of broomsedge, will prevent injurious temperatures. Cover of this kind can be obtained from ''cool-season'' plants like winter ryegrass, oats, vetch, or crimson clover. Such plants can be established on most denuded soils by autumn sowings that are limed and fertilized. By making their growth during cool weather, these cover crops escape heat injury. If they are allowed to stand, their

PLATE 10.—Loblolly pine is a choice species for reclamation of eroding lands,
A, an abandoned hillside on the Ed Eggerson farm near Taylor, Miss., in
1948, and B, the same hillside in 1956, eight years after planting as a
soil stabilization measure (courtesy V. B. MacNaughton, U.S.F.S. 458890
and 485232).

dead foliage shades the soil in summer, permitting the late-season establishment of other species including legumes, loblolly pines, or both (Greene 1953). Excessive costs should be avoided by limiting practical site preparation to measures that have been shown locally to be economical.

Holdover damage from early erosion may need to be appraised, directly or indirectly, prior to the designation of areas where more loblolly pine should be planted to halt further erosion. Indirect appraisal by observation of rates of height growth on scattered residual pines may be the best method. Situations where these pines have developed least rapidly are almost surely the ones where more of them are needed to hold the remaining soil. Goggans (1951) showed that early shoot growth of loblolly pine indicated the thickness of topsoil left (fig. 93).[129]

The continuing retardation of the planted pines is part of the price that must be paid when a commercial species is used primarly to check erosion. Fortunately loblolly pine being more deeply rooted is less sensitive to soil deterioration caused by erosion than are corn or cotton as indirectly reflected in net income (fig. 94), but what to expect was shown by Cooper (1942) working in Newberry County, South Carolina. He classified sheet erosion according to topsoil removed as follows:

Erosion class	Surface soil lost (percent)
0	None apparent
1	Less than 25
2	25 to 50
3	50 to 75
4	Over 75

His observation revealed that the site index for loblolly pine dropped at least 10 feet for each addition of one grade in the erosion class. He concluded that every loblolly pine which now reaches maturity on eroded Piedmont soils is 10 to 30 feet shorter than were the old-growth trees of similar age that grew on comparable uneroded soils.

Localized patching of erosion damage by means of dams in gullies does not affect the fundamental difficulty, a decrease in permeability of the soil. Any permanent rehabilitation of water relations must

[129] The regression formula for this relationship is as follows:
Logarithm of loblolly pine height (feet) equals

$$1.907 - 0.371 \left(\frac{10}{Y} \right) - 0.032 \left(\frac{10}{I} - \frac{10}{YI} \right) \text{ where}$$

age is in years (Y) and depth of the A horizon is in inches (I).

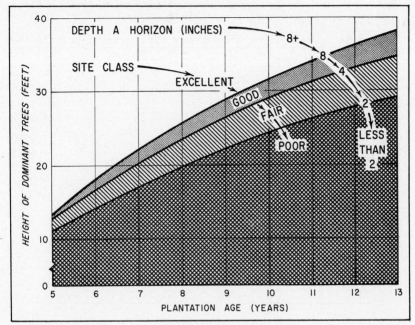

FIGURE 93.—Thickness of topsoil as a key to the quality of eroded Piedmont sites for planting loblolly pine (Goggans 1951).

reestablish adequate pore space within the soil. One way to expedite such a change would be to utilize more of certain species, like red-cedar, that will improve the soil more rapidly than do pines. In some instances it may be advisable to cut down poor stands and use the slash to mulch the ground. The subsequent decay of old root systems under the mulch may improve conditions sufficiently for successful tree planting a few years later.

WATERSHED VALUES

Watershed managers need to understand the phenomena that increase, decrease, or stabilize their water supplies, and what happens in the process to degrade or to improve forest soils.

Moisture lost or retained

Forest cover delays the flashy runoff from sudden storms, prolongs the penetration period, and tends to regulate streamflow (fig. 95, A). As contrasted with storm runoff from forest land, the maximum rate of flow from grassland may be 22 times and that from denuded land 27 times as great (Katana 1955).

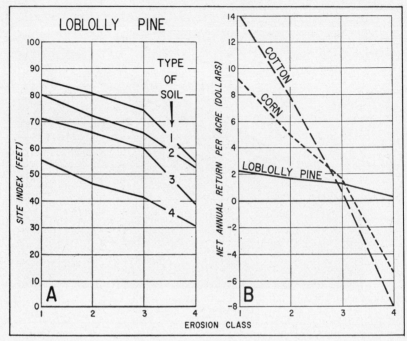

FIGURE 94.—Effect of soil and degree of erosion on site quality. *A*, Soil types are grouped for loblolly pine as follows: (1) Durham sandy loam, Granville sandy loam, Alamance silt loam, and Appling sandy loam; (2) Davidson clay loam, Tirzah silt loam, Georgeville silt loam, Herndon silt loam, and Cecil sandy loam; (3) Whitestore fine sandy loam; and (4) Orange silt loam. *B*, All eleven types are averaged for net annual return, showing the greater sensitivity of agricultural crops to erosion classes (Hostetter 1943).

Moisture lost from extensive forests to the atmosphere can be approximated only indirectly by utilizing meteorological maps and formulas not yet fully verified. On this theoretical basis it can be estimated conservatively (table 48) that a loblolly pine forest returns more than half of its rain water to the air through transpiration. Evapotranspiration losses may vary from 50 to 60 percent in early season and 55 to 70 percent in late season during normal years.

In drought periods, and near the western edge of the loblolly pine range, the loss appears to be greater. Then the transpiration potential from established stands of loblolly pine usually exceeds average summer rainfall, and is less than 100 percent only when moisture reserves are inadequate to maintain the potential rates. Thus west of the Mississippi River, where reserve supplies often may

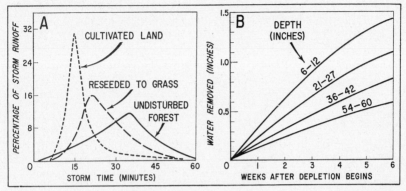

FIGURE 95.—Rate of escape of water from the soil: *A*, Influence of vegetation on peak discharge of rainwater that runs off; *B*, evapotranspiration draft on soil water supplies at different depths (Zahner 1955a and 1955c).

be low, the rain that falls in summer may supply only half the water required by the high potential evapotranspiration (Zahner 1956). The forest thus draws on whatever surplus may remain in the soil from winter and spring rains (fig. 95, *B*). In this process the summer loss may amount to 0.25 inch per day or 2 inches per week. In this way a dense young stand of pine may use up 90 percent of June rainfall and incur a deficiency of some 15 to 20 inches of water in the top 4 feet of soil.

The growth of loblolly pine is retarded and the runoff lowered in drought years, when soil moisture is reduced from saturation in late May nearly to the wilting point by late June (Moyle and Zahner 1954). In general the loss of water appears to be independent of the species composition of a forest (Zahner 1955a), though it may be expected to increase with leaf surface as forest density approaches full stocking.

The disposition of rain falling on a stand of loblolly pine varies with the amount and rate of fall in separate storms. Net interception by a forest canopy may range from 10 to 15 percent of the total yearly precipitation. A trace of rain is caught by and evaporated from foliage; in a rain of less than 0.02 inch little falls through a forest canopy; and even up to 0.10 inch stemflow is negligible. Only a small part of heavy rains is intercepted. Generally in young fully stocked loblolly pine stands about 8 percent evaporates, 20 percent runs down the stems, and 72 percent falls through the canopy (fig. 96).[130]

[130] The net amount received by the soil is $0.954R - 0.034$, where R is 0.10 inch or more rainfall measured in the open (Hoover 1953).

TABLE 48.—*Mean seasonal moisture supply for pine-hardwood forest soils—estimates of water added from and lost to the atmosphere*[1]

Section[2]	Precipitation per month		Transpiration per month	
	March through July	August through November	March through July	August through November
	Inches	Inches	Inches	Inches
Mid-Atlantic.......	4.2	3.6	2.2	1.9
East Gulf.........	4.6	3.9	2.6	2.3
West Gulf.........	4.5	3.4	2.7	2.4

[1] Based on 20-year "normals" of weather observations within the loblolly pine belt only, as adapted from seasonal maps of precipitation (Kincer 1922), temperature (Kincer 1928), and transpiration formulas (Forestry Handbook 1955, Sec. 10, page 7).
[2] Parts of states covered in the three sections are as follows: Mid-Atlantic—Maryland, Virginia, North Carolina, South Carolina; East Gulf—Georgia, Florida, Alabama, Mississippi; West Gulf—Louisiana, Arkansas, Texas.

Litter on the forest floor, like the tops of trees, can retain water only temporarily. The amount is small; only 0.01 to 0.09 inches of precipitation are thus detained (Metz 1958).

Infiltration, percolation, and species composition

After rainwater reaches the ground, a forest cover and litter of any kind helps its entry into the soil, but the rate of infiltration and percolation is influenced by the former land use. Penetration into the upper foot or two of soil is sharply curtailed after certain soils have been farmed and abandoned. For instance the noncapillary pore space may decrease to 12 percent, and the rate of percolation to less than 1 percent of former values at a depth of 1 foot (fig. 97).

Plant succession and species composition also influence the penetration of water. In young stands in the southern Piedmont, the soil under pine is 8 times, and under hardwoods 25 times, more permeable than denuded clay. This relative inferiority of the pines, despite the heavier litter (Broadfoot 1948), may be ascribed to the fact that little humus is added to mineral soil through decomposition of surface litter.

Commonly deep seepage causes negligible loss of water. Through evapotranspiration some 50 to 70 percent of precipitation in the loblolly pine belt is returned to the air (table 48). Most of the rest, including both storm water and the flow of ground water, runs off in streams. Perhaps an inch or two of current rainfall, depending on watershed conditions, remains in the upper 4 to 6 feet of soil where as much as 10 inches of water normally can be stored until withdrawn by the trees. On the Coastal Plain the water tables in relatively impermeable soil is lowered in spring, summer, and autumn by evapotranspiration (Gallup 1954). In poorly drained flatwoods

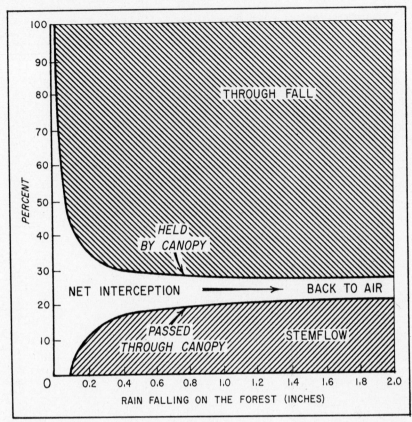

FIGURE 96.—What happens to rainwater falling on a forest varies with the size of the storm. These measurements of throughfall and stemflow were made under a plantation of 760 10-year-old loblolly pines having a basal area of 103 square feet per acre in the Calhoun Experimental Forest, Union, S. C. (Hoover 1953).

(e.g., on Bladen silt loam) the water table is raised by the removal of timber (fig. 12, chapter 2, The Species and Its Environment).

Demonstration watershed

The hydrology of an 88-acre watershed, the Pine Tree Branch in Henderson County, Tennessee, was studied between 1941 and 1950 (U. S. Tennessee Valley Authority 1955). Eroded lands on this tract were stabilized during the first 3 years by planting 78,225 loblolly pines. Although they were beyond the natural range of the species, these plantations thrived. They altered the disposal of rain that continued to fall annually in amounts ranging from 28 to 68 inches. The trees reduced surface runoff by 34 percent, while

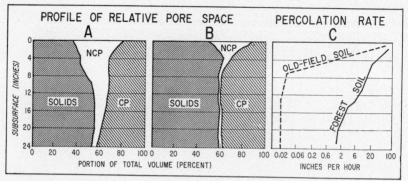

FIGURE 97.—Soil porosity and percolation rates at various depths: *A*, Relative amounts of space in the smaller or capillary pores (*CP*) and in the larger or noncapillary (*NCP*) pores in the surface 2 feet of forested Vance soil; *B*, comparable data for the same soil after its use and abandonment as farmland. *C*, Percolation rates within both the forest and old-field soils (Hoover 1950).

underground runoff increased 82 percent. Surface flow was changed from 69 percent of the total runoff to only 44 percent of the total. The yield of ground water increased from 31 to 56 percent of the total runoff. Peak discharges were reduced in frequency and rate in both winter and summer. The reductions ranged from 61 to 87 percent and were greatest when the soil was dry and the intensity of the rainfall low. The decrease in erosion lowered the sediment load by 50 percent in 2 years, and reduced it 90 percent in 10 years. Before treatment, 54 inches of rain resulted in a soil loss of 24 tons per acre annually. Fifteen years later the rate of loss was down to 1.8 tons per acre per year. The outflow of water did not change significantly.

LIVESTOCK VALUES

The degree to which it is feasible to produce both livestock and timber products on a tract of land varies with the type of forest, kind of animals, and the intensity of management.

This sort of dual use of cut-over lands has been practicable in the South largely on understocked longleaf pine lands. Such use is manifestly incompatible with forestry on hardwood bottom lands. In this respect the loblolly pine-hardwood type of forest is truly intermediate; dual use on a limited scale may be acceptable. As to kind of animals, sheep and goats graze or browse too closely to be used safely outside their own pastures. When cattle range over lands devoted to silviculture there is commonly a little damage to pine reproduction, soil, or both, and some conflict of interests. The conflicts may be insignificant under nonintensive management. Mutual benefits for trees and livestock, however, are usually in evidence only under reasonable control and partial segregation. Under intensive development of land for either purpose, livestock and timber should be concentrated on wholly separate areas. Only in this way can a full crop of each be realized. Despite inescapable limitations, the dual use of loblolly pine forests to raise cattle and trees nonintensively, but under close control, sometimes deserves careful consideration (Brasington 1949).

In many places only a casual type of dual use has developed so far. Cattle are the principal class of domestic stock that ranges on loblolly pine forest areas. They may themselves benefit or suffer and may be either beneficial or damaging to the forest depending on how they are managed. With the exception of plantations and regenerating areas, a mixed forest can be grazed moderately without detriment, though heavy grazing seriously compacts the soil. Nearly everywhere unregulated open-range grazing has been discarded or is gradually being replaced by better management of livestock. Woods grazing under lease, with its greater recognition of property rights, lowers the probability of damage from wildfires and reduces losses from timber theft. Timber stand improvement work is now making increasing use of girdling and herbicides in controlling inferior hardwoods. Where such measures are applied to lands without sufficient advance reproduction of loblolly pine, they may double the production and improve the quality of grass available for cattle.

Grazing practices

Forest grazing operations may take different forms: (1) Yearlong use of the range with supplemental feeding in winter to keep the animals alive, (2) long-season forest grazing, with the use of farm pastures, cover crops, and supplemental feed in winter to keep the stock in fair condition, and (3) short-season forest grazing in spring and early summer only; during the rest of the year the cattle are well nourished on farm pastures, field aftermath, cover crops, and adequate winter feed (Campbell 1944). Typical results of operations (1) and (3) on loblolly pine forest range in Louisiana were as follows:

Operation[1]	Calf crop (percent)	Calf weight (pounds)	Death losses (percent)
1	35-40	250-275	5-10
3	70-80	350+	Under 2

[1] The results from operation No. 2 were intermediate. Calf weights were taken at weaning time

Overstocking with grazing animals may injure soil and loblolly pine seedlings; overstocking of pines leaves scant herbaceous forage for grazing. If properly managed, the middle ground between these extremes can produce both wood and beef. Grass grown under a tree canopy that is one-third to one-half complete, and in a forest perhaps one-half to two-thirds stocked with trees, amounts to 30 to 40 percent of the native forage production of completely open lands in the Coastal Plain. Browsing fortunately retards the broad-leaved competitors of loblolly pine more heavily than it does the pine, thus benefiting pine regeneration on some Piedmont areas. For example, on Piedmont forest ranges where pines remained untouched, the extent of browsing on hardwoods up to 1 inch in d.b.h. was as follows (Shepherd, Kaufman, and Biswell 1946):

	Portion of stand browsed under—	
Seedlings or sprouts	*Moderate grazing* *(percent)*	*Heavy grazing* *(percent)*
Yellow-poplar..........	22	67
Blackgum.............	30	65
Redbud..............	25	54
Hickory..............	3	33
Red maple............	8	20
Dogwood.............	4	16
Sweetgum............	9	15

In the upland forests of that plateau cattle grazing may be permitted because any reduction in hardwoods is beneficial to loblolly pine; but continuous heavy grazing should be avoided because of the danger of erosion and the chance of a large weight loss in the cattle. Forage production is negligible in pine plantations or under fully stocked stands. The carrying capacity of a forest range varies inversely with the tree cover, and the acquired weight of the animals varies inversely with the degree of stocking on the forest range. In open broomsedge areas, or luxuriant honeysuckle, 2 acres per cow per month is sufficient (Kaufman 1949), but as stands of timber close in 8, 10, or more acres per animal per month may be needed.

Fire hazard can be abated in young pine stands and in plantations where broomsedge is plentiful by providing a grazing load just large enough to hold the grass down throughout the season. The short spring grazing season in Piedmont forests may be insufficient for this purpose unless followed by late summer grazing to consume the regrowth. In the coastal flatwoods, where there is no erosion problem, the loblolly pine forest furnishes forage and browse in season, with some shelter, to many head of cattle. They, in turn, reduce accumulations of forest fire fuels from 10 to 75 percent

(Shepherd, Kaufman, and Biswell 1946), depending on ground cover, degree of stocking, and the feasibility of supplemental burning. Controlled burning may help both pines and grass, but ordinarily the use of fire should be prescribed to meet timber rather than grazing needs. The cattle will concentrate on range lands that have been burned.

Herds receiving adequate yearlong nutrition and good care produce 3 to 4 times as much beef per cow as poorly managed herds (Campbell and Cassady 1951). Advances in animal husbandry—better livestock, improved pastures, fence laws, and supplemental feeding of cattle—together with advances in silviculture are making it increasingly possible to manage understocked pine lands profitably (Campbell and Biswell 1944).

Forage production

The bluestems (*Andropogons*), and associated forage species[131] predominate over 50 million acres and make up nearly two-thirds of the forage grazed by cattle in the loblolly pine belt. Such range is best used for grazing only in the spring. Associated species that grow earlier and later than the bluestems lengthen the grazing season and give desirable variety to the diet of cattle.

In undisturbed loblolly pine forest range, forage production decreases with any natural increase in woody vegetative cover. With each increase of 1 percent in tree and shrub cover forage declines about 1.5 percent beneath an overwood or 1.0 percent beneath a cover of shrubs only. A desirable growth of forage can be stimulated materially by reducing the density of an overwood. In the absence of trees and shrubs on the Coastal Plain of Georgia, 9 acres of range are needed from March to January for each 500-pound steer to make maximum gains, or 15 acres for a mature animal. The grass may yield about 1,000 pounds of herbage per acre, but less than half of it is usable under moderate grazing. Fire removes the "rough" of dead grass and weeds and makes nutritious forage more readily available to grazing animals. Where they utilize little more than a third of the native forage, the returns per animal are favorable.

The superiority of fresh spring growth of native forage is shown by chemical analysis. Samples taken in Louisiana (Campbell and Cassady 1951) show a spring protein content of 9 to 15 percent decreasing to about 7 percent in summer and 5 percent or less in

[131] The principal native species are little bluestem, pinehill, and other bluestems, pinewoods dropseed, panicums, *Paspalum* spp., cutover muhly, and legumes. Williams, R. E., Cassady, J. T., Halls, L. K., and Woolfolk, E. J. Range Resources of the South. Ga. Agr. Expt. Bul. N.S. 9, 1955.

winter. Phosphorus content was not adequate at any time of year, even at its peak of 0.14 percent in spring. Calcium was adequate throughout the active growing season. Supplemental protein concentrate or hay is needed for any animals left on the range during autumn and winter.

Little has been done in the South toward nonintensive range improvement through direct seeding of better forage plants. Carpet grass is one accidentally introduced exotic species that can hold its own and advance slowly in competition with native grasses under close grazing along the gulf coast. There, on infertile soils carpetgrass and common lespedeza afford the greatest net return regardless of treatment, but site preparation and reseeding, or transplanting blocks of sod, does speed up establishment and lead to better stands. The tendency for carpetgrass to spread naturally under close grazing is desirable because it checks erosion along old woods roads and improves summer grazing (Ceremello 1942). Yields of 700 to 800 pounds per acre of herbage may be expected from carpetgrass, 75 percent of which is usable for grazing.

Cattle tend to select forage of high palatability or nutritive value, resulting in overgrazing and elimination of some species, like the highly prized southern switch cane. The grazing values on fire lanes or patches of revegetated range benefit from introduction of selected legumes and other forage plants suitable for a given locality. For example in North Carolina certain cool-weather leguminous perennials, such as Ladino, Louisiana white clover, and big trefoil, extend the grazing season and remain noncombustible in autumn and winter. Dallisgrass or lespedeza improve summer grazing. A ground cover composed of a mixture of clover and grass serves to crowd out weeds that have less feed value and present a high fire hazard. Other favorite species have adaptations which enable them to tolerate heavy trampling and cropping by animals. Thus a high ratio of vegetative stems to fruiting stems helps some plants to withstand close utilization (Rechenthin 1956). Bermudagrass and carpetgrass have stolons or rhizomes, or both, that keep the new growth close to the ground. Other grasses, like the native little bluestem, are less nutritious in summer, but possess many short basal nodes to initiate adventitious roots and new primary and secondary roots repeatedly, i.e., to "tiller." These adaptations make certain species efficient producers of forage. Indirectly, of course, improvements in ground cover conserve both watershed and recreation values in the loblolly pine forest.

Range practice should also favor the legumes, because the more vigorous native grasses tend to shade or starve them out. The range value of legumes derives from two qualities: (1) Rich feed value due to high content of protein, vitamins, and mineral salts, especially calcium and phosphorus, and (2) the benefit they extend to other plants growing with them by elaborating nitrogen compounds in their root nodules and subsequently releasing them in the soil.

To the extent that the better forage plants can be propagated under loblolly pines they need not be provided on separate grazing areas. Where forest grazing cannot be managed in conjunction with a farm having commensurate facilities for animal husbandry, grass for cattle may still be established in forest pastures or on the strips of forest land cleared for firebreaks.[132]

Pasturing fire lanes

Well-grazed strip pastures of superior forage do offer an opportunity for low-cost fire protection for extensive Coastal Plain forests. Sod lanes, kept green or closely grazed, can be both productive and nonflammable during the fire season (Shepherd, Kaufman, and Biswell, 1946). Appropriate species established on a system of properly spaced 18- to 66-foot lanes can provide not only forage but also emergency access in case of fire. In sections where grass is only lightly grazed, and hence only partially effective as a barrier, it is best to plow a fire line or build a road in the center of the lane. Marginal fuel reduction, through forage consumption, may then reduce the height of flames enough so that a relatively narrow strip of bare soil will stop the spread of fire. To prepare strip pastures the trees and shrubs should be removed and the ground double-disked to turn under the grass, weeds, and litter several weeks before seeding so that rain can settle the soil. A heavy tandem disk can be drawn by a wheel tractor on average sites or by a crawler tractor on brushy or wet sites. In North Carolina, plowing with a Mathis fire plow, followed by several trips over with a heavy brush-and-bog harrow has been most effective, but chopping with the Marden brush cutter has been the most economical method (Hughes and Rea 1951).

In pure stands, legumes generally give better fire protection than the grasses, but a mixture of grass and a legume is better than either one. Such a mixture tends to provide stronger competition to weeds than either element alone, and a better sod of more suc-

[132] For the improvement of pastures in Louisiana, kudzu and sudangrass are suggested for summer; a mixture of Dallisgrass, carpetgrass, and lespedeza for summer and autumn, and oats or Kentucky 31 fescue for autumn and winter grazing (Campbell and Cassady 1951).

culent forage over a longer period. A mixture of carpetgrass and lespedeza has been successful in Louisiana (Peevy and Cassady 1957). Carpetgrass and white clover are good for fire protection because they encourage close grazing. Two years after establishment, Alta fescue, a cool-season perennial, is green and nonflammable also in winter. It gives excellent protection, and when mixed with white clover, big trefoil, and Dallisgrass the carrying capacity is high in North Carolina (Shepherd 1952). In Georgia excellent winter grazing has been attained through complete fertilization for such crops as oats and Abruzzi rye.

Some fertilization is desirable for establishment, maintenance, and close grazing of nearly all introduced species offering any appreciable improvement over the native range. If well developed and managed, the introduced forage will largely pay for the establishment and maintenance of the fire barriers.

WILDLIFE VALUES

Wildlife inhabitants in loblolly pine forests are of recognized indirect and aesthetic value to man for recreation, angling, and hunting. In this type of forest the damages from wildlife, or direct benefits from its presence, are usually minor. Through cutting, grazing, burning, and soil manipulation much can be done in forest management to favor or reduce fish and wildlife populations (Arnold and Hankla 1958).

Deer

Game management for deer and timber management for loblolly pine are compatible over large areas. On limited areas the combination leads to some conflict of interests when any intensive cultural measures are introduced. Seldom is the control of stocking of either deer or pine sufficient to maintain good balance. Where deer herds grow large they may interfere with regeneration of pine; where silviculture produces dense stands of pine, the deer may be short of forage. Unbalanced populations periodically lead to starvation and disease for deer herds on unimproved range, and before a balance is restored the smallest loblolly pine seedlings may suffer severe browsing damage. Deer herds on southern forest ranges— already as large as 20 to 160 thousand deer in each state—are growing rapidly. Big game in the southeastern national forests alone increased by 22 percent in a recent 5-year period, during which hunting pressure increased 140 percent. But as yet the failure of sportsmen to harvest full crops of deer has not prevented the use of land to grow pine in the South as it has in some northern states.

The loblolly-shortleaf pine type of forest is attractive to deer, particularly if its form is patchy and many-aged. Pure stands of pine are less favorable than those with an admixture of certain hardwoods. Several of these, such as hawthorn, blackgum, persimmon, hickory, and oak occur as associate species or along small streams. Many loblolly pine forests include also some bottom-land hardwoods valuable to game animals (Miller 1956). Sufficiently large breeding herds exist to provide rapid expansion of the deer population in much of the loblolly pine range.

An unpopulated deer range may be initially stocked to advantage with a preponderance of does. Halloran (1943) suggests one buck to 6 does. But to keep a herd in balance with its habitat, current concepts indicate that legal harvests should be nonselective as to sex and age. Composition of large herds may be determined by using kill data from check stations where large samples can be gathered during hunting seasons set without sex or age restrictions. Elsewhere estimates of current populations on limited areas may be based on driving deer out of selected sample areas and counting them as they emerge. Deer pellet counts have been used rather successfully to estimate deer populations.

The rate at which deer reproduce is affected by both the quantity and quality of food available to them. On good range they reproduce each year at the rate of about 2.0 fawns per adult doe, about 1.5 fawns per yearling doe, and about 0.35 fawn per fawn doe. A healthy well-fed herd of 1,000 deer can produce as many fawns as a herd of 1,600 poorly fed deer on overbrowsed range. One deer per 100 acres of forested range represents a low population that may safely be increased under good habitat conditions. One head for each 20 acres is feasible for an autumn concentration in a forest of mixed composition and several age classes. Further increases, however, may lead to starvation causing deterioration in both the herd and range (Baldwin 1957, Barrick 1958).

The manager of deer herds should watch the range in order to recognize excessive browsing on plants preferred as food while there is still time to control populations at a level that can readily be sustained. He should not wait until the symptoms of overstocking become extreme. By the time a well-defined overhead browse line is in evidence the deer are damaging the forest, facing starvation, and destroying their own food supply. This problem can be solved in either or both of two ways: (1) reduce the herd, or (2) log the range to create browse from sprouts. When and where protection of pine regeneration against browsing damage is needed, it may be necessary to reduce deer stocking somewhat below the level of forage availability (Burke 1956). This may be laboriously accomplished by trapping to remove excess deer for distribution to other areas, or by hunting. Controlled hunting is preferable in most cases. Success on the better deer hunts varies, with one deer killed by each 6 to 10 hunters.

Small game

Much of the recreation for hunters is furnished by small animals. There are four small-game hunters to one big-game hunter. Quail, rabbit, and squirrel, for example, provide three-quarters of all the hunting man-hours in North Carolina. Hardwood forest is preferred by most of the smaller birds, though some pine needles are used for nests and pine trees are nesting sites for mourning doves. Loblolly-shortleaf pine forests are attractive to turkey, and to a lesser extent to quail.

Autumn populations of turkey on the better ranges may not exceed one bird per 125 acres (Uhlig and Bailey 1952). There is some evidence that turkeys do not do well with cattle on the range, and, without measures to improve their habitat, they do not thrive in pine forests of less than 15,000 acres (Miller 1956). They may need prescribed burning, supplemental food and water, and special protection. Even so, increases in their populations are slow at best, and artificial restocking with these birds is likely to succeed only if a wild strain is transplanted. An upland pine range suitable for turkey should include some well-watered hardwood sites. Food for turkey should be available adjacent to the pine thickets used for cover—or at least it should not be more than a quarter mile away. Native food plants may be supplemented on 1- to 4-acre clearings or on 80- to 100-foot fire lanes that have been seeded as pastures and maintained by mowing. For this purpose annual browntop millet, winter grains, or perennial Ladino and crimson clover may be suitable (Baldwin 1957).

In southern Georgia foxes are most abundant in areas of mixed woods and cultivation. In the pine forest there are more foxes where the underbrush is least dense (Wood, Davis, and Komerek 1958).

Squirrels show some preference for a pine and hardwood range lightly grazed by cattle. Squirrels are most abundant during the later stages in forest succession when nut bearing trees supply food.

Their preferred food is mast of hickory, white oaks, and to a lesser extent black oaks and pine. They feed on berries and other fleshy fruits when they are in season. Like raccoons, squirrels are attracted to den trees with one or more hollows at least 10 feet above ground. Although opinions differ, four den trees of any species for each 10 acres are believed to be sufficient, provided that the distance between trees does not exceed 7 chains (Vincent 1956).

During the early stages of revegetation of idle lands, the usual ground cover is most attractive to both rabbits and quail. Environmental changes favorable to quail can be induced by landowners under a rotational system of harvesting timber. Some interspersion of various age classes of pine affords protection, food, and nesting cover, and hence is essential to the continued production of quail. An increase in numbers of quail begins with the first opening of a closed forest canopy. It has been observed in Texas (Lay 1940) that during the first 4 years after cutting, the pine forest per covey averages 141 acres. The bird population then rises to a peak, about the eighth year, of 77 acres per covey; then declines to about 95 acres per covey from the 10th to the 15th year. In older tracts of forest there were about 500 acres per covey of quail.

The management of quail is feasible where loblolly pine is being grown, particularly where the reproduction areas can be numerous, small, and scattered. Recommendations include not only protection of the range from heavy grazing, predators, and overshooting, but also brush clearing in spots, plowing with optional planting of feed patches, and some burning of slash under carefully regulated conditions. In Alabama and Georgia, burning has been observed to increase the area occupied by herbaceous quail-food plants (Moore 1956), and the birds prefer a 1-year rough for nesting. Quail will benefit where prescriptions to burn, thin, and prune can be started early. Food patches can be made by fertilizing, disking, and sowing seed of various millets for autumn and annual lespedezas for winter food (Baldwin 1957).

No other use for wildlife in the loblolly pine forest has increased as much in recent years as fishing. In the Southeast there are only about 5 feet of fishing streams per fisherman. Streamside zones in pine stands should be protected so as to provide satisfactory stream conditions. For example, silt buffers help to keep the water clear and shade will keep it relatively cool. Where artificial ponds[133] can

[133] Ponds may carry 100 to 500 pounds of fish per acre, and about half of the weight can be caught annually on a sustained-yield basis. Fertility of watersheds controls the productivity of fishing waters. The yield of fish depends on subsequent management to maintain fertility and a favorable balance

be created within a loblolly pine forest, they provide water for live-stock, for fire fighting, and for recreation.

Habitat and food supply

Improvements in habitat and food supply on game management areas and elsewhere provide the possibility of an overflow of surplus game populations into the surrounding forest, but many species are essentially nonmobile. Hence, in the absence of favorable environ-ment, the repopulation of surrounding areas by this means may be temporary. All strata in a forest contribute something to the habitat: (1) The overstory, mast and dens; (2) the understory, mainly pal-atable browse; (3) the ground cover, forage and game food includ-ing berries and seeds; and (4) the ground itself, available water. Living conditions for wild creatures of the forest are modified most by man through the pattern left by his cutting and burning opera-tions. Maximum diversity in the vegetation is most beneficial, for it is capable of yielding a variety of food over extended periods.

Timber cutting that results in a scattering of small openings augments food supplies for several species of game animals. Even though the resulting increase in understory vegetation may produce abundant browse, some additional timber-growing space may be deliberately sacrificed for mast to maintain game animals. Fire, properly used, can improve the range for deer, turkey, and quail.[134] Removal of dense patches of underbrush destroys the hiding places for animals that prey on turkeys (Hills 1954). Certain shrubs, vines, and minor vegetation, stimulated by fire, are important in their food supply. Berry bushes, herbs, and grass should supply cover without restricting the movement of quail.

Probably no more than a third of the native plants available during the growing season are used by deer. For example, they may feed on yaupon, greenbrier, and water oak, but shun sweetgum, wax-myrtle, and pine. Where natural foods are of poor quality, or in limited supply, the planting and fertilization of pasture crops may be advisable in spots to offset nutrient deficiencies in winter protein and phosphorus. In winter on unimproved range deer subsist on buds, leaves, twigs, and bark. In spring the sprouting of low hard-wood brush, killed back by fire, places fresh foliage within their reach. Where understories are 9 to 12 feet high, the effect of fire

---

between prey and predator species in the pond. There should be about 1 pound of predators to between 3 and 6 pounds of nonpredators.

[134] Stoddard, H. L. Use of fire on southeastern game lands. 19 pp. Coop. Quail Study Assoc., Sherwood Plantation, Thomasville, Ga., 1936.

may be to reduce browse for 2 years, but to increase herbaceous food for at least 3 years with little change in total forage (Lay 1956).

Deer, turkey, and quail suffer some loss of food in the general reduction of mast. Acorns, a winter staple for deer only in years of abundance, supply protein comparable to that given to cattle in their winter supplements. Acorns result in an extra layer of fat that helps the deer through the winter and assists in their reproduction, but they are not indispensable. Winter diets for deer can be improved by planting annual ryegrass or fescue on forest roadways and firebreaks (Miller 1956). Burning may result in a net loss for squirrels, depending on the degree to which they rely on the local understory mast.

McAttee (1936) has systematically listed the genera of plants known to be of most value in providing cover, browse, herbage, mast, fruit, and seeds for wildlife. From one to three of these uses is designated for each plant listed. Among the best of these plants are the herbaceous legumes. A variety of merits makes them valuable in conserving soil and benefiting wildlife. Some species tolerate acid soil, and all of them grow well in mixture with grasses. Many mature early and reseed themselves, especially after a hot fire, but artificial preparation of the site is often preferable. They propagate readily by direct seeding if attention is given to the possible need for scarification, repellents, and inoculation. By adding nitrogen compounds to the soil, legumes benefit neighboring plants. They have high forage value, thrive in well-drained upland game habitats, provide cover, and produce nutritious seeds often available in winter as staple foods. Few legumes are pernicious or poisonous weeds, and legumes do not serve as alternate hosts to any seriously injurious fungi or insects (Graham 1941).

Because pine seeds are vital for forest regeneration only in selected years, there is usually a surplus available to birds and rodents at other times. While the hardwood associates of loblolly pine supply the bulk of the food for wildlife, pine seeds furnish a seasonal source of food for small mammals, doves, quail, and various other ground feeding birds. Twenty or more species of songbirds feed on loblolly pine seeds to some extent. Pine seeds actually supply more than half of the diet for the red crossbill of the finch family.

Essential as food is for wildlife, it often remains unutilized where suitable cover is not sufficiently close. Game animals need cover because of its capacity to serve first as a hiding place and then as an impediment to pursuit by predators. With the possible exception

of turkeys, convenient location of cover in relation to food supplies
is a prime consideration in the evaluation of game habitats (McAtee
1936) within the loblolly pine forest.

Management of wildlife

Long-term wildlife management, together with loblolly pine management, must be considered forestwide, with only such controls as
are required to properly harvest desirable surpluses, and thus protect other values. Large and diversified acreages in blocks of sufficient
size to provide a management unit are required for satisfactory
wildlife production. With the possible exception of quail and squirrel, blocks of less than 5,000 acres do not offer favorable wildlife
opportunities (Miller 1956). On such blocks complete protection
from unregulated fire, livestock, and hunting alone may result in
adequate populations of wildlife, though in places some protection
from predators is advisable.

Many timber management operations to better the accessibility,
composition, structure, and yield of a loblolly pine forest are con-
sonant with game management. Prescriptions for the use of fire, as
well as specifications for firebreaks and roadways, commonly improve the environment for wildlife. Such work may need to be
supplemented by specific measures to achieve a desirable diversity
and distribution of both food and cover. For example, the sowing
and fertilization of isolated openings to grass and legumes benefits
the wildlife.

Scattered trees of seed-bearing species like oak, gum, and dogwood should be retained on perhaps 25 percent of the forest, though
actually occupying less than 10 percent of the area. The timber stands
should be interspersed with openings covering 15 to 20 percent of
the forest. These may include quarter-acre pine reproduction areas
as well as the rights of way for public utilities, service roads, trails,
lanes, and log or pulpwood yards used only periodically.

Timber stand improvement operations can readily reserve some
den trees and adequate numbers of food trees. These measures re-
cur on a given area of pine forest only at rather long intervals during
which sprouting hardwoods produce an abundance of browse. Fires,
prescribed in winter to keep understory vegetation at a low level,
renew the supply of browse within reach of deer. Later, as harvest
time approaches, preparatory, selection, or seed-tree cuttings re-
open the overwood in a manner that stimulates food plants in the
ground cover and benefits quail, deer, and turkey, while rabbits use
the slashings for cover.

Pine regeneration in pure stands, natural or planted, usually develops so rapidly (in the Gulf states east of Texas) that the openings benefit game animals only temporarily. In like manner thinning or improvement cuttings may be too light to benefit wildlife appreciably during the early years of a rotation. These intermediate cuttings, however, together with suspension of controlled burning, commonly permit some hardwoods to grow up with the pines. This development results in little loss to the timber crop and much benefit to wildlife.

A good example of such integration of management for game with that for loblolly pine exists in the Francis Marion National Forest in South Carolina where release cuttings are made on about 1,600 acres annually. There with 60-foot clearings along access roads, each mile provides 7 acres of game food. These strips, together with the grassy patches reserved for game, cover 1 to 4 percent of the forest (Riebold 1956).

A recognized need, in much of the loblolly pine range, is enabling legislation that will permit greater flexibility in the administration of game regulations. Laws are needed that will implement more effective management of both game populations and their habitats by professional game biologists and foresters.

MULTIPLE USE

Skillful management is essential to utilize a loblolly pine forest successfully for a wide variety of purposes. Such utilization is often possible but not always advisable. It is less feasible to attain with small woodlands, or compartments of larger tracts, than with extensive forests. Even then each distinct use can be highly developed only on separate areas. On each of these, the primary use should be recognized and designated. In allocating certain areas of forest among alternative or optional uses, an attempt should be made to achieve ultimately a reasonable balance between the net values obtainable from different products or through various services (Richards 1958).

Intergrated production requires a high degree of skillful management to bring maximum economic returns. Inevitable conflicts arising from overlapping uses are more readily tolerated under nonintensive management, and the rewards from multiple use are most likely to exceed those of any single use in the early stages of a forest enterprise. Even so, many measures taken specifically to improve water relations, soil conditions, or vegetative cover for the benefit of forests or watersheds serve also generally to augment values obtainable from domestic stock, wildlife, or recreation. Thus over wide areas the forestry problem is that of attaining the wise multiple use of loblolly pine land.

SUMMARY

In obtaining timber, as well as various other products and services, from loblolly pine forest lands, soil and water supplies are basic interacting resources that need to be conserved. The fundamental quality of these resources is best realized when the land is managed to promote values obtainable from three principal products other than timber— pure water, domestic stock or wildlife, and recreation.

Revegetation, not only with loblolly pine, but also with grass, forage, and other food or erosion-control plants—if, when, and where needed—is a part of the business of augmenting each of these supplementary forest values.

Although the loblolly pine belt is humid, drought sometimes retards tree growth and reduces runoff. The silt load that varies with the seasons represents erosion losses. It may signify that poor land management has changed too much of the relatively slow subterranean runoff into rapid surface flow. By contrast good management of forest cover promotes steady subsurface percolation of water; it delays and reduces the flashy runoff from swollen streams and stabilizes them. In one 17-year period reforestation with loblolly pine did not alter total annual flow, but it did decrease surface runoff from 69 percent to only 44 percent of that total. Simultaneously in this demonstration of rehabilitation on a 1,715-acre watershed, the decrease in erosion lowered sediment load in the stream by 50 percent in 2 years and by 90 percent in 10 years.

Loblolly pines, more deeply rooted than cotton or corn, are themselves less sensitive to the loss of topsoil. Nevertheless, the value of eroded Piedmont soils as sites for planting pine may be judged by the thickness of the topsoil. Where loblolly pine thrives, its rapid growth and needle cast help to cover and hold denuded soils in place.

Under intensive practice in growing loblolly pine timber the values obtainable from grazing domestic livestock remain secondary, because full development encounters too many conflicting interests. As no individual acre can produce a full crop of both timber and forage, these crops must be grown largely on separate areas either inside or adjoining the forested portion. Potential profits from beef cattle in the forest are highest where adjacent farms provide modern facilities for animal husbandry. Openings made in the forest canopy in operations for timber stand improvement do increase the yield of forage to some extent. However, a pine-hardwood forest can be only moderately grazed by cattle unless improved forage is available on fire lanes or supplemental pastures. Without such auxiliary supplies of forage or feed, cattle tend to lose weight, particularly under heavy stocking and in late season.

The quantity of fresh grass varies with forest cover and with the frequency of fire. In flat terrain the forest floor can sometimes be burned over in a manner that will favor new growth of both grass and pine, but usually strictly silvicultural burning takes precedence. Cattle attracted to the fresh grass on burned areas within the forest may consume enough potential fuel to reduce the incidence of, and damage from, subsequent unwanted fires. It is when the fire lanes are seeded with palatable plants, and hence always grazed closely enough to be relatively nonflammable, that cattle not only make the best gains but also contribute most toward protection of the forest from fire.

The wildlife values to be had from loblolly pine forests add little to the safety of, or profit from, most forestry enterprises, but they do yield recreation dividends. The wild creatures need suitable food, cover, and home sites. Essential silvicultural measures, such as periodic cutting, controlled burning, and scarification of the soil, provide incidental benefits to wildlife populations. Both deer and several kinds of small game, such as quail, are attracted to a forest that is patchy by accident or many-aged by design. A pine-hardwood type of range that is grazed lightly by cattle seems to be preferred by squirrels, but not by wild turkey. Squirrels apparently prefer nut producing trees, and tend to increase where natural den trees are available or where artificial nest boxes are supplied. Some hardwoods may be reserved for mast production. Variety in shrubs and ground cover improves the habitat for all these creatures that contribute to the recreational value of a loblolly pine forest.

A joint consideration of the needs of animals, domestic or wild, and of the soil and water on which they depend, focuses attention on one group of measures. These have to do with the improvement of the native ground cover and the revegetation of bare spots. The best of the forage plants include various legumes and certain grasses of prostrate growth habit with a high ratio of vegetative to fruiting stems. These withstand close grazing, hold soil from erosion and silt from streams, and prepare denuded areas to support pine.

Where the pines have been established, with or without benefit of mulch, they do well in holding the soil, but they crowd out the herbaceous ground cover. Accordingly the various types of useful vegetation should be fostered on appropriate areas in any extensive forest. Fortunately, under multiple-use management, measures to benefit the water regime, soils, and cover in watersheds, also generally benefit livestock, wildlife, and recreation values.

Chapter 10

Properties and Uses

USES FOR LOBLOLLY PINE

SOUTHERN PINE IS NOT ONLY USED extensively in the United States, but is also exported, mostly through Atlantic ports, to more than 70 countries (Wisehart 1946). Loblolly pine wood is used for all purposes served by the southern yellow pines.[135] In fact, loblolly pine timber that passed the "density rule" contributed to the enviable reputation for structural timber enjoyed by our longleaf pine.[136]

No other wood has a wider range of industrial use. The principal uses include lumber for building material, such as joists, frames (plate 11), sheathing, siding, subflooring, floors, ceiling, sash, doors, and interior finish. Other uses are for furnishings and woodenware, frames for upholstered furniture, boxes, crates, package veneers, boats, implements, toys, novelties, slack cooperage, and caskets. Piece products are likewise numerous: posts, poles, piling, timber for bridges and trestles, props and other mine timbers, crossties, and crossarms.

While use for fuel has been decreasing a pulpwood market for rough pine wood has developed. Wood of little value for lumber may be entirely acceptable for pulping. About a third of the cubic volume of our sawtimber trees is more valuable for pulpwood than for saw logs. Our many pulpmills provide a welcome outlet for numerous defective and other inferior trees that must be removed to increase the productivity of our forests.

[135] There is one major exception. An early report (Sargent 1884) indicates that turpentine was occasionally made from loblolly pines, but without commercial success. Longleaf and slash pines alone support the naval stores industry in the United States.

[136] The density rule requires one-third summerwood and not less than six annual rings per inch, or half summerwood with not less than four rings per inch. Estimates are made by visual inspection of the ends of a piece. Wide rings near the pith of boxed-heart pines may be disregarded.

PLATE 11.—Pine, much of it loblolly, remains the principal material used in framing houses (U.S.F.S. Photo).

Sawtimber

A common mistake in growing sawtimber is failure to recognize those logs and trees that can more advantageously be used for some other product of greater or lesser value. It is not enough to know merely what a buyer will accept; it is vital to recognize the minimum size of tree that can be removed with profit.

A basic economic justification for partial cutting is extraction costs which are lower for large than for small trees. Lumber from large trees is worth more per 1,000 board feet than that from small trees. It often costs twice as much to produce 1,000 board feet of lumber from 8-inch as from 24-inch trees, though the lumber from the smaller trees may be worth only three-quarters as much. This relation varies with time and place where "costs and returns" were studied, yet the principle holds. For each operation there is a diameter limit below which trees do not pay their way in lumber production. The effect of this limit on profits should be considered.

For example, it was found (Garver & Miller 1933) that the d.b.h. of the smallest tree which paid its way was 12 inches in second-growth shortleaf and loblolly pine in southern Arkansas, but 16 inches in old-field loblolly pine in northern Louisiana. Under lump-sum purchase a buyer who does not cut for grade may wish to cut down to 11 or 12 inches for the highest gross return, but the greatest return per 1,000 board feet comes from cutting only trees 15 inches in diameter or larger. The economic minimum diameter may be only 10 or 11 inches for crowded loblolly pines of intermediate crown development with a high proportion of B and better lumber, but in general, trees below 13 inches did not pay their way in 1932 (Paul 1932a).

Nevertheless, a recent study in the Piedmont indicated that 62 percent of the pine lumber is being cut with or without profit from 10-inch or smaller logs (Haines 1953a). At small and medium-sized mills, which saw 80 percent of all the pine lumber cut in Alabama, more than half is manufactured from logs less than 10 inches in diameter (fig. 98). Trees under 13 inches should be reserved if sound; if defective they should go to a pulpmill rather than a sawmill.

Ashe (1930a) was one of the first to point out how many more pine trees and logs of small sizes have to be handled to make a given amount of lumber:

Average d.b.h. of pine trees (inches)	Trees to produce 1,000 board feet of lumber (number)	Logs to produce 1,000 board feet of lumber (number)
8	30.0	53.0
10	15.0	44.0
15	4.5	15.0
20	1.7	7.5
25	1.1	4.7

When lumber is cut from 10-inch trees instead of 25-inch trees, it is necessary to handle 13 percent more weight, and it takes twice as long (table 49).

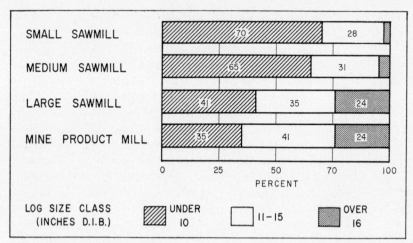

FIGURE 98.—Distribution of pine logs by size classes at Alabama mills (Osborn 1952).

TABLE 49.—*Conversion ratios of logs to boards from trees of different sizes (Ashe 1930a)*

Log d.i.b. (inches)	Board feet per cubic foot	Portion of volume not used for lumber	Weight of wood with bark to produce each board foot
	Bd. ft.	Percent	Pounds
5...............	3.5	71	16.0
8...............	5.2	54	11.0
10...............	6.0	48	9.6
12...............	6.5	44	8.9
14...............	6.9	41	8.3
16...............	7.1	40	8.0
18...............	7.3	39	7.7
20...............	7.4	38	7.5
25...............	7.5	37	7.4

Most mills accept many logs that are too small for economical operation. The prevailing width of boards cut from pines of different sizes on the Piedmont Plateau averages a little more than half the d.b.h. class (McClay 1953a) (table 50). An analysis of log intake at 17 representative mills in Arkansas (Carpenter 1950) showed that less than 30 percent had scaling diameters of more than 12 inches. The size of log most frequently sawed varies between 8 and 11 inches depending on the type of mill (table 51). Had potential values in these trees been distinguished, the poor ones should have been cut for minor uses. Then the milling of the better trees could have been deferred until they became more profitable to saw.

A common procedure in handling old-field pine in the Southeast

TABLE 50.—*Proportion of board widths of rough green lumber sawed from pine logs by circular mills (McClay 1953a)*

Log d.i.b. (inches)	Board width				
	4 in.	6 in.	8 in.	10 in.	12 in.
	Percent	Percent	Percent	Percent	Percent
6	100	..	..	..	..
7	90	10	..	..	..
8	43	57	..	..	..
9	31	69	..	..	..
10	25	64	11	..	..
11	15	41	44	..	..
12	11	24	65	..	..
13	7	22	63	8	..
14	4	17	35	42	2
15	3	14	22	53	8
16	3	11	17	44	25
17	2	7	15	21	55
18	2	7	13	16	62
19	2	5	11	14	67
20	1	5	9	15	70
21	1	5	8	14	72
22	1	5	9	14	71

is to manufacture it into "roofers." These are 1x4- to 1x12-inch air-dried log-run boards, including any and all grades of material in the proportions found. Grading a sample of this material in South Carolina indicated that 85 to 95 percent of it was of the quality of No. 2 common lumber. Pine logs are rarely quartersawn, but better material, suitable for edge-grain flooring or deck planks, can be readily made in this manner from the larger logs.

Utilization is far from complete. In harvesting pines for saw-timber the use of tops for pulpwood in most operations is advantageous, but only 14 percent were so used in one Piedmont area in South Carolina and 54 percent of the slabs and edging were not used for any purpose. The 46 percent that the mill men could dispose of found only low-grade use as follows: 27 percent sold as fuel, 14 percent used at home, and 5 percent given away (Haines 1953b). Investigations are under way to find better uses for this raw wood. New equipment is being developed to remove bark from cull logs, grind them into chips, and load the chips for transport to pulpmills. Chips constituted 9 percent of the pine delivered to pulpmills in 1957. Efficient slab barkers are available and some are in operation; the chief deterrent to this development is the cost of concentrating slabs from scattered mills. If these machines can be made portable and effective without excessive costs, much waste material will be made available to them and the drain on natural resources will be reduced.

Pulpwood

Pulpwood, a wood product of secondary unit value, is rapidly achieving major importance in the economy of the South. A continuing harvest of pulpwood can promote silviculture not merely by reducing waste, but by utilizing countless trees that impede the growth of more valuable products.

About half a cord of pulpwood can be cut from the tops of sawlog trees and another half cord from undesirable small trees removed in a typical selection cutting for saw logs. The forest benefits from thinning and through the release of seedlings formerly suppressed or pinned down by fallen tops. Fire hazard is reduced with debris from tops left closer to the ground where it decays more rapidly. Pulpwood from sawtimber is taken from tops of trees 12 to 26 inches in diameter. It is found largely above the second log in small trees or the third log in large trees (fig. 99). Despite the volume waste in the tops of large trees, the wood requires too much chopping and splitting to yield as much pulpwood as the small trees. The best division of products as between these two uses can advantageously be shifted occasionally in accordance with local market conditions. In 1956 the degree of topwood utilization for pulpwood at Crossett, Ark., was approximately as follows:

| | Average minimum top diameter for | | Merchantable pulpwood cut from tops |
D.b.h. (inches)	Logs (inches)	Pulpwood (inches)	(cubic feet)
12	9	5	2
14	9	5	3
16	10	6	4
18	10	6	5
20	11	7	6
22	11	8	6
24	12	9	7
26	12	11	8
28	13	12	8

For small trees the economic "conversion surplus" in a saw log is absent or so low that it may be the more profitable to utilize the whole tree for pulpwood.[137]

Below 12 inches most of the pines harvested should be used entirely for pulpwood or products other than saw logs. Here, also, the size of tree has a marked effect on extraction costs. For example, McClay (1953c) has shown that a cord of wood produced from 5-inch trees may take nearly 2½ times as much labor as a cord from

[137] Two men with a bow saw can make 1 to 1½ cords of pulpwood per 8-hour man-day from tops of felled trees. When thinning timber stands they can produce 1½ to 2 cords per man-day (Brender 1947).

TABLE 51.—*Proportions of green lumber produced by different classes of mills[1]*

Class of mill	Log diameters (inches)						
	6	8	11	14	17	20	23
	Percent	Percent	Percent	Percent	Percent	Percent	Percent
Band headsaw with resaw	1.2	13.8	35.1	32.1	13.2	4.2	0.4
Solid-tooth circular headsaw with resaw and a shotgun carriage feed	2.7	33.9	41.5	17.0	4.0	.6	.3
Solid-tooth circular headsaw with steam feed (small gun); no resaw	8.1	43.7	33.6	11.0	2.5	1.0	.1
Portable mill with circular headsaw using inserted bits; no resaw	2.9	32.6	42.3	16.0	5.3	.8	.1

[1] Study made in 1948 (Carpenter 1950).

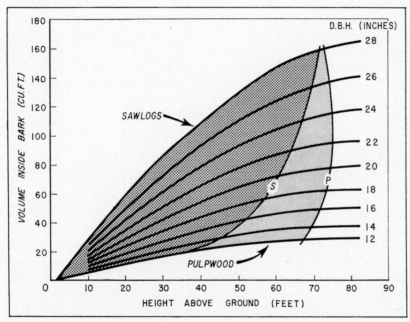

FIGURE 99.—The volume of merchantable wood from loblolly pines of different sizes varies with the diameter and height of the uppermost cut. Top utilization limits as of 1956 in southern Arkansas were as indicated (*S*) for saw logs and (*P*) for pulpwood.

10-inch trees (table 52). The reason for such a difference is reflected also by the man-hour requirements to get the trees down and cut into bolts (table 53). The figures represent only 60 percent of felling, limbing, and bucking time. The other 40 percent, independ-

TABLE 52.—*Relative production time per cord for cutting pine pulpwood, by tree size (McClay 1953)*

(In percent of time required for 10-inch 7-bolt tree)

D.b.h. (inches)	Number of $5\frac{1}{4}$-foot bolts								
	1	2	3	4	5	6	7	8	9
	Percent	Percent	Percent	Percent	Percent	Percent	Percent	Percent	Percent
5	261	240	220						
6		197	186	177					
7			156	151	145	139			
8				130	126	123	120		
9					112	112	110	107	
10					98	100	100	100	
11						90	93	93	93
12						81	84	86	87

TABLE 53.—*Man-hours required per cord to fell, limb, and buck pine pulpwood, by tree size[1] (McClay 1953c)*

D.b.h. (inches)	Felling	Limbing and bucking	Total
	Man-hours	Man-hours	Man-hours
5	0.65	0.93	1.58
6	.44	.78	1.22
7	.33	.67	1.00
8	.28	.57	.85
9	.24	.52	.76
10	.22	.47	.69
11	.20	.44	.64
12	.19	.41	.60

[1] To convert net man-hours per cord to total, including delay time, it is necessary only to divide these figures by 0.60. The above rates (based on work with a 3 hp. chain saw with bow attachment) may have value for comparison purposes, but should not be used directly unless they are being applied to a similar operation.

ent of tree size, is for walking, swamping, hang-ups, and other normal delays.

These estimates may need some modification for changes in methods and crew efficiency, but as expressed in percentage or man-hours they will not change as rapidly as the dollar values. Reynolds (1951b), reporting on the production costs in Arkansas for the previous 10 years, found felling and bucking costs up 198 percent, while the cost of bunching, loading, unloading, and delay had risen 269 percent, and that for hauling 227 percent. The total cost of delivered wood went up 223 perecnt in 10 years.

Costs require separate determination by the job because of the effect of working methods on efficiency. For example, the use of power saws may reduce working time per unit of cross section cut three to six fold in sawtimber (Sundberg 1953), yet with decreasing average diameters as in harvesting pulpwood this advantage may disappear. Bow saws work well on small trees. Piece work tends to increase the weekly earnings of a crew and decrease costs, but it also tends to affect utilization standards adversely (Trousdell 1947). Good supervision and inspection, plus perhaps a penalty system, may be needed to discourage utilization abuses when piece rates are used.

Space between trees affects the efficiency in and profits from felling, bucking, and limbing pulpwood in thinning plantations as follows (Muntz 1948a):

Spacing (feet)	Sticks per cord	Cords per man-day	Remarks
4 x 4	128	2.6	Too close
6 x 6	105	3.0	Good
8 x 8	92	2.9	Good
10 x 10	68	2.6	Too limby

Apparently a moderate spacing distance of 6 or 8 feet facilitates harvest.

Tree size affects not only the operation of harvesting pulpwood, but also the yield of pulp. This stems from the deficiency of the cord as a unit of measure. A run of 6-inch trees yielding 70 cubic feet of solid wood per cord converts to kraft pulp at the rate of about 2 cords per ton; whereas 10-inch trees yielding 85 cubic feet of wood per cord convert at the rate of about 1.6 cords per ton (Duerr 1951).

Obviously the size of trees, logs, and bolts handled, and their concentration on cutting areas influence the cost of logging. In a recent study of cutting pulpwood with one-man chain saws (Guttenberg and Perry 1957) the time requirements per cord harvested under partial cutting was usually less than one man-hour.

As yet, there is no commercial grading of pine pulpwood. It has been suggested (Bethel 1940) that such grades should recognize these three items: (1) Density, the percentage of summerwood; (2) age, the relation of short-fibered core to older wood; and (3) defect, decay, knots, and compression wood.

Poles and piles

Trees that can qualify are usually worth most for piles or poles, next most for saw logs, less for ties, and least for pulpwood. The wood of loblolly pine, like other southern pines and unlike some of its competitors, is suited for poles and piles because it has a much higher percentage of sapwood that is easily penetrated by preservatives. A smaller proportion of loblolly pine timber, however, consists of trees sufficiently straight boled for these uses. In 1955

southern pine was used in 86 percent of all treated poles and 71
percent of all the treated piles in the United States. Piles costing
less than steel and concrete substitutes, continue in demand for
wharfs and piers, and as foundation piles in marsh lands or as
footing for large buildings.

The demand for poles is expected to increase because of the extension of rural telephone lines, power lines for new residence areas,
and lighting for express highways. With a growing demand and
a declining supply stumpage returns from large poles and piles
should continue to increase.

Dealers usually sell poles for an agreed price f.o.b. railroad car
and allow the landowner about 40 percent of that for stumpage.
They prefer to buy only such trees as will produce items on current
orders, but when competition is keen they sometimes buy whole
tracts of timber and resell the saw logs (Wackerman 1945).

For efficient marketing of their timber, landowners need to ascertain whether or not certain selected trees will meet the specialized
requirements for poles or piles (appendix, table 68). The deviation
of a pole from straightness is called sweep. Slight curvature in one
plane is permitted if the sweep does not exceed 1 inch for each 6
feet of length (fig. 100, A). Curvature in two planes or two directions is allowable if a straight line does not intersect the surface of
the pole at any intermediate point (fig. 100, B). Poles must also
be free from localized deviations equal to more than one-half the
mean diameter of the short crooked section (fig. 100, C and D). The
illustration shows typical but not complete examples of shapes that
may disqualify trees for poles. Strict stipulations list numerous
other miscellaneous defects and limit the quantity of each that
will be tolerated. Forest managers should have copies of the complete specifications.[138] Once they have ascertained that certain trees
can pass inspection for poles or piling, and have the prices quoted
for alternative products, the data in table 54 may be useful in estimating the highest value that may be obtained from each tree. In
actual sales the exacting specifications of purchasing agents must
be used.[139]

[138] Complete copies of specifications (ASA 05.1 1948) are available from the
American Standards Association Inc., 70 East 45th St., New York 17, N.Y.
[139] However, an entirely new market for treated poles, developed since 1945
in some areas, utilizes a class of timber for which formerly there was little
market except as pulpwood. Round timber 14 to 25 feet long to a 4- to 6-
inch top may go into pole-frame construction. By setting their treated barn
poles in the ground, farmers not only eliminate high-cost foundations, but they
reduce the need for much structural bracing, thus lowering both material and
labor costs. All farm service buildings in some areas are pole-frame buildings.

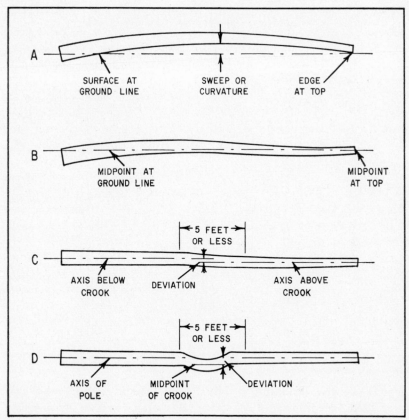

FIGURE 100.—How to measure four typical cases of curvature in poles to meet specifications of the American Standards Association: *A*, Sweep in one plane and one direction; *B*, sweep in two planes (i.e., "double") or in two directions in one plane (i.e., "reverse"); *C*, short crook with the two parts of the reference axis approximately parallel; *D*, short crook with the two parts of the reference axis approximately coincident.

Other uses of the wood

Utilization of loblolly pine wood for miscellaneous purposes continues to change as it is replaced by certain materials for some products, but meanwhile, fabricated in new forms, it is substituted for certain materials in new uses.

Less loblolly pine is used for fuel than formerly although it has 73 percent of the fuel value in white oak, and the ash content is only about 0.25 percent of the dry weight (Sterrett 1914). Little demand remains for either keg staves or wooden laths. Pine for mine tim-

---

This construction is good for carports, equipment shelters, lumber sheds, and warehouses (Osborne 1955).

TABLE 54.—*Number of saw logs, ties, or 5-foot sticks and pulpwood units contained in trees meeting specifications for piles or poles*[1]

Piles or poles			Sawtimber		Railroad ties, 8½ feet long by size (inches)				Pulpwood		
Minimum diameter			Logs per per tree	Volume per tree	7 x 9	7 x 8	6 x 8	6 x 7	Average stick diameter	Sticks	1¼-cord units
Butt	Top	Length									
Inches	Inches	Feet	Number	Bd. ft.	Number	Number	Number	Number	Inches	Number	Number
12½	8	30	2	105	1	0	1	1	10.25	6	0.15
10¾	7	30	2	80	0	0	1	1	8.875	6	.115
12½	8	35	2	105	1	1	0	1	10.0	7	.167
13	8¼	35	2	105	1	1	0	1	10.5	7	.184
13	8	40	2½	145	1	1	1	1	10.5	8	.2078
14½	8¼	45	3	200	2	1	1	1	11.375	9	.2717
13½	7	50	3	160	2	0	1	1	10.25	10	.2484
15	8¼	50	3	200	2	1	1	1	11.625	10	.3137
13½	7	55	3½	180	2	1	0	1	10.25	11	.2733
15½	8¼	55	3½	260	3	1	0	1	11.875	11	.3591
14	6	60	3½	210	2	1	0	1	10.0	12	.2857
16	8¼	60	4	335	3	1	1	1	12.125	12	.4138
14	6	65	4	220	2	1	1	1	10.0	13	.3095
16½	8¼	65	4	335	4	2	0	1	12.375	13	.4643
14	6	70	4	220	2	1	1	1	10.0	14	.3333
17	8¼	70	4½	420	4	2	0	1	12.625	14	.5148
17¼	8¼	75	4½	420	4	2	0	1	12.75	15	.5746

[1] Logs counted to nearest one-half standard log and scaled to the nearest inch of diameter by the International ¼-inch log rule. The unit of pulpwood used is a stack 4 x 5 x 8 feet. From a brochure by M. E. Henegar entitled "Gum naval stores timber land use; information and suggestions." 34 pp. Brunswick, Ga.

bers is likewise declining rapidly. Less than a million cubic feet were used for props in 1956. They are being replaced by concrete and steel.[140] The use of southern pine for treated railroad cross-ties dropped from 12 million in 1946 to 343 thousand in 1956. The former laborious and wasteful practice of hewing pine ties by hand is disappearing in the face of high wages and an active demand for pine for other uses. Sometimes new uses prolong the manufacture of an old product. Pine blocks, set with the end grain as a wearing surface, were formerly used for street paving. Now they serve as industrial flooring, utilizing the equivalent of 33 million board feet in 1954 (Osborne 1955).

Loblolly pine continues to supply shipping containers for a host of commodities. A decline in the use of its wood for box shooks and slack cooperage is offset by an increase in use of its pulp for wrapping paper and corrugated boxes. Although pine veneer for ply-

[140] Without the approval of certain oldtime miners interested in safety. They prefer pine props because, when about to give way under terrific strain from shifting tons of earth above a gallery, a wooden prop emits loud crackling and splintering noises sufficiently ahead of final rupture to allow them to escape.

wood does not compete with Douglas-fir panels, veneer continues in use for fruit box material, baskets, and crates. In fact the successful manufacture of container veneer from small plantation-grown loblolly pine logs has been reported from Australia (Alexander and Watson 1947).

Expanding new uses for loblolly pine are appearing. As a result of recent research and industrial developments we now have laminated arches, various types of fiberboards, and resin-bonded particle boards. Unlike plywood, laminated wood is made by bonding veneer or lumber so that the grain of all layers is parellel. Made with improved modern glue, laminated beams are used as bridge stringers and as rafters for buildings. The newest use is for large arches in assembly halls, factories, gymnasiums, schools, and hangars, and for bridges where wide spans are desired. Arches are now made from southern pine in Wisconsin, Kentucky, Arkansas, and Texas. They lend themselves to the V-type arch popular in church architecture and to the exacting shapes and strength requirements of many ship timbers (Freas 1953). This development promises a major new use for loblolly pine timber.

Residue and waste

Although a million or more cords of pine top wood is now used annually for pulp in the Southeast, there remains about 7 million cords of potentially salvagable residue from logging operations. The economics of this situation were reported by Todd (1953 and 1955) after a study in the Piedmont region. The waste involved in top wood is diminishing steadily as new techniques are developed.

Likewise the large volume of commercially useless mill refuse is continually being reduced. Where pulp is in demand it is no longer economical everywhere to burn slabs and edgings from sawmills. Barking and chipping of pine logs is rapidly becoming standard practice at many large and some small mills. Futhermore several mills are also processing some of their low-grade lumber into pulpwood chips. Of all the potentially usable industrial refuse from southern pine wood (much of it loblolly pine) a third to a half remains unused by the lumber and certain other industries (table 55). This waste is now being steadily reduced as new methods of handling it economically are developed.

A thousand board feet of dressed lumber, containing 61 cubic feet of wood, represents a loss of 139 cubic feet or about 70 percent of the raw material. Of the volume lost 20 percent is left in the woods in tops and broken trees, 60 percent goes into slabs, edgings,

TABLE 55.—*Southwide estimates of residues in the logging and manufacture of pine timber and the degree of current use being made of coarse*[1] *manufacturing residues*

Industry	Coarse residues from—		Unused portion of coarse manufacturing residue	Total coarse and fine manufacturing residues
	Logging	Manufacture		
	Thousand cubic feet	*Thousand cubic feet*	*Percent*	*Thousand cubic feet*
Pulp..........	17,640	30,280	0	74,110
Veneer........	59,983	38,309	9	73,473
Cooperage.....	28,276	12,495	16	24,899
Lumber.......	485,902	574,678	51	1,285,700
Other........	113,704	8,019	33	16,375
All........	705,505	663,781	45	1,474,557

[1] Includes slabs, edgings, trimmings, miscuts, veneer cores, cull pieces, and other material generally suitable for pulpwood chips. Basis: Tables 53-55, appendix, Timber Resources for America's Future. (U. S. Dept. Agr. Forest Resource Rpt. 14, 713 pp. 1958.)

end trim, and sawdust at the mill and the remaining 20 percent becomes planer shavings. For each thousand board feet of lumber produced there is a half cord of pulpwood-size rough wood left in the forest; at the mill are chippable slabs and edgings equal to 0.7 cord of rough round pulpwood. The volume of pine residues is negatively related to cutting as follows:

$$Y \text{ equals } 46.637 - 2.697X$$

where Y is logging residue in cubic feet per MBM, and X is the cut per acre in thousands of board feet (Todd 1953). The average logging residue was 31.1 ± 4.7 cubic feet. Usable mill residues of wood and bark varied from 0.65 to 0.78 cord. Where some logging residue was used (as on $\frac{1}{3}$ of the tracts) less than 15 percent was taken. As a rule the utilization of tops and residual trees together is more profitable than to operate on residual trees alone. An exception is where the tops are dried hard or will yield only one stick of pulpwood each. Todd concluded that the most promising single solution to the whole problem would be establishment of conveniently located concentration yards equipped with debarking, chipping, and chip loading machinery.

Similar studies in Texas (King, W. W., 1953b) indicate that solid pine residues vary inversely as log diameter at all types of mills. Mill equipment, however, may have a secondary effect on waste. Mills in the second class listed in table 56 produced less residue during a study in Louisiana and Arkansas (Carpenter 1950 and 1951) than any of the other mills.

By 1957 some 250 mills, and 11 slab concentration yards, were converting waste wood to chips at an annual rate of more than 1.4 million cords, or over 7 percent of the current supply of wood required by the southern pulping industry. Prospective increases in chip tonnage are to be expected from increases in average size and stability of sawmills, and from further development of portable machines.

TABLE 56.—*Chippable waste per thousand board-feet lumber tally*[1]

Class of mill	Log diameters (inches)							
	6	8	11	14	17	20	23	26
	Cords	Cords	Cords	Cords	Cords	Cords	Cords	Cords
Band headsaw with resaw.......	0.76	0.62	0.47	0.36	0.31	0.33	0.34	....
Solid-tooth circular headsaw with resaw and a shotgun carriage feed......................	.81	.54	.43	.35	.28	.24	.19	.14
Solid-tooth circular headsaw with steam feed (small gun); no resaw....................	.90	.77	.46	.33	.29	.27	.26	....
Portable mill with circular headsaw using inserted bits; no resaw....................	.69	.82	.57	.40	.24	.27	.25	....

[1] Study made in 1948 (Carpenter 1950). There were four sample mills in each class, two in Arkansas and two in Louisiana.

Wood derivatives

Miscellaneous organic substances of present or potential industrial value—such as cellulose, naval stores, fats, sugars, tannin, and lignin—are obtainable from the wood or bark of loblolly pine. Fats, resins, and waxes are highly concentrated in the ray cells. In second-growth southern pine, which is largely sapwood, there is a comparatively small amount (2 to 4 percent) of these substances (Bray 1942a.) Without improved method of recovery this quantity is insufficient to attempt extraction from the wood previous to pulping. Naval stores can be derived as a byproduct of the kraft pulpmills. Sulphate wood turpentine is recovered by condensing the vapors released from the pulping digesters. In this process, soapy curds, consisting of mixed resin and fatty acids, float on the spent cooking liquor called black liquor. This is treated to recover tall oil or liquid rosin.

Sawmill residues contain 50 to 70 percent carbohydrate in the form of cellulose and hemicellulose convertible by acid hydrolysis to sugar solutions suitable for animal feed. Hydrolysis occurs when sawdust, shavings, or wood chips are treated with dilute acids at elevated temperatures. Equipment capable of withstanding high steam pressure is needed. Successful tests of this process have been made with various forms of waste wood such as cull trees and the waste from logging and milling including residues from which resin has been extracted. Mannan is a hexosan that yields mannose on hydrolysis. Mannan, a substance of industrial importance in the production of ethyl alcohol from sulphite liquor and by the hydrolysis of sawdust with catalyzers (Schorger 1917), is present in loblolly pine wood to the extent of about 5 percent. The yield of molasses depends on the amount of cellulose in the wood. About a ton of 50 percent sugar molasses is obtained from a ton of dry wood, or 150 to 190 gallons from a cord of wood (Harris 1950).

Sugars from pine wood are about 80 percent glucose, 3 to 6 percent other hexoses, and 10 to 15 percent pentoses. For nonruminant animals (that cannot use 5-carbon sugars) the sugar from softwood is more suitable than that from hardwood.

The wood molasses should be equivalent to blackstrap in feed value. Cattle eat it best when it is fed with roughage, such as cottonseed hulls, at the rate of 2 gallons to 40 pounds of mixed hulls and meal. In extensive tests most livestock and poultry have made normal gains in weight in feed tests at various state agricultural experiment stations.

Ether extractives (oil basis) from 18-year-old loblolly pine wood are as follows (Max 1945):

	Percent
Unsaponifiable	15.80
Rosin acids	37.20
Fatty acids:	43.60
Saturated	2.28
Unsaturated	41.32
Hannus iodine number	113.5

Pine bark is available in considerable quantity for any use that may be developed for it. The volume of loblolly pine bark is related to unpeeled pulpwood from trees of different sizes as follows:

D.b.h. (inches)	Bark (percent)
6	19.4
8	17.5
10	16.0
12	14.5
14	14.0

Average bark volume is roughly 15 percent (Demmon 1936a). Because of more handling, the logs received at large band mills retain somewhat less bark than those at small circular-saw mills.[141]

[141] At small mills the proportion of pine bark by weight decreases with increased diameter of log as follows:

Bark percentage equals $12.4 - 0.013D^2$ (King 1953b) and varies from 8 to 11 percent.

As yet no commercial use has been found for bark of southern pine except as fuel. It is equal to or slightly higher in heat value than wood. This is attributed to its high percentage of lignin, which contains 62 to 65 percent carbon as compared with 44.5 percent carbon in cellulose material. Loblolly pine bark will burn readily when its moisture content is less than 65 percent. The heat liberated in burning oven-dry bark is 8,500 to 9,000 B.t.u. per pound (Segall and Purves 1946).

In contrast to wood, the bark has less cellulose and its lignin is lower in methoxyl and hydroxyl. Exposure and saprophytic growth may modify the composition of outer bark. The ash and nitrogen contents are higher than for wood. Millions of tons of bark are destroyed or wasted annually.

Extractives from bark have been subjected to elementary chemical analysis and a few qualitative tests only. For detailed chemical study initial extraction will have to be made on a pilot-plant scale. The possibility of making commercial use of the tannin content of pine bark was investigated for the T.V.A. (Snow 1949). The tannin content on an oven-dry weight basis averaged 4.5 percent. The effect of aging up to 8 weeks on tannin content of peeled pine bark was negligible. Because of the small quantity of any individual chemical that could be extracted, it is not to be expected that the recovery of any one valuable substance will be economic. Nor are the residues from such extraction likely to become an economic source of high-grade pulp. Their use as a soil amendment has been suggested. Perhaps some mechanical use for bark fiber can be found, but its chemical utilization appears destined for delay until new chemical techniques are devised for studying it.

Foliage

Two uses for the leaves should be mentioned: (1) potential use of extractives from green needles, and (2) agricultural use of dry needles as mulch.

The so-called "essential oils" are volatile oils produced by steam distillation of coniferous foliage. In the United States they are taken from spruce, fir, hemlock, and arborvitae which yield 0.4 to 0.6 percent oil. They are scenting agents in soap, grease, liniments, inhalants, insecticides, polishes, and cosmetics.

Made from loblolly pine the yield is lower—optimum 0.35 and average 0.30 percent. The specific gravity at 15°C. is 0.871 and refractive index at 20°C. is 1.4742. The major expense is for collection and transport of raw material, estimated at 60 to 75 percent of production cost. Portable stills would be advantageous. Distillation should be in winter, as then the needles can be gathered from dominant trees felled several weeks in advance without excessive evaporation losses that reduce the yield.

Strawberry farmers use pine needles as a mulch to protect the berries from grit, the roots from cold, and the soil from drying. They prefer the ''straw'' (needles) of loblolly pine because it is long, lies flat on the ground, and decomposes less rapidly than grass hay. About 2 acres of pine woodland yields enough strawfall annually to mulch an acre of strawberries (Spillers 1935). Pine straw is baled in Georgia for use at commercial nurseries for an acid mulch around azaleas and other plants that are favored by an acid reaction. It is also used for mulching pine seedbeds. Because it does not have to be chopped up before use the straw of loblolly is preferred to that of slash or longleaf pine in forest nurseries.

CHARACTER OF THE WOOD

The wood of loblolly pine resembles that of the other southern pines. The resin ducts, scattered throughout the annual rings, are readily visible to the naked eye as small dots. The wood rays also are fine, except those which enclose horizontal resin ducts.

Species identity

Structural similarity prevents definite identification of several species of yellow pine on the basis of the wood alone. There is some indication, however, that chemical reagents may be helpful in separating the species. For example, methanol containing a small amount of hydrochloric acid gives a purple coloration after a short-time contact with the sapwood of shortleaf pine, whereas it does not with the sapwood of loblolly pine (Isenberg and Buchanan 1945). More research is needed as the nature of the reaction is unknown and heartwoods were not tested. However, it is reported that the four principal southern pines can be distinguished by absorption spectraphotometric determination in the ultra violet region (Sakornbut 1951) with a high degree of accuracy from samples of the heartwood.

Variation in percentages of mineral constituents of wood cannot be relied upon as distinguishing features because such differences are by far more attributable to the nature of habitats in which the trees grow than to species variations. The very difficulty of distinguishing the species of southern pines by the wood alone, suggests that a knowledge of variability of the wood within species may be of greater practical significance.

Variation in loblolly pine wood

Loblolly pine varies widely in many properties (intrinsic or artificially induced) that affect its utilization. The commonly recognized variations include wood that is (1) strong or weak, (2) heart or sap, (3) old or young, (4) springwood or summerwood, (5) narrow or wide ringed, (6) light or heavy, (7) normal or compression wood, (8) green or seasoned, (9) clear or knotty, (10) sound or defective, (11) untreated or preserved, (12) natural or modified, and (13) high or low grade. In structural use it is obvious that strength is important. With the possible exception of heart or sap the other variations all have an apparent or real bearing on strength or other structural values.

Heartwood

Heartwood in loblolly pine may begin to form any time between 15 and 25 years of age, but in trees less than 20 years old it comprises less than 2 percent. In average second-growth stands the sapwood band normally varies from 3 to 5 inches in width, being wider in trees of rapid growth. The proportion of heartwood to merchantable volume varies directly with age and inversely with the rate of growth (MacKinney and Chaiken 1935b) (fig. 101). Hence, young trees on good sites have the least heartwood. This was observed by Paul (1932a) who related the presence of heartwood to crown width as follows:

Crown width (feet)	Heartwood (percent)	Crown width (feet)	Heartwood (percent)
10	28	20	11
12	22	22	10
14	17	26	9
16	14	30	8
18	12	34	8

Trees of pulpwood size with very little heartwood can be readily found in second-growth stands of any southern pine. For newsprint, sapwood is preferred, but the relatively small amount and light color of the heartwood in typical second-growth does not seriously interfere with its suitability for this purpose. If it is desired to grow loblolly pine with practically no heartwood, a rotation of 20-30 years is suggested, but if 5 percent heart is acceptable, the rotation should not exceed 45 years, or possibly 50 years for open stands on good sites.

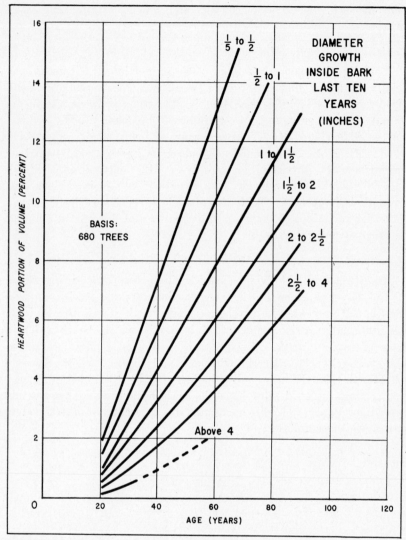

FIGURE 101.—Heartwood increases with elapsed time, hence its proportion in a loblolly pine varies inversely with rate of diameter growth and directly with age.

To distinguish heartwood from sapwood a positive color reaction test with chemicals has been developed (U. S. Forest Products Lab. 1948). To make this test first dissolve 5 grams of benzidine in 23 cc. of 25 percent hydrochloric acid. Next prepare a 10-percent solution of sodium nitrate. Do not mix the two until ready for a test; then mix in equal amounts. This mixture reacts with the wood in a few moments, the sapwood becoming yellowish brown and the heartwood red.

Length and character of wood cells

Springwood fibers of loblolly pine are broad and thin-walled with blunt ends. Pits, which may be thought of as cell wall perforations for the passage of sap, are microscopic but plainly discernible on the surface. In summerwood the fibers may be shorter than in springwood and are thick walled with pointed ends. The pits, seldom seen near the ends, are less pronounced (Nilsson 1926). There is a progressive decrease in the proportion of summerwood in an annual ring from the base to the top of a tree. Four sample trees that averaged 44 percent at breast height showed these proportions at other levels (Young 1952):

Tree height (percent)	Summerwood (percent)
0	48
50	24
65	16
80	10

A sapling pine increased summerwood percentage from pith toward cambium by 2-year intervals as follows: 11, 12, 25, 50, and 60. These two trends can explain the gradients in specific gravity typical of loblolly pine shown in figure 107.

Fiber length increases from the pith outward at least through the 19th ring and from the ground upward to a certain point, then decreases (Jackson 1959). The fibers of maximum length, however, are found progressively higher as a tree gets older. Their location is apparently governed not by the age of the tree but by its height at the time when the ring in question was formed (Bethel 1941). The radial increase in tracheid length is most rapid in the first 10 years (Berkley 1934). This increase occurs at an ever-diminishing rate toward the bark (Kramer 1957). Where rings are over a half inch wide, the length may be 40 to 100 times the width (Teesdale 1914).

Fiber lengths, which vary individually from 0.8 to 4.7 mm. (Beadle and Stevens 1912), average from 2.5 to 4.0 mm., and are commonly 3 mm. (Wells and Rue 1927; Grabow 1923). Beyond the 10th ring Kramer (1957) found the fibers 3.5 to 4.5 mm. long at breast height. Bethel (1940-1941) studying the nature of these variations gives this formula:

Fiber length in mm. equals $2.7743 + 13.6795 h - 15.4573 h^2 + 2.8526 L$ where h is height from the ground as a ratio of tree height

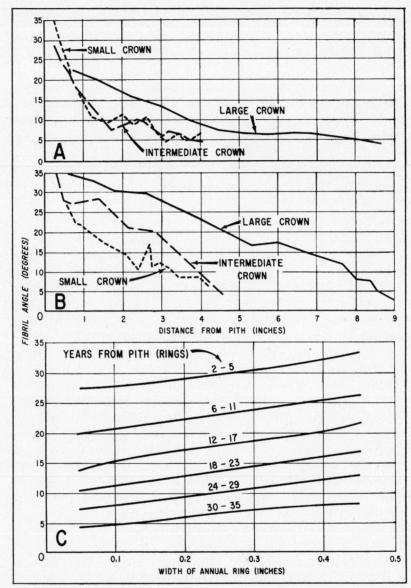

FIGURE 102.—Average fibril angles at various distances from the pith in normal summerwood of loblolly pines 30 to 35 years old: *A,* At intermediate height below crowns of different sizes; *B,* at breast height below crowns of different sizes; *C,* at breast height in relation to age class of rings (Pillow, Terrell, and Hiller 1953).

TABLE 57.—*Estimated fibril angles above breast height in normal summer-wood of second-growth loblolly pine about 30 years old (Pillow, Terrell, & Hiller 1953)*

Rings from pith (number)	Width of annual ring (inches)				
	0.0-0.09	0.10-0.19	0.20-0.29	0.30-0.39	0.40+
	Degrees	Degrees	Degrees	Degrees	Degrees
2-5	15.9	16.0	16.1	16.3	16.4
6-10	8.6	8.8	9.0	9.2	9.4
11-15	5.6	5.8	6.0	6.2	6.4
16-20	4.2	4.4	4.6	4.8	5.0
21+	3.4	3.6	3.7	3.9	4.0

and L is the logarithm of annual-ring numbers counting from the pith out on a cross section. In this study the fibers of maximum length were found at 44 percent of tree height. The zonal distribution of fiber-length classes in relation to age and height is shown in figure 107.

In thickness the fibers show less variation. Wood of slow growth on the average has thicker walled summerwood cells than that of fast growth, but the walls of springwood cells average about the same thickness for both types of wood. Neither springwood nor summerwood cells vary in width with height in the tree (Pew and Knechtges 1939). Within the same growth class, however, fiber thickness in both parts of the ring varies considerably from tree to tree—suggesting possible genetic control.

Fibril angles

Fibrils are microscopic components of the cell walls. They vary considerably in the angle formed by their spiral setting and that variation affects wood properties. In normal summerwood cells the angles range from about 5° to more than 25° depending on distance from the pith and vigor of the tree. The larger angles are found near the pith and in large-crowned trees at upper stem locations (fig. 102, A) and at breast height (fig. 102, B). At any given number of rings from the pith the angle increases slightly with width of ring in the upper stem (table 57).

A general formula for fibrils at crown height in 10- to 15-year saplings is—angle equals $3.805 + 36.46X$ where X is ring width in inches. At breast height the relation is $0.21 + 98.45X$. For trees 30 to 35 years old a better estimate can be made from figure 102, C. For a given age the effect of ring width is small. Closely spaced, narrow-crowned saplings have small fibril angles prior to release; larger angles after liberation. Fibril angles of less than 10° are associated with average or greater strength properties and longitudinal shrinkage of only 0.1 to 0.3 percent. Pulps made from wood with large fibril angles but lacking minute checking are inferior in strength to pulps made from wood with fibrils at small angles (Pillow, Chidester, and Bray 1941). Excessive bleaching is also required for pulp from wood with large fibril angles.

PULPING PROPERTIES

Composition of wood and bark

Making paper from southern pine was delayed until its pulping properties could be compared with those of northern woods. Although the early anxiety about an excess of heartwood volume was quickly dispelled, some concern over resin content remained. Resin content of loblolly pine is about 1.8 percent in fresh wood or 3 percent in dry wood. Resin in the sapwood is least at the base of a tree and increases upward into the crown (Bishop and Marckworth 1933). It has not become troublesome in second growth. In comparison with spruce and true fir, no marked difference in proportion of fiber length to fiber diameter was found, but in southern pine the ratio of length to wall thickness is lower and the percentage of summerwood fiber is higher (Nilsson 1926). However, no differences sufficient to block development of a southern pulpwood industry were found.

Chemical analysis differs somewhat with type of wood. Max (1945) analyzed 18-year-old loblolly pines with 5 rings per inch and a specific gravity of 0.53. His analysis of oven-dry unextracted wood was:

Substance	Percent
Pentosans	8.83
Cross and bevan cellulose	59.00
Lignin	27.10
Uronic acids	0.79

The extractives on an oven-dry unextracted wood basis were:

Solvent	Percent
Alcohol-benzene	2.76
Ether	1.83
Hot water (on alcohol-benzene extracted wood)	1.24
Ether (on steam distilled wood)	1.35
Alcohol (on steam distilled and ether extracted wood)	0.21

A separate analysis by common types of wood is shown in table 58. Note that the lignin content of compression wood is slightly higher and the cellulose content slightly lower than in normal wood (Pillow and Luxford 1937).

TABLE 58.—*Chemical analysis of loblolly pine*[1]

Item	Spring-wood	Summer-wood	Com-pression wood	Entire wood Fast growth	Entire wood Slow growth
	Percent	Percent	Percent	Percent	Percent
Cellulose....................	58.3	59.1	46.2	58.2	58.9
Alpha cellulose..............	43.9	46.4	34.6	43.1	46.5
Lignin......................	28.8	27.4	35.2	27.2	28.5
Pentosans in cellulose........	11.6	10.4	....	10.0	9.1
Total pentosans..............	17.9	12.6	12.2	13.0	11.9
Solubility in—					
Hot 1-percent Na OH solution...............	14.0	12.9	12.6	12.7	9.5
Hot water.................	....	2.0	....	2.6	1.9
Alcohol-benzene...........	4.2	2.5	2.7	4.1	2.8
Ether.....................	3.6	1.5	1.3	3.0	2.0

[1] The wood samples used in this study were estimated to contain at least 90 percent of the desired kind of wood (C. E. Curran 1936).

TABLE 59.—*Analysis of springwood and summerwood from the sap and heart-wood portions of a loblolly pine tree*

Loblolly pine wood	Sapwood Spring	Sapwood Summer	Heartwood Spring	Heartwood Summer
	Percent[1]	Percent[1]	Percent[1]	Percent[1]
Solubility in—				
Cold water................	3.28	2.18	7.50	7.64
Hot water.................	3.49	2.97	7.16	6.44
Sodium hydroxide, 1 percent..	11.11	11.01	18.14	21.19
Constituents:				
Acetic acid................	1.28	1.41	1.00	1.11
Methoxyl..................	4.05	4.18	6.17	6.88
Pentosans.................	11.59	11.12	12.77	12.12
Lignin....................	28.12	26.78	26.78	24.18
Cellulose.................	58.06	61.21	53.44	52.87
Pentosans in cellulose.......	8.78	8.69	11.52	11.20
Moisture.....................	2.82	3.39	3.13	2.16

[1] Of oven-dry sample.

A chemical distinction between the two parts of a growth ring is the higher content of lignin, pentosan, and other extractives in the springwood. These differences were revealed in an early (1926) proximate analysis of loblolly pine wood reported by Ritter and Fleck (1930). In their work the heart and sap portions were studied separately (table 59); the higher extractive content of the heart-wood is manifest.

Springwood and summerwood fibers

With cell walls of equal specific gravity (1.5) springwood of loblolly pine is only half as heavy as summerwood because it has

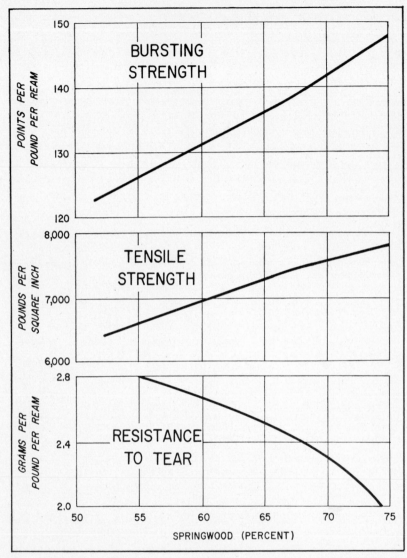

FIGURE 103.—The relation of wood density, expressed as percentage of spring-wood, to the strength of loblolly pine sulphate plup (After Chidester, G. H., Pulpwood Annual, Pulp and Paper 1954).

about 80 percent air space as against about 60 percent in summer-wood. In chemical pulping the ratio between these two types of wood is the most important single factor (Bray and Curran 1937). A variation of 10 percent in springwood content may affect pulp quality more than a change to another species of yellow pine (Paul and Smith 1950). Mild forms of compression wood may not be detrimental to pulp yield if the proportion of summerwood to spring-wood remains low (Pillow, Chidester, and Bray 1941). Compression wood fibers tend to break into fragments along the planes of the checks in the cell wall and fragmentation occurs with little or no fibrillation. Compression wood is undesirable for pulping because the yield of pulp obtained is low and the pulp is dark colored and weak, like that from decayed wood (Johansen 1935).

Yields of loblolly pine pulp increase with wood density which is related to the proportion of summerwood with its thick cell walls. More beating is required to attain maximum strength in the pulp from summerwood, but the fibrils of summerwood are the stronger, lending more tear resistance to paper. Springwood fibers are the more easily fibrillated, but also more easily broken in beating or jordaning. All strength properties of the pulps excepting tear resistance improve with an increase in the springwood content. Tear resistance is increased by both the strength and bonding quality of fibers. Hence, a 50-50 mixture of thick- and thin-walled cells produces a pulp superior to either alone in tear resistance, though the mixture is intermediate in other strength properties (Watson and Hodder 1954).

Fiber length, over the usual range, has only limited effect on tensile and bursting strength of paper. Thin-walled springwood fibers collapse and felt well, making relatively smooth sheets high in these strength qualities (fig. 103).

The distribution of pulping characteristics within loblolly pine trees has often been noted. On cross sections of stems the diameter and wall thickness of both spring and summer fibers commonly increase toward the bark (fig. 104). With increase in elevation in the tree there is an increase in springwood content, a decrease in density, and yields that are lower on a volume basis. Differences in strength properties of pulps prepared from top, middle, and butt portions of trees are shown in figure 105. In general, the pulp yield from sound wood parallels fairly closely the cellulose content of each tree.

The principal processes

The yield of loblolly pine pulp is greatly influenced by the kind and severity of a pulping process. The highest yield, about 95 percent, is from the mechanical process giving groundwood pulp. The lowest yields result from the more drastic chemical digestion in processes that dissolve out undesirable constituents leaving largely pure cellulose (table 60). Loblolly pine reduces readily by the sulphate and mechanical processes. With modification, it can also be pulped by the sulphite process.

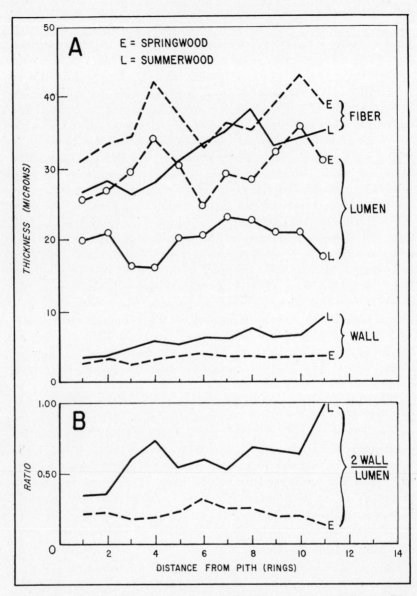

FIGURE 104.—Young loblolly pine wood grown for pulp in Australia: *A*, Ring by ring cross sectional dimensions of the cells, and *B*, a combination of certain measurements to indicate crush resistance of the fibers (Watson and Hodder 1954).

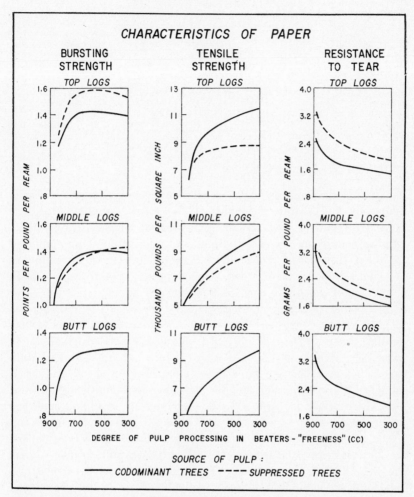

FIGURE 105.—Variation in strength of paper made from wood taken from various positions of the tree in a forest canopy (suppressed or not), position of the log in a tree (top, butt, or middle), and degree of processing the pulp in beaters (Bray, Martin, and Schwartz 1939).

Sulphate process

Beginning about 1916 there has been a tremendous development of the kraft pulping industry in the South to a point where it dominates the American production of this kind of paper products. Herty (1933) was the first to reveal that the pitch troubles encountered in pulping heartwood of old-growth southern pine were absent from the sapwood of second growth. Southern kraft pulps excel northern kraft in tearing strength, bulk, and porosity.

TABLE 60.—*Yield of southern pine pulp from four manufacturing processes*

Mill process	Pulp yield[1]		Wood required per ton of pulp[2]
	Proportion of dry wood	Per cord	
	Percent	Pounds	Cords
Soda..............	40	905	2.210
Sulphite...........	45	1020	1.960[3]
Sulphate..........	48	1085	1.845
Groundwood.......	95	2185	0.915[3]

Forest Products Laboratory, Madison, Wisconsin, Tech. Note 191. 1953. [Processed.]
[1] Based on dry, screened pulp. For the soda and sulphite processes the pulp is bleachable and of paper-making grade.
[2] Based on wood that is dry, and weighing 29 lbs. per cu. ft.
[3] Young wood, essentially free from heartwood.

The sulphate process uses an alkaline cooking liquor of sodium hydroxide and sodium sulphide. It is called "sulphate" because sodium sulphate is used in recovering the chemicals. The sulphate cooking conditions for loblolly pine are similar to those employed for other softwoods. Some 800 to 1,500 pounds of kraft pulp can be obtained per cord of wood, depending on natural variations in cubic feet of wood per cord and in the density of dry wood. For each 2-pound increase in wood density there is a 1-pound increase in pulp yield. High-density wood may yield twice as much as low-density wood. The yield of pulp obtained ranges from 45 to 48 percent by weight of the wood. Strong bleached pine sulphate pulp can be made by employing a little more cooking chemical than is used for the kraft grade, and by bleaching in a multistage process. The kraft grade is used without bleaching in wrapping and bag papers and container boards. The bleached and semibleached sulphate pulps are used extensively in the making of bond type papers.

The yield of screened, kraft-type sulphate pulp increases with the weight of dry pine wood. The approximate yield of moisture-free pulp per cubic foot of wood (weighing 22 to 36 lbs. per cu. ft.) equals the density (expressed in pounds per cu. ft. moisture free) times 0.509 and minus 0.96 (Lehrbas 1950). Roughly each 2-pound increase in wood density produces an extra pound of pulp. Mitchell (1954) reporting a study by Chidester has shown the relation between wood density and kraft pulp yield to be approximately:

$Y = 10.25 + 0.51 (D-22)$, where Y equals pulp yields from oven-dry wood in pounds per cubic foot and D equals wood density in pounds per cubic foot—oven-dry weight and green volume.

Sulphite process

This process uses bisulphite of lime with sulphurous acid. The acid sulphite liquor will not reduce heartwood nor remove resins.

Heartwood and knotty wood fibers must be rejected as screenings or cooked twice.

In one test heartwood chips of loblolly pine from Crossett, Ark., were subjected to the pulping action of calcium, magnesium, and sodium base sulphite liquors before and after air seasoning the chips for 3.5 months. The pulping of the heartwood chips was most complete and effective with the sodium base, somewhat less so with the magnesium base, and least so with the calcium base liquor. The strength values of the various pulps did not vary greatly. The comparatively low bleach requirement of the sodium base pulps made them relatively superior to the others (McGovern and Chidester 1941). The present production of southern pine sulphite pulp is mostly used for making rayon.

Hardboard processes

The pioneer explosion process, in which southern pine fibers were first separated and then rebonded under heavy hydraulic pressure to form hardboard was used successfully for many years. It has recently been modified in a process using hardwoods exclusively, thus opening a new market outlet for fresh green hardwood from trees that previously impeded the growth of loblolly pines.[142] In so far as the new process can utilize chips of hard texture it furnishes a long sought commercial outlet for a large surplus of otherwise unmerchantable hardwoods that continue to obstruct the full use of forest land for crops of loblolly pine. Pine wood in the vicinity of the new plant will be released to meet other urgent demands in existing markets.

Soda process

This is the older and simpler of the alkaline processes. Some pine is pulped by this process, but like the semichemical process it is applied mostly to hardwoods. It is based on the ability of caustic soda to dissolve lignin and hydrolize hemicellulose. The yield of soda pulp is 45 percent or less of the dry weight of wood.

Mechanical process

Mechanical pulp is made by forcing rossed wood against a revolving grindstone. It differs from chemical pulp in that lignin, resins, and tannins are not removed. Blue-stained wood can be used to a limited extent without much detriment to color, and heartwood also causes no color trouble when young fast-growing pine is used.

---

[142] A new plant in Mississippi plans for a 1,000-ton daily capacity, of which only about 12 percent will be derived from manufacturing waste.

The best southern pine groundwood pulp is made from unseasoned wood that is less than 35 years old with fewer than 10 rings per inch (Schafer, Pew, and Curran 1937 and 1958). Though it is difficult to make loblolly pine ground pulp equal in quality to the best that can be made from spruce, a generally good and useful quality of pulp can be produced from the pine with about 20 to 40 percent more energy than ordinarily used for spruce. Knotty wood requires more power than clear wood to produce an equivalent product. Compression wood lowers the strength of the pulp in proportion to the amount present. A dull surface, that is one with well worn grits and rounded edges on the grooves, seems the most suitable for grinding pine. Elevation of grinder temperatures up to 210°F., with other variables constant, results in longer fibered and stronger pulps in relation to the energy consumed.

Southern pine groundwood pulp is used in the manufacture of newsprint paper, paperboard, and insulating board.

PROPERTIES RELATED TO STRENGTH

Information on types of wood is most helpful when interrelationships can be shown. Accordingly each property is reported here in relation to the variables associated with it. If the conditions that influence strength are understood, the safety factors needed in structural design need not be so large. Such factors are necessary, however, as Markwardt and Wood (1953) point out, because under long-time loading wood beams retain little more than half the strength shown under laboratory tests of short duration.

Dimensional stability

Wood does not change in dimensions by shrinking or swelling in the green state; it merely loses or takes up free water in cell cavities and cell openings. If, however, all free water is removed in drying and hygroscopic or "bound" water is removed from the cell wall itself, shrinkage and resultant internal stresses are set up. The point at which all free water is removed from wood and only hygroscopic water remains, is known as the fiber saturation point. It is generally accepted as about 28-30 percent moisture content for most species although it has been accurately measured on only a few. Measurements reported by Berkley (1934) established the fiber saturation point for loblolly pine at 22.5 ± 1 percent moisture content.

The fiber saturation point is important for two major reasons: (1) At the fiber saturation point, shrinkage begins and seasoning

TABLE 61.—*Shrinkage in seasoning loblolly pine*

Type of change	Shrinkage from green size		
	Dried to 20 percent moisture content	Dried to 6 percent moisture content	Dried to 0 percent moisture content
	Percent	Percent	Percent
Radial.................	1.6	3.8	4.8
Tangential..............	2.5	5.9	7.4
Volumetric.............	4.1	9.8	12.3

Condition of 1- by 6-inch boards tested	Moisture content	Shrinkage in	
		Width	Thickness
Sapwood, flat-grained:	Percent	64ths of an inch	64ths of an inch
Green to air-dry.......	25 to 15	10½	1
Air-dry to kiln-dry....	15 to 10	5	½
Green to kiln-dry......	25 to 10	15½	2
Air-dry to house-dry...	15 to 5	10½	1
Kiln-dry to house-dry..	10 to 5	5	½
Heartwood, flat-grained:			
Green to air-dry.......	25 to 15	10	1
Air-dry to kiln-dry....	15 to 10	5	½
Green to kiln-dry......	25 to 10	15	2
Air-dry to house-dry...	15 to 5	10	1
Kiln-dry to house-dry..	10 to 5	5	½
Heartwood, edge-grained:			
Green to air-dry.......	25 to 15	8	1½
Air-dry to kiln-dry....	15 to 10	4	1
Green to kiln-dry......	25 to 10	12	2½
Air-dry to house-dry...	15 to 5	8	1½
Kiln-dry to house-dry..	10 to 5	4	1

Basis: Forest Products Laboratory Note 241 (1933) and Wood Handbook (U.S.F.S. 1955).

defects can occur from internal stress, and (2) most strength properties increase with the loss of moisture below the fiber saturation point.

Shrinkage in loblolly pine generally varies directly with density and is moderate compared with other species, amounting to 4.8 percent radial, 7.4 percent tangential, and 12.3 percent volumetric, from green to oven dry (U.S.F.S. 1955). However, the actual shrinkage of ordinary 6-inch loblolly pine boards in the drying process varies in width from $\frac{1}{128}$-inch up to a maximum of nearly $\frac{1}{4}$-inch depending on the degree of drying and characteristics of the wood (table 61). The wood is easily seasoned with little defect if proper, known seasoning methods are followed.

Longitudinal shrinkage, unlike transverse shrinkage discussed above, seems to vary inversely with wood density, but, since it only amounts to about 0.3 percent from green to oven dry, its effect is not usually important. It appears to be influenced by rate of growth, but is not closely associated with it. For wood with more than 4 rings per inch longitudinal shrinkage tends to remain negligible, but can increase ninefold when there are as few as 2 rings per inch.

Extreme differences in shrinkage, transverse or longitudinal, caused by abnormal wood structure (such as compression wood in softwoods) result in dimensional instability. A common sight in lumber yards cutting old-field pine is the corkscrew or bowed 2 by 4, almost invariably the result of excessive longitudinal shrinkage caused by either compression wood or a sharp contrast in growth rate. Specimens with wide-ringed wood from the center of a tree that shrinks excessively, together with close-ringed outer wood that does not shrink much, become distorted as they dry.

The most common abnormality in loblolly pine wood is known as compression wood. This type of wood is characteristic of softwood trees or logs in which the pith is off center, as might occur in leaning trees. The rings are wide, often eccentric, 15 or 40 percent heavier, and without the usual contrast in color they appear lifeless. Summerwood percentage is usually high. In compression wood the cells are crooked and irregular in length. Nearly circular in cross section, they are not completely joined—leaving intercellular spaces. The slope of spiral checks and striations on the cell walls is greater in compression wood than in normal wood, especially in the springwood portion (Pillow 1951a).

To identify compression wood in its less pronounced forms transmitted light is helpful. If cross sections $\frac{1}{8}$ to $\frac{3}{16}$ inch thick are taken from a sample of compression wood it can be easily recognized (Pillow 1941) because it is opaque rather than translucent.

When adjustments are made for differences in weight, compression wood is lower in nearly all strength properties and in pulp yield as compared to normal wood. Compression wood has lower shock resistance and is inferior in stiffness (fig. 106). It shrinks excessively (over 0.3 percent) along the grain causing butt joints in siding to open (Koehler 1946). More serious difficulty arises when this abnormal wood occurs together with normal wood in the same board. Such lumber tends to bow, crook, or twist if free, or if confined, to check or cross break (Koehler 1946). Few specifications limit compression wood in sawed timber. Some difficulty can be avoided by inspection to eliminate compression wood.

Material with visible compression wood, pith on one surface, less than 4 rings per inch at both ends, or fast and slow growth in close proximity should be viewed with suspicion because these features

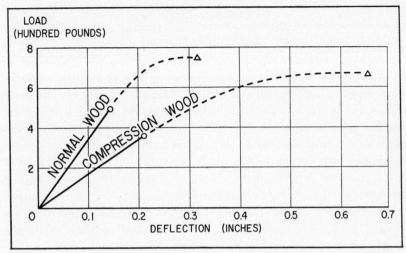

FIGURE 106.—Variation in average load and deflection for normal wood and compression wood of air-dry loblolly pine when tested in static bending (Pillow and Luxford 1937).

affect dimensional stability. Such specimens account for 78 percent of warping in storage (King 1954). The rest of the material should be satisfactory if properly seasoned and used where it will not re-absorb much moisture.

Timber growers who wish to minimize production of abnormal wood should be guided by observations made by Pillow and Luxford (1937) on partially cut loblolly pine stands. Where less than 10 percent of vertical trees had compression wood before logging, about 35 percent produced it in accelerated growth after logging. Among the nonvertical trees reserved and growing 1½ to 2½ inches in 10 years, less than 40 percent of those with slight lean (½° to 2½°) contained compression wood, whereas those with pronounced lean (over 5½°) all had it. Leaning trees should be harvested to avoid that reaction.

Density and weight of wood

Roughly half the weight of green wood is water. Average specific gravity is 0.47 (based on oven-dry weight and green volume). The specific gravity of actual wood substance is 1.52 plus or minus only 4½ percent. Because of this small variation in specific gravity of cell walls, and because resin content accounts for only about 2.3 percent of weight, density of dry loblolly pine wood indicates its substance and strength (Newlin and Wilson 1919). Commercial shortleaf pine wood (which includes loblolly) is roughly 90 percent as heavy as longleaf pine. Because of thinner cell walls, loblolly pine wood of a given density has about 20 percent more summerwood than longleaf pine (Berkley 1934).

An increase of 0.01 in specific gravity brings an increase of about 50 pounds in dry weight of a cord of wood. Specific gravity was recognized early by the Southern Pine Association in judging the quality of structural timber by a "density rule" (p. 421). Because some trees contain nearly twice as much summerwood near the butt as higher in the tree, it is better to judge wood quality at the top end of long timbers. Wood that passes the density rule is stronger on the average than unselected specimens. In laboratory tests a bending strength of 5,170 pounds per square inch was increased to 6,450 pounds or 25 percent by the application of the density rule to exclude the weaker specimens (Wood 1950).

Loblolly pine wood weighs about 36 pounds per cubic foot when dry. After seasoning to 15 or 12 percent moisture, 1,000 actual board feet of lumber weigh about 3,000 pounds; or about 2,200 pounds dressed to standard dimensions of 25/32 by 7½ inches for nominal 1- by 8-inch lumber (Reck 1933, U.S.F.S. 1955).

Betts (1909) reported specific gravity decreasing with height in the tree as follows (basis 14 trees):

Height above stump (inches)	Specific gravity of dry wood
0	0.63
10	.58
20	.53
30	.51
40	.49
50	.48
60	.47

Although these trees were heavier than average, the tendency toward lighter wood in the upper logs has been noted by many observers. There is also a highly significant increase radially in specific gravity from the pith outward (Yandle 1956), owing to some undetermined factor related to age rather than width of ring. A formula (Bethel 1940) expresses this upward and outward increase of density in second-growth loblolly pine as follows: specific gravity = 0.5129 + 0.0442 (logarithm of number of years from the pith) + (− 0.2151) (distance in feet up the tree ÷ total height in feet). A typical distribution of specific gravity resulting from this relationship is shown by the symmetrical zonation in figure 107.

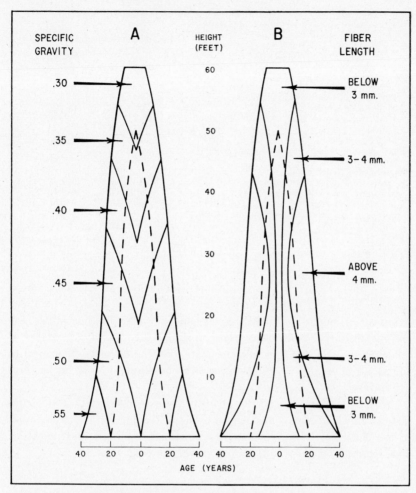

FIGURE 107.—Longitudinal section of a typical pine trunk showing (*A*) zonation of specific gravity of the wood, and (*B*) distribution of fibers by length in relation to age and height (Bethel 1940).

In the gulf states there is a broad geographic downward trend in the average specific gravity of loblolly pine from east to west. Nevertheless, the variation in the specific gravity of mature wood is much greater between individual trees on any one site than it is for average specific gravities between sites or geographic races (Zobel and McElwee 1958a). The bole of a given tree has a higher specific gravity and a greater content of alpha-cellulose in its mature wood than in its juvenile wood.

Strength of the wood, green or dry, may be approximated from

TABLE 62.—*Estimated strength-specific gravity relations for loblolly pine*

Strength property[1]	Specific gravity-strength relations[2]			
	Green wood		Air-dry wood (12 percent moisture)	
Static bending:				
Fiber stress at proportional limit..........p.s.i.	12,720	$G^{1.5}$	21,420	$G^{1.5}$
Modulus of rupture......................p.s.i.	22,700	$G^{1.5}$	35,140	$G^{1.5}$
Work to maximum load.......in.-lb. per cu. in.	37.1	G^{2}	40.0	G^{2}
Total work..................in.-lb. per cu. in.	132	$G^{2.25}$	79.6	$G^{2.25}$
Modulus of elasticity...............1,000 p.s.i.	3,620	$G^{1.25}$	4,180	$G^{1.25}$
Impact bending, height of drop causing complete				
failure...................................in.	136	G^{2}	115	G^{2}
Compression parallel to grain:				
Fiber stress at proportional limit..........p.s.i.	6,550	$G^{1.25}$	11,180	$G^{1.25}$
Maximum crushing strength..............p.s.i.	8,970	$G^{1.25}$	16,430	$G^{1.25}$
Modulus of elasticity...............1,000 p.s.i.	4,010	$G^{1.25}$	4,570	$G^{1.25}$
Compression perpendicular to grain, fiber stress at				
proportional limit......................p.s.i.	3,170	$G^{2.5}$	5,280	$G^{2.5}$
Hardness:				
End....................................lb.	2,770	$G^{2.5}$	4,040	$G^{2.5}$
Side...................................lb.	2,970	$G^{2.5}$	3,710	$G^{2.5}$

[1] P.s.i. equals pounds per square inch.

[2] The properties and values should be read as equations; for example, modulus of rupture of green wood = 22,700 $G^{1.5}$, where G represents the specific gravity based on oven-dry weight and volume at the moisture condition indicated.

exponential equations utilizing various powers of the values for specific gravity (table 62). These formulas are merely estimates of trends; they do not provide accurate determinations of properties for small lots of material and should be applied only in general evaluations.

How variations in specific gravity are associated with stand conditions in the forest have been observed frequently but evaluation of the causes of these relationships remains incomplete and tentative. For example, Paul (1931a) found this trend:

D.b.h. (inches)	Average specific gravity
10..........................	0.49
14..........................	.48
18..........................	.45
22..........................	.39

As this was an even-aged well-stocked stand, the wood from the smaller trees may have been heavy because of suppression or small crowns. The proportion of springwood increased with crown size.

Paul's conclusion, however, was that the development of the summerwood portion of the annual rings depends more upon favorable conditions for continued growth throughout the season. During years of extreme drought the development of the late wood portion of an annual ring is very much below that formed in a

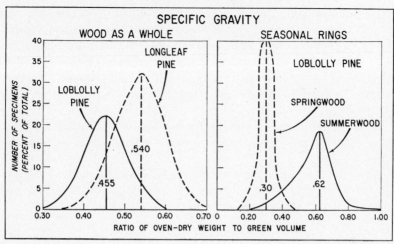

FIGURE 108.—Normal variation in specific gravity of wood found between (*A*) loblolly and longleaf pine (Paul and Smith 1950) and (*B*) springwood and summerwood of loblolly pine (Paul 1939).

summer of heavy rainfall, even though the springwood development for the same year is nearly normal. Heavy wood is produced even in open stands when soil moisture and fertility are such that growth continues throughout the vegetative season sufficiently to keep the proportion of summerwood high.

Zobel and Rhodes (1955), seeking genetic causes for differences in density of wood, found little relation within any given stand between specific gravity at breast height, length of clear bole, or rate of growth. Nor did they find any relation between age of tree (from 25 and 50 years) and specific gravity within any given site. They recognize a strong relation between summerwood percentage and density (fig. 108, *B*), but feel that the environmental causes of variation have been overremphasized. Until it is discovered to what extent the variations are inherited the influence of environment may be questioned but not dismissed.

The wood of loblolly pine normally ranges from 0.30 to 0.60 in specific gravity, averaging about 0.46 (fig. 108, *A*). The reason for the unchallenged direct relation between density and summerwood percentage is apparent in the well-separated peaks of the curves. Summerwood is usually twice as heavy as springwood. Specific gravity averaging about 0.06 higher in old-growth than in second-growth wood appears to increase with number of rings per inch up to about 12 in old growth or 14 in second growth, then to decline. Also for a given percentage of springwood, trees of rapid growth are less dense than those of slow growth. For wood of the same age there is little relationship between growth rate and specific gravity. For rings of the same width occurring in both outer and inner sections, there is less summerwood in the inner zone (Lodewick 1933), reflecting an effect associated with age or radial distance. More research is needed to isolate the principal cause and effect in these relationships.

Bending strength of seasoned wood varies primarily and most directly with density and moisture content below 22.5 percent (fig. 109).

Formulas are available for estimating specific gravity from percentage of summerwood, from rings per inch, or both together (Schafer 1949) using representative specimens.

$$E = 0.00499X + 0.2732$$

where E is the expected specific gravity and X the percentage of summerwood, or

$$E = 0.00673Z + 0.413$$

where Z is the number of rings per radial inch. Using both criteria Schafer's formula is—

$$E = 0.0044X + 0.0037Z + 0.2693$$

Of the total variation in specific gravity encountered in this study summerwood alone accounted for 72 percent and growth rate alone 31 percent. Together they accounted for 80 percent. These relations are derived:

Volume of summerwood (percent)	Ratio: oven-dry weight to green volume (specific gravity)	Rate of growth in rings per inch (number)	Ratio: oven-dry weight to green volume (specific gravity)
15	0.35	2	0.43
25	.40	6	.45
35	.45	10	.48
45	.50	14	.51
55	.55	18	.53
65	.60	22	.56

Turnbull (1947) working with yellow pines in South Africa found that although the density of wood formed in any one year is associated with some function of age rather than rate of growth, overall density for entire cross sections is related to periodic growth by stages in the development of a tree. He concluded that wide spacing in the latter portions of rotations is not apt to reduce specific gravity for it is within the development stage most likely to produce the heavier wood.

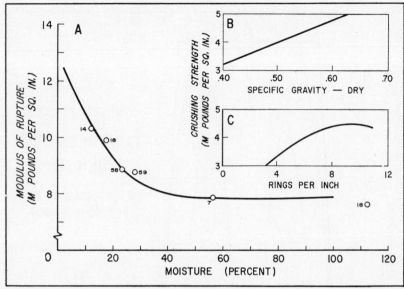

FIGURE 109.—Moisture content, specific gravity, and rate of growth as related to the strength of loblolly pine wood. Bending strength (A) based on numbers of clear 2- by 2- by 30-inch specimens shown on the curve. The crushing strength (B and C) based on tests of 162 clear 2- by 2- by 4-inch specimens (Betts 1909).

The distribution of strength values within the bole, usually symmetrical in vertical trees, varies with age and height above ground. In other trees the pattern becomes irregular, modified by the degree and direction of lean.

For example, the tree at figure 110, A, was a fine straight-grained specimen in old growth with 5 to 8 rings per inch in the first 80 years and 15 to 30 thereafter. Strength increased progressively from the pith only up to a point where growth decreased sharply. Weakest wood was found in the top, the central core, and the over-mature shell. The smaller bole of leaning tree B is stronger, but was inferior because of irregular strength pattern. Although its strength about doubled from pith to bark at stump level on two sides, the contrast between the normal wood on the right and compression wood at the left is unfavorable. The asymmetrical growth on the leaning side warped badly in seasoning.

Height in the tree, environment, or the silviculture used for loblolly pines planted in South Africa greatly influenced the weight of wood found in 16-year-old trees. When they were widely spaced on a low moist site the wood was 29 percent heavier at stump height

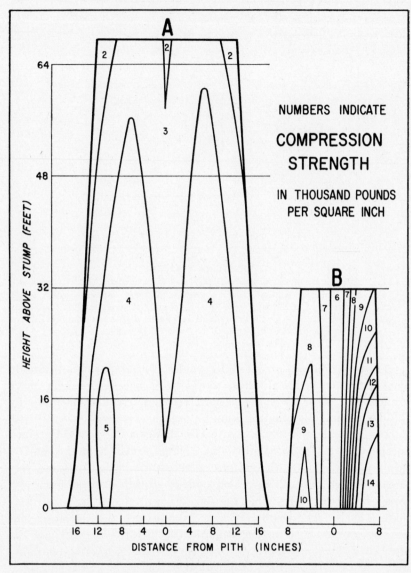

FIGURE 110.—Radial and longitudinal distribution of crushing strength (1,000 lbs. per sq. in.) in two loblolly pines from Mississippi: *A*, A vertical 160-year-old tree, with a relatively uniform pattern of strength in rather light wood, grown on moist sandy clay; *B*, a leaning 50-year-old tree, with a nonuniform pattern of strength in heavier wood, grown on dry clay loam (Brust and Berkley 1935).

than at 22 feet. At 22 feet from the ground the wood was 17 percent heavier from trees widely spaced on a low moist site than from trees closely spaced on a high dry site (Scott and du Plessis 1951).

The influence on specific gravity of the various factors that appear to affect it has not yet been apportioned among them, and will not be until we have more closely controlled experiments.

In general density, elasticity, and strength decrease from low to high points in the bole. Transversely they increase from the pith to a maximum in the outer rings of second-growth trees. In old growth the maxima are usually between the 80th and 100th rings, beyond which they again decrease toward the bark. Most of the variation in specific gravity and strength appear due to position in the tree, age at which the wood is produced, and structural form of the stem, rather than to growth rate (Spurr and Hsiung 1954). Hence, loblolly pine should be grown at the fastest rate commensurate with good natural pruning, form, and knot size.

Moisture content

The average moisture content of green loblolly pine wood varies from 33 percent in heartwood to 110 percent in sapwood. In pole sizes the wood weighs 53 pounds per cubic foot green or 36 pounds air-dry at about 15 percent moisture (U.S.F.S. 1955). At 8 percent, it weighs a pound less. Adjustments in these weights are readily made for moisture changes by adding 0.154 for each 1 percent increase or subtracting it for each 1 percent decrease in moisture.

Strength of clear wood increases as it dries below about 30 percent moisture. Values for several strength properties of both green and dry loblolly pine wood are shown in table 63. In each of these properties dry wood is the stronger. Toughness, however, may be lost in drying as it depends on flexibility as well as on strength.[143] The relationship of toughness or shock resistance to moisture content has been found to be quite complex and differs greatly among species.

Wilson (1932) has indicated that the strength-moisture relations of yellow pine wood may be expressed by an exponential formula of the form Log $S = \log Si + k \ (Mp - M)$ where S is the strength value to be computed for timber of moisture content M, and Si "intersection strength" is the strength value of green wood at or above

[143] When loblolly pine wood of specific gravity 0.47 to 0.51 is dried from 86 percent moisture to 12 percent its toughness (measured in inch-pounds of load applied) is reduced 17 percent on a tangential face, or 36 percent on a radial face—based on laboratory specimens $\frac{5}{8}$ x $\frac{5}{8}$ x 10 inches tested over an 8-inch span.

TABLE 63.—*Strength properties of loblolly pine as measured on small, clear, green or air-dry specimens*[1]

Item and unit	Green specimens	Air-dry specimens
Moisture content..percent	81	12
Specific gravity...	.47	.51
Static bending:		
Fiber stress at proportional limit......................p.s.i.[2]	4,100	7,800
Modulus of—		
Rupture.. p.s.i.	7,300	12,800
Elasticity................................1,000 p.s.i.	1,410	1,800
Work to—		
Proportional limit......................in.-lb. per cu. in.	.68	1.92
Maximum load......................... ”	8.2	10.4
Impact bending (50-lb. hammer), height of drop causing		
failure..inches	30	30
Compression parallel to the grain:		
Fiber stress at proportional limit......................p.s.i.	2,550	4,820
Maximum crushing strength...........................p.s.i.	3,490	7,080
Compression perpendicular to the grain, fiber stress at		
proportional limit....................................p.s.i.	480	980
Shear parallel to the grain, maximum shearing strength.....p.s.i.	850	1,370
Tension perpendicular to grain, maximum tensile strength...p.s.i.	260	470
Hardness: load required to embed a 0.444-inch ball to $\frac{1}{2}$ its diameter:		
End...pounds	420	750
Side..pounds	450	690

[1] Wood Handbook, p. 76 (U.S.F.S. 1955).
[2] P.s.i. equals pounds per square inch.

"Mp"—21 percent for loblolly pine—and k a constant with average values ranging roughly from 0.012 to 0.035 for different strength properties. The logarithm of average strength values varies inversely and uniformly[144] with moisture content below 21 percent and is unchanging above that point (fig. 111). The horizontal portions of these curves represent the strength of wood that is green or soaked, and the left ends of the sloping lines represent the average strength of wood seasoned to 12 percent moisture. The equation and chart apply to strength as tested on small specimens of clear wood in which moisture was distributed uniformly. They do not apply to large timbers with an irregular distribution of moisture.

The data for air-dry wood (12 percent moisture content) in table 63 may be used to approximate the strength of wood at other moistures below about 20 percent moisture content. Correction factors in percent for the various strength properties of loblolly pine for each 1 percent change in moisture content are as follows:

[144] This uniformity is an approximation in that the exact relation tends to be slightly curvilinear, meeting the fiber-saturation point at some moisture content a little above 21 percent.

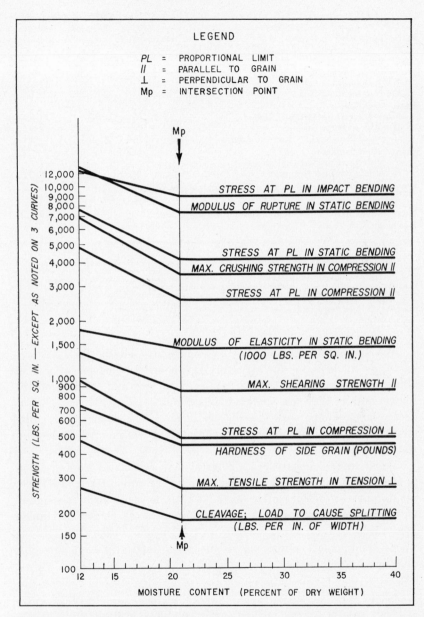

FIGURE 111.—Strength-moisture relations for 2- by 2-inch specimens of clear loblolly pine wood. Moisture at 12 percent represents air-seasoned lumber and at 21 percent or more, lumber that is green or soaked (Markwardt and Wilson 1935).

Strength property	Curve no. in figure 111	Correction factor[1] (percent)
Static bending:		
Fiber stress at proportional limit	3	7.4
Modulus of rupture	2	6.4
Modulus of elasticity	6	2.8
Work at proportional limit		11.2
Work to maximum load		2.6
Impact bending:		
Fiber stress at proportional limit	1	3.4
Work to proportional limit		3.8
Height of drop causing complete failure		.1
Compression parallel to grain:		
Fiber stress at proportional limit	5	7.3
Maximum crushing strength	4	8.2
Compression perpendicular to grain, fiber stress at proportional limit	8	8.3
Shear parallel to grain, maximum shearing strength	7	5.4
Hardness:		
End		6.5
Side	9	4.9

[1] Corrections to the strength properties must be applied successively for each 1 percent change in moisture content until the total change has been covered. For each 1 percent decrease in moisture content the strength is multiplied by $(1 + P)$ where correction P is expressed as a decimal. For each 1 percent increase in moisture (up to about 20 percent) the strength is divided by $(1 + P)$. Successive multiplications or divisions can be avoided by raising the factor $(1 + P)$ to the power n, where n is the total moisture change to be covered, and then multiplying or dividing the original strength by the ratio so calculated. A compound interest table may serve the purpose. This correction procedure is standard practice at the Forest Products Laboratory at Madison, Wis.

Working stresses

Wooden building materials vary widely in strength. Basic stresses for clear lumber and for structural timbers are reported (U.S.F.S. 1955, pp. 137-164) as they are related to size and quality of the pieces, and as they are modified by various types of defects such as decay, holes, knots, shakes, cross grain, etc. The details of grading structural timber are important engineering considerations beyond the scope of this treatise.

Wood technologists may be interested in cell structure as related to strength in timber and the nature of its fracture. Garland (1939) points out that failure of brash loblolly pine seems to be associated with relatively low strength among specimens of large fibril angle (see discussion of fibril angles in section on "Character of the wood") and that splintering occurs with relatively high strength and small fibril angles.

Thermal conductivity

The rate at which loblolly pine conducts heat is intermediate between that of a light coniferous wood such as northern white-cedar and a heavy hardwood like hickory. Thermal conductivity increases directly with moisture content. For loblolly pine, conductivity may be computed from the formula

$$K = S\,(1.39 + 0.028M) + 0.165\ ^{[145]}$$

where S is specific gravity based on volume at current moisture content and weight when oven dry, and M is moisture content in percent. For moistures above 30 percent a constant value for S equal to 0.47 may be used.

Nail holding capacity

Loblolly pine is much like Douglas-fir in retaining nails, but superior to ponderosa pine. Loblolly wood holds nails only about four-fifths as tenaciously as the other southern yellow pines. In laboratory tests cement-coated 7d nails were driven to a depth of 1¼ inches and pulled at once. The load required for withdrawal was 179 pounds for end surface, 271 radial, and 335 tangential. The density of the pine sample was 0.59. Resistance to withdrawal decreased with the specific gravity of the wood (U.S. Forest Serv. Forest Products Lab. Tech. Note 236, 1931).

DEFECTS AND GRADES

Wounds and decay in standing timber

Much of the waste in manufacturing and many of the defects in sawed wood products stem from imperfections in trees and logs. Log volumes have to be scaled down to allow for losses from crook, sweep, fusiform cankers, and redheart. Heart rots affect second-growth timber much less than the old growth because of shorter rotations. Redheart caused by *Fomes pini* was observed to vary from 5 percent in a 40- to 90-year-old stand of loblolly pine in Virginia to 72 percent of the volume in a stand 190 to 230 years old. Insofar as loblolly pines are more limby than shortleaf, they may develop more rot, but usually it does not exceed 15 percent of the volume in second growth at 70 to 80 years, even in unmanaged stands. In a 58-year-old stand of loblolly pine in southern Arkansas the volume loss in logs infected with redheart was about 4 percent, but degrade from incipient decay brought the total financial loss up to 8 percent (Hepting and Chapman 1938).

Cull results from fire wounds in standing timber because decay, insects, or pitch soaking often follow. The volume of butt cull is closely related to the width and age of scars made by fire or in logging. Owing to size limitations, average wound widths vary with diameter of the trees (fig. 112, A). Although wide scars take

[145] K is the quantity of heat in British thermal units that flows in 1 hour through a 1-inch thickness of material, 1 square foot in area, when the temperature difference between the two surfaces is 1°F. (U.S.F.S. 1955, p. 47).

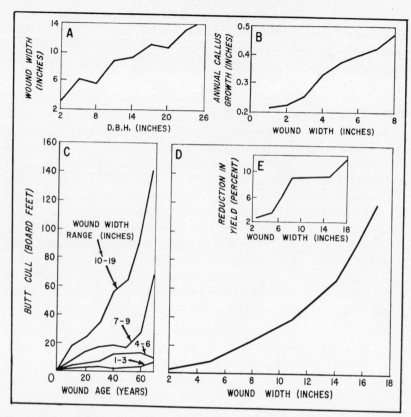

FIGURE 112.—Relations between the dimensions of loblolly pine trees, their basal wounds, rate of healing, and volume of cull wood: (*A*) Tree diameter limits wound width, (*B*) wider wounds heal faster, (*C*) butt cull increases with wound width and time since injury, (*D*) volume loss accelerates with increase in wound width after 30 years, and (*E*) percentage reduction in yield increases with width of wound (Garren 1941).

longer to heal, their rate of healing is faster than for narrow ones (fig. 112, *B*). In loblolly pine more than half the wounds appear to have no importance in relation to decay in saw-log-sized trees. Scars 1 to 3 inches wide produce little cull, regardless of age, but scars 4 to 6 inches wide produce some cull. There is an abrupt increase in cull from wounds wider than 6 inches (fig. 112, *E*). Wounds 7 to 12 inches wide result in considerable cull after 30 years, while those over 12 inches wide become serious in 10 years (fig. 112, *C* and *D*).

A loss of 9 to 12 percent in lumber volume may be expected from wounds wider than 7 inches. For any given wound age, cull volume increases approximately with the square of wound width

(Garren 1941). The extent of fire injury in a stand depends on such factors as frequency, severity, and season of burning, but the prevalence of scarred trees standing at a given time is affected not only by the incidence of fire but also by the capacity of a species to survive various degrees of wounding. As fires occur less frequently, and partial cutting more often, logging scars may account for a somewhat larger portion of butt rot and other defects in trees.

Insects cause their share of the common defects in timber. In pine products the so-called pin holes, or grub holes less than ⅛ inch in diameter, with adjacent dark streaks usually result from ambrosia beetles, *Platypus flavicornis,* in felled trees, green logs, or unseasoned lumber. Holes that are larger than ⅛ or ¼ inch are usually the work of timber worms in living trees. If such holes are oval and filled with powdery dust or loose shreds ("frass") they result from round-headed borers, *Monochamus titillator,* or from powder-post beetles in green or seasoned lumber. "Powder-post" is a form of damage caused by various insects. Unstained holes tightly packed with granular boring dust (pellets of digested and excreted wood) are made by flatheaded borers in living or green felled trees (Snyder 1927).

Stain and minor defects

Brown and blue stains result from fungus attack, but are not necessarily accompanied by decay. Their presence, however, indicates that conditions have been favorable to decay, and decay might also be present. Species of *Ceratostomataceae* are responsible for most of the initial blue stain in southern pine lumber and logs (Davidson 1935). Blue stain fungi are most active from late May to early September. Most stain develops in sapwood of green logs and lumber during air seasoning, before the moisture content is reduced to 20 percent of the dry weight (Scheffer and Lindgren 1940). Important stain also develops in beetle-killed trees. Spradling (1936) studying the penetration of the mold *Trichoderma lignorum* into the sapwood of loblolly pine found it mainly in ray cells and resin ducts. Unlike the wood destroying fungi, however, it causes only a small reduction in strength.

Decay in round products

About 60 percent of the strength at the midpoint of a telephone pole depends upon the outer inch of wood in its cross section. Hence, any fungus growth at all in the outer fibers of a pole may be expected to reduce its strength. Of course, most poles are treated against decay, and a recent discovery indicates that certain fungi actually improve the absorption of preservative without causing any loss in strength (Lindgren 1952).

In studying four decay-producing fungi, Richards (1950) found that neither position within the sapwood of a log nor its original density had any consistent effect on the decay resistance of loblolly pine.

Loblolly pine pulpwood stored in the forest deteriorates in both summer and winter. Decay and stain are greater in peeled than in rough wood stored 2 months in summer or 4 to 5 months in winter, but for longer periods peeling is advantageous (Lindgren 1953). For rough bolts, specific gravity is reduced about 7 percent after 4 months of storage in late spring and summer, as compared to 2 percent for late fall and winter storage. After 9 to 12 months the losses range from 10 to 15 percent (Lindgren 1951). Storage losses can be reduced in rough wood by using large bolts, spraying freshly cut wood with 4 percent aqueous solution of sodium fluoride or ammonium bifluoride, or by storing in large tight piles or under water. Losses in peeled wood are reduced by storing in open piles, splitting large bolts, and by dipping bolts in one of the chemical solutions. Research indicates that current deterioration in round southern pine pulpwood (as in certain western conifers) can be reduced by storing the wood in the form of chips in large out-door piles. A high moisture content of the chips apparently favors success with this method, but the length of satisfactorily storing loblolly pine chips in this manner has not been determined.

Significant early decay in pine poles and posts, as well as pulpwood, seems to be caused mostly by one fungus, *Peniphora gigantea*, which can be detected in sapwood by a simple color test (Lindgren 1955). A small amount of a water solution of Alizarine Red S is sprayed on freshly exposed end-grain surfaces. Infected wood turns yellow, while the uninfected turns pink to red. Fortunately the presence of the minor staining or molding fungi, which also turn red, do not interfere with the test. The indicator should be useful in the rejection of material not worthy of preservative treatment. After 6 month's storage more destructive fungi, like *Lenzites saepiaria*, become common (Lindgren 1951).

Log and tree grades

Until about 1915 the timber industry judged quality in its materials by ocular inspection without benefit of any recognized standards. Even then, however, the superiority of large butt logs over

the upper logs and of large trees over the smaller ones was conspicuous. This was well shown for loblolly pine by a mill-scale
study using the lumber grades of the North Carolina Pine Association (Sterrett 1914).

During the next 30 years the standard lumber grades of the
Southern Pine Association achieved South-wide recognition. It remained for the Forest Service, studying the financial aspects of
forestry at Crossett, Ark., to test the application of the first tentative grades for logs. This work quickly confirmed the early study
by Ashe (1929b) showing that in small sizes both trees and logs
cost more and are worth less at a sawmill (fig. 113).

Subsequently a number of grade-yield studies were made by the
Southern Pine Association and Forest Service researchers, using the
Crossett log grades, modifications thereof, or other systems. Each
local application of a system achieved good stratification of the
values in study logs of various sizes and species of pine found in
that specific situation.

The so-called U. S. Forest Service "interim grades" (see appendix), resulting from these early studies, are the best available
so far. They are still subject to revision, but certain facts indicate
progress. These grades are simple to apply with a choice of viewing logs from 2, 3, or 4 sides. They do segregate value classes within a local area, regardless of pine species, though they cannot yet
serve as a basis for value appraisals without local grade-yield data.
The discrepancies may stem from differences between mills, sawyers,
grades, or markets. To correct this deficiency further area-coordinated
research on log quality is in progress. The results from grading logs
from widely separate localities by a given set of rules must be compared at a single manufacturing plant using the grade yields obtained
under uniform conversion to lumber and grading of values. To be
widely useful in value appraisals the chosen system of grading must
pass such tests.

The prime need now is for wide acceptance of a single system of
grading logs. The second need is to translate the accepted log grades
into tree grades to permit more precise evaluation of merchantable
timber. The third need is to combine this with a workable method
of classifying silvical quality in standing pines of all sizes and ages.
Such a classification will involve recognition of intrinsic differences
in the current or potential vigor of individual pines. Fulfillment of
this third need will implement the judgment of timber cruisers
and foresters in selecting trees to cut or leave so as to continue to
build up the quality of growing stocks. Quality classes that will em-

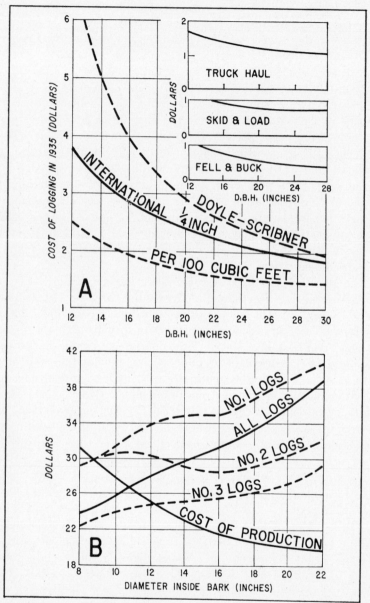

FIGURE 113.—Cost of logging loblolly pine trees of different sizes and the value of lumber from logs of different sizes, based on early Crossett log grades: A, Costs per M board feet or per 100 cubic feet; B, values or cost per M feet mill tally in 1935 (Reynolds, Bond, and Kirkland 1944).

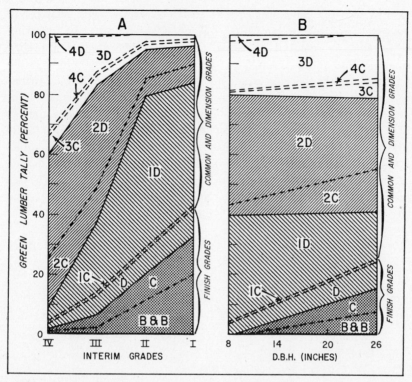

FIGURE 114.—Lumber grade yields from 124 loblolly pines in Mississippi: *A*, Logs of all sizes in each of four "interim" log grades, and *B*, ungraded logs from trees of all diameters (from unpublished data, Southeastern Forest Experiment Station).

brace growing-stock values, as well as market values, for loblolly pine trees eventually will make forest valuation more realistic in terms of future growth potential.

Part of the increase in value of logs with increase in their diameter is due to an increase in the width of boards sawed from the larger logs and trees, and from the higher lumber grades recovered. Grades of lumber obtainable from four grades of logs and from ungraded trees of different sizes are given in fig. 114, wherein lines show the percentage of sample in and above the indicated grade, while shaded areas cover grades of approximately equal sales value. Note that for ungraded timber (fig. 114, *B*) 11-inch trees contain 1 percent of B and Better lumber, whereas 20-inch trees contain 5 percent. Grade II logs contain 10 percent, and grade I logs nearly 20 percent of such lumber (fig. 114, *A*).

For logs the commercial value shifts constantly with changes in market prices and dollar values. Some of the difficulty in following these shifts is removed by using a technical device called "quality index." The index is based on the observation that, throughout the fluctuations, the various grade prices of lumber maintain a rather constant proportion of the current price for standard length, kiln-dried, 1- by 8-inch S4S boards classed as No. 2 Common lumber. The marginal cost of production has tended to fluctuate about this price. The index for such lumber, and other grades of equal value, is shown as 100 percent in table 64. Note that 5- and 10-inch boards of grade C are worth twice as much, and 12-inch "B and Better boards" three times as much as No. 2 Common boards of the same size.

TABLE 64.—*Quality indices for loblolly or shortleaf yellow pine lumber based on grade, width, and thickness*

Nominal thickness (inches)	Grade	Nominal width (inches)				
		4	6	8	5 and 10	12
1....................	B and B	220	220	220	235	310
	C	180	180	180	200	245
	#1 Com.	155	155	155	165	200
	#2 Com.	85	100	100	100	115
	#3 Com.	60	80	85	85	85
	#4 Com.	45	45	45	45	45
5/4, 6/4, 7/4..........	B and B	240	240	240	280	340
	Other	(¹)	(¹)	(¹)	(¹)	(¹)
2....................	B and B	265	260	260	280	340
	#1D	110	100	105	115	130
	#2D	100	90	95	100	110
	#3D	65	65	65	65	65
3 or more.............	#1 Tbr.	105	105	105	125	135
	#2 Tbr.	90	90	90	100	120

Basis: 8- to 20-ft. lengths for timber, 16-ft. length for dimension, standard lengths for others. "Rough green" for timbers, kiln dried and S4S for other No. 2 or better material, air dried and S4S for other material. Index base is No. 2 Common 1″ x 8″ board price, equivalent to 100 in the above table. Lumber grades are those of the Southern Pine Inspection Bureau of the Southern Pine Association, New Orleans, La.
¹ Indices same as for corresponding width and grade of 1-inch material.

Where local grade yields are being studied, quality indices for lumber in this table may be used to appraise relative log values. A prerequisite is sawmill data, or estimates, to show the number of board feet in each grade. A weighted average index is then computed as in the following example for a 16-foot log 10.1 inches in scaling diameter:

Lumber grade	Thickness and width (inches)	Lumber content (bd. ft.)	Quality of lumber (index)	Weighted indices
C.................	1 x 4	5.3	180	954
1 Com............	1 x 6	24.0	155	3,720
2 Com............	1 x 4	5.3	155	822
3 Com............	1 x 4	10.7	85	910
		45.3		6,406

$$\text{Quality index for log} = \frac{6,406}{45.3} = 141$$

An evaluation of this kind, applied to the interim southern pine log grades during tests in South Carolina and Georgia, resulted in log quality indices as shown in table 65. It indicates that, in the Atlantic Coastal Plain, 1,000 board feet sawed from 11-inch grade 4 logs is worth only 6 percent more than the current price of No. 2C 8-inch boards, whereas 1,000 board feet cut from 20-inch grade 2 logs is worth twice as much—i.e., 212 percent of No. 2C lumber.

TABLE 65.—*Average log quality indices by log grade and diameter for short-leaf and loblolly pine, on a mill tally basis[1]*

Log d.i.b. (inches)	Index for Atlantic Coastal Plain near Charleston, S. C., when log grade is—				Index for southern Piedmont near Macon, Ga., when log grade is—			
	1	2	3	4	1	2	3	4
6......................	...	...	125	98	...	...	134	113
7......................	...	...	128	100	...	...	136	115
8......................	...	...	130	102	...	...	139	116
9......................	...	...	132	103	...	...	141	118
10.....................	...	160	135	104	...	179	143	119
11.....................	...	165	138	106	...	184	146	120
12.....................	...	170	140	107	...	189	148	122
13.....................	...	176	142	108	...	194	151	123
14.....................	...	181	145	110	...	200	153	125
15.....................	...	186	147	111	...	205	156	126
16.....................	...	192	150	112	...	210	158	127
17.....................	230	197	152	114	...	...	...	...
18.....................	236	202	154	115	...	...	...	...
19.....................	242	207	156	116	...	...	...	...
20.....................	249	212	159	117	...	...	...	...
21.....................	255	218	...	...	...	...	...	...
22.....................	262	223	...	...	...	...	...	...
Average..............	244	190	146	107		189	146	118

[1] In these indices the f.o.b. car price of No. 2 Common, standard length, 1 x 8, kiln-dried, S4S boards has an index value of 100 (McClay 1954b).

Any classification of sawtimber trees by quality may utilize log grades, and possibly will hinge on the grade of the butt log, for it presents the maximum volume, value, and variation in quality. Tentative tree classes developed at the Santee and Hitchiti Experimental Forests from the interim system of log grades are as follows:

Butt log No. 1 and second log No. 2 or better......   1-2
Butt log No. 1 and second log No. 3..............   1-3
Butt log No. 2................................   2
Butt log No. 3................................   3

Current studies indicate another possibility. It may be that trees can be classified as to economic value on the basis of characteristics visible on the lower 20 feet of the bole, or on some specified proportion of the merchantable height. Ultimately, of course, such a classification must also be integrated with silvical vigor classes of trees, so that cruisers can appraise the potential as well as the present economic value of timber.

In an effort to apply log grades in estimating the quality of saw-log trees McClay and Pawek (1955) observed the following variation in quality index:

Tree quality No. by grade of butt log	Range of d.b.h. (inches)	Associated range in tree quality index
1....................	20-30	149-166
2....................	12-24	116-142
3 or 4..............	10-24	108-125

SEASONING

Loblolly pine, like all wood products, must be seasoned before it is completely suitable for most uses.[146] In living trees its moisture averages 110 percent in the sapwood and 33 percent in the heartwood (U.S.F.S. 1955). Seasoning is needed for four main reasons: (1) To prevent infection by mold and fungi that attack wood only when it contains more than 20 percent moisture, (2) to reduce weight for shipping, (3) to stabilize shrinkage within the range of moisture contents expected in service, and (4) to increase strength to meet the needs of the final product. In addition to these major reasons, seasoning improves machining, gluing and finishing, electrical, and insulation properties.

Moisture in poles and posts should be reduced to 20 or 30 percent to condition them for preservative treatment. To obtain air circulation and rapid drying, round products should be debarked and piled crib fashion.

Where product investments are large, such as with telephone

[146] The moisture content of wood in trees varies from 30 to 300 percent of its dry weight. It is not higher in summer than in winter (U.S. Forest Serv. Forest Prod. Lab. Tech. Note F-15, 1953). For use as construction lumber, this moisture must be reduced to 12-15 percent, for furniture and interior trim to 7-9 percent, for flooring to 5-7 percent, and for veneer to 3-4 percent before gluing.

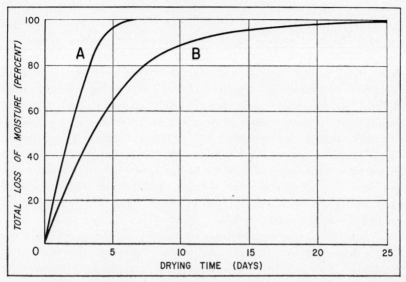

FIGURE 115.—Air drying of inch-thick loblolly pine lumber from green condition to 18 percent moisture content takes four times as long in the absence of forced draft ventilation: *A*, Average rate in four predrying runs under high air circulation; *B*, average for four methods of piling in twenty tests of open-air drying without fans (Page 1958).

poles, recent developments have shown the advantages of forced drying such as kiln drying, controlled air seasoning (Vaughan 1954), and vapor drying (Hudson 1947).

Air seasoning sawed products

The bulk of loblolly pine lumber and timber is air seasoned. Conventional methods of piling loblolly pine for air seasoning are (1) handpiled, flat stacks with slope and pitch, (2) end-piled lumber piled against inverted V-frames, (3) crib-piled lumber crisscrossed in triangular or rectangular fashion, (4) end-racked lumber X-piled on a long A-frame, and (5) package-piled lumber in flat, level tiers of packages handled by mechanized equipment.

Air seasoning requires from 3 weeks to a year or more, depending on thickness, species, weather conditions, and piling methods. Under optimum summer weather conditions, it was found that 1-inch pine dried in 3 to 5 weeks in Georgia. In subsequent studies, Page (1958) determined the rate of air drying under summer conditions in Georgia by four piling methods and the rate of predrying under high air circulation (fig. 115).

Excessive degrade in seasoning loblolly pine is frequently en-

countered. Bluestain is most severe, accounting for 73 percent of
the total degrade loss. This is followed by warp, 11 percent; surface
and end checks, 4 percent; and miscellaneous, 12 percent (Page and
Carter 1958). It was also found that high moisture contents per-
sisted in all piling methods where green boards were lapped without
stickers. Recommended practices for air seasoning green lumber
include the following: (1) An antistain chemical dip, (2) good
foundations to keep lumber at least 12 to 18 inches above ground,
(3) well-aligned dry stickers, (4) bolsters aligned with stickers,
(5) stickers at end of lumber which should be box-piled, (6) roofs
on all piles with space of 6 to 12 inches between top of lumber pile
and roof, (6) adequate space between and behind piles, (7) good
yard sanitation with elimination of weeds, and (8) unobstructed
yards open to prevailing winds.

Predrying lumber is a recently developed method of speeding the
drying process by creating air circulation in a closed shed with fans,
usually in the absence of additional heat. Unpublished research by
Page and Gaby shows that pine can usually be predried to 18 percent
in 6 days (fig. 115), with elimination of most of the degrade occurring in air seasoning.

Kiln drying

When loblolly pine with a moisture content below 15 percent is
required, it is placed in a dry kiln having controlled temperature,
air circulation, and relative humidity, and dried the required amount.
Also, considerable pine is dried in a kiln from the green condition
to 18 percent moisture content for shipping, thus saving time and
yard inventory, and reducing stain and other air-seasoning degrade.
Lumber, however, should not be considered kiln dried in the usual
sense of the term unless the moisture content is below 12 percent.

There are numerous types of dry kilns in use varying from not
much more than hot boxes with natural draft to elaborate 150-foot
kilns with controlled air circulation, temperature, and relative humidities. Most of the kilns used for drying southern pine are operated on a progressive basis, with lumber loads entering the kiln
daily and an approximately equal quantity being removed each day,
the drying progressing as the lumber is moved through the kiln in
a 3- to 5-day schedule. In these kilns the temperature varies from
130°F. to 150° at the green end to 160° to 200° at the dry end.

In compartment kilns, the kiln is fully loaded with lumber at
one time, and the temperature is increased and relative humidity
lowered as the lumber dries. Newer kilns of this type in the south-

ern pine area are usually package loaded. Kiln doors are sufficiently large to permit a fork-lift truck to load and unload the kiln with package lumber, thus dispensing with tracks and kiln trucks, and often eliminating double handling of the lumber. With experience, the kiln can be operated on a time schedule, but the safest method is to base the operation on the moisture content of the lumber as determined from sample boards. Using the latter method, the schedule recommended by the Forest Products Laboratory (Rpt. D1791. 1957) for all species of southern pine up to 2 inches thick is as follows:

Moisture content of lumber (percent)	Dry bulb temperature (degrees F.)	Wet bulb temperature (degrees F.)	Equilibrium moisture content (percent)
Green to 35	180	170	11.1
35 to 30	180	166	9.4
30 to 25	190	170	7.4
25 to 20	190	155	4.9
20 to final	200	150	3.3

A major manufacturer of kiln-drying equipment (Moore **Dry** Kiln Company—Instructions, Bulletin 0638) recommends the following time schedule for all common grades of southern pine up to 2 inches thick dried in compartment type kilns:

Hours in kiln	Dry bulb temperature (degrees F.)	Wet bulb temperature (degrees F.)	Equilibrium moisture content (percent)
1 to 24	165	150	9.3
25 to 48	170	150	7.8
49 to final	175	150	6.6

Special seasoning processes

Numerous special seasoning methods have been tried on southern pine such as vapor drying, boiling in oil, high-frequency heating, infrared heating, and solvent seasoning. Of these, vapor drying (Hudson 1947) has been very successful for round products, but the other methods have had limitations of cost or degrade or both that prevented their widespread use.

Vapor drying is accomplished in a closed cylinder where the air has been removed and replaced by an organic vapor at a temperature of 230° to 350°F. As the water is removed from the wood, it combines with the liquified organic material and is separated as the combination leaves the cylinder. The organic solvent is then reheated, vaporized, and recirculated through the cylinder. One-inch pine can be dried in 3 to 6 hours by this method. The major limitations of this method are the expensive equipment required and the possible reduction in strength of the wood caused by the higher temperatures.

Storage and handling

Loblolly pine, like all wood, is hygroscopic and will thus absorb water in a moist atmosphere. Once lumber is dried to a specific moisture content, it should be protected. Air-dried lumber under cover will not rise to more than 16 to 18 percent moisture under most U. S. conditions. As long as it is protected from rain or other sources of free moisture, it can be dead-piled (without stickers) for long periods of time without danger of decay. Certain insects, however, will attack dry lumber but can be controlled by soaking the lumber for at least 3 minutes in light petroleum oil solutions of 5 percent pentachlorophenol or 1 percent lindane.

Kiln-dried lumber should be stored where the temperature and relative humidity will keep it at its low moisture content. A simple method is to store the lumber in a closed room where the inside temperature remains 10 to 15 degrees above outside temperature at all times. This will maintain a wood moisture content of about 8 percent.

In cases where southern pine logs, pulpwood, or other items need to be kept in a green condition without deterioration, they can be stored under water indefinitely or in a cold room where the temperature is maintained below 40°F. For logs chemical sprays are helpful (see section on "Stain and decay in wood products" in chapter 3, Protection).

PRESERVATION

Choice of treatment

The preservatives for wood that are effective on loblolly pine fall into two general categories, those that are oil soluble and those that are water soluble. The oil-soluble preservatives include creosote, pentachlorophenol, and some of the copper compounds. The water-borne preservatives include a variety of toxic salts, such as chromated zinc chloride, copperized chromated zinc chloride, Tanalith (Wolman Salts), acid copper chromate (Celcure), zinc meta arsenite, ammoniacal copper arsenite (Chemonite), chromated zinc arsenate (Boliden salt), and chromated copper arsenate (Greensalt or Erdalith), and "double diffusion" of copper sulphate followed by sodium arsenate.

Preservatives are applied to loblolly pine wood by several methods, one of the most common being treatment by pressure in a closed cylinder. Preservatives also may be put into the wood by cold soaking, hot- and cold-bath treatments, brushing, dipping, and spraying. Any of the preservatives can be applied by any of the methods mentioned.

Generally it can be stated that the effectiveness of any wood preservative is directly related to the depth of penetration and the amount of absorption, i.e., the total retention of preservative per cubic foot of wood. In addition to the penetration and absorption of preservative, the service life may depend also on the ability of the chemical to withstand leaching from the wood during wet weather or periods of high humidity. The oil-borne preservatives generally resist leaching much better than the water-borne salts.

Thus the choice of a preservative for loblolly pine and the method adopted may not be so important as the effectiveness of the particular treatment used in obtaining penetration and retention, and the exposure to which the wood subsequently will be subjected. When wood is to be used in contact with the soil or constantly subjected to wetting, deep penetration and a high degree of retention of a nonleachable chemical are essential, and this points to pressure treatment with one of the oil-soluble preservatives. There are uses, however, where most of the hazards can be removed by the design of the structure and by keeping wood relatively dry and away from contact with the soil or water. In such cases lighter treatments or even surface treatments give worthwhile protection. Table 66 suggests treatments by exposure classes where the wood will be in contact with the ground or water.

Creosoted loblolly pine wood is resistant to attack by termites to a degree determined by the penetration and retention of preservative. Well-treated wood is not attacked, but may be bypassed by termites. Defense against these insects in houses involves the use of soil poison, termite shields, good drainage, proper clearance between the ground and the wood, ventilated crawl space, and provision for at least annual inspection of substructures. Soil poisons are especially needed for buildings constructed on concrete slabs.

Pressure treatments

Production of treated lumber has increased eightfold since 1930. Some 173 wood preserving plants in the loblolly pine belt between Virginia and Texas treated 130 million cubic feet of wood in 1954. Ninety-five percent of the volume of this wood was pressure treated, 85 percent with creosote, and only 15 percent with the newer chem-

TABLE 66.—*Minimum retention per cubic foot of creosote and oil-borne preservatives necessary to preserve wood products under varying exposures[1]*

Product and Exposure	Coal tar creosote	Creosote-coal tar solutions	Creosote-petroleum oil solutions	Pentachlorophenol 5% in petroleum oil	Copper naphthenate (0.75% Cu) in petroleum oil
	Pounds	*Pounds*	*Pounds*	*Pounds*	*Pounds*
Lumber and structural timber in contact with—					
Fresh water or ground......	10	10	12	10	10
Salt water......	20	20	..	..	..
Posts in the ground.	6	6	7	6	6
Poles in the ground.	8	..	..	8	8
Ties on the ground..	8	8	9	..	..
Piles in—					
Coastal water...	20	20	..	..	..
Fresh water or ground......	12	12	14	..	..

[1] The various water-borne preservatives may also be injected under pressure to obtain retentions varying from one-third to somewhat over one pound of dry salt per cubic foot, but they are not generally used for poles, ties, piles, or any structure exposed to marine borers. Basis: Interim Federal Specification TT-W-00571d(GSA-FSS).

icals. Pressure treatments (Hunt and Garratt 1938, MacLean 1952) involve the use of closed cylinders and high pressures to inject preservative into wood. Two principal processes are used for loblolly pine. In the full cell process a preliminary vacuum is first applied to remove air from the wood; the preservative is then added and pressure applied to force it in. The aim of this treatment is to retain as much of the preservative as possible. In the empty cell process, the object is to inject preservative under pressure and then force part of it out, thus obtaining as deep a penetration as possible with minimum amount of preservative. This may be accomplished by introducing the preservative under atmospheric conditions, then injecting it under pressure, or the wood is first placed under pressure and kept under pressure as the preservative is introduced. This provides a cushion of compressed air in the wood to expel excess preservative when the pressure is released.

When green material is to be treated it is customary to condition loblolly pine wood by a special heat treatment at 240° and 259°F. so that it can be penetrated with the preservative. After 3 to 18 hours under steam pressure of 20 pounds per square inch, a vacuum is applied for ½ to 3 hours. The conditioning treatment generally removes 5 or 6 pounds of moisture per cubic foot and also heats the wood to a more favorable treating temperature (MacLean 1952).

The sapwood of loblolly pine is easily treated, but the heartwood is moderately difficult to penetrate. Longitudinal penetration is about 20 times the radial and 80 times the tangential penetration. An absorption of 10 to 12 pounds of creosote per cubic foot extended the service life of loblolly pine ties for one railroad fivefold—from 5.3 to about 27 years.[147]

Nonpressure treatments

A number of nonpressure treatments, very effective for certain uses, are becoming more widely used each year. For instance, the hot-and-cold-bath process and the vacuum process for treating fence posts and similar materials with oil-borne preservatives often result in retentions and penetrations higher than those under pressure treatment; this may even be a disadvantage because too much preservative in the treated wood runs the cost up more than it should. Southern pine posts that have been infected by *Trichoderma* frequently take up excessive preservative even in cold soaking. Thus it must be reemphasized that the results attained, rather than the method of treatment, is of utmost importance.

The "double diffusion" process, developed by the Forest Products Laboratory, involves soaking green wood in a solution of cooper sulphate followed by a second soaking in sodium arsenate. The reaction of these chemicals forms an insoluble toxic substance inside the wood that prevents termite and decay damage. Tests indicate that fence posts preserved by this process should last at least 32 years.

Many of the water-borne salts are applied by soaking or spray treatments after which the treated material is piled under cover and the preservatives allowed to diffuse into the wood. These treatments can be very effective for loblolly pine if properly applied. Millwork, sash, siding, and similar items are now commonly treated very effectively by the vacuum method and by simple dip treatments. Water repellents which break capillary attraction and thus prevent rainwater penetration in joists, sash, siding, etc., have recently come into vogue. They are very effective in preventing decay and some types of paint failure. Water repellents, however, are relatively ineffective in preventing the movement of water vapor. Thus swelling due to humidity changes is only partially controlled by water

---

[147] According to Hudson (1952) there have been occasional failures in creosoted southern pine poles due to *Poria radiculosa,* a creosote-tolerant decay fungus.

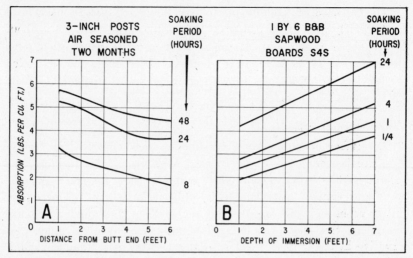

FIGURE 116.—Nonpressure absorption of preservative in cold soaking treatments with low viscosity oil solution of 5 percent pentachlorophenol at about 70°F.: *A*, Absorption in different sections of posts with 18 to 22 percent moisture content; *B*, effect of depth of immersion on absorption in lumber (Burkman and Pera 1942).

repellents and is very little affected by even the more penetrating treatments of water-borne salts.

In the so-called nonpressure treatments the forces that move the preservative into loblolly pine wood are capillarity, plus mild pressure from the head of liquid above the immersed wood. In tests ¾-inch boards absorbed 1.9 to 7.0 pounds of preservative varying with depth and time (fig. 116, *B*). Less was absorbed by thicker lumber. Absorption varied from 1.0 to 4.7 pounds for 2 x 6 plank (Buckman and Pera 1942).

Untreated loblolly pine fence posts often fail after the first 2 or 3 years (Blew and Kulp 1954). Although posts treated by pressure with creosote, pentachlorophenol, and other oil-soluble preservatives have·been in test for many years and show service lives of 25 years or more, most of the nonpressure treatments and some of the newer preservatives have not been in test long enough to determine fully the expected service life. Southern yellow pine, however, should last 18 to 20 years or longer on the average when treated 48 hours by cold soaking (Blew 1956) with creosote or pentachlorophenol in oil solutions. Until long-time service tests have been made for many of the newer preservatives and the simpler treating methods such as dipping, spraying, and painting or brushing, it is unwise to predict what service life may be expected even though it may be materially longer than that for untreated wood.

Permeability of infected wood

Mold, blue-stain, and decay fungi increase the permeability of dry loblolly pine wood for liquids, both water and oil (Lindgren 1952, Lindgren and Scheffer 1939). Infections, however, can decrease absorption of preservatives by favoring a high moisture content. Water absorbed by posts exposed to 2 days of drizzling rain averaged 28 to 30 pounds per cubic foot in heavily molded wood and only 7 to 8 pounds in bright wood. Increased porosity is believed to be due to partial breakdown of ray parenchyma or to fungus penetration holes in tracheid walls or pits, depending on the type of fungus present. A common mold *Trichoderma,* often occurring naturally with blue stain, is particularly effective in increasing penetration. Nonpressure absorption of oil, of about 1 pound in fungus-free pine wood, reached 8 or 9 pounds per cubic foot in heavily molded wood. Side penetration of posts 3 to 4 inches in diameter is often complete in molded wood, in contrast to shallow 0.1-inch or less penetration in bright wood. Heavily molded and bright wood should not be treated in the same batch. Small to moderate amounts of fungus infection normally occurring in the seasoning of posts may explain some of the success of soak treatments of fence posts (fig. 116, *A*).

Fireproofing and painting

Test treatments with inorganic chemicals indicate that there are at least 30 which can make loblolly pine wood less combustible (Truax, Harrison, and Baechler 1935). Of these substances seventeen were also effective against wood-destroying fungi. It is possible, therefore, to protect wood against both fire and decay by impregnation with chemicals, but the retention of preservative required to protect against fire is several times greater than that required to protect against decay. Also at the present time all of the more effective fire-retardant chemicals are water soluble and will leach away in rain or ground water. Much more research is needed to develop effective water insoluble fire retardants.

Loblolly pine does not hold paint as well as cedar, cypress, redwood, or white pine. Grade, texture, and density affect retention of paint. Knots, pitch pockets, and other defects do not paint well. In clear lumber the density and angle of cut of a board may hasten paint failure. Wood with narrow rings and much springwood holds paint the best. Edge grain is better than flat grain. Among the flat-grained boards, those surfaced and painted on the bark side do better than those painted on the side toward the pith. The paint lasts longer in shade than in sunlight (Browne 1930, 1951). Changes in commercial house paints in recent years have not altered the effects exerted by the wood on paint behavior. Some recent inovations which radically modify loblolly pine improve its paintability. For example hard fiberboard is readily painted, as are also lumber or plywood surfaced with resin-impregnated paper. Paper-faced southern pine has already withstood outdoor exposure in Wisconsin for more than 5 years without need of repainting. A special modi- fied wood product called "impreg" holds paint better than natural wood of similar density and grain structure.

SUMMARY

Lumber and pulpwood are the principal uses for loblolly pine. Within the usual limits, an increase in the size of trees, logs, or bolts harvested or manufactured increases profit per unit of volume in the product. Profit is now being sacrificed at small mills cutting more than half their lumber from logs less than 10 inches in diameter. Pines under 13 inches should be left standing if sound, or, if defec- tive, should go to a pulpmill rather than a sawmill. Advantage of higher prices should be taken for all trees meeting the exacting specifications for poles or piling. A market for both pine and hard- wood mine timbers offers a means of restoring depleted forests near mines in Alabama. The various residues from lumber manufacture add up to nearly 70 percent of the forest raw material. There is still no economic way to use bark other than for fuel.

Within-species variation in the character of southern pine wood is more important to understand than are the distinctions between the principal species. For example, an abnormal type called com- pression wood is inferior both in strength and pulping properties as well as dimensional stability. Leaning trees, commonly con- taining it, should be eliminated. Density, elasticity, and strength generally decrease upward in pine trees. A density rule helps in- spectors to segregate the strong wood of high specific gravity needed for some purposes. The rule works because the summerwood band in a ring is conspicuous and about twice as heavy as the springwood portion. Formulas are given to compute density from ocular esti- mates of summerwood, and others to approximate different strength values from the density determinations. The effect of growth rate on strength, formerly overestimated, is considered minor. Hence, loblolly pine should be grown at the fastest rate compatible with satisfactory pruning, form, and knot size. Green wood is weaker than seasoned wood. Factors for correcting strength estimates for changes in moisture content to be expected in service locations are given. Grade and defect in structural timbers must be considered in estimating working stresses.

In standing second-growth trees heart rot seldom exceeds 5 percent of volume. A higher percentage of the 5-foot butt section may be decayed by certain fungi that enter through roots or fire scars. Butt rot within scarred trees increases with age and is related to the square of wound width. Posts or poles that do not qualify for preservative treatment because of decay can be detected with a chemical color test. The so-called interim specifications for pine log grades now being developed promise a useful means of recognizing true log values throughout the South. Inasmuch as the varying prices of lumber maintain a rather constant proportion of the current price for No. 2 Common boards, an index of quality based on this relationship is available to remove much of the former difficulty in appraising log values. The next step will be to develop tree classes that utilize both the recognized log grades and the varying capacity of trees for rapid growth.

Seasoning loblolly pine wood serves to reduce fungus attacks, stabilize shrinkage, and increase strength. Certain defects may be minimized by drying lumber to the degree most appropriate to its situation in use. Time can be saved by proper predrying, kiln-drying, or vapor drying. Choice between various methods of preserving wood should likewise be based on the varying requirements in different service conditions. To a limited extent for certain uses the new chemical preservative treatments are beginning to compete with creosote injected under pressure—a treatment so far unexcelled in imparting long service life to pine wood in contact with soil or sea water.

Fiber characteristics, important in pulp and paper, vary with position in the tree. At the higher levels there is an increase in springwood content, a decrease in density, and pulp yields that are lower on a volume basis. All strength properties of the pulps, excepting tear resistance, improve with an increase in springwood content. The thin-walled springwood fibers collapse and flatten out into ribbons upon drying, thus providing a greater surface of contact between fibers. Thus, they felt and bond well into smooth sheets. Loblolly pine can be pulped by each of the three main processes:

sulphite, sulphate, and mechanical. The mechanical process, producing groundwood pulp containing most of the wood components yields twice as much pulp per unit of wood as the other processes, but serves only certain purposes. Yields on a volume basis increase with specific gravity of the wood. By the sulphate process, the increase is roughly 1 pound of pulp for each 2-pound increase in weight per cubic foot.

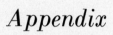

Appendix

TABLE 67.—*Formulas for upper stem diameters inside bark on loblolly pines of various heights and any given breast-high outside-bark diameter "D"*[1]

TREES LESS THAN 75 YEARS OLD

Height of measurement (feet)	Formulas for upper stem diameter inside bark (inches) when total height of tree in feet is—											Length merchantable where upper d.i.b. meets minimum requirements[2]
	20	30	40	50	60	70	80	90	100	110	120	
Above ground, 4.50	30.81D	30.83D	0.84D−0.6	0.87D−0.6	0.87D−0.4	0.88D−0.4	0.81D+0.4	0.90D−0.3	0.92D−0.6	0.88D−0.1	0.92D−0.5	
Above stump:[2]												
8.15	3.63D	3.71D	.76D−0.5	.82D−0.7	.82D−0.4	.81D−0.1	.84D−0.2	.84D−0.1	.86D−0.1	.85D−0.0	.87D−0.2	½
16.30		3.53D	.65D−0.6	.74D−0.7	.73D+0.2	.74D+0.2	.77D−0.3	.80D−0.1	.82D−0.2	.83D−0.4	.83D−0.3	1
24.45			.49D−0.5	.64D−0.6	.66D−0.2	.69D+0.3	.72D+0.3	.76D−0.1	.80D−0.4	.79D−0.3	.81D−0.5	1½
32.60			.25D−0.3	.48D−0.4	.55D−0.2	.64D−0.2	.66D+0.5	.72D−0.1	.78D−0.8	.76D−0.3	.78D−0.7	2
40.75				.26D−0.2	.47D−0.2	.57D+0.1	.59D+0.7	.70D−0.5	.74D−0.9	.75D−0.9	.75D−0.8	2½
48.90						.45D+0.1	.52D−0.5	.66D−0.9	.69D−0.9	.69D−0.6	.69D−0.5	3
57.05						.31D−0.1	.42D+0.4	.61D−1.4	.65D−1.3	.65D−0.8	.66D−0.7	3¾
65.20							.28D+0.3	.52D−1.6	.60D−1.7	.59D−0.8	.62D−1.1	4
73.35								.40D−1.6	.52D−1.8	.55D−1.2	.54D−0.4	4½
81.50									.41D−1.6	.47D−1.1	.49D−0.7	5
89.65										.36D−1.0	.43D−0.9	5½
97.80											.33D−0.6	6
Girard form class[4]	340	355	Quotients 59-60	Quotients 68-69	Quotients 71-72	Quotients 75-76	Quotients 78-79	Quotients 79-80	Quotients 80-81	Quotients 80-81	Quotients 81-82	

TREES OVER 75 YEARS OLD

Height of measurement (feet)	Formulas for upper stem diameter inside bark (inches) when total height of tree in feet is—						Length merchantable where upper d.i.b. meets minimum requirements²
	90	100	110	120	130	140	
Above ground, 4.50	$0.88D-0.2$	$0.88D-0.0$	$0.90D-0.3$	$0.91D-0.4$	$0.90D+0.0$	$0.85D+1.7$	
Above stump:²							
8.15	.84D−0.3	.82D+0.5	.82D+0.5	.85D−0.0	.84D−0.3	.81D+1.5	½
16.30	.79D−0.0	.78D+0.6	.78D+0.6	.80D+0.3	.80D+0.5	.75D+2.1	1
24.45	.77D−0.2	.77D+0.1	.77D+0.3	.76D+0.6	.75D+1.1	.70D+2.8	1½
32.60	.76D−0.8	.74D−0.1	.75D+0.1	.73D+0.8	.71D+1.4	.67D+2.9	2
40.75	.70D−0.6	.71D−0.2	.72D−0.0	.72D+0.2	.69D+1.2	.65D+2.8	2¼
48.90	.63D−0.4	.66D−0.1	.69D−0.1	.69D−0.0	.68D+0.6	.62D+2.8	3
57.05	.56D−0.5	.61D−0.2	.65D−0.3	.66D−0.1	.65D+0.6	.60D+2.6	3½
65.20	.45D−0.4	.56D−0.6	.60D−0.4	.63D−1.4	.62D+0.5	.56D+2.9	4
73.35	.32D−0.4	.47D−0.7	.53D−0.5	.60D−1.0	.59D−0.2	.51D+3.4	4½
81.50	.16D−0.1	.36D−0.8	.45D−0.6	.55D−1.4	.56D−0.3	.47D+3.3	5
89.65			.34D−0.6	.49D−1.9	.52D−0.8	.43D+3.2	5½
97.80				.40D−2.1	.45D−0.8	.39D+2.6	6
105.95					.37D−1.1	.33D+2.4	6½
114.10					.25D−0.7	.26D+2.1	7
Girard form class⁴	Quotients 79-80	Quotients 80-81	Quotients 80-82	Quotients 81-82	Quotients 81-83	Quotients 82-84	

¹ Computed from data by W. W. Ashe, N. C. Geol. and Econ. Survey Bul. 24: 29-37. 1915.
² These heights correspond to usual log and half-log lengths in all trees, but represent actual logs only in trees large enough to produce them.
³ Approximated from TVA data for 800 trees in 10 states—Tech. Note 10, table 6 (Potts 1952).
⁴ D.i.b. at 16.3 feet above stump in percentage of d.o.b. at breast height—4.5 feet above ground.

TABLE 68.—*Standard dimensions for southern pine poles*[1]

MINIMUM CIRCUMFERENCE AT 6 FEET FROM BUTT

Length of pole (feet)	Ground line distance from butt (feet)	Class of creosoted pole (minimum top circumference in inches)									
		1 (27)	2 (25)	3 (23)	4 (21)	5 (19)	6 (17)	7 (15)	(18)	[2]9 (15)	[2]10 (12)
		Inches	Inches	Inches	Inches	Inches	Inches	Inches		Inches	Inches
16	3½	....	....	....	....	21.5	19.5	18.0	([3])	16.0	13.0
18	3½	....	....	26.5	24.5	22.5	21.0	19.0	([3])	17.0	13.5
20	4	31.5	29.5	27.5	25.5	23.5	22.0	20.0	([3])	17.5	14.0
22	4	33.0	31.0	29.0	26.5	24.5	23.0	21.0	([3])	18.5	14.5
25	5	34.5	32.5	30.0	28.0	26.0	24.0	22.0	([3])	19.5	15.0
30	5½	37.5	35.0	32.5	30.0	28.0	26.0	24.0	([3])	20.5	....
35	6	40.0	37.5	35.0	32.0	30.0	27.3	25.5	([3])		
40	6	42.0	39.5	37.0	34.0	31.5	29.0	27.0	([3])		
45	6½	44.0	41.5	38.5	36.0	33.0	30.5	28.5	([3])		
50	7	46.0	43.0	40.0	37.5	34.5	32.0	29.5	([3])		
55	7½	47.5	44.5	41.5	39.0	36.0	33.5	....	([3])		
60	8	49.5	46.0	43.0	40.0	37.0	34.5	....	([3])		
65	8½	51.0	47.5	44.5	41.5	38.5	....	....	([3])		
70	9	52.5	49.0	46.0	42.5	39.5	....	....	([3])		
75	9½	54.0	50.5	47.0	44.0	....	....	....	([3])		
80	10	55.0	51.5	48.5	45.0	....	....	....	([3])		
85	10½	56.5	53.0	49.5	....	....	....	....	([3])		
90	11	57.5	54.0	50.5	....	....	....	....	([3])		

MINIMUM TOP CIRCUMFERENCE OF STUBS[2] FOR REA POLES

Length of pole (feet)	Length of stub (feet)	Class of creosoted pole						
		1	2	3	4	5	6	7
		Inches	Inches	Inches	Inches	Inches	Inches	Inches
30	10½	36.0	33.5	31.0	28.5	26.5	24.5	22.5
35	11	38.0	35.5	33.0	30.0	28.0	25.5	23.5
40	11½	40.0	37.5	35.0	32.0	29.5	27.0	25.0
45	12½	42.0	39.5	36.5	34.0	31.0	28.5	26.5
50	13	43.5	40.5	37.5	35.0	32.0	29.5	27.0

[1] Complete copies of these specifications including limiting defects are available from the American Standards Association, Inc., 70 E. 45th St., New York 17, N. Y.
[2] Figures for poles in this class and for stubs are from Rural Electrification Administration specifications—electric (Spec. No. DT-5A), telephone (Spec. No. PE-9). Except as noted for classes 9 and 10, REA uses ASA specifications for their poles.
[3] No butt requirement.

U. S. Forest Service interim log grades for southern pine

Definitions

Face —Any quarter cylindrical surface running full length of log.

Overgrown—Any limb stub buried beneath the bark surface, indicated by a distortion in
knot the bark pattern or bump on the log surface.

Sound —Any limb or limb stub which shows no evidence that a hole or wood rot
knot penetrates deeper into the log than two radial inches.

Unsound —Any limb or limb stub which shows evidence that a hole or wood rot pene-
knot trates deeper into the log than two radial inches.

D —Average diameter of log inside bark at small end to nearest whole inch.

K —Number of overgrown knots plus sum of diameters of sound exposed knots
plus twice sum of diameters of unsound knots. Diameters are measured to
nearest whole inch at the point where the limb would normally be trimmed.

Sweep —Greatest deviation in whole inches of log axis from the straight line con-
necting centers at both ends of log. It is analagous to the middle ordinate of
an arc.

Bad knot —Any knot in the 1-inch class or larger which has a diameter larger than
$\dfrac{D}{6}$ or which is unsound.

Specifications

	When grading by—		
	4 faces	*3 faces*	*2 faces*
Grade 1: D=17 or more and K is equal to or less than...........	$\dfrac{D}{5}$	$\dfrac{D}{7}$	$\dfrac{D}{10}$
Grade 2: D=10 or more and K is equal to or less than...........	$\dfrac{D}{2}$	$\dfrac{D}{3}$	$\dfrac{D}{4}$
(and greater than Grade 1 maxima)			

Grade 3: D=5 or more and K is greater than Grade 2 maxima.

Grade 4: Grade 3 degraded for any cause listed below.

N.B.: Degrade any log one grade if sweep equals or exceeds both 3 inches and $\dfrac{D}{3}$.

Degrade any log one grade if wood-rot fruiting body or punk knot pierces bark
surface.

Degrade any Grade 3 log to Grade 4 if it is impossible to encompass all bad knots
within a continuous surface area no longer than $\frac{1}{4}$ log length and no wider than $\frac{1}{4}$
log circumference.

TABLE 69.—*Number of pulpwood bolts per tree and merchantable volume inside bark to a 4-inch top outside bark for second-growth loblolly pine (MacKinney and Chaiken 1956)*[1]

FIVE-FOOT BOLTS

Diameter breast high outside bark (inches)	Total height of tree (feet)								
	20	30	40	50	60	70	80	90	100
	No.	No.	No.	No.	No.	No.	No.	No.	No.
6	2.0	2.9	3.9	4.6	5.6	6.6	7.5	....	....
8	2.3	3.8	5.0	6.4	7.7	9.6	10.7	11.6	....
10	...	4.3	5.5	7.2	8.8	10.9	12.3	12.8	....
12	...	4.5	5.9	7.6	9.5	11.6	12.9	13.5	14.7
14	...	4.5	6.1	7.7	9.8	11.9	13.3	14.0	15.3
16	...	...	6.2	7.8	9.9	12.0	13.5	14.4	15.6
18	...	...	...	7.8	10.0	12.1	13.7	14.6	15.7
20	...	...	...	7.9	10.1	12.2	13.8	14.7	15.7

VOLUME

Diameter breast high outside bark (inches)	Total height of tree (feet)								
	20	30	40	50	60	70	80	90	100
	Cu. ft.	Cu. ft.	Cu. ft.	Cu. ft.	Cu. ft.	Cu. ft.	Cu. ft.	Cu. ft.	Cu. ft.
6	0.7	1.3	2.1	3.0	3.8	4.5	5.4	....	....
8	1.6	3.0	4.3	5.7	7.1	8.5	9.9	11.4	....
10	...	4.9	7.0	9.1	11.3	13.5	15.7	18.0	....
12	...	7.3	10.4	13.3	16.4	19.5	22.7	25.9	29.2
14	...	10.1	14.2	18.2	22.4	26.6	30.9	35.2	39.5
16	...	....	18.5	23.9	29.3	34.7	40.7	46.4	53.0
18	...	...	....	30.2	36.9	44.3	52.2	59.4	66.7
20	...	...	....	37.1	46.0	55.4	64.1	73.0	81.9

[1] Basis: 457 trees from 32 stands in the Coastal Plains of the Carolinas. Volume includes peeled stem above a 0.7-foot stump to a top diameter outside bark of 4.0 inches. These tables, issued originally in 1939, were revised in 1946 and reprinted in 1956. The above condensation is from tables 2 and 7 of the 1956 version.

TABLE 70.—*Pulpwood volumes available as a byproduct where small trees of average form are removed in timber stand improvement and tops from sawtimber trees are utilized (bark excluded)*

SMALL TREES USED IN THINNING—VOLUME[1] PER TREE

D.b.h. (inches)	Total height (feet)					
	30	40	50	60	70	80
	Cu. ft.	Cu. ft.	Cu. ft.	Cu. ft.	Cu. ft.	Cu. ft.
5	1.1	1.5	1.8	....	....	....
6	1.8	2.4	3.1	4.0	5.3	....
7	2.7	3.4	4.5	5.8	7.4	....
8	3.6	4.6	6.2	7.8	9.9	11.6
9	4.6	6.0	7.8	10.1	12.6	15.2

SAWTIMBER TREES, TOPS ONLY, USED IN SALVAGE—VOLUME PER TREE[2]

Upper limit (inside bark)		D.b.h. classes (inches)					
Saw logs	Pulpwood	10	12	14	16	18	20
Inches	Inches	Cu. ft.	Cu. ft.	Cu. ft.	Cu. ft.	Cu. ft.	Cu. ft.
6	4	2.3	1.6	1.2	...	...	...
6	5	1.8	1.1	0.8	...	...	...
8	4	7.8	5.8	4.6	...	...	...
8	5	7.1	5.2	3.8	2.9	2.3	2.1
8	6	...	...	...	2.2	1.7	1.6
10	5	...	...	...	8.1	6.2	5.0
10	6	...	...	...	7.3	5.3	4.3

SAWTIMBER TREES, TOPS ONLY, USED IN SALVAGE—VOLUME PER M BOARD FEET (INTERNATIONAL $\frac{1}{4}$-INCH RULE)

6	4	34	14	7	..	..	..
6	5	27	10	4	..	..	..
8	4	186	60	27	..	..	..
8	5	169	54	23	11	7	5
8	6	...	..	..	9	5	4
10	5	...	..	..	36	19	12
10	6	...	..	..	33	16	11

[1] Volumes per tree to a 3-inch top for pines in the Tennessee Valley (Potts 1952, Minor 1950). Stand volumes based on these figures may be converted to standard cords of rough stacked wood by dividing by 65 for plantations or 70 for natural stands of loblolly pine.

[2] U. S. Forest Service data (McClay 1954a) for Westvaco and Santee Experimental Forests, South Carolina. A similar study at Crossett, Ark., showed an average difference of only 0.1 cubic foot per treetop utilized.

TABLE 71.—*Volume of stacked cordwood, with bark, for loblolly pines of different heights*[1]

D.b.h. (inches)	Total height (feet)									Basis, trees
	30	40	50	60	70	80	90	100	110	
	Cords	Cords	Cords	Cords	Cords	Cords	Cords	Cords	Cords	Number
4.....................	0.0090	0.0140	0.0190	0.0238	0.0279					33
6.....................	.0235	.0341	.0445	.0531	.0615	0.0690	0.0769			99
8.....................	.0445	.0620	.0799	.0960	.113	.128	.143	0.158	0.174	83
10.....................	.0715	.0994	.127	.151	.177	.201	.226	.255	.280	38
12.....................		.147	.183	.219	.258	.290	.330	.270	.450	26
14.....................			.252	.300	.350	.398	.451	.502	.548	23
16.....................			.329	.395	.454	.520	.589	.647	.706	25
18.....................				.495	.568	.655	.734	.810	.882	9
20.....................				.598	.691	.788	.886	.975	1.07	4
22.....................					.817	.928	1.04	1.15	1.26	1
24.....................					.947	1.07	1.20	1.33	1.46	1
26.....................					1.08	1.22	1.36	1.51	1.66	3
	No.	No.	No.	No.	No.	No.	No.	No.	No.	
Basis, trees..............	5	47	67	60	51	44	50	15	6	345

[1] Abridged from table 3 of U.S.D.A. Misc. Pub. 50 (1929). Blocks indicate extent of basic data. Stump height 1 foot; top d.i.b. 3 inches. Average deviation of individual tree volumes from tabular values, ±7.7 percent; aggregate difference, −0.22 percent.

TABLE 72.—*Timber volumes for use with aerial photographs (Minor 1953a)*[1]

CUBIC FEET (INSIDE BARK)

Crown diameter (feet)	Total visible height (feet)						
	50	60	70	80	90	100	110
10	10.9	13.0	15.2	17.4	19.6		
12	13.3	17.0	18.5	21.1	24.1	26.7	
14	16.3	19.7	22.7	26.0	29.3	32.7	36.0
16		22.6	26.2	30.0	33.8	37.6	41.5
18		26.2	30.5	34.9	39.5	43.8	48.1
20		30.0	35.0	40.0	45.0	50.0	55.0
22		34.5	40.2	46.0	51.9	57.6	63.3
24			45.7	52.3	58.9	65.4	72.0
26			50.2	57.4	64.7	71.9	79.2
28			55.9	63.9	72.0	80.0	88.0
30			61.8	70.6	79.4	88.2	97.1

BOARD FEET (INTERNATIONAL $\frac{1}{4}$-INCH RULE)

Crown diameter (feet)	50	60	70	80	90	100	110
10	64	77	90	103	115		
12	80	103	120	128	146	161	
14	101	122	140	161	182	203	223
16		144	166	190	215	239	263
18		170	198	227	256	285	313
20		198	231	264	297	330	363
22		231	270	308	348	386	424
24			311	355	400	445	490
26			344	394	443	493	542
28			386	441	497	552	607
30			429	491	552	613	675

[1] For rough estimates of southern pine (other than longleaf) in all-aged or low density even-aged saw-log stands, assuming that form class averages 80.

TABLE 73.—*International ¼-inch board-foot volumes for loblolly pines of different heights*[1]

D.b.h. (inches)	Total height (feet)								Basis, trees
	40	50	60	70	80	90	100	110	
	Bd. ft.	Bd. ft.	Bd. ft.	Bd. ft.	Bd. ft.	Bd. ft.	Bd. ft.	Bd. ft.	Number
6	14	15	16	19					2
7	16	18	21	25	32	39			35
8	18	24	29	36	45	55	63		52
9	24	31	40	49	62	75	89		30
10		40	53	65	83	100	118		17
11			69	85	108	128	150		21
12			87	108	135	160	187	217	10
13			107	130	163	194	228	261	16
14			128	156	193	229	270	308	14
15			151	182	224	267	313	355	9
16				205	255	306	357	404	11
17				232	290	348	404	456	14
18				260	325	391	452	510	3
19				290	362	434	502	569	6
20				320	400	480	556	627	3
21				351	440	527	611	688	1
22				384	480	576	669	750	1
23				417	522	629	727	814	...
24				452	567	681	786	878	1
25				486	613	733	846	945	...
26				521	658	787	906	1010	1
27				559	706	843	967	1077	2
	No.	No.	No.	No.	No.	No.	No.	No.	
Basis, trees....	4	30	51	49	45	50	14	6	249

[1] Calculated from table 5 of U.S.D.A. Misc. Pub. 50 (1929). Blocks indicate extent of basic data. Stump height 1 foot; logs scaled in 16-foot lengths, with 0.3 foot trimming allowance and additional upper sections to top d.i.b. of 5 inches. Average deviation of individual tree volumes from tabular values, ±12.6 percent; aggregate difference, −0.9 percent.

TABLE 74.—*Volumes of loblolly pine saw-log trees of outside-bark form class 86 (Buell 1942)*[1]

GROSS VOLUME IN BOARD FEET (INTERNATIONAL $\frac{1}{4}$-INCH RULE)

D.b.h. (inches)	Number of 16.3-foot logs											
	½	1	1½	2	2½	3	3½	4	4½	5	5½	6
10	21	34	44	54	63	72						
12	33	52	69	84	98	111	124	136	147			
14	47	76	100	122	143	161	180	197	213	230	245	
16	65	105	139	169	197	223	248	272	294	317	338	359
18	..	139	184	224	262	296	330	362	392	421	450	478
20	..	180	238	290	337	383	425	466	505	542	579	615
22	..	...	299	365	425	481	535	586	635	684	730	774
24	..	...	369	450	524	594	661	724	785	843	902	957
26	..	...	...	546	637	721	802	879	953	1,023	1,094	1,161
28	..	...	...	653	760	863	959	1,052	1,140	1,225	1,309	1,387
30	..	...	...	...	900	1,019	1,132	1,242	1,346	1,445	1,545	1,641
32	..	...	...	...	...	1,191	1,324	1,452	1,574	1,690	1,803	1,914
34	..	...	...	...	...	1,377	1,535	1,679	1,820	1,959	2,089	2,218
36	..	...	...	...	...	1,585	1,762	1,928	2,089	2,249	2,399	2,547

FACTORS BY WHICH TO MULTIPLY VOLUMES IN ABOVE TABLE TO OBTAIN BOARD-FOOT (INT. $\frac{1}{4}$-INCH) VOLUMES FOR OTHER FORM CLASSES[2]

OUTSIDE-BARK CLASSES

Form class (tens)	Form class (units)									
	0	1	2	3	4	5	6	7	8	9
7	0.65	0.66	0.68	0.70	0.72	0.74	0.76	0.78	0.80	0.83
8	.85	.87	.90	.92	.95	.97	1.00	1.03	1.06	1.09
9	1.12	1.15	1.18	1.21	1.24	1.28	1.31	1.35	1.39	1.43

GIRARD INSIDE-BARK CLASSES

	0	1	2	3	4	5	6	7	8	9
7	....	....	....	....	....	....	....	1.03	1.07	1.11
8	1.14	1.18	1.21	1.24	1.26	....	....	....	....	....

[1] To a variable top diameter as utilized. Block indicates extent of basic data from 378 sample trees from Piedmont and northern Coastal Plain counties of South Carolina. Average deviation ±5.4 percent, and aggregate difference—estimated values 0.25 percent low.

[2] According to Horn (1956) the average form class in a loblolly pine stand is within ±2 of the average ratio of d.i.b. at 7 feet to d.o.b. at 2.25 feet. Constants to use in a formula for changing the volumes in o.b. form-class tables like the above to i.b. form-class tables utilizing 3 different log rules are available on page 7 of the original (Buell 1942) publication.

TABLE 75.—*Approximate saw-log volumes contained in southern pines that will yield finished poles meeting standard specifications*[1]

Length (feet)	Pole class								
	1	2	3	4	5	6	7	8	9
	Bd. ft.	Bd. ft.	Bd. ft.	Bd. ft.	Bd. ft.	Bd. ft.	Bd. ft.	Bd. ft.	Bd. ft.
25..............	...	...	70	55	45	35	25	..	20
30..............	125	105	85	70	55	45	35	..	25
35..............	155	135	115	90	75	·	..		
40..............	205	175	150	130	100	..			
45..............	245	210	180	145	120				
50..............	280	240	205	170					
55..............	335	295	250						
60..............	385	325	280						
65..............	420	365							
70..............	495	425							
75..............	535								
80..............	570								

[1] These estimates, by E. T. Hawes, are for trees of Girard form class 80. D.b.h. outside bark equals 1.136 times rough pole diameter at midpoint of class. Taper above 16 feet, and volumes by Scribner scale, are from tables 2 and 6 of U.S. Forest Service pocket manual by Mesavage and Girard (1956).

TABLE 76.—*Weight of freshly cut loblolly pine pulpwood (green wood with bark) by height and diameter of trees*[1]

Diameter breast high outside bark (inches)	By total heights of trees (feet)							
	30	40	50	60	70	80	90	100
	Lbs.	Lbs.	Lbs.	Lbs.	Lbs.	Lbs.	Lbs.	Lbs.
6....................	88	139	195	242	280	329	.....	.....
7....................	141	212	275	338	399	459	520	.....
8....................	206	289	375	457	536	612	691	.....
9....................	271	377	484	588	690	791	886	.....
10....................	342	477	608	737	863	985	1,103	.....
11....................	...	588	748	905	1,057	1,201	1,347	1,485
12....................	...	720	902	1,087	1,267	1,441	1,613	1,781
13....................	...	847	1,071	1,286	1,498	1,706	1,907	2,096
14....................	...	994	1,251	1,502	1,751	1,990	2,219	2,440
15....................	...	1,153	1,448	1,740	2,023	2,292	2,591	2,849
16....................	...	1,320	1,664	1,997	2,312	2,655	2,958	3,310
17....................	...	1,503	1,893	2,264	2,629	3,009	3,409	3,750
18....................	...	.....	2,136	2,550	2,990	3,449	3,842	4,220
19....................	...	.....	2,391	2,892	3,361	3,858	4,296	4,720
20....................	...	.....	2,662	3,222	3,794	4,297	4,787	5,259
21....................	...	.....	.....	3,537	4,237	4,732	5,247	5,795

[1] Based on volumes by MacKinney and Chaiken (reprinted 1956) and volume-weight ratios by Barron and Osborn—courtesy Union Bag-Camp Paper Corporation, Franklin, Va.

TABLE 77.—*Approximate volume inside bark and weight outside bark of green loblolly pine pulpwood by tree diameter classes*

Dimensions of average pine tree			Weight[3] per—		Stacked volume[4] occupied	Trees per unit[5]	Volume per unit[5]
D.b.h.	Height[1]	Volume[2]	Cu. ft.	Tree			
Inches	Feet	Cu. ft.	Pounds	Pounds	Percent	Number	Cu. ft.
4	30	0.6	66.4	40	58.0	162	97
	38	1.2	66.0	79	59.3	83	99
6	45	2.5	65.6	164	60.5	41	101
	51	4.3	65.3	281	61.7	24	103
8	56	6.5	64.9	422	62.7	16	105
	62	9.4	64.6	607	63.7	11	107
10	67	12.8	64.4	824	64.6	8	108
	71	16.7	64.3	1074	65.5	7	110
12	75	21.1	64.2	1355	66.2	5	111
	78	26.1	64.1	1673	66.8	4	112
14	82	31.8	64.0	2035	67.4	4	113

[1] Forest-grown trees (fig. 50, A).
[2] Merchantable to 4-inch outside-bark top (table 69).
[3] Adapted from basic data in a detailed study by foresters N. T. Barron and R. M. Osborn, Union Bag-Camp Corporation, Franklin, Va. The data in column 4 show a slight decline in weight per cubic foot with an increase in size of trees. This is the net effect of opposite trends in weight associated with diameter and height. For a given height class of trees density increases with diameter, but for a given diameter class the density decreases with height.
[4] Wood with bark (MacKinney and Chaiken 1956, fig. 63).
[5] A stack 5¼ by 4 by 8 feet, gross volume 168 cubic feet, and rough green weight 6,800 ±400 pounds.

TABLE 78.—*Stand density units by average d.b.h. (in inches and tenths), for computing stand density index, a product of the number of trees per acre and one of the following units (Reineke 1933)*[1]

Average d.b.h. (inches)	Decimal part of diameter (tenths of an inch)									
	0	1	2	3	4	5	6	7	8	9
1............	0.025	0.029	0.033	0.037	0.042	0.047	0.052	0.057	0.063	0.069
2............	.075	.082	.089	.096	.103	.110	.117	.124	.131	.138
3............	.145	.153	.161	.169	.177	.185	.193	.202	.211	.220
4............	.229	.239	.249	.259	.269	.279	.289	.299	.309	.319
5............	.329	.340	.351	.362	.373	.384	.395	.406	.417	.428
6............	.440	.452	.464	.476	.488	.500	.512	.525	.538	.551
7............	.564	.577	.590	.603	.616	.629	.643	.657	.671	.685
8............	.699	.713	.727	.741	.755	.769	.784	.799	.814	.829
9............	.844	.859	.874	.889	.904	.920	.936	.952	.968	.984
10............	1.000	1.016	1.032	1.048	1.064	1.080	1.096	1.113	1.130	1.147
11............	1.164	1.181	1.198	1.215	1.232	1.249	1.267	1.285	1.303	1.321
12............	1.339	1.357	1.375	1.393	1.411	1.429	1.447	1.466	1.485	1.504
13............	1.523	1.542	1.561	1.580	1.599	1.618	1.637	1.656	1.675	1.695
14............	1.715	1.735	1.755	1.775	1.795	1.815	1.835	1.855	1.875	1.895
15............	1.916	1.937	1.958	1.979	2.000	2.021	2.042	2.063	2.084	2.105
16............	2.126	2.147	2.168	2.189	2.211	2.233	2.255	2.277	2.299	2.321
17............	2.343	2.365	2.387	2.409	2.431	2.453	2.476	2.499	2.522	2.545
18............	2.568	2.591	2.614	2.637	2.660	2.683	2.706	2.730	2.754	2.777
19............	2.801	2.825	2.849	2.873	2.897	2.921	2.946	2.970	2.994	3.018
20............	3.042	3.066	3.091	3.115	3.140	3.165	3.190	3.215	3.240	3.265

[1] Include all trees 1.5 inches d.b.h. and larger, and use diameter of the tree of average basal area.

TABLE 79.—Growth and yield of loblolly pine in fully stocked stands[1]

Site index (feet)	Age (years)	Height of dominant stand	Basal area per acre		Stand per acre		Average d.b.h.		Mean annual growth per acre			Yield per acre		
			Trees 2 inches and over	Dominant stand	Trees 2 inches and over	Dominant trees	Trees 2 inches and over	Dominant stand	Trees 2 inches and over (peeled)	Trees 4 inches and over (rough)	Trees 7 inches and over (Int. ¼-in.)	Trees 2 inches and over (rough)	Trees 4 inches and over (rough)	Dominant stand (Int. ¼-in.)
		Feet	Sq. ft.	Sq. ft.	No.	No.	Ins.	Ins.	Cu. ft.	Cords	Bd. ft.	Cu. ft.	Cords	Bd. ft.
60	20	32	121	86	1600	670	3.6	4.6	68	0.60	....	1,900	12	....
	30	45	138	96	850	390	5.4	6.6	75	.83	136	2,900	25	4,100
	40	54	147	104	585	290	6.8	8.1	75	.88	226	3,750	35	8,100
	50	60	152	111	440	230	7.9	9.4	72	.82	271	4,350	41	12,200
	60	64	156	116	360	200	8.9	10.4	66	.77	287	4,750	46	14,900
	70	67	158	120	310	175	9.7	11.2	59	.70	284	5,000	49	16,700
	80	69	160	123	275	160	10.4	11.9	54	.64	271	5,150	51	18,500
70	20	38	125	88	1185	510	4.3	5.4	82	.85	68	2,200	17	1,400
	30	52	143	101	640	315	6.5	7.8	92	1.03	256	3,400	31	6,800
	40	63	151	111	435	230	8.1	9.6	92	1.05	362	4,450	42	12,700
	50	70	157	118	325	180	9.4	10.9	87	1.00	398	5,200	50	17,200
	60	75	160	125	270	160	10.6	12.1	79	.92	400	5,700	55	20,400
	70	78	163	129	230	140	11.5	13.0	72	.84	381	6,000	59	23,100
	80	80	165	132	205	130	12.3	13.8	66	.78	362	6,250	62	25,300
80	20	43	129	90	950	430	5.0	6.2	98	1.10	136	2,550	22	2,700
	30	59	147	106	510	260	7.4	8.7	108	1.27	377	4,000	38	10,000
	40	72	156	117	345	195	9.2	10.7	110	1.28	498	5,250	51	16,700
	50	80	162	126	255	155	10.7	12.2	104	1.20	534	6,150	60	22,600
	60	85	165	132	210	130	12.0	13.6	95	1.10	520	6,700	66	26,200
	70	89	168	137	185	115	13.1	14.6	86	1.00	491	7,100	70	29,900
	80	92	170	141	160	105	14.0	15.5	78	.91	458	7,400	73	32,100
90	20	48	133	93	790	370	5.6	6.9	115	1.35	226	3,000	27	4,500
	30	67	152	111	420	225	8.2	9.6	128	1.53	513	4,750	46	13,100
	40	81	162	125	290	170	10.2	11.7	130	1.52	644	6,200	61	21,700

	Age	33	37	61	36	60	34	59	40	47	54	38	46	63
	50	90	167	134	220	135	12.0	13.6	123	1.42	679	7,250	71	28,500
	60	96	171	141	180	115	13.4	15.0	112	1.30	648	7,850	78	33,500
	70	100	174	146	150	100	14.6	16.2	101	1.17	607	8,300	82	37,500
	80	103	176	150	135	95	15.6	17.2	92	1.06	566	8,600	85	40,300
100	20	54	138	98	690	330	6.1	7.4	138	1.60	339	3,450	32	6,300
	30	74	158	118	375	205	9.0	10.4	152	1.77	663	5,500	53	17,200
	40	90	168	133	255	155	11.2	12.8	152	1.78	804	7,200	71	27,600
	50	100	174	143	190	125	13.1	14.7	144	1.68	824	8,450	84	36,200
	60	107	178	150	155	105	14.6	16.2	132	1.53	792	9,150	92	42,100
	70	112	181	155	135	95	15.9	17.6	120	1.37	737	9,600	96	46,200
	80	115	182	159	115	85	17.1	18.6	109	1.25	684	9,950	100	49,300
110	20	59	145	103	615	300	6.6	7.9	158	1.85	452	3,950	37	8,100
	30	81	166	126	335	190	9.7	11.2	177	2.07	830	6,250	62	21,300
	40	99	176	141	225	140	12.1	13.7	176	2.05	973	8,300	82	33,900
	50	110	182	152	170	115	14.1	15.7	168	1.92	986	9,700	96	44,300
	60	118	186	160	140	100	15.9	17.4	154	1.77	950	10,550	106	50,700
	70	122	189	166	120	90	17.3	18.8	139	1.60	879	11,100	112	55,700
	80	126	191	170	105	80	18.4	20.0	126	1.45	809	11,400	116	58,800
120	20	64	152	109	560	280	7.1	8.5	182	2.10	588	4,400	42	10,400
	30	89	174	134	305	180	10.4	11.9	202	2.33	995	7,050	70	26,200
	40	108	185	151	205	130	13.0	14.6	204	2.32	1166	9,350	93	40,700
	50	120	192	162	155	105	15.1	16.8	192	2.20	1167	11,000	110	52,000
	60	128	196	171	125	90	17.0	18.6	176	2.02	1101	12,000	121	58,800
	70	133	199	177	105	80	18.5	20.0	160	1.83	1028	12,650	128	65,600
	80	137	201	181	95	70	19.7	21.2	146	1.68	945	13,050	134	69,700

Original source of data: U.S.D.A. Misc. Pub. 50 (1929) table number .... 33 | 37 | 61 | 36 | 60 | 34 | 59 | 40 | 47 | 54 | 38 | 46 | 63

1 A word of caution is needed to avoid possible misuse of the data in table 79. In theory so called "normal" yield tables for any type of timber represent full development, and show yields at maximum capacity expected from typical even-aged stands at various ages. In loblolly pine the classic concept is that pure stands of near equilibrium stocking can be kept in production close to the maximum rate continuously. Such an ideal is seldom, if ever, attained in practice.

Actually table 79 portrays ideal timber stands only in a limited way because of its inherent weakness. Necessarily the data were taken on a series of small unmanaged, but presently fully stocked plots, chosen within each class and without regard to undetermined abnormalities in early developmental stages. Hence they overestimate the yields obtainable through management of extensive areas. With due allowance for understocking and deceleration in the approach to normal, some long-term predictions can be based on table 79, but table 25 is a better guide to the management of second-growth loblolly pine timber.

LIST OF ECONOMIC OR POTENTIALLY ECONOMIC
INSECTS ON LOBLOLLY PINE—TREES OR WOOD

Compiled by the Division of Forest Insect Research, Southeastern
Forest Experiment Station, U. S. Forest Service, July 1956.

1. *Acanthocinus nodosus* (F.), lesser pine borer.
   Common borer under bark of dying pines and green logs.
   A. obsoletus is associated. Hasten deterioration of trees or
   logs.

2. Anobiidae, furniture and death watch beetles.
   This group contains a number of species of powder-post
   beetles, some of which are particularly destructive to pine
   timbers in buildings.

3. *Aphrophora parallela* (Say), pine spittlebug.
   Attacks twigs; potentially dangerous. May weaken trees.

4. *Asemum atrum* (Esch.), pine borer.
   Borer in sapwood of dying pines, green logs, and stumps.
   Damage common but not severe.

5. *Atta texana* (Buckl.), Texas leaf-cutting ant.
   Precludes pine regeneration, natural or planted, in spots up
   to 10 acres in size around their large colonies.

6. *Buprestis apricans* Hbst., turpentine borer.
   Wood borer attacking scarred areas on living trees.
   Most important in fire-scarred trees.

7. *Callidium antennatum* (Newn.), black-horned pine borer.
   Bores in phloem of dead trees; sometimes in lumber; often of
   economic importance in rustic work and houses.

8. *Catorama* spp., powder-post beetles [Anobiidae].
   Reared from cones and twigs. Infests stored pine cones in
   South.

9. *Chalcophora virginiensis* (Drury).
   Bores in injured, dead, and dying trees and stumps; mines
   sapwood and heartwood. May completely destroy butt log
   on injured trees.

10. *Chrysobothris* spp., flatheaded borers.
    C. dentipes (Germ.) attacks living trees.
    C. floricola Gory and *C. pusilla* Cast.
    Borers in cambium area of weakened and dying trees. Gen-
    erally not serious.

11. *Cinara taedae* Tissot, aphid.
    Causes needle discoloration and drop. Possible potential pest.

12. *Conophthorus taedae* Hopk., cone beetle.

   Attack developing cones and cause cone drop; important reductions of seed crop.

13. *Dendroctonus frontalis* Zimm., southern pine beetle.

   Attacks cambium area of trunk. Causes extensive tree mortality in pine stands during drought, etc. One of the most important southern forest insects.

14. *Dendroctonus terebrans* (Oliv.), black turpentine beetle.

   Attacks and kills pines. Causes heavy losses especially in normally wet areas following selective logging operations. *D. valens* (Lec.) in northern part of range is similar but less aggressive.

15. *Dicerca punctulata* (Sch.), flatheaded borer.

   Borer in dead and dying pines.

16. *Dioryctria amatella* (Hulst.), cone moth.

   Destroys cones. Also damages twigs, shoots of reproduction. Attacks wounds also.

17. *Ernobius granulatus* Lec., powder-post beetle [Anobiidae].

   Reared from cones and twigs. Attacks stored cones. Minor importance.

18. *Exoteleia pinifoliella* (Chamb.), pine needle miner.

   Larvae mine needles. Cause unsightly browning of trees; may affect increment.

19. *Gnathotrichus materiarius* (Fitch), ambrosia beetle.

   Bores in dying trees, logs, etc. Minor importance.

20. *Hylastes porculus* Er. and *Hylastes tenuis* Eichh.

   Frequently attack roots of small trees. May kill pine transplants or young plantation trees. Commonly breed in logs, stumps, etc. Minor importance.

21. *Hylobius pales* (Hbst.), pales weevil.

   Adults girdle seedlings. Serious pest of reproduction following fires or cutting of pine.

22. *Hylotrupes bajulus* (L.), old house borer.

   A roundheaded borer which is becoming a serious pest of pine timber in construction.

23. *Ips* spp., pine engraver beetles.

   I. avulsus (Eichh.), *I. calligraphus* (Germ.), and *I. grandicollis* (Eichh.).

   Important bark beetles. Attack slash, logs, dying trees, and live trees under adverse conditions.

24. *Laspeyresia erotella* (Hein.) and *L. toreuta* (Grote), cone moths.

Feed on seeds in cones. Believed to be a minor pest of pine seed crop.

25. *Matsucoccus gallicola* Morrison, pine twig gall scale.

Sucking insects under bark scales can kill or badly deform young trees. Periodically serious.

26. *Monochamus* spp., pine sawyers.

M. carolinensis (Oliv.) and *M. titillator* (Fab.).

Attack dying trees and logs. Cause extensive damage to wood.

27. *Neodiprion* spp., pine sawflies.

About 9 species in this complex group of defoliators attack loblolly pine. Damage by some species causes growth loss; others may lead to mortality.

28. *Neodiprion exitans* Roh., pine sawfly.

Southern species from Delaware to Texas. Late summer and fall defoliation or earlier in Deep South.

29. *Neodiprion lecontei* (Fitch), red-headed pine sawfly.

Serious defoliator of young or open grown trees. Can be two or more generations per year, feeds year round in Deep South. Causes seedling mortality.

30. *Neodiprion taedae linearis* Ross, loblolly pine sawfly.

Causes severe defoliation to loblolly pine which results in high growth loss. Common in Arkansas, Louisiana, and Texas.

31. *Pachylobius picivorus* (Germ.), pitch-eating weevil.

Adults girdle seedlings in recently cutover areas and in plantations near such areas. Very important economically.

32. *Phenacaspis pinifoliae* (Fitch), pine needle scale.

Infests needles, causing yellowing and loss of tree vigor.

33. *Phyllophaga* spp., white grubs.

P. luctuosa (Horn), *P. prununculina* (Burmeister), *P. soror* Davis, etc.

Root feeding by larvae causes serious seedling losses in nurseries and in plantations. Adults feed on needles or on leaves of hardwoods.

34. *Pissodes nemorensis* Germ., deodar weevil.

Adults may girdle seedlings following cutting, fire, etc. Breeds in recently killed pines and live deodar cedar. Attacks living pine under adverse conditions.

35. *Pityophthorus* spp., bark beetles.

This group has many species which usually attack the twigs

of southern pines. *P. pulicarius* Zimm. is the most aggressive species; it has attacked slash pine scions in genetics studies.

36. *Platypus flavicornis* (F.).

    Most common ambrosia beetle attacking dying trees and logs. Causes severe lumber degrade.

37. *Pseudophilippia quaintancii* Ckll., woolly pine scale.

    Attacks young trees at base of needles. Common but importance unknown.

38. Ptinidae, spider beetles.

    Species of this family are destructive to pine wood. The brown spider beetle, *Ptinus brunneus* Dufts, is rather common in old buildings.

39. *Reticulitermes* spp., subterranean termites.

    This common and widely distributed group of termites is destructive to most species of wood improperly used in construction. In the forest they can be found attacking pines soon after their death.

40. *Retinodiplosis* spp., resin midge.

    Causes resin blisters on twigs and may kill twigs when abundant.

41. *Rhyacionia frustrana* (Comst.) and *R. rigidana* (Fern.), pine tip moths.

    Bore in buds and new shoots. Cause considerable damage in young pine stands, particularly on poor sites.

42. *Stenocorus inquisitor* (L.), ribbed pine borer.

    Cambium borer of recently dead trees. Very common. Hastens deterioration of timber.

43. *Stephanopachys rugosus* (Oliv.), powder-post beetle [Bostrichidae.]

    Attacks recently cut or milled pine. Continues to mine seasoned wood 1 to 5 years.

44. *Tetralopha robustella* Zell., pine webworm.

    Defoliates seedlings and small trees. Occasionally kills young seedlings. Large webbed masses indicate presence.

45. *Toumeyella pini* (King), pine scale.

    Rather common mahogany-colored soft scale on twigs. Causes black sooty mold. Results in needle drop; little mortality.

46. *Xylotrechus sagittatus* (Germ.), wood borer.

    Common in dying pine and green logs. Bores in wood. Causes degrade and deterioration.

LIST OF ECONOMIC OR POTENTIALLY ECONOMIC FUNGI ON LOBLOLLY PINE—TREES OR WOOD

Compiled by the Division of Forest Disease Research, Southeastern Forest Experiment Station, U. S. Forest Service, July 1956.

1. *Atropellis tingens* Lohm. and Cash.
   A minor stem-canker fungus.
2. *Ceratocystis ips* (Rumb.) Mor.
   A blue-stain fungus usually associated with Ips bark beetles.
3. *Ceratocystis pilifera* (Fr.) Mor.
   A major cause of blue stain in lumber.
4. *Ceratocystis minor* (Hedgc.) Hunt.
   A blue-stain fungus associated with attacks by *Dendroctonus frontalis* and possibly other bark beetles.
5. *Coleosporium apocynaceum* Cooke.
   A minor needle rust. Alternate stage on *Amsonia.*
6. *Coleosporium delicatulum* (A. & K.) Hedgc. & Long.
   A minor leaf rust with an alternate stage on *Euthamia,* one of the goldenrods.
7. *Coleosporium elephantopodis* (Schw.) Thuem.
   A minor needle rust. Alternate host on *Elephantopus,* elephant's-foot.
8. *Coleosporium ipomoeae* (Schw.) Burr.
   A common needle rust. Alternate stage on certain Convolvulaceae.
9. *Coleosporium laciniariae* Arth.
   A minor needle rust with an alternate stage on *Liatris.*
10. *Coleosporium minutum* Hedgc. & Hunt.
    A minor needle rust with an alternate stage on *Adelia.*
11. *Coleosporium solidaginis* (Schw.) Thuem.
    A very common needle rust. Alternate stage on Carduaceae.
12. *Coleosporium terebinthinaceae* (Schw.) Arth.
    A minor needle rust with alternate stage on *Parthenium, Polymnia, Silphium.*
13. *Coleosporium vernoniae* B. & C.
    A common needle rust. Alternate stage on *Vernonia.*
14. *Coniophora puteana* (Schum. ex Fr.) Karst.
    A brown rot common on various products exposed both in and above ground.
15. *Cronartium cerebrum* Hedgc. & Long.
    A rust causing round galls on stems. Alternate stage on oak leaves. Seldom serious.

16. *Cronartium comptoniae* Arth.

A minor stem rust with alternate stage on sweetfern and sweetgale. (Reported on loblolly pine planting stock in New Jersey.)

17. *Cronartium fusiforme* Hedgc. & Hunt.

Causes the most important stem rust of loblolly. Alternate stage on oak leaves.

18. *Daedalea berkeleyi* Sacc.

Causes a common brown rot of wood products.

19. *Dasyscypha ellisiana* (Rehm) Sacc.

A weak parasite on twigs and branches.

20. *Diplodia megalospora* B. & C.

Probably minor. On branches, twigs, roots, lumber, etc.

21. *Diplodia natalensis* Evans.

A common blue-stain fungus in lumber.

22. *Fomes annosus* (Fr.) Cke.

A root and butt rot that may become important in plantations.

23. *Fomes pini* (Thore) Lloyd.

The most important heart-rot fungus on loblolly pine.

24. *Hypoderma lethale* Dearn.

Common killer of foliage in late winter and spring.

25. *Lentinus lepideus* Syd.

A brown rot of the wood under exposed conditions.

26. *Lenzites saepiaria* (Wulf.) Fr.

A very common cause of rot of slash and of wood in service.

27. *Lenzites trabea* Pers. ex Fr.

A brown rot common on wood in service above ground.

28. *Lophodermium pinastri* (Schrad.) Chev.

Occurs widely in association with needle browning but may not be primary.

29. *Merulius lacrymans* (Wulf.) Fr.

A cause of so-called dry rot in buildings.

30. *Peniophora gigantea* (Fr.) Massee.

A very common cause of decay in stored pulpwood and in other unseasoned pine products.

31. *Phytophthora cinnamomi* Rands.

A root parasite associated with littleleaf disease.

32. *Polyporus abietinus* (Dicks.) ex Fries.

A common sapwood rot of pulpwood and other wood exposed to moisture.

33. *Polyporus palustris* B. & C.
    Brown cubical wood rot.
34. *Polyporus schweinitzii* Fr.
    Commonest cause of root and butt rot.
35. *Polyporus volvatus* Pk.
    Causes a minor sapwood decay in standing dead trees.
36. *Poria cocos* (Schw.) Wolf.
    Causes tuckahoes on roots of living trees, and a brown rot
    of the wood.
37. *Poria incrassata* (B. & C.) Curt.
    The major cause of so-called dry-rot or water conducting rot
    in buildings.
38. *Poria monticola* Murr.
    A brown rot common on a variety of wood products.
39. *Poria radiculosa* (Peck) Sacc.
    A decay of wood, notably poles and posts, exposed to soil.
40. *Poria subacida* (Peck) Sacc.
    Found on downed trees in three states and suspected as a
    cause of butt rot.
41. *Pythium* spp.
    Sometimes causes loblolly pine seedlings to damp-off.
42. *Rhizoctonia solani* Kuehn.
    A principal cause of damping-off on all of the southeastern
    species of pine.
43. *Rhizopogon parasiticus* Cok. and Tott.
    An ocassional root parasite. Forms mycorrhizae.
44. *Scirrhia acicola* (Dearn.) Siggers.
    A common cause of needle blight, often appearing in the fall.
45. *Miscellaneous.* Root rot complex at W. W. Ashe Nursery. This
    is an important disease of loblolly pine and nematodes are
    currently ascribed as the primary cause. However, the fol-
    lowing fungi were commonly isolated from diseased roots and
    probably play a role in the trouble: *Torula marginata* Jack-
    son, *Fusarium* sp., *Sclerotium bataticola* Taub., and *Pestaloz-
    zia funera* Desm.
46. The following fungi have been found capable of inducing mycor-
    rhizae on loblolly pine roots: *Boletus granulatus, B. exinus,
    B. brevipes, B. chromapes, B. subluteus, Boletinus pictus,
    Cantharellus cibarius, Russula lepida, Cenococcum grani-
    forme, Amanita muscaria, Rhizopogon* sp.

Bibliography

Anonymous. 1906. *American Forest Trees: Loblolly or North Carolina Pine (29th Paper).* Hardwood Rec. 21 (10) : 14-15.

———. 1910. *Loblolly Pine (Pinus Taeda).* U. S. Dept. Agr. Forest Serv. Cir. 183, 4 pp.

———. 1928. *Loblolly Plantation in New Jersey Makes Good Growth.* U. S. Forest Serv. Forest Worker 4 (2) : 15.

———. 1931. *Nail-Holding Power of American Woods.* U. S. Forest Serv. Forest Prod. Lab. Tech. Note 236, 4 pp.

———. 1933. *Shrinkage Table for Softwood Lumber.* U. S. Forest Serv. Forest Prod. Lab. Tech. Note 241, 4 pp.

———. 1935. *Loblolly Pine (Pinus Taeda Linaeus).* Amer. Forests 41 : 126-127.

———. 1937. *A Visual Method of Distinguishing Longleaf from Shortleaf and Loblolly Pine.* U. S. Forest Serv. Forest Prod. Lab. Tech. Note 141, 3 pp.

———. 1940. *Report of 30th. Annual Inspection of C., B. and Q. R. R. Experimental Ties.* Wood Preserv. News 18 (1) : 1-4.

———. 1941. *Computed Thermal Conductivity of Common Woods.* U. S. Forest Serv. Forest Prod. Lab. Tech. Note 248, 4 pp.

———. 1947. *Strength Properties of Pinus Taeda.* New Zeal. Forest Serv. Rpt. 1946-47 : 36.

———. 1947. *Nutriment Requirements of Pinus Caribaea and P. Taeda.* Queensland Dept. Agr. Rpt. 1946-7 : 41. Forestry Abs. 9 (4) : 436. 1948.

———. 1948. *Fertilizer Experiments in Pine Plantations.* Austral. Council Sci. & Indus. Res. Ann. Rpt. 1946-47 : 18. Forestry Abs. 10 (2) : 165. 1948.

———. 1948. *Exotic Pines.* Austral. Timber Jour. 14 (4) : 210. Forestry Abs. 10 (2) : 179.

———. 1948. *Mycorrhiza on Seedling Pines Grown in Uninoculated Soil.* Nyasaland Dept. Forestry Rpt. 1946 : 7. Forestry Abs. 10 (2) : 165. 1948.

———. 1953. *Density, Fiber Length, and Yields of Pulp for Various Species of Wood.* U. S. Forest Serv. Forest Prod. Lab. Tech. Note 191, 10 pp.

———. 1954. *Newsprint Production from Hardwoods.* In Study of Newsprint Expansion: Part II. Dept. Com. House Comm. Rpt., 83d Cong. 2nd Sess., 368 pp.

Abel, G. W. 1947. *Suppression of Hardwood on Pine Land.* Miss. Farm Res. [Miss. Sta.] 10 (2) : 1, 8.

Addoms, R. M. 1937. *Nutritional Studies on Loblolly Pine.* Plant Physiol. 12: 199-205.

———. 1950. *Notes on the Structure of Elongating Pine Roots.* Amer. Jour. Bot. 37: 208-211.

Afanasiev, M. 1957. *Growth in Volume and Basal Area in a Loblolly Pine-Shortleaf Pine-Hardwood Stand in Southeastern Oklahoma.* Okla. Agr. Expt. Sta. Bul. B-498, 20 pp.

Akerman, A. 1926. *The Loblolly Pine.* Ga. State Forestry Dept. Leaflet 1, 4 pp.

———. 1928. *An Experiment in Thinning Loblolly Pine.* Jour. Forestry 26: 487-499.

Alexander, C., and Watson, A. J. 1947. *Peeling and Drying of Veneer from Plantation-Grown Loblolly Pine and Slash Pine.* Div. Forest Prod., Coun. Sci. Industr. Res., Aust., 4 pp.

Allen, J. C. 1950. *Pine Planting Tests in the Copper Basin.* Tenn. Acad. Sci. Jour. 25: 199-216.

——— and Cummings, W. H. 1953. *Tree Volume Equivalents for Small Pines.* U. S. Tenn. Val. Authority, Div. Forestry Relat. Tech. Note 13, 5 pp.

Ames, F. E. 1906. *A Report on Loblolly Pine Lumbering in South Carolina.* Thesis, Yale Univ. School Forestry.

Anderson, D. A. 1945. *Southern Pine Bark Beetles.* Tex. Forest Serv. Bul. 33, 8 pp. rev. 1949.

———. 1952. *The Use of Methyl Bromide and Chlordane for the Control of the Texas Leaf-Cutting Ant.* Tex. Forest Serv. Res. Note 1, 8 pp.

Anderson, G. A. 1946. *An Experimental Study of the Effects of Strip Cuttings and Cleanings on Loblolly Pine Reproduction in the Duke Forest.* Thesis, Duke Univ. School Forestry.

———. 1953. *Silviculture of Southern Pines from the Standpoint of Integrated Utilization of Products.* Jour. Forestry 51: 93-94.

Anderson, M. H. 1941. *Natural Reproduction Following a Partial Cutting in Loblolly-Shortleaf Types on Selected Areas.* Thesis, La. State Univ. School Forestry.

Anderson, R. F. 1948. *Host Selection by the Pine Engraver.* Jour. Econ. Ent. 41: 596-602.

Anderson, W. C. 1954. *Pine Sawmilling Costs by Log Size: An Estimating Method.* U. S. Forest Serv. Southeast. Forest Expt. Sta. Paper 43, 14 pp.

———. 1955. *Can Slabs from Small Sawmills Be Salvaged at a Profit?* South. Lumberman 191 (2393) : 185-188.

———. 1957. *Sawtimber Prices are Highest in the Fall.* U. S. Forest Serv. Southeast. Forest Expt. Sta. Res. Notes 105.

Andrews, L. K. 1941. *Effects of Certain Soil Treatments on the Development of Loblolly Pine Nursery Stock.* Jour. Forestry 39: 918-921.

Applequist, M. 1941. *Stand Composition of Upland Hardwood Forests as Related to Soil Type in the Duke Forest.* Thesis, Duke Univ. School Forestry.

Arnold, F., and Hankla, D. J. 1958. *Good Forestry Can Make Good Hunting.* Wildlife in N. C. 22 (9) : 14-17.

Ashe, W. W. 1894. *The Forests, Forest Lands, and Forest Products of Eastern North Carolina.* N. C. Geol. Survey Bul. 5, 128 pp.

———. 1895. *Forest Fires: Their Destructive Work, Causes and Prevention.* N. C. Geol. Survey Bul. 7, 66 pp.

———. 1910. *Management of Loblolly and Shortleaf Pines.* Soc. Amer. Foresters Proc. 5 : 84-100.

———. 1915. *Loblolly or North Carolina Pine.* N. C. Geol. and Econ. Survey Bul. 24, 176 pp.

———. 1916. *Cost of Logging Large and Small Timber.* Forestry Quart. 14 : 441-452.

———. 1925. *Cutting to Increase the Margin of Profit.* South. Lumberman 121 (1573) : 39-40.

———. 1926a. *Adjustment of the Volume Removed in Selection Felling.* Jour. Forestry 24 : 862-873.

———. 1926b. *Profit in Cutting Timber for a Permanent Yield.* South. Lumberman 123 (1597) : 44-46.

———. 1928. *Profit or Loss in Cutting Shortleaf and Loblolly Pines in Alabama.* Ala. State Comn. Forestry Bul. 2, 64 pp.

———. 1929. *The Less You Cut the More You Cut.* Jour. Forestry 27 : 761-767.

———. 1930a. *Small Trees Wasteful to Cut for Saw Timber.* U. S. Dept. Agr. Leaflet 55, 5 pp.

———. 1930b. *The Tree that Does Not Yield a Profit.* Sci. Monthly 31 (4) : 319-327.

Averell, J. L. 1945. *Rules of Thumb for Thinning Loblolly Pine.* Jour. Forestry 43 : 649-651.

Avery, T. E. 1955. *Gross Volume Estimation Using "Plotless Cruising" in Southeast Arkansas.* Jour. Forestry 53 : 206-207.

Bailey, L. F. 1948. *Leaf Oils from Tennessee Valley Conifers.* Jour. Forestry 46 : 882-889.

Baird, P. K. 1931. *Results of Paper Making Experiments with Southern Woods.* South. Lumberman 143 (1804) : 47-48.

Baker, F. S. 1949. *A Revised Tolerance Table.* Jour. Forestry 47 : 179-181.

Balch, R. E. 1928. *The Influence of the Southern Pine Beetle on Forest Composition in Western North Carolina.* Thesis, N. Y. State Col. Forestry, Syracuse Univ.

Baldwin, W. T. 1957. *Management of Pine Stands for Timber and Wildlife.* Sixth Ann. Forestry Symposium Proc., La. State Univ. School Forestry 1957 : 80-89.

Ball, D. H., and others. 1956. *The Structure of the Hemicelluloses of Loblolly Pine.* Tappi 39 (6) : 438-443.

Barker, W. J., and others. 1953. *Longer Life for Fence Posts.* Clemson Agr. Col. S. C. Ext. Serv. Cir. 262, 15 pp. (rev.).

Barney, C. W. 1947. *A Study of Some Factors Affecting Root Growth of Loblolly Pine (Pinus Taeda L.).* Thesis, Duke Univ. School Forestry.

———. 1951. *Effects of Soil Temperature and Light Intensity on Root Growth of Loblolly Pine Seedlings.* Plant Physiol. 26 : 146-163.

Barrett, L. I. 1928. *Fire Damage to Mature Loblolly Pine.* Naval Stores Rev. 38 (18) : 11.

———. 1940. *Requirements for Restocking Cutover Loblolly and Short-leaf Pine Stands.* South. Lumberman 161 (2033) : 200-202.

——— and Downs, A. A. 1943. *Hardwood Invasion in Pine Forests of the Piedmont Plateau.* Jour. Agr. Res. 67 : 111-128.

——— and Righter, F. I. 1929. *Working Plan for Experimental Thinnings in Shortleaf and Loblolly Pines.* Jour. Forestry 27 : 782-803.

Barrick, F. B. 1958. *A Study in Deer Productivity.* Wildlife in N. C. 22 (6) : 6-10.

Barron, N. T. 1951. *A Method of Converting an Unmanaged Loblolly Pine Stand to Sustained Yield.* Forest Farmer 10 (11) : 7, 14-15.

Barton, J. H. 1954. *How Much Does It Cost to Plant Trees?* Forest Farmer 14 (2) : 4-5.

Barton, L. V. 1928. *Hastening the Germination of Southern Pine Seed.* Jour. Forestry 26 : 774-785.

———. 1935. *Storage of Some Coniferous Seeds.* Boyce Thompson Inst. Contrib. 7 : 379-404.

Beadle, C., and Stevens, H. P. 1912-13. *The Length of Fibers of Pulps Produced from Different Kinds of Pulp Woods.* Paper Maker and Brit. Paper Trade Jour. 45 : 150-157.

——— and Stevens, H. P. 1916. *The Fiber Lengths of Southern Pine.* Paper 17 (18) : 18.

Beal, J. A. 1927. *Weather as a Factor in Southern Pine Beetle Control.* Jour. Forestry 25 : 741-742.

———. 1933. *Temperature Extremes as a Factor in the Ecology of the Southern Pine Beetle.* Jour. Forestry 31 : 329-336.

———. 1942. *Mortality of Reproduction Defoliated by the Red-Headed Pine Sawfly (Neodiprion Lecontei Fitch).* Jour. Forestry 40 : 562-563.

———. 1952. *Forest Insects of the Southeast: with Special Reference to Species Occurring in the Piedmont Plateau of North Carolina.* Duke Univ. School Forestry Bul. 14, 168 pp.

——— and McClintick, K. B. 1943. *The Pales Weevil in Southern Pine.* Jour. Econ. Ent. 36 : 792-794.

——— and Massey, C. L. 1945. *Bark Beetles and Ambrosia Beetles (Coleoptera: Scolytoidea): with Special Reference to Species Occurring in North Carolina.* Duke Univ. School Forestry Bul. 10, 178 pp.

Behre, C. E. 1945. *Growing Stock, Cutting Age, and Sustained Yield.* Jour. Forestry 43 : 477-483.

Bell, M. T. 1949. *The Wild Turkey in Southeast Louisiana.* Thesis, La. State Univ. School Forestry.

Benjamin, D. M. 1955. *The Biology and Ecology of the Red-Headed Pine Sawfly.* U. S. Dept. Agr. Tech. Bul. 1118, 57 pp.

Bennett, J., and Fletcher, P. W. 1947. *Loblollies and the Land.* Soil Conserv. 13 : 114-115.

Bennett, W. H. 1955a. *Pine Tip Moth.* Tex. Forest Serv. Cir. 46, 4 pp.

———. 1955b. *Texas Leaf-Cutting Ant.* Tex. Forest Serv. Cir. 44, 4 pp.

———. 1955c. *Pine Bark Beetles.* Tex. Forest Serv. Cir. 43, 12 pp.

———. 1955d. *Pales Weevil, Hylobius Pales (Hbst.).* Tex. Forest Serv. Cir. 41, 4 pp.

————. 1956. *Important Insect Enemies of Southern Pines.* U. S. Forest Serv. South. Forest Expt. Sta. South. Forest Pest Reporter 10, 21 pp.

Berkley, E. E. 1934. *Certain Physical and Structural Properties of Three Species of Southern Yellow Pine Correlated with the Compression Strength of Their Wood.* Mo. Bot. Gard. Ann. 21 (2) : 241-338.

Berkman, A. H. 1928. *The pH Value of Some Texas Soils and Its Relation to the Incidence of Certain Woody Plant Species.* Soil Sci. 25 (2) : 133-142.

Berliner, J. F. T. 1941. *Seasoning and Treating Southern Lumber with Urea.* South. Lumberman 163 (2057) : 189-195.

Bethel, J. S. 1940. *Loblolly Pine Pulping Qualities.* Paper Indus. and Paper World 22 : 358-359.

————. 1941. *The Effect of Position within the Bole Upon Fiber Length of Loblolly Pine (Pinus Taeda L.).* Jour. Forestry 39 : 30-33.

————. 1947. *The Influence of Stand Density Upon the Quality of Wood Produced in Young Loblolly Pine Stands.* Thesis, Duke Univ. School Forestry.

Betts, H. S. 1909. *Properties and Uses of the Southern Pines.* U. S. Dept. Agr. Forest Serv. Cir. 164, 30 pp.

————. 1917. *The Seasoning of Wood.* U. S. Dept. Agr. Bul. 552, 28 pp.

————. 1954. *The Southern Pines.* *In* American Woods, U. S. Forest Serv., 13 pp.

Bilan, M. V. 1957. *The Stimulation of Cone and Seed Production in Pulpwood-Size Loblolly Pine.* Thesis, Duke Univ. School Forestry.

Bishop, G. N., and Marckworth, G. D. 1933. *Some Factors Influencing Resin Concentration in Loblolly and Slash Pines.* Jour. Forestry 31 : 953-960.

Bitting, K. G. 1909. *The Histological Difference Between Pinus Taeda and Pinus Palustris.* Ind. Acad. Sci. Proc. 1908 : 127-129.

Blackman, M. W. 1922. *Mississippi Bark Beetles.* Miss. Agr. Expt. Sta. Tech. Bul. 11, 130 pp.

Blew, J. O., Jr. 1956. *Treating Wood in Pentachlorophenol Solutions by the Cold-Soaking Method.* U. S. Forest Serv. Forest Prod. Lab. Rpt. R1445, 19 pp.

———— and Champion, F. J. 1952. *Preservative Treatment of Fence Posts and Farm Timbers.* U. S. Dept. Agr. Farmers' Bul. 2049, 33 pp.

———— and Kulp, J. W. 1954. *Service Records on Treated and Untreated Fence Posts.* U. S. Forest Serv. Forest Prod. Lab. Rpt. R2005, 41 pp.

Boggess, W. R., and Bryan, J. E. 1940. *Selectivity Studies on Slash Pine and Loblolly Pine Underplanted in an Existing Hardwood Stand.* Ala. Agr. Expt. Sta. Ann. Rpt., pp. 30-32.

———— and Lorenz, R. W. 1949. *Growth and Early Thinning of Loblolly Pine in Southern Illinois.* Ill. Agr. Expt. Sta. Forestry Note 7, 3 pp.

———— Swarthout, P. A., and Toole, E. R. 1941. *Results of the Survey on the Littleleaf Disease of Southern Pines in Alabama.* Ala. Agr. Expt. Sta. Dept. Mimeo., 15 pp.

Bond, W. E. 1938. *The Integration of Forest Industries in the Southeastern United States.* Jour. Forestry 36 : 549-554.

————. 1939. *Costs and Returns of Managing 100,000 Acres of Short-*

leaf and Loblolly Pine for Sustained Yield. U. S. Forest Serv. South. Forest Expt. Sta. Occas. Paper 79, 15 pp.

──────. 1940. *Dollars-and-Cents Control in Forest Management.* South. Lumberman 161 (2033): 193-196.

──────. 1947. *Costs and Realization Values in Producing Pulp Wood.* U. S. Forest Serv. South. Forest Expt. Sta. South. Forestry Notes 52.

──────. 1951. *Cutting for Profit in Southern Pine Woodlands.* U. S. Dept. Agr. Farmers' Bul. 2027, 24 pp.

──────. 1952a. *Financial Maturity—a Guide in Thinning.* First Ann. Forestry Symposium Proc., La. State Univ. School Forestry 1952: 83-87.

──────. 1952b. *Growing Stock Differences in Even-Aged and All-Aged Forests.* Jour. Forestry 50: 691-693.

──────. 1953. *The Case for All-Aged Management of Southern Pines.* Jour. Forestry 51: 90-93.

────── and Campbell, R. S. 1951. *Planted Pines and Cattle Grazing, a Profitable Use of Southwest Louisiana's Cut-Over Pine Land.* La. Forestry Comn. Bul. 4, 28 pp.

────── and Spillers, A. R. 1935. *Use of Land for Forests in the Lower Piedmont Region of Georgia.* U. S. Forest Serv. South Forest Expt. Sta. Occas. Paper 53, 49 pp.

────── Wahlenberg, W. G., and Kirkland, B. P. 1937. *Profitable Management of Shortleaf and Loblolly Pine for Sustained Yield.* U. S. Forest Serv. South. Forest Expt. Sta. Occas. Paper 70, 37 pp.

Bormann, F. H. 1953. *Factors Determining the Role of Loblolly Pine and Sweetgum in Early Old-Field Succession in the Piedmont of North Carolina.* Ecol. Monog. 23: 339-358.

──────. 1956. *Ecological Implications of Changes in the Photosynthetic Response of Pinus Taeda Seedlings During Ontogeny.* Ecology 37: 70-75.

Bourne, R. 1951. *A Fallacy in the Theory of Growing Stock.* Forestry 24: 6-18.

Boyce, J. S., Jr. 1951. *Lophodermium Pinastri and Needle Browning of Southern Pines.* Jour. Forestry 49: 20-24.

──────. 1952a. *Scirrhia Acicola, a Cause of Loblolly Pine Needle Browning.* (Abs.) Assoc. South. Agr. Workers Proc. 49: 134.

──────. 1952b. *Loblolly Pine Needle Blight Caused by the Brown-Spot Fungus.* U. S. Forest Serv. Southeast. Forest Expt. Sta. Res. Notes 11, 1 p.

──────. 1952c. *A Needle Blight of Loblolly Pine Caused by the Brown-Spot Fungus.* Jour. Forestry 50: 686-687.

──────. 1953. *Needle Blights of Pines in the Southeast.* Arborist's News 18: 89-91.

──────. 1954a. *Hypoderma Needle Blight of Southern Pines.* Jour. Forestry 52: 496-498.

──────. 1954b. *Forest Plantation Protection Against Diseases and Insect Pests.* FAO Forestry Devlpmt. Paper 3, 41 pp.

──────. 1958. *Needle Cast of Southern Pines.* U. S. Forest Serv. Forest Pest Leaflet 28, 4 pp.

Boyce, S. G. 1951. *Plant Succession in a Thinned Loblolly Pine Stand in a Piedmont County.* Thesis, N. C. State Col. School Forestry.

Bramble, W. C., Worley, D. P., and Brynes, W. R. 1953. *Effect of Placement of Dormant Basal Spray on Top-Killing and Sprouting of Scrub Oak.* Northeast. Weed Control Conf. Proc. 7: 309-311.

Brasington, J. J. 1948. *Pull-Cut-or Poison?* Forest Farmer 7 (5): 14.

———. 1949. *Forest Grazing in South Alabama and West Florida.* Forest Farmer 9 (3): 8.

———. 1950. *Poisoning Scrub Oaks with the Cornell Tool.* Forest Farmer 9 (6): 5.

Bray, M. W. 1942a. *Recovery of Fats, Waxes, Resins, and Turpentine from Wood.* Paper Trade Jour. 115 (10): 41-42.

———. 1942b. *Development, Problems, and Possibilities of the Southern Pulping Industry.* South. Pulp and Paper Jour. 4 (10): 6-10, 14, 16.

———and Curran, C. E. 1937. *Sulphate Pulping of Southern Yellow Pines: Effect of Growth Variables on Yield and Pulp Quality.* Paper Trade Jour. 105 (20): 39-46.

——— Martin, J. S., and Schwartz, S. L. 1939. *Effect of Growth Variables on Yield and Pulp Quality.* In Sulphate Pulping of Southern Yellow Pines. South. Pulp and Paper Jour. 2 (6): 35-41.

Brender, E. V. 1947. *Pulpwood from Tops.* South. Lumberman 175 (2201): 238, 240.

———. 1949. *Logging Costs in Loblolly Pine.* Forest Farmer 9 (3): 5, 10.

———. 1952a. *From Forest to Farm to Forest Again.* Amer. Forests 58: 24-25, 40-41, 43.

———. 1952b. *Woodlands Can Add Cash to Farm Incomes.* Soil Conserv. News. December.

———. 1955. *Drought Damage to Pines.* Forest Farmer 14 (10): 7, 15.

———. 1957a. *Loblolly Pine not Suited for Bud Pruning.* Jour. Forestry 55: 214-215.

———. 1957b. *Clear-Cutting and Planting Loblolly Pine in the Lower Piedmont.* South. Lumberman 195 (2441): 188-190.

———. 1958. *A 10-Year Record of Pine Seed Production on the Hitchiti Experimental Forest.* Jour. Forestry 56: 408-410.

——— and Barber, J. C. 1956. *Influence of Loblolly Pine Overwood on Advance Reproduction.* U. S. Forest Serv. Southeast. Forest Expt. Sta. Paper 62, 12 pp.

——— and Cooper, R. W. 1949. *Testing Machine Planting in Cutover Piedmont Areas.* Forest Farmer 9 (3): 4, 9.

——— and Hodges, C. S. 1957a. *When Drought Strikes Your Pines.* Forest Farmer 16 (12): 8-9.

——— and Hodges, C. S. 1957b. *Honeysuckle or Trees?* U. S. Forest Serv. Southeast. Forest Expt. Sta. Res. Notes 103.

———and Nelson, T. C. 1952. *Re-Establishing Pine on Piedmont Cut-Over Land.* U. S. Forest Serv. Southeast. Forest Expt. Sta. Paper 18, 8 pp.

Brenneman, D. L. 1953. *Fertilization of Loblolly Pine Plantations.* First year results embodied in thesis by Dwight L. Brenneman. Third year's observations and measurements summarized by D. A. Dubow in thesis, 1954. N. C. State Col. School Forestry.

Brinkman, K. A., and Swarthout, P. A. 1942. *Natural Reproduction of Pines in East-Central Alabama.* Ala. Agr. Expt. Sta. Cir. 86, 12 pp.

Broadfoot, W. M. 1948. *Soil and Litter under Pine Plantations.* U. S. Forest Serv. South. Forest Expt. Sta. South. Forestry Notes 55, pp. 3-4.

————. 1951a. *Forest Planting Sites in North Mississippi and West Tennessee.* U. S. Forest Serv. South. Forest Expt. Sta. Occas. Paper 120, 15 pp.

————. 1951b. *Soil Rehabilitation Under Eastern Redcedar and Loblolly Pine.* Jour. Forestry 49: 780-781.

Bronson, A. H. 1941. *The Nantucket Pine Tip Moth (Rhyacionia Frustrana Comst.) and Its Occurrence on the Duke Forest.* Thesis, Duke Univ. School Forestry.

Browne, F. L. 1930. *Why Some Wood Surfaces Hold Paint Longer Than Other.* U. S. Dept. Agr. Leaflet 62, 3 pp.

————. 1951. *Wood Properties That Affect Paint Performance.* U. S. Forest Serv. Forest Prod. Lab. Rpt. R1053, 42 pp.

Bruce, D. 1955. *A New Way to Look at Trees.* Jour. Forestry 53: 163-167.

Bruner, M. H. 1938. *Pulpwood in the Management of Pine Stands.* Ark. Agr. Col. Ext. Cir. 249, 17 pp.

————. 1955. *Loblolly Pine Takes Over Black Locust Planting.* Jour. Forestry 53: 137-138.

————and Goebel, N. B. 1958. *Is Loblolly Pine Adapted to the Upper Piedmont?* Forest Farmer 17 (10): 12.

Brust, A. W., and Berkley, E. E. 1935. *The Distribution and Variations of Certain Strength and Elastic Properties of Clear Southern Yellow Pine Wood.* Thirty-eighth Amer. Soc. Testing Mater. Proc. Vol. 35, pt. II, pp. 643-673.

Bryan, M. B. 1954. *Some Effects of Winter Applications of Inorganic Fertilizers to Pine Seedlings in the Nursery.* Thesis, N. C. State Col. School Forestry.

Buckholz, J. T. 1918. *Suspensor and Early Embryo of Pinus.* Bot. Gaz. 66 (3): 185-228.

Buckley, S. B. 1860. *The Cutting Ant of Texas.* Acad. Nat. Sci. Phila. Proc. 12: 233-236.

Buckman, S. J. 1934. *What Is the Relationship between Durability and Specific Gravity of Wood?* Jour. Forestry 32: 725-728.

———— and Pera, J. D. 1942. *Non-Pressure Treatment of Wood. Cold Soaking Treatment of Southern Pine Sapwood with a Low Viscosity Oil Solution of Pentachlorphenol.* South. Lumberman 165 (2081): 223-226.

Buell, J. H. 1940. *Effect of Season of Cutting on Sprouting of Dogwood.* Jour. Forestry 38: 649-650.

————. 1942. *Outside-Bark Form Class Volume Tables for Some Southern Appalachian Species.* U. S. Forest Serv. Appalachian Forest Expt. Sta. Tech. Note 53, 76 pp.

Bull, H. 1934. *Profit from Improving a Second-Growth Forest of Lob-*

lolly and Shortleaf Pines and Hardwoods. U. S. Forest Serv. South. Forest Expt. Sta. Occas. Paper 38, 8 pp.

————. 1934a. *Thinning Loblolly Pine in Even-Aged Stands.* U. S. Forest Serv. South. Forest Expt. Sta. Occas. Paper 35, 12 pp.

————. 1934b. *Thinnings in Southern Pines.* Prog. Farmer 50 (3) : 15.

————. 1936. *Pulpwood Yields from Experimental Thinnings in Old-Field Stands of Loblolly and Shortleaf Pines.* U. S. Forest Serv. South. Forest Expt. Sta. Occas. Paper 57, 9 pp.

————. 1938. *Board-Foot Growth After Improvement Cutting.* South. Lumberman 157 (1985) : 154-156.

————. 1939a. *Loblolly Pine Versus Cotton: A Comparison of Annual Cellulose Production per Acre.* Jour. Forestry 37 : 570-571.

————. 1939b. *Increased Growth of Loblolly Pine as a Result of Cutting and Girdling Large Hardwoods.* Jour. Forestry 37 : 642-645.

————. 1942. *How Much Profit in Pruning Old-Field Loblolly Pine?* South. Lumberman 165 (2081) : 229-232.

————. 1944. *Growing More Wood on Fewer Trees.* South. Lumberman 169 (2129) : 195-198.

————. 1945. *Increasing the Growth of Loblolly Pine by Girdling Large Hardwoods.* Jour. Forestry 43 : 449-450.

————. 1950a. *Cord Mortality in Unthinned Stands.* U. S. Forest Serv. South. Forest Expt. Sta. South. Forestry Notes 70.

————. 1950b. *Pointers on Thinning Southern Pine.* South. Lumberman 181 (2273) : 259-260.

———— and Campbell, R. S. 1949. *Recent Research in Poisoning Southern Weed Hardwoods.* South. Weed Conf. Proc. 2: 1-7.

———— and Reynolds, R. R. 1943. *Further Study Needed of Management of Loblolly Pine.* Jour. Forestry 41: 722-726.

———— Williams, E. B., and Judson, G. M. 1948. *Harvest-Cutting Studies in East Texas Loblolly and Shortleaf Pine.* South. Lumberman 177 (2225) : 282, 284-286, 288.

Buller, G. B., and Gibbs, J. A. 1952. *Planted Loblolly Pines Respond to Mulching.* Jour. Forestry 50: 317-318.

Burke, H. D. 1956. *Game Habitat and Multiple Use of Southern Forest Ranges.* Jour. Range Mangt. 9: 164-166.

Burns, J. D. 1948. *Some Effects of Forest Fires on Mortality and Growth of Certain Species of Southern Pines.* Thesis, La. State Univ. School Forestry.

Butts, D., and Buckholz, J. T. 1940. *Cotyledon Numbers in Conifers.* Ill. Acad. Sci. Trans. 33 (2) : 58-62.

Byram, G. M. 1948. *Vegetation Temperature and Fire Damage in Southern Pines.* U. S. Forest Serv. Fire Control Notes 9 (4) : 34-36.

————. 1954. *Atmospheric Conditions Related to Blowup Fires.* U. S. Forest Serv. Southeast. Forest Expt. Sta. Paper 35, 34 pp.

———— and Nelson, R. M. 1952. *Lethal Temperatures and Fire Injury.* U. S. Forest Serv. Southeast. Forest Expt. Sta. Res. Notes 1, 2 pp.

Cain, S. A. 1940. *The Identification of Species in Fossil Pollen of Pinus by Size-Frequency Determinations.* Amer. Jour. Bot. 27: 301-308.

Caird, R. W. 1935. *Physiology of Pines Infested with Bark Beetles.* Bot. Gaz. 96: 709-733.

Calder, A. 1946. *The Paper Industry and Union Bag and Paper Corporation.* South. Pulp & Paper Jour. 9 (9): 26, 30, 32, 36, 49.

Campbell, R. A. 1946. *Pine Pulpwood Production—A Study of Hand and Power Methods.* U. S. Forest Serv. Southeast. Forest Expt. Sta. Tech. Note 66, 20 pp.

Campbell, R. S. 1944. *Grazing Cattle on Southern Pine Forests.* South. Lumberman 169 (2129): 188-191.

―――― and Biswell, H. H. 1944. *Cattle in the Pines.* Amer. Forests 59: 238-239, 260, 262, 264, 265.

―――― and Cassady, J. T. 1951. *Grazing Values for Cattle on Pine Forest Ranges in Louisiana.* La. State Univ. Bul. 452, 31 pp.

―――― and Peevy, F. A. 1950. *Poisoning Certain Undesirable Southern Hardwoods for Forest and Range Improvement.* Amer. Midland Nat. 44: 495-505.

Campbell, W. A. 1949. *Needle Cast of Southern Pines.* Forest Farmer 9 (1): 4, 10.

――――. 1951. *The Occurrence of Phytophthora Cinnamomi in the Soil Under Pine Stands in the Southeast.* Phytopathology 41: 742-746.

―――― and Copeland, O. L., Jr. 1954. *Littleleaf Disease of Shortleaf and Loblolly Pines.* U. S. Dept. Agr. Cir. 940, 41 pp.

Carmean, W. H. 1947. *The Effects of Clear-Cutting in Patches on the Reproduction of Old Field Loblolly Pine in the Duke Forest.* Thesis, Duke Univ. School Forestry.

Carmelich, J. N. F. 1951. *The Growth of Pinus Taeda.* Rev. Fac. Agron. Vet., B. Aires 13 (1): 26-46.

Carow, J. 1954. *The University of Michigan Photo-Interpreters Scale.* Mich. Forestry No. 6, 2 pp.

Carpenter, R. D. 1950. *Amount of Chippable Waste at Southern Pine Sawmills.* U. S. Forest Serv. South. Forest Expt. Sta. Occas. Paper 115, 7 pp.

――――. 1951. *Volume of Heavy Waste at Southern Pine Sawmills.* South. Lumberman 182 (2277): 62, 64.

Carvell, K. L. 1955. *Translocation of Ammate.* Forest Sci. 1: 41-43.

――――. 1956. *The Use of Chemicals in Controlling Forest Stand Composition in the Duke Forest.* Jour. Forestry 54: 525-530.

Cassady, J. T., Hopkins, W., and Whitaker, L. B. 1955. *Cattle Grazing Damage to Pine Seedlings.* U. S. Forest Serv. South. Forest Expt. Sta. Occas. Paper 141, 14 pp.

―――― and Peevy, F. A. 1948. *From Scrubby Hardwoods to Merchantable Pines—Timber Owners Kill Defective Hardwoods with Chemicals.* South. Lumberman 177 (2225): 115-119.

Cech, F. C. 1958. *The Vegetative Propagation of Pinus Taeda L. (Loblolly Pine).* Thesis, Tex. Agr. Col.

―――― and Goddard, R. E. 1957. *Selecting Drought Resistant Loblolly Pine in Texas.* South. Conf. Forest Tree Impr. Proc. 4: 30-33.

Ceremello, P. J. 1942. *Carpet Grass Sod on Forest Roads.* U. S. Forest Serv. South. Forest Expt. Sta. South. Forestry Notes 45.

Chaiken, L. E. 1939. *The Approach of Loblolly and Virginia Pine Stands Toward Normal Stocking.* Jour. Forestry 37: 866-871.

————. 1941. *Growth and Mortality During 10 Years Following Partial Cuttings in Loblolly Pine.* Jour. Forestry 39: 324-329.

————. 1949. *The Behavior and Control of Understory Hardwoods in Loblolly Pine Stands.* U. S. Forest Serv. Southeast. Forest Expt. Sta. Tech. Note 72, 27 pp.

————. 1950a. *This Hardwood Problem.* Forest Farmer 9 (6): 8-9.

————. 1950b. *Control of Undesirable Hardwoods.* (Abs.) Assoc. South. Agr. Workers Proc. 47: 91-92.

————. 1951a. *Tree Poisoning with 2, 4, 5-T in Frills.* Forest Farmer 10 (9): 9, 12.

————. 1951b. *Chemical Control of Inferior Species in the Management of Loblolly Pine.* Jour. Forestry 49: 695-697.

————. 1951c. *The Use of Chemicals to Control Inferior Trees in the Management of Loblolly Pine.* U. S. Forest Serv. Southeast. Forest Expt. Sta. Paper 10, 34 pp.

————. 1952a. *Control Inferior Tree Species.* South. Lumberman 184 (2306): 38-39.

————. 1952b. *Annual Summer Fires Kill Hardwood Root Stocks.* U. S. Forest Serv. Southeast. Forest Expt. Sta. Res. Notes 19, 1 p.

————. 1952c. *Extent of Loss of Loblolly Pine Seed in Winter Fires.* U. S. Forest Serv. Southeast. Forest Expt. Sta. Res. Notes 21, 2 pp.

————. 1955. *Control of Undesirable Hardwoods.* Forest Farmer 15 (1): 18, 24.

————. 1956. *Progress in the Control of Undesirable Hardwoods.* Forest Farmer 15 (6): 7-9, 16.

———— and Legrande, W. P., Jr. 1949. *When to Burn for Seedbed Preparation.* Forest Farmer 8 (11): 4.

Chamberlin, H. H., Sample, L. A., and Hayes, R. W. 1945. *Private Forest Land Ownership and Management in the Loblolly-Shortleaf Type in Southern Arkansas, Northern Louisiana, and Central Mississippi.* La. Agr. Expt. Sta. Bul. 393, 46 pp.

Chandler, R. F., Jr. 1939. *The Calcium Content of the Foliage of Forest Trees.* N. Y. (Cornell) Agr. Expt. Sta. Mem. 228, 15 pp.

———— Schoen, P. W., and Anderson, D. A. 1943. *Relation Between Soil Types and the Growth of Loblolly Pine and Shortleaf Pine in East Texas.* Jour. Forestry 41: 505-506.

Chapman, A. D. 1952. *Treated Wood Lasts.* South. Lumberman 185 (2321): 246, 248, 250, 252.

———— and Scheffer, T. C. 1933. *New Chemical Treatments for the Control of Sap Stain and Mold in Southern Pine and Hardwood Lumber.* South. Lumberman 146 (1851): 25-30.

———— and Scheffer, T. C. 1940. *Effect of Blue Stain on Specific Gravity and Strength of Southern Pine.* Jour. Agr. Res. 61: 125-133.

Chapman, C. S. 1905. *A Working Plan for Forest Lands in Berkeley County, S. C.* U. S. Dept. Agr. Bur. Forestry Bul. 56, 62 pp.

Chapman, H. H. 1917. *Second Growth Pine as a Solution of the Cutover Lands Problem in the South.* Lumber World Rev. 32 (10): 21-25.

————. 1921. *Yield of Old-Field Pine.* Timberman 22 (11): 41.

————. 1922. *A New Hybrid Pine (Pinus Palustris X Pinus Taeda).* Jour. Forestry 20: 729-734.

————. 1923. *The Recovery and Growth of Loblolly Pine After Suppression.* Jour. Forestry 21: 709-711.

————. 1940. *Forest Fires in 1938.* Jour. Forestry 38: 64-65.

————. 1941. *Comments on "Growth and Mortality During 10 Years Following Partial Cuttings in Loblolly Pine."* Jour. Forestry 39: 721.

————. 1942a. *Effect of Annual Spring Fires on Stump Taper of Loblolly Pine.* Jour. Forestry 40: 962-963.

————. 1942b. *Management of Loblolly Pine in the Pine-Hardwood Regions in Arkansas and Louisiana West of the Mississippi River.* Yale Univ. School Forestry Bul. 49: 1-150.

————. 1943. *Common Sense Needed in Management of Loblolly Pine.* Jour. Forestry 41: 726-727.

————. 1944a. *Fire and Pines.* Amer. Forests 50: 62-64, 91-93.

————. 1944b. *"Selection" Cutting in Loblolly Pine.* Jour. Forestry 42: 838-839.

————. 1945. *The Effect of Overhead Shade on the Survival of Loblolly Pine Seedlings.* Ecology 26: 274-282.

————. 1948. *How to Grow Loblolly Pine Instead of Inferior Hardwoods.* Soc. Amer. Foresters Proc. 1947: 347-353.

————. 1951. *Should Small Woodlots be Managed for Sustained Annual Yield?* Jour. Forestry 49: 343-344.

————. 1953. *Effects of Thinning on Yields of Forest-Grown Longleaf and Loblolly Pines at Urania, La.* Jour. Forestry 51: 16-26.

———— and Bryant, R. C.   1913. *Prolonging the Cut of Southern Pine.* Yale Univ. School Forestry Bul. 2, 32 pp.

Chen, W. H. W., and Cameron, F. K.   1942. *Cellulose Content of Cotton and Southern Woods.* Indus. and Engin. Chem. Indus. Ed. 34: 224-225. 1942. Forestry Abs. 4 (2): 114.

Chesley, K. G., Hair, J. C., and Swartz, J. N.   1956. *Underwater Storage of Southern Pine Pulpwood.* Tappi 39 (9): 609-614.

Chidester, G. H., McGovern, J. M., and McNaughton, C. C.   1938. *Comparison of Sulphite Pulps from Fast-Growth Loblolly, Shortleaf, Longleaf, and Slash Pines.* Paper Trade Jour. 107 (4): 36-39.

Chidester, M. S.   1942. *The Effect of a Mold, Trichoderma Lignorum, on Loblolly Pine Sapwood.* Amer. Wood Preservers' Assoc. Proc. 38: 134-139.

Chisman, H. H., and Schumacher, F. X.   1940. *On the Tree-Area Ratio and Certain of its Applications.* Jour. Forestry 38: 311-317.

Clapp, C. E.   1954. *Seedling Production and Planting.* South. Lumberman 189 (2369): 176.

Clark, H. D., Jr.   1948. *The Effect of Ground Cover on Germination and Establishment of Loblolly and Shortleaf Pines.* Thesis, La. State Univ. School Forestry.

Clark, J. A.   1912. *Loblolly, the King of Southern Pines.* St. Louis Lumberman 49 (10): 55.

Clark, R. H.   1954. *Underplanting of Southern Pine.* Third Ann. Forestry Symposium Proc., La. State Univ. School Forestry 1954: 80-86.

Clark, S. F.   1947a. *Releasing Pine from Hardwood Competition.* U. S. Forest Serv. South. Forest Expt. Sta. South. Forestry Notes 50.

————. 1947b. *Forest Enemy Number Two.* South. Lumberman 175 (2201) : 182-184.

————. 1952. *Logging Costs in East Texas as Affected by Cut per Acre and Log Size.* South. Lumberman 184 (2301) : 76, 78.

———— and Hebb, E. A. 1951a. *Mortality in Pine Stands During First Year After Logging.* South. Lumberman 183 (2297) : 256, 258.

———— and Hebb, E. A. 1951b. *Mortality Following Harvest Cutting.* U. S. Forest Serv. South. Forest Expt. Sta. South. Forestry Notes 74.

———— and Williston, H. L. 1948. *Cost of Girdling Low-Grade Hardwoods.* U. S. Forest Serv. South. Forest Expt. Sta. South. Forestry Notes 58.

Clements, J. B. 1943. *The Introduction of Pines into Nyasaland.* Nyasaland Dept. Agr. Quart. Jour. 1 (4) : 5-15. 1941. Forestry Abs. 5 (1) : 31. 1943.

Cloud, M. C., Jr. 1950. *Effect of Nitrogen Fertilization on the Radial Growth of Southern Pines.* Thesis, Ga. Univ. School Forestry.

Cobb, B. C. 1957. *Logging with Farm Tractors.* South. Lumberman 194 (2425) : 72, 74, 76.

Coile, T. S. 1933. *Soil Reaction and Forest Types in the Duke Forest.* Ecology 14 : 323-333.

————. 1936. *The Effect of Rainfall and Temperature on the Annual Radial Growth of Pine in the Southern United States.* Ecol. Monog. 6 : 533-562.

————. 1937a. *Composition of the Leaf Litter of Forest Trees.* Soil Sci. 43 : 349-355.

————. 1937b. *Forest Soil Problems in the Piedmont Plateau.* Jour. Forestry 35 : 344-348.

————. 1937c. *Distribution of Forest Tree Roots in North Carolina Piedmont Soils.* Jour. Forestry 35 : 247-257.

————. 1938. *Forest Classification: Classification of Forest Sites with Special Reference to Ground Vegetation.* Jour. Forestry 36 : 1062-1066.

————. 1940. *Soil Changes Associated with Loblolly Pine Succession on Abandoned Agricultural Land of the Piedmont Plateau.* Duke Univ. School Forestry Bul. 5, 85 pp.

————. 1942. *Some Physical Properties of the B Horizons of Piedmont Soils.* Soil Sci. 54 : 101-103.

————. 1948. *Relation of Soil Characteristics to Site Index of Loblolly and Shortleaf Pines in the Lower Piedmont Region of North Carolina.* Duke Univ. School Forestry Bul. 13, 78 pp.

————. 1950a. *Influence of Soil and Other Factors on the Stocking of Hardwoods in the Pine Stands.* (Abs.) Assoc. South. Agr. Workers Proc. 47 : 90-91.

————. 1950b. *Effect of Soil on the Development of Hardwood Understories in Pine Stands of the Piedmont Plateau.* Soil Sci. Soc. Amer. Proc. 14 : 350-352.

————. 1952a. *Soil and the Growth of Forests.* Adv(s). in Agron. 4 : 330-398.

————. 1952b. *Soil Productivity for Southern Pines. Part I. Shortleaf and Loblolly Pines.* Forest Farmer 11 (7) : 10, 11, 13.

—————— and Schumacher, F. X. 1953a. *Relation of Soil Properties to Site Index of Loblolly and Shortleaf Pines in the Piedmont Region of the Carolinas, Georgia, and Alabama.* Jour. Forestry 51: 739-744.

—————— and Schumacher, F. X. 1953b. *Site Index of Young Stands of Loblolly and Shortleaf Pines in the Piedmont Plateau Region.* Jour. Forestry 51: 432-435.

Colley, R. H., and Rumbold, C. T. 1930. *Relation Between Moisture Content of the Wood and Blue Stain in Loblolly Pine.* Jour. Agr. Res. 41: 389-399.

Conarro, R. M. 1942. *The Place of Fire in Southern Forestry.* Jour. Forestry 40: 129-131.

Conway, E. M., and Schnell, R. L. 1952. *Fence Post Treating.* U. S. Tenn. Val. Authority, Div. Forestry Relat., 20 pp.

Cooke, C. W. 1936. *Geology of the Coastal Plain of South Carolina.* U. S. Geol. Survey Bul. 867.

Cooper, W. E. 1942. *Forest Site Determination by Soil and Erosion Classification.* Jour. Forestry 40: 709-712.

Cope, J. A. 1921a. *A Dream Come True: Maryland Loblolly Pine to the Front.* Jour. Forestry 19: 399-401.

——————. 1921b. *Thinnings in Loblolly Pine at a Profit.* Jour. Forestry 19: 759-761.

——————. 1923a. *Loblolly Pine in Maryland.* Md. State Dept. Forestry. 96 pp.

——————. 1923b. *Loblolly Pine on the "Eastern Shore."* Amer. Forestry 29: 368-371.

——————. 1924. *A Progress Report on the Reseeding of Cutover Lands to Loblolly Pine.* Jour. Forestry 22: 171-174.

——————. 1926. *Loblolly Pine: a Woodland Crop.* Md. Univ. Ext. Bul. 41, 49 pp.

Copeland, O. L., Jr. 1949. *Some Relations Between Soils and the Littleleaf Disease of Pine.* Jour. Forestry 47: 566-568.

——————. 1952. *Root Mortality of Shortleaf and Loblolly Pine in Relation to Soils and Littleleaf Disease.* Jour. Forestry 50: 21-25.

Cossitt, F. M. 1947. *Mineral Spirits as a Selective Herbicide in Southern Pine Seed-Beds.* South. Lumberman 175 (2201): 203-204.

Cox, G. S. 1948. *The Influence of Soil Fertility on the Growth of Certain Forest Tree Seedlings as Affected by Soil Moisture and Light Intensity.* Thesis, Duke Univ. School Forestry.

——————. 1953. *The Effect of Soil Properties on the Site Index of Loblolly Pine in the Southeastern Coastal Plain.* Thesis, Duke Univ. School Forestry.

Coyne, J. F. 1954. *Destructive Insects of Southern Pine.* Forests and People 4 (1): 18-20.

——————. 1959. *Neodiprion Taedae Linearis, a Pest of Loblolly and Shortleaf Pines.* U. S. Forest Serv. Forest Pest Leaflet 34, 4 pp.

Craib, I. J. 1939. *Thinning, Pruning, and Management Studies on the Main Exotic Conifers Grown in South Africa.* Union So. Africa Dept. Agr. and Forestry Sci. Bul. 196, 179 pp.

——————. 1947. *The Silviculture of Exotic Conifers in South Africa.* British Empire Forestry Conf., 35 pp., City Printing Works, Ltd., Pieter-maritzburg, South Africa.

Craig, R. B. 1949. *Virginia Forest Resources and Industries.* U. S. Dept. Agr. Misc. Pub. 681, 64 pp.

Craighead, F. C. 1925a. *The Dendroctonus Problems.* Jour. Forestry 23: 340-354.

———. 1925b. *Bark-Beetle Epidemics and Rainfall Deficiency.* Jour. Econ. Ent. 18: 577-586.

———. 1928. *Interrelation of Tree-Killing Barkbeetles (Dendroctonus) and Blue Stains.* Jour. Forestry 26: 886-887.

———. 1950. *Insect Enemies of Eastern Forests.* U. S. Dept. Agr. Misc. Pub. 657, 679 pp.

——— and Middleton, W. 1930. *An Annotated List of the Important North American Forest Insects.* U. S. Dept. Agr. Misc. Pub. 74, 30 pp.

Crow, A. B. 1941. *Distribution, Establishment, Growth, and Management of Loblolly Pine in the Northeastern Part of Its Range.* Thesis, Yale Univ. School Forestry.

———. 1958. *Fourth-Year Results from a Local Geographic Seed-Source Test on Planted Loblolly Pine.* La. State Univ. Forestry Notes 21.

Cruikshank, J. W. 1940a. *Forest Resources of the Tennessee Valley of North Alabama.* U. S. Forest Serv. South. Forest Expt. Sta. Forest Survey Release 49, 39 pp.

———. 1940b. *Forest Resources of North Central Alabama.* U. S. Forest Serv. South. Forest Expt. Sta. Forest Survey Release 50, 36 pp.

———. 1940c. *Forest Resources of the Southern Coastal Plain of North Carolina.* U. S. Forest Serv. Southeast. Forest Expt. Sta. Forest Survey Release 4, 46 pp.

———. 1940d. *Forest Resources of the Northern Coastal Plain of North Carolina.* U. S. Forest Serv. Southeast. Forest Expt. Sta. Forest Survey Release 5, 48 pp.

———. 1940e. *Forest Resources of the Piedmont Region of North Carolina.* U. S. Forest Serv. Southeast. Forest Expt. Sta. Forest Survey Release 6, 55 pp.

———. 1944. *North Carolina Forest Resources and Industries.* U. S. Dept. Agr. Misc. Pub. 533, 76 pp.

———. 1948. *Southern Pulpwood Production and the Timber Supply.* U. S. Forest Serv. Southeast. Forest Expt. Sta. Forest Survey Release 24, 12 pp.

———. 1952a. *Rates of Net Annual Growth in Cords Applicable to Large Forested Areas in Florida.* U. S. Forest Serv. Southeast. Forest Expt. Sta. Res. Notes 6, 2 pp.

———. 1952b. *Rates of Net Annual Growth in Board Feet Applicable to Large Forested Areas in Florida.* U. S. Forest Serv. Southeast. Forest Expt. Sta. Res. Notes 7, 2 pp.

———. 1952c. *1951 Pulpwood Production in the South.* U. S. Forest Serv. Southeast. Forest Expt. Sta. Forest Survey Release 38, 28 pp.

———. 1952d. *Pulpwood Production in the Southeast Increases Nearly 300 Percent from 1939-1951.* U. S. Forest Serv. Southeast. Forest Expt. Sta. Res. Notes 13, 2 pp.

———. 1952e. *10-Year Diameter Growth of Selected Tree Species in*

South Georgia. U. S. Forest Serv. Southeast. Forest Expt. Sta. Res. Notes 21, 1 p.

————. 1954a. *1953 Pulpwood Production in the South.* U. S. Forest Serv. Southeast. Forest Expt. Sta. Forest Survey Release 43, 32 pp.

————. 1954b. *Site Index of the Major Pine Forest Types in the Southeast.* U. S. Forest Serv. Southeast. Forest Expt. Sta. Res. Notes 50.

———— and Anderson, W. C. 1955. *Pine Sawtimber Stumpage Prices in South Carolina, 1948-1954.* U. S. Forest Serv. Southeast. Forest Expt. Sta. Paper 57, 14 pp.

———— and Eldredge, I. F. 1939. *Forest Resources of Southeastern Texas.* U. S. Dept. Agr. Misc. Pub. 326, 37 pp.

————and McCormack, J. F. 1956. *1955 Pulpwood Production in the South.* U. S. Forest Serv. Southeast. Forest Expt. Sta. Forest Survey Release 47, 29 pp.

Cummings, W. H. 1952a. *Loblolly Pine Shows Early Differences with Source of Seed and Locality of Planting.* Jour. Forestry 50: 626-627.

————. 1952b. *Post Yield, Production Costs, and Growth Response from First Thinning of Loblolly and Shortleaf Pine Plantations.* First Ann. Forestry Symposium Proc., La. State Univ. School Forestry 1952: 99-102.

———— and Thurmond, A. K. 1952. *Thin Your Pine Plantation for Fence Posts.* Forest Farmer 11 (12): 4-5, 8.

Cuno, J. B. 1939. *Production of Loblolly Pine Pulpwood in the Mid-Atlantic Region.* South. Pulp & Paper Jour. 1 (4): 13-16 and 1 (6): 9-15, 26.

Curran, C. E. 1936. *Some Relations Between Growth Conditions, Wood Structure and Pulping Quality.* Paper Trade Jour. 103 (11): 36-40.

————. 1938. *Relation of Growth Characteristics of Southern Pine to Its Use in Pulping.* U. S. Forest Serv. Forest Prod. Lab. Rpt. R1168, 11 pp.

———— and Bray, M. W. 1931. *White Paper from Southern Pines. Part I. Pulping Loblolly Pine for Strong, Easy-Bleaching Sulphate Pulp.* Paper Trade Jour. 92 (1): 47-52.

Cushman, R. A. 1927. *The Parasites of the Pine Tip Moth, Rhyacionia Frustrana (Comstock).* Jour. Agr. Res. 34: 615-622.

Darby, S. P., Jr. 1950. *Effects of Seedbed Preparation on the Germination and Initial Establishment of Loblolly Pine in the Piedmont Forest.* Thesis, Ga. Univ. School Forestry.

————. 1956. *Georgia's New Dewinger.* Jour. Forestry 54: 579-581.

Darker, G. D. 1932. *The Hypodermataceae of Conifers.* Arnold Arboretum Contrib. I, 131 pp.

Davidson, R. W. 1935. *Fungi Causing Stain in Logs and Lumber in the Southern United States, Including Five New Species.* Jour. Agr. Res. 50: 789-807.

Davis, D. E. 1949. *Some Effects of Calcium Deficiency on the Anatomy of Pinus Taeda.* Amer. Jour. Bot. 36: 276-282.

Davis. E. M. 1927. *The Density of Southern Pine. Its Significance in Terms of Properties and Grades.* South. Lumberman. 129 (1681): 161-164.

Davis, J. E. 1949. *Loblolly Recommended for Northeast Mississippi Area.* Miss. Farm Res. [Miss. Sta.] 12 (10): 1, 8.

———. 1950a. *Winter Is the Time to Plant Trees in Mississippi Forests.* Miss. Farm Res. [Miss. Sta.] 13 (1): 1, 7.

———. 1950b. *Loblolly Better Than Black Locust for Upstate Forests.* Miss Farm Res. [Miss. Sta.] 13 (3): 8.

Davis, J. R., and Duke, W. B. 1955. *Quick, Bunyan, the Needle!—Tree Injector Kills Cull Hardwoods.* South. Lumberman 191 (2393): 171-172.

Davis, K. P. 1954. *American Forest Management.* 482 pp. New York.

———. 1959. *Forest Fire—Control and Use.* 584 pp. New York.

Davis, V. B. 1940. *Forest Site Quality in Georgia.* U. S. Forest Serv. South. Forest Expt. Sta. South. Forestry Notes 33.

Davis, W. C., Wright, E., and Hartley, C. 1942. *Diseases of Forest-Tree Nursery Stock.* Fed. Security Agency Civilian Conserv. Corps Forestry Pub. 9, 79 pp.

Decker, J. P. 1944. *Effect of Temperature on Photosynthesis and Respiration in Red and Loblolly Pines.* Plant Physiol. 19: 679-688.

———. 1947. *The Effect of Air Supply on Apparent Photosynthesis.* Plant Physiol. 22: 561-571.

Deetlefs, P. P. du T. 1953. *Means of Expressing and Regulating Density in Forest Stands.* So. African Forestry Assoc. Jour. 23: 1-12.

———. 1954. *The Relationship Between Stand Density, Crown Size and Basal Area Growth in Stands of Pinus Taeda in the Native Habitat of this Species.* So. African Forestry Assoc. Jour. 24: 1-28.

Demmon, E. L. 1935. *The Silvicultural Aspects of the Forest-Fire Problem in the Longleaf Pine Region.* Jour. Forestry 33: 323-331.

———. 1936a. *Influence of Forest Practice on the Suitability of Southern Pine for Newsprint.* Jour. Forestry 34: 202-210.

———. 1936b. *Rate of Formation of Heartwood in Southern Pines.* Jour. Forestry 34: 775-776.

———. 1942. *Periodicity of Forest Fires in the South.* South. Lumberman 165 (2081): 220-222.

Derr, H. J., and Mann, W. F., Jr. 1954. *Future Forests by Direct Seeding.* Forests and People 4 (4): 22-23, 38-39.

DeVall, W. B. 1944. *A Bark Character for the Identification of Certain Florida Pines.* Fla. Acad. Sci. Proc. 7: 101-103.

Diftler, N. 1947. *The Invasion of Hardwoods in Pine Stands as Related to Soil Texture on the Upland Soil Types of the Lower Piedmont Plateau Region of Durham County and Its Adjacent Area.* Thesis, Duke Univ. School Forestry.

Dixon, R. D. 1947. *Financial Aspects of Artificial and Natural Regeneration of Loblolly Pine in the Piedmont Section of Georgia.* Thesis, Ga. Univ. School Forestry.

Doak, C. C. 1935. *Evolution of Foliar Types, Dwarf Shoots, and Cone Scales of Pinus, with Remarks Concerning Similar Structures in Related Forms.* Illinois Biol. Monog. 13 (3): 1-106.

Doane, R. W., Van Dyke, E. C., Chamberlin, W. J., and Burke, H. E. 1936. *Forest Insects.* 463 pp. New York and London.

Doi, T., and Morikawa, K. 1929. *An Anatomical Study of the Leaves of the Genus Pinus.* Kyushu Imp. Univ. Dept. Agr. Jour. 2 (6) : 149-198.

Doolittle, W. T. 1955. *Axe or Machine Girdling?* South. Lumberman 191 (2393) : 152, 157.

Dorman, K. W., and Barber, J. C. 1956. *Time of Flowering and Seed Ripening in Southern Pines.* U. S. Forest Serv. Southeast. Forest Expt. Sta. Paper 72, 15 pp.

Downey, E. J. 1937. *Open Tank Creosote Treatment of Shortleaf and Loblolly Pine Poles.* Jour. Forestry 35 : 349-352.

Downs, A. A. 1942. *The Influence of Silvicultural Practice on the Costs of Felling and Bucking Loblolly Pine Pulpwood.* Jour. Forestry 40 : 37-41.

———. 1947. *Choosing Pine Seed Trees.* Jour. Forestry 45 : 593-594.

——— and Barrett, L. 1943. *Growth Response of White Pine in the Southern Appalachians to Green Pruning.* Jour. Forestry 41 : 507-510.

Downs, R. J., and Borthwick, H. A. 1956. *Effects of Photoperiod on Growth of Trees.* Bot. Gaz. 117 : 310-326.

Dubow, D. A. 1954. *The Relationship Between Crown and Bole Length and Their Ratios with Diameter Growth in Young Loblolly Pine Plantations.* Thesis, N. C. State Col. School Forestry.

Duerr, W. A. 1951. *Guides to Profitable Forest Management.* Jour. Forestry 49 : 771-773.

——— and Bond, W. E. 1950. *Private Forest Management in the Lower South.* Ames Forester 37 (i.e. 38) : 32-47.

——— and Bond, W. E. 1952. *Optimum Stocking of a Selection Forest.* Jour. Forestry 50 : 12-16.

——— Fedkiw, J., and Guttenberg, S. 1956. *Financial Maturity: a Guide to Profitable Timber Growing.* U. S. Dept. Agr. Tech. Bul. 1146, 74 pp.

——— and Vaux, H. J. 1953. *Research in the Economics of Forestry.* Charles Lathrop Pack Forestry Found., 475 pp. Washington, D. C.

Duffield, J. W. 1952. *Relationships and Species Hybridization in the Genus Pinus.* Ztschr. f. Forstgenetik u. Forstpflanzenzücht. 1 : 93-97.

——— and Righter, F. I. 1953. *Annotated List of Pine Hybrids Made at the Institute of Forest Genetics.* U. S. Forest Serv. Calif. Forest and Range Expt. Sta. Forest Res. Notes 86, 9 pp.

Duncan, W. H. 1939. *Wilting Coefficient and Wilting Percentage of Three Forest Soils of the Duke Forest.* Soil Sci. 48 : 413-420.

———. 1941. *A Study of Root Development in Three Soil Types in the Duke Forest.* Ecol. Monog. 11 : 141-164.

Dyer, C. D. 1955. *Thinning Pine Stands.* Ga. Univ. Ext. Cir. 347, 7 pp.

Easley, L. T. 1954. *Loblolly Pine Seed Production Areas.* Jour. Forestry 52 : 672-673.

Egler, F. E. 1954. *Vegetation Management for Rights-of-Way and Roadsides.* Smithson. Inst. Ann. Rpt. 1952/53 : 299-322.

Eldredge, I. F. 1947. *The 4 Forests and the Future of the South.* Charles Lathrop Pack Forestry Found., 65 pp. Washington, D. C.

Elliott, F. A., and Pomeroy, K. B. 1948. *Artificial Regeneration of Loblolly Pine on a Prescribed Burn.* Jour. Forestry 46 : 296-298.

Evans, T. C. 1942. *The Distribution of Commercial Forest Trees in*

Virginia. U. S. Forest Serv. Appalachian Forest Expt. Sta. Forest Survey Release 10, 32 pp.

——— and McClay, T. A. 1952. *Rules-of-Thumb for Volume and Value in Pulpwood Trees.* U. S. Forest Serv. Southeast. Forest Expt. Sta. Res. Notes 4, 2 pp.

Ferguson, E. R. 1955. *Fire-Scorched Trees—Will They Live or Die?* Fourth Ann. Forestry Symposium Proc., La. State Univ. School Forestry 1955: 102-113.

———. 1956. *Causes of First-Year Mortality of Planted Loblolly Pines in East Texas.* Soc. Amer. Foresters Proc. 1956: 89-92.

———. 1957a. *Prescribed Burning in Shortleaf-Loblolly Pine on Rolling Uplands in East Texas.* U. S. Forest Serv. Fire Control Notes 18 (3): 130-132.

———. 1957b. *Stem-Kill and Sprouting Following Prescribed Fires in a Pine-Hardwood Stand in Texas.* Jour. Forestry 55: 426-429.

———. 1958. *Response of Planted Loblolly Pines to Reduction of Competition.* Jour. Forestry 56: 29-32.

——— and Duke, W. B. 1954. *Weevil Damage on Fresh-Cut Pineland.* U. S. Forest Serv. South. Forest Expt. Sta. South. Forestry Notes 94.

——— and Thatcher, R. C. 1956. *Preplanting Dip for Controlling Pales Weevil.* Jour. Forestry 54: 469-470.

Fernow, B. E. 1896. *Southern Pine—Mechanical and Physical Properties.* U. S. Dept. Agr. Div. Forestry Cir. 12, 12 pp.

Ferree, M. J. 1953. *A Method of Estimating Timber Volumes from Aerial Photographs.* N. Y. State Col. Forestry, Syracuse Univ. Tech. Pub. 75, 50 pp.

Ferrell, W. K. 1953. *Effect of Environmental Conditions on Survival and Growth of Forest Tree Seedlings Under Field Conditions in the Piedmont Region of North Carolina.* Ecology 34: 667-688.

Fields, J. G. 1947. *The Relationship of Stump Height Diameter to Diameter Breast High for Loblolly and Shortleaf Pines.* Thesis, Ga. Univ. School Forestry.

Fiori, A. 1934. *I Pini Delle Sezioni "Taeda" E "Australes."* Alpe (Florence) 21 (8-9): 353-358.

Flick, F. J. 1947. *Bibliography: Management of Loblolly-Shortleaf Pine-Hardwood Forests.* U. S. Dept. Agr. Library and South. Forest Expt. Sta., 6 pp.

Florence, R. G., and McWilliam, J. R. 1956. *The Influence of Spacing on Seed Production.* Ztschr. f. Forstgenetik u. Forstpflanzenzücht. 5 (4): 97-102.

Flory, C. H., Nettles, W. C., and Barker, W. J. 1955. *Forest Insects and Diseases of South Carolina Trees.* Clemson Agr. Col. S. C. Ext. Serv. Bul. 116, 40 pp.

Folweiler, A. D. 1953. *Forest Tree Improvement Research.* South. Lumberman 187 (2345): 200-203.

——— and Brown, A. A. 1946. *Fire in the Forests of the United States.* 183 pp. John S. Swift, St. Louis.

——— and Vaux, H. J. 1944. *Private Forest Land Ownership and Management in the Loblolly-Shortleaf Type of Louisiana.* Jour. Forestry 42: 783-790.

Forbes, R. D. 1923. *The Passing of the Piney Woods*. Amer. Forestry 29 (351) : 131-136.

————. 1924. *Fire in Loblolly Pine, Urania, La.* U. S. Forest Serv. Bul. 8 (17) : 5-6.

————. 1930. *Timber Growing and Logging and Turpentining Practices in the Southern Pine Region.* U. S. Dept. Agr. Tech. Bul. 204, 115 pp.

————and Bruce, D. 1930. *Rate of Growth of Second-Growth Southern Pines in Full Stands.* U. S. Dept. Agr. Cir. 124, 76 pp.

Forestry Committee of South Carolina. 1946. *Minimum Cutting Practices for South Carolina.* S. C. State Comn. Forestry and Clemson Agr. Col. S. C., 35 pp.

Foster, A. A. 1956a. *Opening Case-Hardened Southern Pine Cones.* Jour. Forestry 54: 466-467.

————. 1956b. *Fumigation of Forest Nurseries in the Southeast for Control of Weeds and Root Rot.* Tree Planters' Notes 26: 1-2.

————. 1956c. *The Effect of Seedbed Density on Seedling Production at the Georgia Forest Nurseries.* Tree Planters' Notes 25: 1-3.

————. 1956d. *Diseases of the Forest Nurseries of Georgia.* Plant Dis. Rptr. 40: 69-70.

————. 1959. *Nursery Diseases of Southern Pines.* U. S. Forest Serv. Forest Pest Leaflet 32, 7 pp.

———— and Henry, B. W. 1956. *Nursery Control of Fusiform Rust Demands Careful Spraying.* Tree Planters' Notes 24: 13-15.

Fowells, H. A., and Krauss, R. W. 1959. *The Inorganic Nutrition of Loblolly Pine and Virginia Pine with Special Reference to Nitrogen and Phosphorus.* Forest Sci. 5: 95-112.

Freas, A. D. 1953. *Laminated Southern Pine.* South. Lumberman 187 (2345) : 168-169.

Freese, F. 1950. *Pine Growth Doubled by Improvement Cutting.* Jour. Forestry 48: 855.

————. 1951. *Best Trees for Strip-Mined Land in Alabama.* U. S. Forest Serv. South. Forest Expt. Sta. South. Forestry Notes 76.

————. 1954. *Tree Species for Planting Spoil Banks in North Alabama.* Tree Planters' Notes 17: 15-18.

Frothingham, E. H., and Nelson, R. M. 1944. *South Carolina Forest Resources and Industries.* U. S. Dept. Agr. Misc. Pub. 552, 72 pp.

Gabriel, W. J. 1950. *The Effect of Some Treatments on the Establishment of Loblolly Pine in the Duke Forest.* Thesis, Duke Univ. School Forestry.

Gaiser, R. N. 1950. *Relation between Soil Characteristics and Site Index of Loblolly Pine in the Coastal Plain Region of Virginia and the Carolinas.* Jour. Forestry 48: 271-275.

Gallup, L. E. 1954. *Some Interrelationships of Drainage, Water Table, and Soil on the Hoffman Forest in Eastern North Carolina.* Thesis, N. C. State Col. School Forestry.

Gardner, F. E. 1929. *The Relationship Between Tree Age and the Rooting of Cuttings.* Amer. Soc. Hort. Sci. Proc. 26: 101-104.

Garin, G. I. 1955. *Pruning Southern Pines.* Forest Farmer 15 (2) : 6-8, 19.

Garland, H. 1939. *A Microscopic Study of Coniferous Wood in Relation to Its Strength Properties.* Bot. Gard. Ann. Rpt. 26, 95 pp.

Garren, K. H. 1939. *Studies on Polyporus Abietinus. III. The Influence of Certain Factors on the Rate of Decay of Loblolly Pine Sapwood.* Jour. Forestry 37: 319-323.

———. 1941. *Fire Wounds on Loblolly Pine and Their Relation to Decay and Other Cull.* Jour. Forestry 39: 16-22.

———. 1943. *Effects of Fire on Vegetation of the Southeastern United States.* Bot. Rev. 9: 617-654.

Garver, R. D. 1933. *The Portable Band Sawmill and Selective Logging in Second-Growth Loblolly Pine.* Jour. Forestry 31: 68-75.

——— and Cuno, J. B. 1932. *The Portable Band Sawmill and Selective Logging in the Loblolly Pine Forests of North Carolina.* U. S. Dept. Agr. Tech. Bul. 337, 30 pp.

——— Cuno, J. B., Korstian, C. F., and MacKinney, A. L. 1931. *Selective Logging in the Loblolly Pine-Hardwood Forests of the Middle Atlantic Coastal Plain with Special Reference to Virginia.* Va. Forest Serv. Pub. 43, pp. 1-50.

——— and Miller, R. H. 1933. *Selective Logging in the Shortleaf and Loblolly Pine Forests of the Gulf States Region.* U. S. Dept. Agr. Tech. Bul. 375, 54 pp.

Gemmer, E. W. 1939. *Reproduction of Loblolly Pine.* U. S. Forest Serv. South. Forest Expt. Sta. South. Forestry Notes 28.

———. 1941. *Loblolly Pine Establishment as Affected by Grazing, Overstory, and Seedbed Preparation.* Jour. Forestry 39: 473-477.

Gevorkiantz, S. R. 1940. *Comments on "The Approach of Loblolly and Virginia Pine Stands Toward Normal Stocking."* Jour. Forestry 38: 512-513.

Gibbs, J. A. 1948a. *Tree Plantings Control Erosion and Produce Wood.* Forest Farmer 8 (2): 5.

———. 1948b. *Growth of Tree Plantings for Erosion Control in the Southeastern Region.* Iowa State Col. Jour. Sci. 22: 371-386.

Gilmore, A. R. 1957. *Physical and Chemical Characteristics of Loblolly Pine Seedlings Associated with Drought Resistance.* South. Conf. Forest Tree Impr. Proc. 4: 34-39.

Girard, J. W. 1933. *Volume Tables for Mississippi Bottomland Hardwoods and Southern Pines.* Jour. Forestry 31: 34-41.

Goddard, R. E. 1954. *Killing Small Undesirable Hardwoods by Use of the Cornell Tool.* Down to Earth (Dow Chemical Co.) 10 (2): 5.

———. 1955. *Basal Spray Treatments of Small Hardwoods with Chemical Herbicide 2,4,5-T.* Tex. Forest Serv. Res. Note 13, 20 pp.

Goggans, J. F. 1949. *Cronartium Fusiforme on Slash and Loblolly Pine in the Piedmont Region of Alabama.* Jour. Forestry 47: 978-980.

———. 1951. *Slash and Loblolly Pine Plantations in Alabama's Piedmont Region.* Ala. Agr. Expt. Sta. Cir. 99, 22 pp.

———. 1957. *Southern Fusiform Rust.* Ala. Agr. Expt. Sta. Bul. 304, 19 pp.

——— and Schultz, E. F. 1958. *Growth of Pine Plantations in Alabama's Coastal Plain.* Ala. Agr. Expt. Sta. Bul. 313, 19 pp.

Golden, E. A. 1951. *The Hess Creek Logging Area: Stand Condition*

After Fifteen Years of Management. Thesis, La. State Univ. School Forestry.

Golfari, L. 1954. *Pulpwood from Plantations of Exotic Conifers in the Parana Delta.* (Informal English translation of original Spanish). FAO United Nations Rpt.

Goodwin, O. C., Jr. 1947. *Comparative Costs of Producing Pine Pulpwood with a Chain Saw and with a Crosscut Saw in the Piedmont Region of North Carolina.* Thesis, Duke Univ. School Forestry.

Grabow, R. H. 1923. *Suitability of Various American Woods for Pulp and Paper Making.* Jour. Forestry 21: 462-474.

Graham, D. P. 1952. *The Effect of Trichoderma and Penicillium Molds on the Toughness of Loblolly Pine.* Thesis, La. State Univ. School Forestry.

Graham, E. H. 1941. *Legumes for Erosion Control and Wildlife.* U. S. Dept. Agr. Misc. Pub. 412, 153 pp.

Graham, S. A. 1939. *Principles of Forest Entomology.* Ed. 2, 410 pp. New York and London.

Grano, C. X. 1949. *Is Litter a Barrier to the Initial Establishment of Shortleaf and Loblolly Pine Reproduction?* Jour. Forestry 47: 544-548.

――――. 1951a. *What Loblollies Are Likely Cone Producers.* Jour. Forestry 49: 734.

――――. 1951b. *Can Hardwood Root Grafts Transmit Poison?* Forest Farmer 10 (7): 6.

――――. 1952a. *Effectiveness of Ammate in Controlling Hardwoods.* South. Lumberman 185 (2316): 44, 46, 48, 50.

――――. 1952b. *2,4,5-T for Unwanted Southern Hardwoods.* U. S. Forest Serv. South. Forest Expt. Sta. South. Forestry Notes 78.

――――. 1952c. *How do Sulfamate Poisons Kill Trees?* Jour. Forestry 50: 318.

――――. 1953a. *Chemical Control of Weed Hardwoods.* South. Lumberman 186 (2332): 46-47.

――――. 1953b. *Wind-Firmness of Shortleaf and Loblolly Pines.* South. Lumberman 187 (2345): 116.

――――. 1954. *Re-Establishment of Shortleaf-Loblolly Pine under Four Cutting Methods.* Jour. Forestry 52: 132-133.

――――. 1955a. *Behavior of South Arkansas Oaks Girdled in Different Seasons.* Jour. Forestry 53: 886-888.

――――. 1955b. *Girdle Your Weed Trees in the Spring.* Forest Farmer 14 (4): 6, 16.

――――. 1956. *Growing Loblolly and Shortleaf Pine in the Mid-South.* U. S. Dept. Agr. Farmers' Bul. 2102, 25 pp.

――――. 1957a. *Growth of Loblolly Pine Seed Trees in Relation to Crown Density.* Jour. Forestry 55: 852.

――――. 1957b. *Indices to Potential Cone Production of Loblolly Pine.* Jour. Forestry 55: 890-891.

Grant, B. F., and Patterson, A. E. 1946. *Forest Facts of Georgia.* Ga. Forestry Dept. Bul. 10.

Greene, G. E. 1953. *Soil Temperatures in the South Carolina Piedmont.* U. S. Forest Serv. Southeast. Forest Expt. Sta. Paper 29, 16 pp.

Greene, M. F. 1956. *Forest Fire Insurance as It Affects Forest Management and Fire Control Activities.* Soc. Amer. Foresters Proc. 1956: 181-185.

Gregory, G. R., and Person, H. L. 1946. *Pine Log Grades and Lumber Recovery.* South. Lumberman 173 (2177): 168-169.

———— and Person, H. L. 1949. *Lumber Values for East Texas Pine Logs.* U. S. Forest Serv. South. Forest Expt. Sta. Occas. Paper 113, 31 pp.

Grigsby, H. C. 1952. *The Relationship of Some Soil Factors to the Site Index of Loblolly Pine in Southeastern Louisiana.* Thesis, La. State Univ. School Forestry.

Griswold, N. B. 1949. *Mine Wood Market—a Potential Aid to Forest Management.* Forest Farmer 8 (10): 6, 8.

————. 1952. *Improvement Cuttings as a Means of Increasing the Value of Forest Lands in North-Central Alabama.* Ala. Acad. Sci. Jour. 21/22: 30-32.

———— and McKnight, J. S. 1947. *Wood Use by Alabama Mines.* U. S. Forest Serv. South. Forest Expt. Sta. Occas. Paper 109, 12 pp.

———— and McKnight, J. S. 1948. *Wood—an Important Resource to Alabama Mine Operators.* Ala. Purchaser 4 (3): 24-25.

Grosenbaugh, L. R. 1952a. *Shortcuts for Cruisers and Scalers.* U. S. Forest Serv. South. Forest Expt. Sta. Occas. Paper 126, 24 pp.

————. 1952b. *Plotless Timber Estimates—New, Fast, Easy.* Jour. Forestry 50: 32-37.

————. 1955. *Better Diagnosis and Prescription in Southern Forest Management.* U. S. Forest Serv. South. Forest Expt. Sta. Occas. Paper 145, 27 pp.

————. 1958. *Point-Sampling and Line-Sampling: Probability Theory, Geometric Implications, Synthesis.* U. S. Forest Serv. South. Forest Expt. Sta. Occas. Paper 160, 34 pp.

Gruschow, G. F., and Trousdell, K. B. 1958. *Incidence of Heart Rot in Mature Loblolly Pine in Coastal North Carolina.* Jour. Forestry 56: 220-221.

Guttenberg, S. 1949. *Good Trees—Good Lumber—Surer Profits.* South. Lumberman 179 (2249): 132-135.

————. 1950. *The Rate of Interest in Forest Management.* Jour. Forestry 48: 3-7.

————. 1953. *Loblolly Crown Length—Clue to Vigor.* U. S. Forest Serv. South. Forest Expt. Sta. South. Forestry Notes 88.

————. 1954. *Growth and Mortality in an Old-Field Southern Pine Stand.* Jour. Forestry 52: 166-168.

————. 1956. *Influence of Timber Characteristics Upon Stumpage Prices.* U. S. Forest Serv. South. Forest Expt. Sta. Occas. Paper 146, 14 pp.

———— and Duerr, W. A. 1949. *A Guide to Profitable Tree Utilization.* U. S. Forest Serv. South. Forest Expt. Sta. Occas. Paper 114, 18 pp.

———— and Perry, J. D. 1957. *Pulpwooding with Less Manpower.* U. S. Forest Serv. South. Forest Expt. Sta. Occas. Paper 154, 34 pp.

———— and Reynolds, R. R. 1953. *Cutting Financially Mature Loblolly and Shortleaf Pine.* U. S. Forest Serv. South. Forest Expt. Sta. Occas. Paper 129, 18 pp.

Hahn, V. W. 1942. *The Effect of Soil and Air Temperatures on the Re-*

sumption of Growth of Tree Seedlings in the Spring. Thesis, Duke Univ. School Forestry.

Haig, I. T. 1938. *Fire in Modern Forest Management.* Jour. Forestry 36: 1045-1049.

———. 1950a. *Solving the Riddle of Low Grade Hardwoods.* Amer. Forests 56 (2): 28-30, 40-41.

———. 1950 b. *The Control of Undesirable Hardwoods in Southern Forests.* Forest Farmer 9 (11): 9, 11, 14.

Haines, W. H. B. 1953a. *62 Percent of Pine Lumber is Cut from 10-Inch or Smaller Logs in the Central Piedmont of South Carolina.* U. S. Forest Serv. Southeast. Forest Expt. Sta. Res. Notes 36, 2 pp.

———. 1953b. *86 Percent of Tops and 54 Percent of Slabs and Edgings Unused in Central Piedmont of South Carolina.* U. S. Forest Serv. Southeast. Forest Expt. Sta. Res. Notes 35, 2 pp.

Haliburton, W. 1943. *Some Factors in the Environmental Resistance of Ips Degeer.* Thesis, Duke Univ. School Forestry.

Hall, W. L. 1939. *Building Up a Shortleaf-Loblolly Pine Forest in Arkansas.* Jour. Forestry 37: 538-540.

———. 1945. *Is Pine Coming or Going in South Arkansas?* Jour. Forestry 43: 634-637.

———. 1947. *Prescribed Burning in the Loblolly Pine Type.* Jour. Forestry 45: 209-212.

——— and Maxwell, H. 1911. *Uses of Commercial Woods of the United States. II. Pines.* U. S. Dept. Agr. Forest Serv. Bul. 99, 96 pp.

Halloran, A. F. 1943. *Management of Deer and Cattle on the Aransas National Wildlife Refuge, Texas.* Jour. Wildlife Mangt. 7 (2): 203-216.

Halls, L. K. 1957. *Grazing Capacity of Wiregrass-Pine Ranges of Georgia.* Jour. Range Mangt. 10: 1-5.

——— Burton, G. W., and Southwell, B. L. 1957. *Some Results of Seeding and Fertilization to Improve Southern Forest Ranges.* U. S. Forest Serv. Southeast. Forest Expt. Sta. Paper 78, 26 pp.

——— Hale, O. M., and Knox, F. E. 1957. *Seasonal Variation in Grazing Use, Nutritive Content, and Digestibility of Wiregrass Forage.* Ga. Agr. Expt. Sta. Tech. Bul. (n.s.) 11, 28 pp.

Hamilton, J. R. 1949. *The Fungicidal Treatment of Stratified and Unstratified Loblolly and Shortleaf Pine Seed to Prevent Damping-Off.* Thesis, Ga. Univ. School Forestry.

———. 1956a. *An Evaluation of Southern Pine Plantations in the Georgia Piedmont Plateau.* Ga. Agr. Expt. Sta. Bul. (n.s.) 20, 41 pp.

———. 1956b. *Effect of Season of Year and Length of Seasoning Time on Absorption and Distribution of Zinc Chloride Solution in Unpeeled Fence Posts.* Ga. Agr. Expt. Sta. Cir. (n.s.) 3, 8 pp.

Hamilton, S. W. 1943. *Ratios of Clean and Rough Seed.* Jour. Forestry 41: 63-64.

Haney, G. P. 1956. *Effect of Burning and Discing Before Logging on Establishment of Loblolly Pine and on Recovery of Brush.* Thesis, N. C. State Col. School Forestry.

Hansbrough, T. 1956. *Growth of Planted Loblolly and Slash Pines in North Louisiana.* La. State Univ. Forestry Notes 10, 2 pp.

——— and Hollis, J. P., 1957. *The Effect of Soil Fumigation for the*

Control of Parasitic Nematodes on the Growth and Yield of Loblolly Pine Seedlings. Plant Dis. Rptr. 41: 1021-1025.

Hardtner, Q. T., Jr. 1954. *Forestry and Southern Pine.* South. Lumberman 189 (2369): 127-128.

Harkin, D. A. 1957. *Every Seedling from Selected Seed.* Jour. Forestry 55: 842-843.

Harlow, W. M., and Harrar, E. S. 1941. *Textbook of Dendrology.* Ed. 2, 542 pp. New York and London.

Harper, R. M. 1913. *Geographical Report, Including Descriptions of the Natural Divisions of the State, Their Forests and Forest Industries, with Quantitative Analyses and Statistical Tables.* In Economic Botany of Alabama, pt. 1, Ala. Geol. Survey Monog. 8, 228 pp.

————. 1917. *A Quantitative, Volumetric, and Dynamic Study of the Vegetation of the Pinus Taeda Belt of Virginia and the Carolinas.* Torrey Bot. Club Bul. 44: 39-57.

————. 1928. *Catalogue of the Trees, Shrubs, and Vines of Alabama, with Their Economic Properties and Local Distribution.* In Economic Botany of Alabama, pt. 2, Ala. Geol. Survey Monog. 9, 357 pp.

————. 1943. *Forests of Alabama.* Ala. Geol. Survey Monog. 10, 230 pp.

Harrar, E. S. 1934. *Identification and Microscopy of Wood and Wood Fibers Used in the Manufacture of Pulp. Pt. 1. Coniferous Pulpwoods.* Paper Indus. 15: 630-637.

Harrington, T. A. 1955a. *2,4,5-T Basal Spray on Hardwoods Does Not Harm Loblolly Planted Next Day.* U. S. Forest Serv. South. Forest Expt. Sta. South. Forestry Notes 95.

————. 1955b. *Tip Moth and Webworm in East Texas.* U. S. Forest Serv. South. Forest Expt. Sta. South. Forestry Notes 97.

————. 1955c. *More Power to Girdling.* Forest Farmer 14 (8): 12, 16-17.

————. 1956. *Loblolly Seedling Survival After Hardwood Control by 2,4,5-T.* Jour. Forestry 54: 39-40.

———— and Stephenson, G. K. 1955. *Repeat Burns Reduce Small Stems in Texas Big Thicket.* Jour. Forestry 53: 847.

Harris, E. E. 1950. *Wood Molasses for Stock and Poultry Feed.* U. S. Forest Serv. Forest Prod. Lab. Rpt. R-1731, 21 pp. (Revised Oct. 1955).

Harrison, R. P. 1957. *Pine Bark Beetles and Their Control in Georgia.* Ga. Forest Res. Council Rpt. 2, 8 pp.

Hartley, C. 1929. *Forest Tree Seedlings Kept from Damping-Off by Aluminum Sulphate.* U. S. Dept. Agr. Yearbook 1928: 332-334.

Hartman, A. W. 1949. *Fire as a Tool in Southern Pine.* U. S. Dept. Agr. Yearbook 1949: 517-527.

Hastings, A. B. 1935. *Forest Fire Control in the Coastal Plains Section of the South.* Jour. Forestry 33: 320-323.

Hatch, A. B., and Doak, K. D. 1933. *Mycorrhizal and Other Features of the Root Systems of Pinus.* Arnold Arboretum Jour. 14 (1): 85-99.

Hawley, R. C., and Smith, D. M. 1954. *The Practice of Silviculture.* Ed. 6, 525 pp. New York.

Hayes, R. W., and Wakeley, P. C. 1929. *Survival and Early Growth of Planted Southern Pine in Southeastern Louisiana.* La. State Univ. Bul. 21 (3): pt. 2, 48 pp.

Hebb, E. A. 1948. *A Study of the Influence of Overstory on the Incidence of Cronartium Cankers on Loblolly Pine*. Thesis, La. State Univ. School Forestry.

Hedgcock, G. G. 1928. *A Key to the Known Aecial Forms of Coleosporium Occurring in the United States and a List of the Host Species.* Mycologia 20 (2) : 97-100.

———— and Siggers, P. V. 1949. *A Comparison of the Pine-Oak Rusts.* U. S. Dept. Agr. Tech. Bul. 978, 30 pp.

Heeren, R. D. 1956. *The Regeneration of Loblolly Pine under the Shelterwood Method in the Duke Forest.* Thesis, Duke Univ. School Forestry.

Heiberg, S. O. 1939. *Forest Soil in Relation to Silviculture.* Jour. Forestry 37 : 42-46.

Heller, R. C., Coyne, J. F., and Bean, J. L. 1955. *Airplanes Increase Effectiveness of Southern Pine Beetle Surveys.* Jour. Forestry 53 : 483-487.

Hendrickson, B. H. 1949. *Tenth-Year Progress Report, Field Tests of Farm Woodland Practices, Tree Planting Studies, Southern Piedmont Soil and Water Conservation Experiment Station, Watkinsville, Georgia, December 1948.* U. S. Soil Conserv. Serv. Region 2, 20 pp.

Henry, B. W. 1953. *A Root Rot of Southern Pine Nursery Seedlings and Its Control by Soil Fumigation.* Phytopathology 43 : 81-88.

———— and Bercaw, T. E. 1956. *Shortleaf-Loblolly Hybrid Pines Free of Fusiform Rust After 5 Years' Exposure.* Jour. Forestry 54 : 779.

Hepting, G. H. 1934. *Eastern Forest Tree Diseases in Relation to Stand Improvement.* Emergency Conserv. Work Forestry Pub. 2., 28 pp.

————. 1935. *Blue Stain Development in Peeled Shortleaf and Loblolly Pine Pulpwood.* Paper Indus. 17 : 402-404.

————. 1942. *Reducing Losses from Tree Diseases in Eastern Forests and Farm Woodlands.* U. S. Dept. Agr. Farmers' Bul. 1887, 21 pp.

————. 1944. *Little-Leaf—a Shortleaf and Loblolly Pine Problem.* Amer. Forests 50 : 244.

————. 1945a. *Reserve Food Storage in Shortleaf Pine in Relation to Little-Leaf Disease.* Phytopathology 35 : 106-119.

————. 1945b. *Decay and Staining of Southern Pine Pulpwood.* Paper Indus. and Paper World 27 (3) : 379-382.

————. 1949. *Managing Pines in Littleleaf Areas.* Forest Farmer 8 (11) : 7, 10.

————. 1952. *Disease Factors in the Management of Young, Even-Aged Southern Pine.* First Ann. Forestry Symposium Proc., La. State Univ. School Forestry 1952 : 37-41.

————. 1953. *Diseases of Forest Trees in Virginia.* Va. Forests 8 (5) : 8-10.

———— and Chapman, A. D. 1938. *Losses from Heart Rot in Two Shortleaf and Loblolly Pine Stands.* Jour. Forestry 36 : 1193-1201.

———— and Lindgren, R. M. 1950. *Common Southern Forest Tree Diseases.* Forest Farmer 9 (5) : 31-33.

———— and Roth, E. R. 1950. *The Fruiting of Heart-Rot Fungi on Felled Trees.* Jour. Forestry 48 : 332-333.

Herrick, A. M. 1945. *A Numerical Evaluation of Stand Structure.* Jour. Forestry 43 : 891-899.

Herty, C. H. 1933. *White Paper from Young Southern Pines.* Paper Trade Jour. 96 (13) : 23-27.

Hetrick, L. A. 1940. *Some Factors in Natural Control of the Southern Pine Beetle, Dendroctonus Frontalis Zimm.* Jour. Econ. Ent. 33: 554-556.

——. 1941. *Life History Studies of Neodiprion Americanum (Leach).* Jour. Econ. Ent. 34: 373-377.

——. 1942. *Some Observations of Ips Bark Beetle Attack on Pine Trees.* Jour. Econ. Ent. 35: 181-183.

——. 1949. *Some Overlooked Relationships of Southern Pine Beetle.* Jour. Econ. Ent. 42: 466-470.

——. 1956. *Life History Studies of Five Species of Neodiprion Sawflies.* Forest Sci. 2: 181-185.

Heyward, F., Jr. 1939. *Some Phases of Pine Forest Management for Pulpwood.* South. Pulp and Paper Jour. 1 (6) : 16-18, 25.

Hills, J. T. 1954. *Prescribed Burning Gets Results.* U. S. Forest Serv. Fire Control Notes 15 (3) : 21.

——. 1957. *Prescribed Burning Techniques in Loblolly and Longleaf Pine on the Francis Marion National Forest.* U. S. Forest Serv. Fire Control Notes 18 (3) : 112-113.

Hinds, W. E. 1912. *The Southern Pine Beetle and Its Control.* Ala. Agr. Expt. Sta. Cir. 15: 45-58.

Hobbs, J. E. 1947. *A Study of the Relationship Between Soil Texture and Establishment of Pine Reproduction, as Affecting Silvicultural Practices on Upland Piedmont Soils in Durham County and Vicinity in N. C.* Thesis, Duke Univ. School Forestry.

Hocker, H. W., Jr. 1953. *Relative Growth and Development of Loblolly Pine and Yellow Poplar on a Series of Soil-Sites in the Lower Piedmont of North Carolina.* Thesis, N. C. State Col. School Forestry.

——. 1955. *Climatological Summaries for Selected Stations in and Near the Southern Pine Region, 1921-1950.* U. S. Forest Serv. Southeast. Forest Expt. Sta. Paper 56, 11 pp.

——. 1956. *Certain Aspects of Climate as Related to the Distribution of Loblolly Pine.* Ecology 37: 824-834.

Hodgkins, E. J. 1952. *Effect of Different Heat Treatments upon the Viability and Vigor of Pine Pollen.* Jour. Forestry 50: 450-452.

——. 1956. *Testing Soil-Site Index Tables in Southwestern Alabama.* Jour. Forestry 54: 261-266.

——. 1957. *Some Early Effects of Prescribed Burning on the Soil, Forest Floor, and Vegetation in the Loblolly-Shortleaf Pine Forest of the Upper Coastal Plain of Alabama.* Abs., *In* Diss. Abs. 17 (6) 1957 (1176).

——. 1958. *Effects of Fire on Undergrowth Vegetation in Upland Southern Pine Forests.* Ecology 39 (1) : 38-46.

Hoffmann, C. H., and Anderson, R. F. 1945. *Effect of Southern Pine Beetle on Timber Losses and Natural Restocking.* Jour. Forestry 43: 436-439.

Holley, D. P. 1947. *The Value of Pine Thinnings from Farm Woodlands in the Piedmont Region of N. C.* Thesis, Duke Univ. School Forestry.

Hollick, A. 1897. *Oldfield Pine in New Jersey.* Forester 3: 136.

Hoover, M. D. 1950. *Hydrologic Characteristics of South Carolina Piedmont Forest Soils.* Soil Sci. Soc. Amer. Proc. 14: 353-358.

———. 1953. *Interception of Rainfall in a Young Loblolly Pine Plantation.* U. S. Forest Serv. Southeast. Forest Expt. Sta. Paper 21, 13 pp.

——— Olson, D. F., Jr., and Greene, G. E. 1953. *Soil Moisture Under a Young Loblolly Pine Plantation.* Soil Sci. Soc. Amer. Proc. 17: 147-150.

——— Metz, L. J., and Olson, D. F., Jr. 1954. *Soil Sampling for Pore Space and Percolation.* U. S. Forest Serv. Southeast. Forest Expt. Sta. Paper 42, 28 pp.

Hopkins, A. D. 1899. *Report on Investigations to Determine the Cause of Unhealthy Conditions of the Spruce and Pine from 1880-1893.* W. Va. Agr. Expt. Sta. Bul. 56, 461 pp.

———. 1903. *Some of the Principal Insect Enemies of Coniferous Forest in the United States.* U. S. Dept. Agr. Yearbook 1902: 265-282.

———. 1909a. *Some Insects Injurious to Forests. Insect Depredations in North American Forests and Practical Methods of Prevention and Control.* U. S. Bur. Ent. Bul. 58, pt. 5, pp. 57-101.

———. 1909b. *Practical Information on the Scolytid Beetles of North American Forests. I. Barkbeetles of the Genus Dendroctonus.* U. S. Bur. Ent. Bul. 83, 169 pp.

———. 1910. *Insect Injuries to the Wood of Dying and Dead Trees.* U. S. Bur. Ent. Cir. 127, 3 pp.

———. 1921. *The Southern Pine Beetle: a Menace to the Pine Timber of the Southern States.* U. S. Dept. Agr. Farmers' Bul. 1188, 15 pp.

Hopkins, W. 1949. *Machine Planting—No Cinch!* South. Lumberman 179 (2249): 172-175.

Hopkins, W. C. 1948. *Intermediate Operations in the Management of Loblolly Pine.* Thesis, Yale Univ. School Forestry.

———. 1957. *Factors Which Influence the Production of Clear Loblolly Pine Lumber.* (Abs.) Assoc. South. Agr. Workers Proc. 54: 164-165.

———. 1958. *Relationship of Stand Characteristics to Quality of Loblolly Pine.* La. Agr. Expt. Sta. Bul. 517, 27 pp.

Horn, A. F. 1956. *A Simplified Method for Estimating Form Class of Loblolly and Shortleaf Pine Stands in Mississippi.* Jour. Forestry 54: 185-187.

Hostetter, R. D. 1943. *The Profitability of Corn, Cotton, Loblolly Pine, and Shortleaf Pine When Grown on Eleven Durham County Soils.* Thesis, Duke Univ. School Forestry.

Hubbard, F. W., Jr. 1955. *Estimating the Age of Southern Pine by Bark Characteristics.* U. S. Forest Serv. Region 8 Serv. Forester Tech. 4.

Huberman, M. A. 1940a. *Normal Growth and Development of Southern Pine Seedlings in the Nursery.* Ecology 21: 323-334.

———. 1940b. *Studies in Raising Southern Pine Nursery Seedlings.* Jour. Forestry 38: 341-345.

Huckenpahler, B. J. 1948. *Loblolly Pine Is Superior to Shortleaf.* Miss. Farm Res. [Miss. Sta.] 11 (7): 8.

———. 1949a. *Which Is Best? a Study of Loblolly vs. Shortleaf.* South. Lumber Jour. 53 (3): 19, 108.

————. 1949b. *Underplanted Loblolly Pines Need Early Release.* U. S. Forest Serv. South. Forest Expt. Sta. South. Forestry Notes 61.

————. 1950. *Development of Nineteen-Year-Old Southern Pine Plantations in Tennessee.* Jour. Forestry 48: 722-723.

————. 1952. *Ax or Poison?* South. Lumberman 185 (2321): 180-182.

————. 1953a. *Source of Seed Affects Pine Survival and Growth.* Miss. Farm Res. [Miss. Sta.] 16 (6): 6.

————. 1953b. *Loblolly Best in North Mississippi Despite Tip Moth and Webworm.* Jour. Forestry 51: 640.

————. 1954. *Poisoning Versus Girdling to Release Underplanted Pines in North Mississippi.* Jour. Forestry 52: 266-268.

————. 1955. *Underplanted Loblolly Pine Responds to Delayed Release.* Jour. Forestry 53: 512.

Hudson, M. S. 1947. *Vapor Drying: the Artificial Seasoning of Wood in Vapor of Organic Chemicals.* Forest Prod. Res. Soc. Proc. 1: 124-146.

————. 1952. *Poria Radiculosa, a Creosote-Tolerant Organism.* Forest Prod. Res. Soc. Jour. 2 (2): 73-74.

Huffman, J. B. 1955. *Distribution of Resinous Extractives in Loblolly Pine Lumber After Seasoning.* Forest Prod. Res. Soc. Jour. 5 (2): 135-138.

Hughes, R. H., and Rea, J. L., Jr. 1951. *Forage for Fire Protection—Grazed Firebreaks in the North Carolina Coastal Plain.* South. Lumberman 183 (2297): 157-160.

Humphrey, C. J., and Siggers, P. V. 1933. *Temperature Relations of Wood-Destroying Fungi.* Jour. Agr. Res. 47: 997-1014.

Hunt, F. M. 1951. *Effects of Flooded Soil on Growth of Pine Seedlings.* Plant Physiol. 26: 363-368.

Hunt, G. M., and Garratt, G. A. 1938. *Wood Preservation.* 457 pp. New York and London.

Huntemann, J. W. 1952. *Stem and Crown Development Relationships of Loblolly Pine in a Portion of the Georgia Piedmont.* Thesis, Ga. Univ. School Forestry.

Hunter, W. D. 1912. *Two Destructive Texas Ants.* U. S. Bur. Ent. Cir. 148, 7 pp.

Hyler, J. E. 1956. *Modern Sawmilling.* South. Lumberman 192 (2398): 33-34, 36.

Isenberg, I. H., and Buchanan, M. A. 1945. *A Color Reaction of Wood with Methanolhydrochloric Acid.* Jour. Forestry 43: 888-890.

Jackson, L. W. R. 1945. *Root Defects and Fungi Associated with the Little-Leaf Disease of Southern Pines.* Phytopathology 35: 91-105.

————. 1952. *Radial Growth of Forest Trees in the Georgia Piedmont.* Ecology 33: 336-341.

————. 1958. *Spacing and Growth.* Forest Farmer 18 (3): 12-13, 18-19.

————. 1959. *Loblolly Pine Tracheid Length in Relation to Position in Tree.* Jour. Forestry 57: 366-367.

———— and Greene, J. T. 1958. *Tracheid Length Variation and Inheritance in Slash and Loblolly Pine.* Forest Sci. 4: 316-318.

———— Thompson, G. E., and Lund, H. O. 1954. *Forest Diseases and Insects of Georgia's Trees.* Ga. Forestry Comn., 39 pp.

Jeffords, A. I., Jr. 1956. *Trends in Pine Pulpwood Marketing in the South.* Jour. Forestry 54: 463-466.

Jemison, G. M., and Korstian, C. F. 1944. *Loblolly Pine Seed Production and Dispersal.* Jour. Forestry 42: 734-741.

———— Lindenmuth, A. W., and Keetch, J. J. 1949. *Forest Fire-Danger Measurement in the Eastern United States.* U. S. Dept. Agr. Handb. 1, 68 pp.

———— and others. 1945. *Cutting Practices for the Carolinas.* Committee report. Jour. Forestry 43: 861-870.

Jiles, R. A., Jr. 1957. *Pine Stumpage Sales for Pulpwood and Sawlogs in East Tennessee.* U. S. Tenn. Val. Authority, Div. Forestry Relat. Tech. Note 30, 20 pp.

Johansson, D. 1935. *Effect of Quality of Wood in Manufacture of Sulfate and Sulfite Pulp.* Svenska Skogsvardsfor. Tidskr. 33 (1): 77-101. Biol. Abs. 9 (9): Item 19486. 1935.

Johnson, E. A., and Kovner, J. L. 1956. *Effect on Streamflow of Cutting a Forest Understory.* Forest Sci. 2 (2): 82-91.

Johnson, J. W., and others. 1956. *Proceedings of Southeastern Direct Seeding Conference.* Woodlands Res. Dept., Union Bag-Camp Paper Corp., 66 pp. Savannah, Ga.

Johnston, H. R. 1944. *Control of the Texas Leaf-Cutting Ant with Methyl Bromide.* Jour. Forestry 42: 130-132.

————. 1952. *Insect Control: Practical Methods for the Control of Insects Attacking Green Logs and Lumber.* South. Lumberman 184 (2307): 37-39.

———— and Eaton, C. B. 1942. *Tests with Various Chemicals for the Control of White Grubs in Forest Nurseries of the Carolinas.* Jour. Forestry 40: 712-721.

———— and Kowal, R. J. 1949. *New Insecticides for the Prevention of Attack by Ambrosia Beetles on Logs and Lumber.* South. Lumberman 179 (2249): 183-188.

Johstono, H. E., Jr. 1954. *A Study Concerning the Diameter Increment of Residual Pine Saplings in the Southern Piedmont.* Thesis, Ga. Univ. School Forestry.

Jokela, J. J., and Lorenz, R. W. 1955. *A Comparison of Three Methods of Eliminating Cull Trees from Woodlands with 2,4,5-T.* Jour. Forestry 53: 901-904.

Jones, E. E., Jr. 1947. *Cost Analysis of a Mechanized Pulpwood Operation in Eastern Virginia.* Thesis, Duke Univ. School Forestry.

Jones, G. D., and Ford, J. E. 1952. *The Turpentine Beetle in North Carolina.* N. C. Agr. Ext. Serv. Ext. Folder 91.

————. 1954. *Ips Engraver Beetles in North Carolina.* N. C. Agr. Ext. Serv. Ext. Folder 108.

Jones, J. K. N., and Painter, T. J. 1957. *The Hemicelluloses of Loblolly Pine Wood. Part I. The Isolation of Five Oligosaccharide Fragments.* Chem. Soc. Jour. 1957: 669-673.

Jordan, C. R., and Dyer, C. D. 1956. *The Black Turpentine Beetle and Its Control.* Ga. Agr. Col. Ext. Cir. 404, 12 pp.

Katana, M. S. 1955. *Some Comparisons of Precipitation, Streamflow, and*

Soil on a Denuded, a Grass-Covered, and a Forested Watershed in the Copper Basin of Tennessee. Thesis, N. C. State Col. School Forestry.

Kauffman, E. 1955. *The Forest Fire Problem in the South.* South. Lumberman 191 (2393) : 144-146.

———. 1956. *More and Better Trees from Our Nurseries.* Forest Farmer 16 (1) : 4-6.

Kaufman, C. M. 1949. *Forest Grazing in the North Carolina Piedmont.* Soc. Amer. Foresters Proc. (1948) 2 : 39-244.

Keetch, J. J. 1954. *Instructions for Using Forest Fire Danger Meter Type 8.* U. S. Forest Serv. Southeast. Forest Expt. Sta. Paper 33, 7 pp.

Keever, N. C. 1950. *Causes of Succession on Old Fields of the Piedmont, North Carolina.* Ecol. Monog. 20 : 229-250.

Kelso, W. C., Jr. 1951. *The Effect of Insect Peeling on the Strength of Loblolly Pine Fence Posts.* Thesis, Yale Univ. School Forestry.

Ker, J. W. 1953. *The Relationship Between the Number of Trees Per Acre and the Percentage Stocking of Reproduction.* Jour. Forestry 51 : 342-344.

———. 1954. *Distribution Series Arising in Quadrat Sampling of Reproduction.* Jour. Forestry 52 : 838-841.

Kilbourne, R. D. 1957. *Water and the TVA Forestry Program.* Forest Farmer 16 (8) : 11-13.

Kincer, J. B. 1936. *Climate (Part I, 1922), Temperature, Sunshine, and Wind (Part II, Sec. B, 1928).* In Atlas of American Agriculture. U. S. Dept. Agr., 34 pp. Washington, D. C.

King, D. B. 1955. *A Test of Krilium Soil Conditioner in Gully Planting.* Jour. Forestry 53 : 731-732.

King, H. C. 1946. *Notes on the Three Cyclones in Mauritius in 1945: Their Effect on Exotic Plantations, Indigenous Forest and on Some Timber Buildings.* Empire Forestry Jour. 24 (2) : 192-195. Forestry Abs. 8 (1) : 147. 1946.

King, W. W. 1953a. *Progress Report on Durability Tests of Posts Treated by Non-Pressure Methods and with Various Wood Preservatives.* Tex. Forest Serv. Res. Note 5.

———. 1953b. *The Effect of Log Diameter and Milling Equipment on Sawmill Residues.* Jour. Forestry 51 : 897-906.

———. 1954. *Cause of and Remedy for Warped Southern Pine 2 x 4's.* South. Lumberman 189 (2361) : 31-34.

Kirby, J. 1954. *Death Strikes the Woods.* Forest Farmer 13 (6) : 5, 10-11.

Klawitter, R. W. 1957. *Most Cankered Trees Are Good Risks in Loblolly Pine Sawtimber Stands.* U. S. Forest Serv. Southeast. Forest Expt. Sta. Res. Notes 107.

Knapp, G. E. 1946. *Mechanization in Southern Pulpwood Logging.* South. Pulp and Paper Jour. 9 (3) : 30-32, 34, 62.

Knight, F. B. 1951. *Survey Gives New Information on Insect Damage to Loblolly Pine Cones.* Forest Farmer 10 (11, i.e. 12) : 8.

———. 1952. *Insect Damage to Loblolly Pine [Pinus Taeda] Cones.* Va. Forests 7 (1) : 14-15.

Koehler, A. 1917. *Guidebook for the Identification of Woods Used for Ties and Timbers.* U. S. Dept. Agr. Forest Serv. Misc. RL-1, 79 pp.

————. 1938. *Rapid Growth Hazards Usefulness of Southern Pine.* Jour. Forestry 36: 153-158.

————. 1946. *Longitudinal Shrinkage of Wood.* U. S. Forest Serv. Forest Prod. Lab. Rpt. R1093, 21 pp.

Korstian, C. F., and Bilan, M. V. 1957. *Some Further Evidence of Competition Between Loblolly Pine and Associated Hardwoods.* Jour. Forestry 55: 821-822.

———— and Coile, T. S. 1938. *Plant Competition in Forest Stands.* Duke Univ. School Forestry Bul. 3, 125 pp.

———— and Maughan, W. 1935. *The Duke Forest: a Demonstration and Research Laboratory.* Duke Univ. School Forestry Bul. 1, 74 pp.

Korstian, K. C. 1939. *The Amount of Forest Floor and Incorporation of Organic Matter in Several Forest Types of Piedmont North Carolina.* Thesis, Yale Univ. School Forestry.

Kowal, R. J. 1948. *Pine Sawfly in Southern Arkansas.* Forest Farmer 8 (2): 3, 10.

————. 1949. *Control of Wood-Boring Insects in Green Logs and Lumber.* Forest Prod. Res. Soc. Proc. 3: 469-479.

————. 1950. *Insects Commonly Attacking Forest Trees and Unseasoned Timber in the Southern States.* Forest Farmer 9 (5): 28-31.

————. 1953. *Insects—Forest Enemy No. 1?* Forest Farmer 12 (10): 5-7.

————. 1955a. *Ips Beetles Are Killing Pines: What Shall We Do About It?* U. S. Forest Serv. Southeast. Forest Expt. Sta. Res. Notes 81.

————. 1955b. *Where We Stand in Our Fight Against Forest Insects.* Forest Farmer 14 (10): 4-6.

———— and Coyne, J. F. 1951. *The Black Turpentine Beetle Can Kill Trees.* AT-FA Jour. 13 (9): 7, 14-15.

Kozlowski, T. T. 1941. *The Transpiration Rate of Some Forest Tree Species During the Dormant Season.* Thesis, Duke Univ. School Forestry.

————. 1943. *Transpiration Rates of Some Forest Tree Species During the Dormant Season.* Plant Physiol. 18: 252-260.

————. 1947. *Light and Water in Growth and Competition of Piedmont Forest Tree Species.* Thesis, Duke Univ. School Forestry.

————. 1949. *Light and Water in Relation to Growth and Competition of Piedmont Forest Tree Species.* Ecol. Monog. 19: 207-231.

————. 1957. *Effect of Continuous High Light Intensity on Photosynthesis of Forest Tree Seedlings.* Forest Sci. 3: 220-224.

———— and Scholtes, W. H. 1948. *Growth of Roots and Root Hairs of Pine and Hardwood Seedlings in the Piedmont.* Jour. Forestry 46: 750-754.

———— and Schumacher, F. X. 1943. *Estimation of Stomated Foliar Surface of Pines.* Plant Physiol. 18: 122-127.

Kramer, P. J. 1936. *Effect of Variation in Length of Day on Growth and Dormancy of Trees.* Plant Physiol. 11: 127-137.

————. 1942. *Species Differences with Respect to Water Absorption at Low Soil Temperatures.* Amer. Jour. Bot. 29: 828-832.

————. 1943. *Amount and Duration of Growth of Various Species of Tree Seedlings.* Plant Physiol. 18: 239-251.

————. 1949. *Plant and Soil Water Relationships.* 347 pp. New York, Toronto, and London.

————. 1951. *Effects of Respiration Inhibitors on Accumulation of Radioactive Phosphorus by Roots of Loblolly Pine.* Plant Physiol. 26: 30-36.

————. 1953. *Plant Physiology in Relation to Forest Competition and Succession.* (Abs.) Assoc. South. Agr. Workers Proc. 50: 206-207.

————. 1957. *Some Effects of Various Combinations of Day and Night Temperatures and Photoperiod on the Height Growth of Loblolly Pine Seedlings.* Forest Sci. 3 (1): 45-55.

———— and Clark, W. S. 1947. *A Comparison of Photosynthesis in Individual Pine Needles and Entire Seedlings at Various Light Intensities.* Plant Physiol. 22: 51-57.

———— and Decker, J. P. 1942. *The Effect of Light Intensity on Photosynthesis in Pine and Oak Seedlings.* (Abs.) Elisha Mitchell Sci. Soc. Jour. 58, p. 134.

———— and Decker, J. P. 1944. *Relation Between Light Intensity and Rate of Photosynthesis of Loblolly Pine and Certain Hardwoods.* Plant Physiol. 19: 350-358.

———— and Hodgson, R. H. 1954. *Differences Between Mycorrhizal and Non-Mycorrhizal Roots of Loblolly Pine.* Eighth Internatl. Bot. Cong., Paris, Sect. 13: 133-134.

———— Oosting, H. J., and Korstian, C. F. 1952. *Survival of Pine and Hardwood Seedlings in Forest and Open.* Ecology 33: 427-430.

———— and Wilbur, K. M. 1949. *Absorption of Radioactive Phosphorus by Mycorrhizal Roots of Pine.* Science 110: 8-9.

Kramer, P. R. 1957. *Tracheid Length Variation in Loblolly Pine.* Tex. Forest Serv. Tech. Rpt. 10, 22 pp.

Kurth, E. F. 1947. *The Chemical Composition of Barks.* Chem. Rev. 40 (1): 33-39.

Labyak, L. F., and Schumacher, F. X. 1954. *The Contribution of Its Branches to the Mainstem Growth of Loblolly Pine.* Jour. Forestry 52: 333-337.

Lamb, H. 1937. *Rust Canker Diseases of Southern Pines.* U. S. Forest Serv. South. Forest Expt. Sta. Occas. Paper 72, 7 pp.

———— and Sleeth, B. 1940. *Distribution and Suggested Control Measures for the Southern Pine Fusiform Rust.* U. S. Forest Serv. South. Forest Expt. Sta. Occas. Paper 91, 5 pp.

Lange, K. D. 1952. *Guide for First Thinning of Plantations of Loblolly and Shortleaf Pine.* First Ann. Forestry Symposium Proc., La. State Univ. School Forestry 1952: 103-109.

Larson, R. W. 1957. *How Long Does It Take to Grow Pine Pulpwood or Sawtimber in North Carolina?* U. S. Forest Serv. Southeast. Forest Expt. Sta. Res. Notes 106.

Lay, D. W. 1940. *Bob-White Populations as Affected by Woodland Management in Eastern Texas.* Tex. Agr. Expt. Sta. Bul. 592, 37 pp.

————. 1956. *Effects of Prescribed Burning on Forage and Mast Production in Southern Pine Forests.* Jour. Forestry 54: 582-584.

————. 1957. *Browse Quality and the Effects of Prescribed Burning in Southern Pine Forests.* Jour. Forestry 55: 342-347.

Lebold, W. R. 1948. *Silvicultural Aspects of Pine-Hardwood Stands in the Coastal Plain of Southeast Georgia, and Their Possible Conversion to Pure Pine.* Thesis, Duke Univ. School Forestry.

Lee, R. E., and Coyne, J. F. 1955. *Suggested Guides for Detecting the Black Turpentine Beetle.* Tex. Forest News 34 (6): 4-5.

———— and Smith, R. H. 1955. *The Black Turpentine Beetle, Its Habits and Control.* U. S. Forest Serv. South. Forest Expt. Sta. Occas. Paper 138, 14 pp.

Lehrbas, M. M. 1950. *Wood Density Influences Pulp Yields.* U. S. Forest Serv. South. Forest Expt. Sta. South. Forestry Notes 68.

Lemieux, F. J. 1936. *Log Rules, Taper Tables, and Volume Tables for Use in the South.* Jour. Forestry 34: 970-974.

Lewis, H. F. 1950. *The Significant Chemical Components of Western Hemlock, Douglas Fir, Western Red Cedar, Loblolly Pine, and Black Spruce.* Tappi 33: 299-301.

Leysath, E. F. 1947. *An Investigation of the Possibilities of Sustained Yield Management on a Coastal Plain Forest.* Thesis, Duke Univ. School Forestry.

Lightle, P. C., and Starr, J. W. 1957. *Heartrot in Southern Pines.* U. S. Forest Serv. South. Forest Expt. Sta. South. Forestry Notes 108.

Lindenmuth, A. W., Jr., and Byram, G. M. 1948. *Headfires Are Cooler Near the Ground Than Backfires.* U. S. Forest Serv. Fire Control Notes 9 (4): 8-9.

Lindgren, R. M. 1948. *Care Needed in Thinning Pines with Heavy Fusiform Rust Infection.* Forest Farmer 7 (12): 3.

————. 1950. *Damage from Heavy Fusiform Cankering in '49 Can Be Reduced.* Forest Farmer 9 (4): 9.

————. 1951. *Reducing Deterioration of Southern Pine Pulpwood During Storage.* Forest Products Res. Soc. 1951 Preprint 161, 12 pp.

————. 1952. *Permeability of Southern Pine as Affected by Mold and Other Fungus Infection.* Amer. Wood Preservers' Assoc. Proc. 48: 158-174.

————. 1953. *Deterioration Losses in Stored Southern Pine Pulpwood.* Tappi 36 (6): 260-264.

————. 1955. *Color Test for Early Storage Decay in Southern Pine.* U. S. Forest Serv. Forest Prod. Lab. Rpt. R2037, 5 pp.

———— and Scheffer, T. C. 1939. *Effect of Blue Stain on the Penetration of Liquids into Air-Dry Southern Pine Wood.* Amer. Wood Preservers' Assoc. Proc. 35: 325-336.

———— and Verrall, A. F. 1950. *Fungus Control in Unseasoned Forest Products.* Forest Farmer 9 (5): 53-54.

Little, E. L., Jr. 1953. *Check List of Native and Naturalized Trees of United States (Including Alaska).* U. S. Dept. Agr. Handb. 41, 472 pp.

Little, S., and Mohr, J. J. 1954. *Reproducing Pine Stands on the Eastern Shore of Maryland—Using a Seed Tree Cutting and Preparing Seedbeds with Machinery and Summer Fires.* U. S. Forest Serv. Northeast. Forest Expt. Sta. Paper 67, 11 pp.

———— and Mohr, J. J. 1957a. *Seedbed Treatment Increases Dominance of Natural Loblolly Pine Reproduction.* U. S. Forest Serv. Northeast. Forest Expt. Sta. Res. Note 76, 4 pp.

——— and Mohr, J. J. 1957b. *Growth and Mortality of Residual Loblolly Pines After a Seed-Tree Cutting.* U. S. Forest Serv. Northeast. Forest Expt. Sta. Res. Note 75, 4 pp.

——— Mohr, J. J., and Spicer, L. L. 1958. *Salt-Water Damage to Loblolly Pine Forests.* Jour. Forestry 56: 27-28.

——— and Moore, E. B. 1952. *Mechanical Preparation of Seedbeds for Converting Oak-Pine Stands to Pine.* Jour. Forestry 50: 840-844.

——— and Somes, H. A. 1958. *Results 18 Years After Planting Loblolly Pines at Different Spacings.* U. S. Forest Serv. Northeast. Forest Expt. Sta. Res. Note 80, 3 pp.

Livingston, K. W. 1948. *A Comparison of Tree Site Index of Young Loblolly Pine Plantations with Site Index Estimated from the Soil.* Thesis, Duke Univ. School Forestry.

———. 1952. *The Effect of Early Thinning on the Growth and Yield of Young Southern Pine Plantations.* First Ann. Forestry Symposium Proc., La. State Univ. School Forestry 1952: 43-52.

———. 1956. *Thin—or Not to Thin?* Highlights Agr. Res. [Ala. Sta.] 3 (3): 4.

Lodewick, J. E. 1933. *Some Summer-Wood Percentage Relationships in the Southern Pines.* Jour. Agr. Res. 46: 543-556.

Lorenz, R. C. 1939. *High Temperature Tolerance of Forest Trees.* Minn. Agr. Expt. Sta. Tech. Bul. 141, 25 pp.

Lotti, T. 1953. *Good Seed Trees Pay Off.* South. Lumberman 187 (2336): 43-44.

———. 1955. *Summer Fires Kill Understory Hardwoods.* U. S. Forest Serv. Southeast. Forest Expt. Sta. Res. Notes 71, 2 pp.

———. 1956a. *Eliminating Understory Hardwoods with Summer Prescribed Fires in Coastal Plain Loblolly Pine Stands.* Jour. Forestry 54: 191-192.

———. 1956b. *Growing Loblolly Pine in the South Atlantic States.* U. S. Dept. Agr. Farmers' Bul. 2097, 33 pp.

———. 1956c. *Good Seed Production from a Young Stand of Loblolly Pine.* U. S. Forest Serv. Southeast. Forest Expt. Sta. Res. Notes 97, 2 pp.

———. 1957. *An Effective Control for Cull Hardwoods.* U. S. Forest Serv. Southeast. Forest Expt. Sta. Res. Notes 108.

——— and Chaiken, L. E. 1948. *Tree Grades for Loblolly and Shortleaf Pine.* South. Lumberman 177 (2225): 107-109.

——— and Evans, T. C. 1942. *Virginia's Forests.* U. S. Forest Serv. Appalachian Forest Expt. Sta. Forest Survey Release 11, 75 pp.

——— and McCulley, R. D. 1951. *Loblolly Pine: Maintaining This Species as a Subclimax in the Southeastern United States.* Unasylva 5: 107-113.

Louisiana State University. 1954. *Recent Developments in Planting and Direct Seeding in the Southern Pine Region.* Third Ann. Forestry Symposium Proc., La. State Univ. School Forestry, 104 pp.

Lowe, E. N. 1921. *Plants of Mississippi.* Miss. State Geol. Survey Bul. 17, 292 pp.

Lowther, E. J., and Murray, R. V. 1946. *Labor Requirements in Southern Pine Lumber Production.* Monthly Labor Rev. 63: 941-953.

Luckhoff, H. A. 1949. *The Effect of Live Pruning on the Growth of Pinus Patula, P. Caribaea, and P. Taeda.* So. African Forestry Assoc. Jour. 18: 25-55.

———. 1955. *Two Hitherto Unrecorded Fungal Diseases Attacking Pines and Eucalypts in South Africa.* So. African Forestry Assoc. Jour 26: 47-61.

Ludbrook, W. V. 1941. *Boron Deficiency Symptoms on Pine Seedlings in Water Culture.* Austral. Council Sci. & Indus. Res. Jour. 13: 186-190. Forestry Abs. 2 (4): 284.

———. 1943. *Fertilizer Trials in Southern New South Wales Pine Plantations.* Austral. Council Sci. & Indus. Res. Jour. 15: 307-314. Forestry Abs. 5 (2): 89.

Lyle, E. S., and Gilmore, A. R. 1958. *The Effect of Rough Handling of Loblolly Pine Cones on Seed Germination.* Jour. Forestry 56: 595.

——— Gilmore, A. R., and May, J. T. 1958. *Survival and Growth of 2-0 Longleaf and Loblolly Seedlings in the Field.* Tree Planters' Notes 33: 26-27.

Lynch, D. W., Davis, W. C., Roof, L. R., and Korstian, C. F. 1943. *Influence of Nursery Fungicide-Fertilizer Treatments on Survival and Growth in a Southern Pine Plantation.* Jour. Forestry 41: 411-413.

MacAndrews, A. H. 1926. *The Biology of the Southern Pine Beetle.* Thesis, N. Y. State Col. Forestry, Syracuse Univ.

MacKinney, A. L. 1933. *Increase in Growth of Loblolly Pines Left After Partial Cutting.* Jour. Agr. Res. 47: 807-821.

———. 1934a. *Logging Damage in Selectively Logged Loblolly Pine Stands.* Jour. Forestry 32: 94-96.

———. 1934b. *A Suggestion for Cleaning Loblolly Pine Seed.* U. S. Forest Serv. Appalachian Forest Expt. Sta. Tech. Note 6, 1 p.

———. 1934c. *Storage of Loblolly Pine Seed.* U. S. Forest Serv. Appalachian Forest Expt. Sta. Tech. Note 7, 2 pp.

———. 1935. *Effects of a Light Fire on Loblolly Pine Reproduction.* U. S. Forest Serv. Appalachian Forest Expt. Sta. Tech. Note 9, 2 pp.

———. 1936. *Recent Site Index Curves for Second-Growth Loblolly Pines.* U. S. Forest Serv. Appalachian Forest Expt. Sta. Tech. Note 22, 4 pp.

——— and Chaiken, L. E. 1935a. *A Method of Determining Density of Loblolly Pine Stands.* U. S. Forest Serv. Appalachian Forest Expt. Sta. Tech. Note 15, 3 pp.

——— and Chaiken, L. E. 1935b. *Heartwood in Second-Growth Loblolly Pine.* U. S. Forest Serv. Appalachian Forest Expt. Sta. Tech. Note 18, 3 pp.

——— and Chaiken, L. E. 1936. *Converting Factors for Loblolly Pine Pulpwood.* U. S. Forest Serv. Appalachian Forest Expt. Sta. Tech. Note 20, 9 pp.

——— and Chaiken, L. E. 1956. *Volume, Yield, and Growth of Loblolly Pine in the Mid-Atlantic Coastal Region.* U. S. Forest Serv. Southeast. Forest Expt. Sta. Tech. Note 33, 58 pp.

——— and Korstian, C. F. 1932. *Felling, Girdling and Poisoning Undesirable Trees in Forest Stands.* Jour. Forestry 30: 169-177.

——— and Korstian, C. F. 1938. *Loblolly Pine Seed Dispersal.* Jour. Forestry 36: 465-468.

——— and McQuilkin, W. E. 1938. *Methods of Stratification for Loblolly Pine Seeds.* Jour. Forestry 36: 1123-1127.

——— Schumacher, F. X., and Chaiken, L. E. 1937. *Construction of Yield Tables for Non-Normal Loblolly Pine Stands.* Jour. Agr. Res. 54: 531-545.

MacLean, J. D. 1952. *Preservative Treatment of Wood by Pressure Methods.* U. S. Dept. Agr. Handb. 40, 160 pp.

MacNaughton, V. B. 1953. *Uncle Sam's Gully Rangers—a New Kind of Forester.* South. Lumberman 187 (2345): 99-100.

MacNaughton, W. G. 1935. *Ground Wood and Sulphite Pulp from Southern Pine.* Paper Mill and Wood Pulp News 58 (29): 9, 11, 13-15.

Maki, T. E. 1953. *Some Aspects of Inorganic Fertilizer Applications in Forest Nurseries.* (Abs.) Assoc. South. Agr. Workers Proc. 50-207.

———. 1955. *The Role of Superior Trees in Forest Management.* Unit 58: 88-97.

——— and Henry, B. W. 1951. *Root-rot Control and Soil Improvement at the Ashe Forest Nursery.* U. S. Forest Serv. South. Forest Expt. Sta. Occas. Paper 119, 23 pp.

——— and Marshall, H. 1945. *Effects of Soaking with Indolebutyric Acid on Root Development and Survival of Tree Seedlings.* Bot. Gaz. 107: 268-276.

——— Marshall, H., and Ostrom, C. E. 1946. *Effects of Naphthaleneacetic-Acid Sprays on the Development and Drought Resistance of Pine Seedlings.* Bot. Gaz. 107: 297-312.

——— and Slocum, G. K. 1956. *Put Pines in the Piedmont.* Res. & Farming [N. C. Sta.] 15:10-11.

Mann, W. F., Jr. 1949. *Releasing Loblolly and Shortleaf Reproduction.* Forest Farmer 8 (8): 3, 10.

———. 1950a. *Industry Releases Pine for Profit.* South. Lumberman 180 (2257): 38-39.

———. 1950b. *Quick Returns from Releasing Pine.* U. S. Forest Serv. South. Forest Expt. Sta. South. Forestry Notes 67.

———. 1950c. *Competition for Light, Water, and Nutrients.* U. S. Forest Serv. South. Forest Expt. Sta. South. Forestry Notes 69.

———. 1951a. *Profits from Release of Loblolly and Shortleaf Pine Seedlings.* Jour. Forestry 49: 250-253.

———. 1951b. *Today You Can Improve Your Timberlands at a Profit.* South. Lumber Jour. 55 (1): 84-85.

———. 1951c. *1,200 Feet Per Acre Growth? Its Possible on Good Sites.* South. Lumber Jour. 55 (11): 96-97.

———. 1951d. *Pruning Loblolly Pine in the Farm Forest.* The Forest Farmer 10 (11, i.e. 12): 5.

———. 1952a. *Loblolly Pruning Scars Heal Rapidly.* U. S. Forest Serv. South. Forest Expt. Sta. South. Forestry Notes 77.

———. 1952b. *Stratified Pine (Pinus Taeda) Seed for Direct Seeding.* Tree Planters' Notes 11: 3.

———. 1952c. *Rapid Growth of Loblolly Pine (Pinus Taeda).* Forests and People 2 (1) : 14-15, 39.

———. 1952d. *Response of Loblolly Pine to Thinning.* Jour. Forestry 50: 443-446.

———. 1952e. *Thirty-Six Years of Thinning Research with Loblolly Pine.* First Ann. Forestry Symposium Proc., La. State Univ. School Forestry 1952: 1-7.

———. 1952f. *More on Competition for Light and Water.* U. S. Forest Serv. South. Forest Expt. Sta. South. Forestry Notes 79.

———. 1953a. *Pine Best-Suited to Choice Sites in Mid-Louisiana: Loblolly [Pinus Taeda].* Forests and People 3 (3) : 23, 39.

———. 1953b. *Pruning Increases Profits from Pine.* Forests and People 3 (4) : 27, 33.

———. 1953c. *Thinning of Loblolly Pine.* Pulp and Paper 27 (4) : 78, 81.

———. 1953d. *Loblolly Outgrows Slash on Good Sites.* U. S. Forest Serv. South. Forest Expt. Sta. South. Forestry Notes 86.

———. 1954a. *Thinning of Loblolly Pine.* Forests and People 4 (2) : 20-21.

———. 1954b. *Direct Seeding Research with Longleaf, Loblolly, and Slash Pines.* Third Ann. Forestry Symposium Proc., La. State Univ. School Forestry 1954: 9-18.

———. 1956. *Direct-Seeding the Southern Pines.* Tree Planters' Notes 25: 12-19.

———. 1957. *Direct-Seeding the Southern Pines.* Forest Farmer 17 (2) : 8-9, 12, 16-18.

———. 1959. *Industry Tests Loblolly Direct Seeding.* Forests and People 9 (1) : 22, 23, 30, 32.

——— and Derr, H. J. 1954a. *Count Your Cottontails.* U. S. Forest Serv. South. Forest Expt. Sta. South. Forestry Notes 89.

——— and Derr, H. J. 1954b. *Direct Seeding of Southern Pines.* South. Lumberman 189 (2369) : 115-117.

Markwardt, L. J. 1930. *Comparative Strength Properties of Woods Grown in the United States.* U. S. Dept. Agr. Tech. Bul. 158, 39 pp.

——— and Wilson, T. R. C. 1935. *Strength and Related Properties of Woods Grown in the United States.* U. S. Dept. Agr. Tech. Bul. 479, 99 pp.

——— and Wood, L. W. 1953. *The Testing of Timber—Strength Studies of Timber and the Development of Structural Timber Grades in the United States.* Inc. Assoc. Architects and Surveyors, London, England. Pt. IV. Inst. Civ. Engin. Joint Comm. Mater. Testing.

Marquis, R. W. 1939. *Economics of Private Forestry.* 219 pp. New York and London.

Marshall, H., and Maki, T. E. 1946. *Transpiration of Pine Seedlings as Influenced by Foliage Coatings.* Plant Physiol. 21: 95-101.

Martin, A. C., Zim, H. S., and Nelson, A. L. 1951. *American Wildlife and Plants.* 500 pp. New York.

Martin, S. C., and Clark, F. B. 1954. *Controlling Hardwood Sprouts with Foliage Sprays.* U. S. Forest Serv. Cent. States Forest Expt. Sta. Tech. Paper 145, 10 pp.

Mathewson, J. S. 1930. *The Air Seasoning of Wood.* U. S. Dept. Agr. Tech. Bul. 174, 56 pp.

Matte, L. 1944. *Pulpwood Volume Tables for Southeastern Pines.* Thesis, Duke Univ. School Forestry.

―――. 1949. *The Taper of Coniferous Species with Special Reference to Loblolly Pine.* Forestry Chron. 25 (1): 21-31.

Matthews, D. M. 1942. *Cost Control in the Logging Industry.* 374 pp. New York and London.

Mattoon, W. R. 1920. *Making Woodlands Profitable in the Southern States.* U. S. Dept. Agr. Farmers' Bul. 1071, 30 pp. (Revised 1926).

―――. 1926. *Loblolly Pine Primer.* U. S. Dept. Agr. Farmers' Bul. 1517, 38 pp.

―――. 1929. *Shortleaf and Loblolly Pine Litter and Humus a Valuable Fertilizer.* U. S. Forest Serv. Forest Worker 5 (2): 14-15.

―――. 1942. *Pruning Southern Pines.* U. S. Dept. Agr. Farmers' Bul. 1892, 34 pp.

Max, K. W. 1945. *Chemical Analysis of Green Loblolly Pine.* South. Pulp and Paper Jour. 7 (8): 36.

May, J. T. 1933. *Effect of Density of Stocking on the Growth and Development of Longleaf, Loblolly, and Slash Pine Seedlings.* Thesis, Ga. Univ. School Forestry.

McAlpine, R. G. 1957. *Age of Tree and Root Development by Air-Layers in Loblolly Pine.* South. Conf. Forest Tree Impr. Proc. 4: 59-63.

McAtee, W. L. 1936. *Groups of Plants Valuable for Wildlife Utilization and Erosion Control.* U. S. Dept. Agr. Cir. 412, 11 pp.

McClay, T. A. 1951a. *Comparative Stumpage Prices for Pine Sawtimber and Pulpwood in the Lower Piedmont.* Forest Farmer 10 (9): 7.

―――. 1951b. *Annual Income Possibilities from Southern Piedmont Farm Woodlands.* U. S. Forest Serv. Southeast. Forest Expt. Sta. 4 pp.

―――. 1952. *Comparative Stumpage Prices for Small Pine Sawtimber and Pulpwood.* U. S. Forest Serv. Southeast. Forest Expt. Sta. Paper 16, 7 pp.

―――. 1953a. *Estimating Board Widths Obtainable from Pine Trees of Different Diameters.* U. S. Forest Serv. Southeast. Forest Expt. Sta. Res. Notes 25, 2 pp.

―――. 1953b. *Estimating Time Requirements for Tree Poisoning with Ammate.* U. S. Forest Serv. Southeast. Forest Expt. Sta. Res. Notes 27, 2 pp.

―――. 1953c. *Relation of Tree Size to Production Rates When Cutting Pine Pulpwood with a Chain Saw.* U. S. Forest Serv. Southeast. Forest Expt. Sta. Res. Notes 28, 2 pp.

―――. 1953d. *Growth, Mortality, and Regeneration After Cutting in Loblolly Pine Pulpwood Stands.* U. S. Forest Serv. Southeast. Forest Expt. Sta. Paper 28, 15 pp.

―――. 1953e. *The Relation of Growth to Severity and Season of Pruning Open-Grown Loblolly Pine.* Jour. Forestry 51: 287-288.

―――. 1954a. *Loblolly Pine Topwood Volumes.* U. S. Forest Serv. Southeast. Forest Expt. Sta. Res. Notes 61, 2 pp.

―――. 1954b. *Lumber Grade Yields in the Loblolly-Shortleaf Pine Type by the Southern Pine Log Grades.* U. S. Forest Serv. Southeast. Forest Expt. Sta. Paper 37, 12 pp.

―――. 1955a. *Loblolly Pine Growth as Affected by Removal of Understory Hardwoods and Shrubs.* U. S. Forest Serv. Southeast. Forest Expt. Sta. Res. Notes 73, 2 pp.

―――. 1955b. *The Relation of Growth to Site and Residual Density in Loblolly Pine Pulpwood Stands.* U. S. Forest Serv. Southeast. Forest Expt. Sta. Res. Notes 78, 2 pp.

――― and Pawek, H. J. 1955. *The Southern Pine Log Grades—Their Application in a Stumpage Appraisal.* South. Lumberman 190 (2379) : 70, 72, 74, 76.

McCormack, J. F. 1949a. *Forest Resources of Northeast Florida, 1949.* U. S. Forest Serv. Southeast. Forest Expt. Sta. Forest Survey Release 30, 36 pp.

―――. 1949b. *Forest Resources of Central Florida, 1949.* U. S. Forest Serv. Southeast. Forest Expt. Sta. Forest Survey Release 31, 36 pp.

―――. 1950a. *Forest Resources of Northwest Florida, 1949.* U. S. Forest Serv. Southeast. Forest Expt. Sta. Forest Survey Release 32, 36 pp.

―――. 1950b. *Forest Resources of South Florida, 1949.* U. S. Forest Serv. Southeast. Forest Expt. Sta. Forest Survey Release 33, 21 pp.

―――. 1950c. *Forest Statistics for Florida, 1949.* U. S. Forest Serv. Southeast. Forest Expt. Sta. Forest Survey Release 36, 73 pp.

―――. 1952. *Southern Pulpwood Production Hits New High.* U. S. Forest Serv. Southeast. Forest Expt. Sta. Res. Notes 15, 2 pp.

―――. 1953. *D.B.H. in Relation to Stump Diameter at Various Heights for Southern Yellow Pines and Hardwoods.* U. S. Forest Serv. Southeast. Forest Expt. Sta. Res. Notes 43, 1 p.

―――. 1955a. *Forest Statistics for the Northern Coastal Plain of North Carolina, 1955.* U. S. Forest Serv. Southeast. Forest Expt. Sta. Forest Survey Release 45, 44 pp.

―――. 1955b. *An Allowance for Bark Increment in Computing Tree Diameter Growth for Southeastern Species.* U. S. Forest Serv. Southeast. Forest Expt. Sta. Paper 60, 6 pp.

―――. 1958. *1957 Pulpwood Production in the South.* U. S. Forest Serv. Southeast. Forest Expt. Sta. Forest Survey Release 53, 15 pp.

――― and Cruikshank, J. W. 1949. *South Carolina's Forest Resources, 1947.* U. S. Forest Serv. Southeast. Forest Expt. Sta. Forest Survey Release 28, 122 pp.

――― and Cruikshank, J. W. 1954. *Forest Statistics for Georgia, 1951-1953.* U. S. Forest Serv. Southeast. Forest Expt. Sta. Forest Survey Release 44, 77 pp.

McCulley, R. D. 1950a. *Wet-Weather Logging Hazard to Loblolly Pine Seed Trees.* Forest Farmer 10 (2) : 13.

―――. 1950b. *A Check on the Effectiveness of Ammate in Coastal Virginia.* Forest Farmer 10 (3) : 9.

―――. 1951. *Release of Seed Source as a Factor in Loblolly Pine Management.* Unit 37 : 16-20.

―――. 1953a. *Controlling Seed Production and Seed Utilization in Loblolly Pine.* (Abs.) Assoc. South. Agr. Workers Proc. 50 : 117-118.

——. 1953b. *The Seed-Tree System; a Summary of Recent Research in Loblolly Pine.* South. Lumber Jour. 57 (8) : 20, 22, 90-91.

——. 1953c. *Estimating Growing Space Liberated by the Removal of Residual Hardwoods.* U. S. Forest Serv. Southeast. Forest Expt. Sta. Res. Notes 31, 2 pp.

——. 1953d. *Gunning for Loblolly Pine Cones.* U. S. Forest Serv. Southeast. Forest Expt. Sta. Res. Notes 40, 1 p.

——. 1953e. *Natural Regeneration of Loblolly Pine in the Southeastern Coastal Plain.* U. S. Forest Serv. Southeast. Forest Expt. Sta. Paper 26, 14 pp.

——. 1953f. *The Case for Even-Aged Management of Southern Pine.* Jour. Forestry 51 : 88-90.

—— and Elliott, F. A. 1952. *A Test of Research Predictions.* Va. Forests 7 (2) : 10-11.

McGough, R. B. 1947. *A Quantitative Analysis of the Weight of the A_0 Horizon of Loblolly Pine and White Oak-Black Oak-Red Oak Stands of the Duke Forest and Vicinity.* Thesis, Duke Univ. School Forestry.

McGovern, J. N., and Chidester, G. H. 1941. *Pulping Loblolly Pine Heartwood with Calcium-, Magnesium-, and Sodium-Base Sulphite Liquors.* Paper Trade Jour. 113 (16) : 33-35.

McGregor, W. H. D. 1958. *Seasonal Changes in the Rates of Photosynthesis and Respiration of Loblolly Pine and White Pine.* Thesis, Duke Univ. School Forestry.

—— and Kramer, P. J. 1957. *The Effect of Photoperiod on Photosynthesis, Respiration, and Growth of Loblolly Pine Seedlings from Two Sources.* (Abs.) Plant Physiol. 32 (sup.) : x-xi.

McKeller, A. D. 1942. *Ice Damage to Slash Pine, Longleaf Pine, and Loblolly Pine Plantations in the Piedmont Section of Georgia.* Jour. Forestry 40 : 794-797.

McKinnon, A. D. 1946. *Development of Southern Pines in Auckland Conservancy.* New Zeal. Jour. Forestry 5 (2) : 127-132. Forestry Abs. 8 (2) : 226.

McLemore, B. F. 1957. *Effect of Geographic Origin of Seed on the Dry Matter Content of Loblolly Pine Needles.* Thesis, La. State Univ. School Forestry.

McLintock, T. F. 1942. *Stratification as a Means of Improving Results of Direct Seeding of Pines.* Jour. Forestry 40 : 724-728.

McQuilkin, W. E. 1939. *Natural Establishment of Pine in Abandoned Fields in the Piedmont Region.* U. S. Forest Serv. Appalachian Forest Expt. Sta. Tech. Note 37, 3 pp.

——. 1946. *Tests of Direct Seeding with Pines in the Piedmont Region.* Jour. Agr. Res. 73 : 113-136.

——. 1955. *Use Ammate for Deadening Trees Only During Growing Season.* South. Lumberman 191 (2388) : 70.

Meade, F. M. 1955. *Converting Low-Grade Hardwood Stands to Conifers in the Arkansas Ozarks.* Ark. Agr. Expt. Sta. Bul. 551, 26 pp.

——. 1956. *Effects of Spacing on Growth of Loblolly Pine.* Ark. Farm Res. 5 (3) : 9.

Meginnis, H. G. 1933a. *Tree Planting to Reclaim Gullied Lands in the South.* Jour. Forestry 31 : 649-656.

————. 1933b. *Using Soil-Binding Plants to Reclaim Gullies in the South.* U. S. Dept. Agr. Farmers' Bul. 1697, 17 pp.

————. 1935. *Influence of Forest Litter on Surface Run-Off and Soil Erosion.* Amer. Soil Survey Assoc. Bul. 16, pp. 115-118.

————. 1939. *Soil-Collecting Trenches as Substitutes for Temporary Check Dams in Reforesting Gullies.* Jour. Forestry 37: 764-769.

Mergen, F. 1954. *Mechanical Aspects of Wind-Breakage and Windfirmness.* Jour. Forestry 52: 119-125.

Merkel, E. P. 1954. *The Pine Needle Miner on the North Carolina National Forest.* U. S. Forest Serv. Southeast. Forest Expt. Sta. Forest Pest Survey Rel. 3, 4 pp.

———— and Kulman, H. M. 1955. *Beetle Conditions in North-Central South Carolina.* South. Lumberman 191 (2389): 60, 62.

Merrifield, R. G. 1958. *Annual Growth of Loblolly Pine as Related to Several Soil Moisture Deficiencies.* Thesis, La. State Univ. School Forestry.

Mesavage, C. 1946. *New Tables for Estimating Board-Foot Volume of Timber.* South. Lumberman 173 (2177): 153-156.

————. 1947a. *Tables for Estimating Cubic-Foot Volume of Timber.* U. S. Forest Serv. South. Forest Expt. Sta. Occas. Paper 111, 71 pp.

————. 1947b. *Board-Foot Volume Tables for Southern Lumberman.* South. Lumberman 175 (2201): 195-197.

———— and Girard, J. W. 1946. *Tables for Estimating Board-Foot Volume of Timber.* (A pocket manual reprinted 1956). U. S. Dept. Agr., 94 pp.

Metcalf, C. L., and Flint, W. P. 1939. *Destructive and Useful Insects.* Ed. 2, 981 pp. New York.

Metz, L. J. 1950. *Relationship Between Soil Properties and the Growth of Loblolly Pine in the Southeastern Coastal Plain.* Thesis, Duke Univ. School Forestry.

————. 1952a. *Weight and Nitrogen and Calcium Content of the Annual Litter Fall of Forests in the South Carolina Piedmont.* Soil Sci. Soc. Amer. Proc. 16: 38-41.

————. 1952b. *Calcium Content of Hardwood Litter Four Times That from Pine; Nitrogen Double.* U. S. Forest Serv. Southeast. Forest Expt. Sta. Res. Notes 14, 2 pp.

————. 1954. *Forest Floor in the Piedmont Region of South Carolina.* Soil Sci. Soc. Amer. Proc. 18: 335-338.

————. 1958. *Moisture Held in Pine Litter.* Jour. Forestry 56: 36.

Meyer, H. A., and Worley, D. P. 1957. *Volume Determinations from Aerial Stand Volume Tables and Their Accuracy.* Jour. Forestry 55: 368-372.

Meyer, W. H. 1942. *Yield of Even-Aged Stands of Loblolly Pine in Northern Louisiana.* Yale Univ. School Forestry Bul. 51: 1-39.

————. 1955. *Some Treatment Effects on Loblolly and Shortleaf Pine Reproduction.* Jour. Forestry 53: 895-900.

Middleton, W. 1921. *Leconte's Sawfly, an Enemy of Young Pines.* Jour. Agr. Res. 20: 741-760.

————. 1922. *A Sawfly Injurious to Young Pines.* U. S. Dept. Agr. Farmers' Bul. 1259, 11 pp.

Mignery, A. L. 1952. *Good Management Reduces Drouth Losses.* U. S. Forest Serv. South. Forest Expt. Sta. South. Forestry Notes 79.

———— and Gregory, G. R. 1949. *Better Timber Crops from East Texas Farm Woodlands.* Forest Farmer 9 (3) : 7-9.

Miller, H. A. 1956. *Opportunities in Wildlife.* Forest Farmer 16 (3) : 10-12, 16 and 16 (4) : 10-11, 17-18.

Miller, R. H. 1941. *Measuring Green Southern Yellow Pine Pulpwood by Weight or Cord.* South. Pulp and Paper Jour. 4 (1) : 10, 11, 19.

Miller, R. H. P. 1955. *Debarkers Used in the South and East.* U. S. Forest Serv. Forest Prod. Lab. Rpt. R2038, 18 pp.

Miller, W. D. 1954. *Pine or Hardwoods? A Comparison of the Growth Rates of Loblolly and Virginia Pines and Upland Hardwoods in the Piedmont of North Carolina.* South. Lumberman 188 (2355) : 32-34.

———— and Tissue, O. C. 1956. *Results of Several Methods of Release of Understory Loblolly Pine in Upland Hardwood Stands.* Jour. Forestry 54 : 188-189.

Minckler, L. S. 1942. *One-Parent Heredity Tests with Loblolly Pine.* Jour. Forestry 40 : 505-506.

————. 1948. *Planted Pines on Claypan Soils in Southern Illinois.* U. S. Forest Serv. Cent. States Forest Expt. Sta. Note 44, 2 pp.

————. 1950. *Effect of Seed Source on Height Growth of Pine Seedlings.* Jour. Forestry 48 : 430-431.

————. 1951. *Southern Pine from Different Geographic Sources Show Different Responses to Low Temperatures.* Jour. Forestry 49 : 915-916.

————. 1952. *Loblolly Pine Seed Source and Hybrid Tests in Southern Illinois.* U. S. Forest Serv. Cent. States Forest Expt. Sta. Tech. Paper 128, 8 pp.

———— and Chapman, A. G. 1948. *Tree Planting in the Central, Piedmont, and Southern Appalachian Regions.* U. S. Dept. Agr. Farmers' Bul. 1994, 39 pp.

———— and Deitschman, G. H. 1949. *Thinning a 13-Year-Old Loblolly Pine Plantation on Claypan Soil in Southern Illinois.* U. S. Forest Serv. Cent. States Forest Expt. Sta. Note 56, 2 pp.

———— and Deitschman, G. H. 1953a. *Success of Planted Pines Varies with Species and Site.* U. S. Forest Serv. Cent. States Forest Expt. Sta. Note 76, 2 pp.

———— and Deitschman, G. H. 1953b. *Growth of Thinned and Unthinned Loblolly Pine in Southern Illinois.* U. S. Forest Serv. Cent. States Forest Expt. Sta. Note 73, 2 pp.

———— and Downs, A. A. 1946. *Machine and Hand Direct Seeding of Pine and Cedar in the Piedmont.* U. S. Forest Serv. Southeast. Forest Expt. Sta. Tech. Note 67, 10 pp.

Minor, C. O. 1950. *Form Class Volume Tables for Use in Southern Pine Pulpwood Timber Estimating.* La. Agr. Expt. Sta. Bul. 445, 39 pp.

————. 1951. *Stem-Crown Diameter Relations in Southern Pine.* Jour. Forestry 49 : 490-493.

————. 1952. *Short Cuts to Estimating Volume Growth of Pine Pulpwood.* Forest Farmer 11 (10) : 8.

————. 1953a. *Preliminary Volume Tables for Use with Aerial Photographs.* Forest Farmer 12 (10) : 9-10, 11.

————. 1953b. *Loblolly Pine Bark Thickness.* La. State Univ. Forestry Notes 1, 2 pp.

————. 1953c. *Miscellaneous Converting Factors for Southern Pine Sawtimber Volumes.* La. State Univ. Forestry Notes 4, 2 pp.

Mirov, N. T. 1954. *Chemical Composition of Gum Turpentines of Pines of the United States and Canada.* Forest Prod. Res. Soc. Jour. 4: 1-7.

———— Wang, T. H., Haagen-Smit, A. J., and Thurlow, J. 1949. *Chemical Composition of Gum Turpentines of Pines: a Report on Pinus Strobus, P. Cembra, P. Taeda, P. Radiata, and P. Virginiana. Composition of Gum Turpentine of P. Lambertiana.* Amer. Pharm. Assoc. Jour. (Sci. Ed.) 38 (7): 403-409.

Mississippi Forest Commission. 1956. *Predicted Annual Growth Percent During Next Two Inches of Diameter Growth.* Miss. Forest Serv. Tech. 5, 2 pp.

Mitchell, H. C. 1943. *Regulation of Farm Woodlands by Rule of Thumb.* Jour. Forestry 41: 243-248.

————. 1952. *The D-Plus Principle of Forest Stand Structures and Its Application to Plantation Spacing and the Thinning of Southern Pine Stands.* First Ann. Forestry Symposium Proc., La. State Univ. School Forestry 1952: 93-98.

Mitchell, H. L. 1954. *Greater Pulp Yields Per Acre Per Year.* U. S. Forest Serv. Forest Prod. Lab. Rpt. R1993, 8 pp.

———— and Wheeler, P. R. 1959. *The Search for Wood Quality.* Forest Farmer 18 (4): 4-6, and 18 (5): 10-12.

Mohr, C. 1897. *The Timber Pines of the Southern United States.* U. S. Dept. Agr. Div. Forestry Bul. 13, rev. ed., 176 pp.

————. 1901. *Plant Life of Alabama.* U. S. Natl. Herbarium, Vol. VI, 921 pp.

Moller, C. M., and others. 1954. *Thinning Problems and Practices in Denmark.* N. Y. State Col. Forestry, Syracuse Univ. Tech. Pub. 76, 92 pp.

Moon, D. G. 1956. *Where Are We Headed?* South Pulp & Paper Mfr. 19 (10): 42, 44.

Moore, W. H. 1956. *Effects of Certain Prescribed Fire Treatments on the Distribution of Some Herbaceous Quail Food Plants in Loblolly-Shortleaf Pine Communities of the Alabama Upper Coastal Plain.* (Abs.) Ala. Acad. Sci. Jour. 28: 120.

Moreland, D. E. 1950a. *The Translocation of Radioactive Phosphorus in Loblolly Pine.* Thesis, N. C. State Col. School Forestry.

————. 1950b. *A Study of the Translocation of Radioactive Phosphorus in Loblolly Pine (Pinus Taeda L.)* Elisha Mitchell Sci. Soc. Jour. 66: 175-181.

Morgan, H. L., Jr. 1947. *Relationship Between Density and Basal Area of Natural Loblolly Pine Stands in the Georgia Piedmont.* Thesis, Ga. Univ. School Forestry.

Morgan, R. B. 1955. *Survival and Height Growth of Loblolly Pine as Affected by Seedling Size and Depth of Planting.* Soc. Amer. Foresters Note, 1 p.

Morriss, D. J. 1958. *Basal Area Thinning Guides for Thinning in the South.* Jour. Forestry 56: 903-905.

Mortimer, M. F. 1941. *The Life History and Control of the Pine Tip Moth Rhyacionia Frustrana (Comstock), (Family: Tortricidae) at Nashville, Tennessee.* Tenn. Acad. Sci. Jour. 16: 190-206.

Moses, F. H., and Hyatt, A. J. 1957. *Seventy-Year-Old Pine Plantation Found in Alabama.* Jour. Forestry 55: 850.

Moulds, F. R. 1957. *Southern Pines in Australia.* Forest Farmer 16 (10): 6-7.

Moyle, R. C. 1956. *Leaping Loblolly.* U. S. Forest Serv. South. Forest Expt. Sta. South. Forestry Notes 105.

———— and Zahner, R. 1954. *Soil Moisture as Affected by Stand Conditions.* U. S. Forest Serv. South. Forest Expt. Sta. Occas. Paper 137, 14 pp.

Mulloy, G. A. 1943. *Stand Density Units.* Canad. Forest Serv. Silvic. Leaflet 16, 2 pp.

Munns, E. N. 1938. *The Distribution of Important Forest Trees of the United States.* U. S. Dept. Agr. Misc. Pub. 287, 176 pp.

Muntz, H. H. 1947. *Ice Damage to Pine Plantations.* South. Lumberman 175 (2201): 142-145.

————. 1948a. *Profit from Thinning Variously Spaced Loblolly Pine Plantations.* South. Lumberman 177 (2225): 125-128.

————. 1948b. *Slash Pine Versus Loblolly in Central Louisiana.* Jour. Forestry 46: 766-767.

————. 1950. *Releasing Pine Planted Under Scrub Oak.* South. Lumberman 181 (2273): 200-201.

————. 1951. *Converting Scrub Oak Areas to Pine Plantations.* Jour. Forestry 49: 714-715.

————. 1952. *Time Requirements for Timber Stand Improvement in North Alabama.* South. Weed Conf. Proc. 5: 148-151.

———— and Derr, H. J. 1949. *Early Release Helps Underplanted Pines.* U. S. Forest Serv. South. Forest Expt. Sta. South. Forestry Notes 64.

Myers, J. W., Jr. 1955. *Forest Fire Insurance Now a Reality.* Forest Farmer 14 (7): 4-5.

Nelson, M. L. 1938. *Preliminary Investigations on Dry, Cold Storage of Southern Pine Seed.* U. S. Forest Serv. South. Forest Expt. Sta. Occas. Paper 78, 19 pp.

————. 1940. *Successful Storage of Southern Pine Seed for Seven Years.* Jour. Forestry 38: 443-444.

————. 1941. *Polyembryony in Seeds of Southern Pines.* Jour. Forestry 39: 959-960.

Nelson, R. M. 1931. *Decay in Loblolly Pine on the Atlantic Coastal Plain.* Va. Forest Serv. Pub. 43, pp. 58-59.

————. 1934. *The Effect of Bluestain Fungi on Southern Pines Attacked by Bark Beetles.* Phytopath. Ztschr. 7: 327-353.

————. 1952. *Observations on Heat Tolerance of Southern Pine Needles.* U. S. Forest Serv. Southeast. Forest Expt. Sta. Paper 14, 6 pp.

————. 1955a. *How to Measure Forest Fire Danger in the Southeast.* U. S. Forest Serv. Southeast. Forest Expt. Sta. Paper 52, 22 pp.

————. 1955b. *The Principles and Uses of Fire Danger Measurement.* Fourth Ann. Forestry Symposium Proc., La. State Univ. School Forestry 1955: 36-45.

————. 1959. *Drought Estimation in Southern Forest Fire Control.* U. S. Forest Serv. Southeast. Forest Expt. Sta. Paper 99, 22 pp.

———— and Beal, J. A. 1929. *Experiments with Bluestain Fungi in Southern Pines.* Phytopathology 19: 1101-1106.

Nelson, T. C. 1951. *Ice Damage High for Spindly Residual Saplings.* Forest Farmer 10 (11, i.e. 12): 6.

————. 1957. *The Original Forests of the Georgia Piedmont.* Ecology 38: 390-397.

Nestler, R. B. 1946. *Germination of Seeds of Some Wild and Cultivated Plants After 5½ Years of Storage.* Jour. Forestry 44: 683-684.

Newins, H. S. 1945. *Arboriculture in the South.* Nineteenth Natl. Shade Tree Conf. Proc. 1943: 26-30.

Newlin, J. A., and Wilson, T. R. C. 1917. *Mechanical Properties of Woods Grown in the United States.* U. S. Dept. Agr. Bul. 556, 47 pp.

———— and Wilson, T. R. C. 1919. *The Relation of the Shrinkage and Strength Properties of Wood to Its Specific Gravity.* U. S. Dept. Agr. Bul. 676, 35 pp.

Newman, I. V. 1956. *On Fluting of the Trunk in Young Trees of Pinus Taeda L. (Loblolly Pine) with an Appendix on the Measurement of Radial Growth as Ring-Width.* Austral. Jour. Bot. 4: 1-12.

New Zealand State Forest Service. 1947. *Utilization Technology (Chap. X).* New Zeal. State Forest Serv. Ann. Rpt. 1946-47: 35-38.

————. 1948. *Specific Gravity of Exotic Coniferous Timbers in New Zealand.* New Zeal. State Forest Serv. Ann. Rpt. 1947-48: 47-48.

Nilsson, T. H. 1926. *A Critical Study of Southern Pine Fibre.* Paper Mill and Wood Pulp News 49 (49): 4, 6.

North Carolina Forestry Association. 1954. *Desirable Cutting Practices for North Carolina Forests.* 22 pp. Raleigh, N. C.

Nyasaland Department of Forestry. 1947. *Annual Report of the Forestry Department (Nyasaland) for the Year Ended 31 December 1945.* 16 pp. Forestry Abs. 8 (3): 368.

Olmstead, F. E. 1902. *A Working Plan for Forest Lands Near Pine Bluff, Arkansas.* U. S. Dept. Agr. Bur. Forestry Bul. 32, 48 pp.

Oosting, H. J. 1942. *An Ecological Analysis of the Plant Communities of Piedmont, North Carolina.* Amer. Midland Nat. 28: 1-126.

————. 1944. *The Comparative Effect of Surface and Crown Fire on the Composition of a Loblolly Pine Community.* Ecology 25: 61-69.

———— and Kramer, P. J. 1946. *Water and Light in Relation to Pine Reproduction.* Ecology 27: 47-53.

Osborn, R. M. 1951. *Costs of Cutting Mine Props from Pine and Hardwoods.* U. S. Forest Serv. South. Forest Expt. Sta. South. Forestry Notes 71.

————. 1952. *Division of Big and Little Logs among Alabama Mills.* Ala. Lumberman 4 (5): 18-19, 27.

Osborne, R. 1955. *New Markets for Treated Timber.* Forest Farmer 15 (3): 8-10, 16.

Ostrom, C. E. 1945. *Effects of Plant Growth Regulators on Shoot Development and Field Survival of Forest-Tree Seedlings.* Bot. Gaz. 107: 139-183.

Page, R. H. 1958. *Relative Efficiency of Four Stacking Methods in Air-*

Seasoning Southern Pine Lumber. Ga. Forestry Comn. and U. S. Forest Serv. [Forest Util. Serv.] Tech. Paper 1, 20 pp.

———— and Carter, R. M. 1958. *Variations in Moisture Content of Air-Seasoned Southern Pine Lumber in Georgia.* Forest Prod. Jour. 8 (6): 15A-18A.

Parker, J. 1949. *Effects of Variations in the Root-Leaf Ratio on Transpiration Rate.* Plant. Physiol. 24: 739-743.

————. 1950a. *The Effects of Flooding on the Transpiration and Survival of Some Southeastern Forest Tree Species.* Plant Physiol. 25: 453-460.

————. 1950b. *Planting Loblolly Pine outside Its Natural Range.* Jour. Forestry 48: 278-279.

————. 1955. *Survival of Some Southeastern Pine Seedlings in Northern Idaho.* Jour. Forestry 53: 137.

Parker, J. R., and Aull, G. H. 1953. *Farm Marketing of Sawtimber and Pulpwood in a Selected Area of South Carolina.* S. C. Agr. Expt. Sta. Bul. 403, 29 pp.

Patterson, A. E., and Weddell, D. J. 1943. *Management of Georgia's Woodlands.* Ga. Univ. George Foster Peabody School Forestry Bul. 1, 34 pp.

Paul, B. H. 1927. *Producing Dense Southern Pine Timber in Second-Growth Forest.* South. Lumberman 128 (1668): 46-48.

————. 1930a. *The Application of Silviculture in Controlling the Specific Gravity of Wood.* U. S. Dept. Agr. Tech. Bul. 168, 20 pp.

————. 1930b. *Heartwood in Second-Growth Southern Pine.* South. Lumberman 140 (1788): 46.

————. 1931a. *Relation of Forest Conditions to Quality and Value of Loblolly Pine Timber.* Va. Forest Serv. Pub. 43, pp. 51-57.

————. 1931b. *Pruning Young Loblolly Pine Trees Makes Timber Growing More Profitable.* South. Lumber Jour. 35 (14): 32.

————. 1932a. *The Relation of Certain Forest Conditions to the Quality and Value of Second-Growth Loblolly Pine Lumber.* Jour. Forestry 30: 4-21.

————. 1932b. *Quality Versus Size as an Index of a Profitable Tree: Loblolly Pine.* Jour. Forestry 30: 831-833.

————. 1932c. *Mixed Stands Produce Pine Lumber of Higher Grade.* South. Lumberman 145 (1821): 44-45.

————. 1933. *Mixed Stands Produce Pine Lumber of Higher Grade.* South. Lumber Jour. 37 (4): 26.

————. 1938a. *Knots in Second-Growth Pine and the Desirability of Pruning.* U. S. Dept. Agr. Misc. Pub. 307, 35 pp.

————. 1938b. *Reducing Bowing and Crooking of Lumber Cut from Second-Growth Southern Yellow Pine.* South. Lumberman 156 (1962): 48-50.

————. 1938c. *When to Prune Southern Pine.* South. Lumberman 157 (1985): 143-145.

————. 1939. *Variation in the Specific Gravity of the Springwood and Summerwood of Four Species of Southern Pines.* Jour. Forestry 37: 478-482.

————. 1952. *Variability in Wood of Southern Pines as Influenced by*

Silvicultural Practices. U. S. Forest Serv. Forest Prod. Lab. Rpt. R1923, 10 pp.

———— and Smith, D. M. 1950. *Summary on Growth in Relation to Quality of Southern Pine.* U. S. Forest Serv. Forest Prod. Lab. Rpt. D1751.

Pearse, A. S. 1943. *Effects of Burning-Over and Raking-Off Litter on Certain Soil Animals in the Duke Forest.* Amer. Midland Nat. 29: 406-424.

————. 1946. *Observations on the Microfauna of the Duke Forest.* Ecol. Monog. 16: 127-150.

Peck, E. C. 1956. *Air Drying of Lumber.* U. S. Forest Serv. Forest Prod. Lab. Rpt. R1657, 21 pp.

Peevy, F. A. 1949. *How to Control Southern Upland Hardwoods with Ammate.* U. S. Dept. Agr. M-5296, 7 pp.

————. 1951. *New Poisons for Undesirable Hardwoods.* U. S. Forest Serv. South. Forest Expt. Sta. South. Forestry Notes 72.

————. 1952. *Keep Stored Ammate Dry.* U. S. Forest Serv. South. Forest Expt. Sta. South. Forestry Notes 82.

————. 1953. *Chemical Control of Southern Upland Hardwoods.* Second Ann. Forestry Symposium Proc., La. State Univ. School Forestry 1953: 35-42.

————. 1954. *Woody Plant Control in Southern Forests.* South. Weed Conf. Proc. 7: 261-264.

———— and Campbell, R. S. 1947. *Poisoning Undesirable Hardwoods.* Forest Farmer 6 (7): 6-7.

———— and Campbell, R. S. 1949. *Poisoning Southern Upland Weed Trees.* Jour. Forestry 47: 443-447.

———— and Cassady, J. T. 1957. *Case for the Seeded Firebreak.* Forest Farmer 16 (10): 4, 16-18.

———— and Grano, C. X. 1952. *ABC's of Hardwood Control.* South. Lumberman 185 (2321): 211-213.

———— and Mann, W. F., Jr. 1952. *Slash and Loblolly Pine Plantation Destroyed by Hogs.* Forests and People 2 (4): 20, 37.

Pennefather, M. 1948. *A Comparison of the Management of Slash and Loblolly Pine in South Africa and the United States.* Thesis, Yale Univ. School Forestry.

Perry, T. O., and Wang, C. W. 1957a. *Cooperative Forest Genetics Research Program.* Fla. Univ. School Forestry Res. Rpt. 4, 28 pp.

———— and Wang, C. W. 1957b. *Collection, Shipping, and Storage of Slash and Loblolly Pine Cuttings.* Jour. Forestry 55: 122-123.

Pessin, L. J. 1928. *Mycorrhiza of Southern Pines.* Ecology 9: 28-33.

————. 1933. *Forest Associations in the Uplands of the Lower Gulf Coastal Plain (Longleaf Pine Belt).* Ecology 14: 1-14.

Pew, J. C., and Knechtges, R. G. 1939. *Cross-Sectional Dimensions of Fibers in Relation to Paper-Making Properties of Loblolly Pine.* Paper Trade Jour. 109 (15): 46-48.

Phillips, J. E. 1941. *Effect of Day Length on Dormancy in Tree Seedlings.* Jour. Forestry 39: 55-59.

Pillow, M. Y. 1930. *Compression Wood Cause of Bowing and Twisting.* Wood Working Indus. 8 (5): 26-27.

————. 1941. *A New Method of Detecting Compression Wood.* Jour. Forestry 39: 385-387.

————. 1951a. *What Is Compression Wood and Tension Wood: and What Is Their Practical Significance?* South. Lumberman 182 (2277): 52.

————. 1951b. *Variability in Anatomical Features and Their Effects on Properties of Second-Growth Yellow Pines.* U. S. Forest Serv. Forest Prod. Lab. Rpt. SR-21, 4 pp.

————. 1954. *Specific Gravity Relative to Characteristics of Annual Rings in Loblolly Pine.* U. S. Forest Serv. Forest Prod. Lab. Rpt. R1989, 21 pp.

———— Chidester, G. H., and Bray, M.W. 1941. *Effect of Wood Structure of Properties of Sulfate and Sulphite Pulps from Loblolly Pine.* South. Pulp and Paper Jour. 4 (7): 6-12.

———— and Luxford, R. F. 1937. *Structure, Occurrence, and Properties of Compression Wood.* U. S. Dept. Agr. Tech. Bul. 546, 32 pp.

———— Terrell, B. Z., and Hiller, C. H. 1953. *Patterns of Variation in Fibril Angles in Loblolly Pine.* U. S. Forest Serv. Forest Prod. Lab. Rpt. D1935.

Pinchot, G., and Ashe, W. W. 1897. *Timber Trees and Forests of North Carolina.* N. C. Geol. Survey Bul. 6, 227 pp.

Place, I. C. M. 1953. *"Selective Cutting" and the All-Aged Stand.* Forestry Chron. 29 (3): 248-253.

Pomerening, D. A. 1951. *Results of the Two-Cut Shelterwood Method in Loblolly Pine Pulpwood-Size Stands in the Carolinas and Virginia.* Thesis, Duke Univ. School Forestry.

Pomeroy, K. B. 1948. *Observations on Four Prescribed Fires in the Coastal Plain of Virginia and North Carolina.* U. S. Forest Serv. Fire Control Notes 9 (2 and 3): 13-17.

————. 1949a. *Can Hardwoods Be Controlled?* Va. Forests 4 (2): 6-7, 11, 12.

————. 1949b. *Loblolly Pine Seed Trees: Selection, Fruitfulness, and Mortality.* U. S. Forest Serv. Southeast. Forest Expt. Sta. Paper 5, 17 pp.

————. 1949c. *Application of Strip Cutting in Loblolly Pine Management.* Forest Farmer 9 (1): 4.

————. 1949d. *The Germination and Initial Establishment of Loblolly Pine under Various Surface Soil Conditions.* Jour. Forestry 47: 541-543.

————. 1950a. *Bugs in the Loblolly Pine Cones.* Forest Farmer 9 (7): 15.

————. 1950b. *Twenty Years without Fire Protection.* Forest Farmer 10 (3): 12.

———— and Barron, N. T. 1950. *Hardwoods Versus Loblolly Pines.* Jour. Forestry 48: 112-113.

———— and Korstian, C. F. 1949. *Further Results on Loblolly Pine Seed Production and Dispersal.* Jour. Forestry 47: 968-970.

———— and Trousdell, K. B. 1948. *The Importance of Seed-Bed Preparation in Loblolly Pine Management.* South. Lumberman 177 (2225): 143-144.

Posey, H. G. 1957. *Indications of Linear Dependence of D.O.B. Increases* on D.I.B. Increases in Loblolly Pine at 17.3 Feet. Jour. Forestry 55: 145.

———— and May, J. T. 1954. Some Effects of Sawdust Mulching of Pine Seedlings. Ala. Agr. Expt. Sta. Leaflet 42, 4 pp.

Potts, S. M. 1952. Volume Tables for Small-Diameter Loblolly (Pinus Taeda) and Shortleaf (P. Echinata) Pines. U. S. Tenn. Val. Authority, Div. Forestry Relat. Tech. Note 10, 23 pp.

Pruitt, A. A. 1947. A Study of the Effects of Soils, Water Table, and Drainage on the Height Growth of Slash and Loblolly Pine Plantations on the Hofmann Forest. Thesis, N. C. State Col. School Forestry.

Raber, O. 1937. Water Utilization by Trees, with Special Reference to the Economic Forest Species of the North Temperate Zone. U. S. Dept. Agr. Misc. Pub. 257, 97 pp.

Ralston, C. W. 1947. A Study of Soil Characteristics Associated with Site Index of Loblolly Pine on Alluvial Soils Near Durham, North Carolina. Thesis, Duke Univ. School Forestry.

Ralston, J. 1955. The Relative Productivity of Loblolly Pine and Sweet Gum on Forest Sites in the Lower Piedmont of North Carolina. Thesis, N. C. State Col. School Forestry.

Ramsey, H. 1941. Fauna of Pine Bark. Elisha Mitchell Sci. Soc. Jour. 57: 91-97.

Rawls, I. W. 1952. Large Logs Cost Less to Log Than Small Logs. South. Lumberman 185 (2321): 125-126.

Ray, H. 1957. New Developments in Chemical Brush Control in Arkansas. Jour. Range Mangt. 10 (4): 151-155.

Read, R. A. 1950. Relation Between Time of Treatment and Sprouting of Poisoned Trees. Science 111: 264.

Rechenthin, C. A. 1956. Elementary Morphology of Grass Growth and How It Affects Utilization. Jour. Range Mangt. 9: 167-170.

Reck, E. C. 1933. Specific Gravity and Related Properties of Softwood Lumber. U. S. Dept. Agr. Tech. Bul. 343, 24 pp.

Record, S. J. 1907. The Forests of Arkansas. Forestry Quart. 5: 296-301.

Reed, F. W. 1905. A Working Plan for Forest Lands in Central Alabama. U. S. Forest Serv. Bul. 68, 71 pp.

Reed, J. F. 1939. Root and Shoot Growth of Shortleaf and Loblolly Pines in Relation to Certain Environmental Conditions. Duke Univ. School Forestry Bul. 4, 52 pp.

Reed, R. T. 1946. The Portable Saw in Selective Cutting of Pine Pulpwood. Farmers Fed. News 26 (7): 10-11, 27.

Reigner, I. C. 1953. Do Not Plant Trees Too Soon After Using Weed Killers. U. S. Forest Serv. Northeast. Forest Expt. Sta. Res. Notes 20: 3-4.

Reineke, L. H. 1926. Comparison of Caliper and Diameter Tape Measurements of Second-Growth Loblolly Pine. Jour. Forestry 24: 306.

————. 1933. Perfecting a Stand-Density Index for Even Aged Forests. Jour. Agr. Res. 46: 627-638.

Reines, M., and Greene, J. T. 1958. Early Cone Production in Loblolly Pine. Jour. Forestry 56: 855.

Reynolds, R. R. 1933. Truck Logging of Pine in Mississippi and Louis-

iana. U. S. Forest Serv. South. Forest Expt. Sta. Occas. Paper 28, 10 pp.

————. 1934. *Volume Tables to Fixed Top Diameters.* Jour. Forestry 32: 29-31.

————. 1936. *Good Forestry Is Good Business.* South. Lumberman 153 (1937): 127-128.

————. 1937a. *Factors for Converting Log and Tree Volumes or Values from One Common Scale to Another.* U. S. Forest Serv. South. Forest Expt. Sta. Occas. Paper 68, 4 pp.

————. 1937b. *Pulpwood Production Studies in Shortleaf-Loblolly Pine Stands.* U. S. Forest Serv. South. Forest Expt. Sta. Occas. Paper 71, 5 pp.

————. 1937c. *Forest Management in Shortleaf-Loblolly Pine Regions of the South.* Ames Forester 25: 27-33.

————. 1939a. *Improvement Cuttings in Shortleaf and Loblolly Pine.* Jour. Forestry 37: 568-570.

————. 1939b. *Possible Returns from Planted Loblolly Pine.* Jour. Forestry 37: 250-254.

————. 1939c. *Truck Logging with Detachable Trailers.* U. S. Forest Serv. South. Forest Expt. Sta. Occas. Paper 85, 5 pp.

————. 1939d. *Management of the Forest for Maximum Production.* Mich. Forester 20: 12-15, 63.

————. 1940a. *Pulpwood and Log Production Costs as Affected by Type of Road.* Jour. Forestry 38: 925-931.

————. 1940b. *Lightning as a Cause of Timber Mortality.* U. S. Forest Serv. South. Forest Expt. Sta. South. Forestry Notes 31.

————. 1941a. *Some Principles of Farm Woodland Management.* Miss. Farm Res. [Miss. Sta.] 4 (9): 6.

————. 1941b. *Five Years of Selective Cutting.* South. Lumberman 163 (2047): 54-57.

————. 1941c. *Economical Spacing of Forest Roads.* South. Lumberman 163 (2057): 165-168.

————. 1942. *Labor Requirements for Operating Second-Growth Pine Lands.* U. S. Forest Serv. South. Forest Expt. Sta. South. Forestry Notes 44.

————. 1943a. *Employment Requirements of Well-Managed Timberland.* South. Lumberman 167 (2105): 149-150, 152.

————. 1944. *Farm Forestry Pays.* South. Lumberman 169 (2129): 163-164.

————. 1946. *Trees a Profitable Crop.* Natl. Farm Chemurg. Council Chemurg. Papers 444, 6 pp.

————. 1947a. *Timber—A Modern Crop.* U. S. Dept. Agr. Yearbook 1943-47: 461-464.

————. 1947b. *Business Opportunities in Growing Timber.* Jour. Forestry 45: 81-84.

————. 1947c. *Management of Second-Growth Shortleaf-Loblolly Pine-Hardwood Stands.* Jour. Forestry 45: 181-187.

————. 1947d. *Tree Size Holds Up Under Selective Cuts.* U. S. Forest Serv. South. Forest Expt. Sta. South. Forestry Notes 49.

——. 1948a. *Ten Years of Selective Timber Management.* South. Lumberman 177 (2225): 121-124.

——. 1948b. *Get Your Money's Worth from Forestry.* U. S. Forest Serv. South. Forest Expt. Sta. Occas. Paper 112, 7 pp.

——. 1949a. *Defoliation by Sawfly Retards Pine Growth.* U. S. Forest Serv. South. Forest Expt. Sta. South. Forestry Notes 60.

——. 1949b. *Some Results of Forest Management Research at the Crossett Experimental Forest.* U. S. Forest Serv. South. Forest Expt. Sta., 9 pp.

——. 1950a. *Sidelights on Managing Mixed Pine-Hardwood Stands Under the Selection System.* Jour. Forestry 48: 108-111.

——. 1950b. *Tree Growth in Pictures.* South. Lumberman 181 (2273): 164-166.

——. 1951a. *Timber Stand Improvement Job in Southwest Arkansas.* South. Lumberman 183 (2289): 43-45.

——. 1951b. *Pulpwood Production Costs and Methods in Southeastern Arkansas.* South. Pulp and Paper Mfr. 14 (9): 28, 30, 32.

——. 1951c. *Costs of Intensive Commercial Forest Management.* Forest Farmer 10 (10): 15.

——. 1951d. *Improvement Cutting in Shortleaf and Loblolly Pine.* South. Lumberman 183 (2297): 237-239.

——. 1951e. *Guide to the Crossett Experimental Forest.* U. S. Forest Serv. South. Forest Expt. Sta., 65 pp.

——. 1952a. *Profit Possibilities from Intensive Management of Loblolly Pine.* Jour. Forestry 50: 294-296.

——. 1952b. *Are Suppressed Pines Inferior?* South. Lumberman 185 (2321): 182-183.

——. 1953a. *Is Tree Farming Profitable?* South. Lumberman 187 (2336): 76, 78.

——. 1953b. *Fifteen Years of Management on the Crossett Farm Forestry Forties.* U. S. Forest Serv. South. Forest Expt. Sta. Occas. Paper 130, 27 pp.

——. 1954a. *Management Increases Growth Rate.* U. S. Forest Serv. South. Forest Expt. Sta. South. Forestry Notes 92.

——. 1954b. *Growing Stock in the All-Aged Forest.* Jour. Forestry 52: 744-747.

——. 1955. *Managed Growth.* U. S. Forest Serv. South. Forest Expt. Sta. Occas. Paper 142, 16 pp.

——. 1956. *Upland Hardwoods in South Arkansas Pine Stands— Aerial or Underground Fifth Column?* Jour. Forestry 54: 585-586.

——. 1958. *Drought Can Be Costly to Timber-Land Owners.* South. Lumberman 196 (2447): 32-33.

—— Bond, W. E., and Kirkland, B. P. 1944. *Financial Aspects of Selective Cutting in the Management of Second-Growth Pine-Hardwood Forests West of the Mississippi River.* U. S. Dept. Agr. Tech. Bul. 861, 118 pp.

—— and Bruce, D. 1940. *Check of Central States Fire-Danger Meter.* U. S. Forest Serv. Fire Control Notes 4 (2): 77-79.

—— and Clark, S. F. 1948. *Keep Small Trees Growing.* U. S. Forest Serv. South. Forest Expt. Sta. South. Forestry Notes 54.

————and Rawls, I. W. 1945. *Grade of Material Removed in First Selection Cut in Crossett Experimental Forest Stands.* South. Lumberman 171 (2153) : 139-140.

Rhodes, R. R. 1953. *Survey of Survival, Growth, and Adaptability of Hardwood and Coniferous Tree Species Planted in East Central Texas.* Tex. Forest Serv. Res. Note 4, 18 pp.

Richards, A. B. 1958. *Some Economic Considerations in the Multiple Use of Forest Land.* Land Econ. 34 (3) : 263-268.

Richards, B. N. (n.d.) *The Development of Thinning Schedules for Plantations of Slash and Loblolly Pine in Queensland.* Queensland Forest Serv. Res. Notes 3, 43 pp.

————. 1955. *Thinning of Slash and Loblolly Pines in Queensland.* Austral. Forestry 19 : 67-73.

————. 1956. *The Effect of Phosphate on Slash and Loblolly Pine in Queensland.* Queensland Forest Serv. Res. Notes 5, 11 pp.

Richards, C. A., and Chidester, M. S. 1940. *The Effect of Peniophora Gigantea and Schizophyllum Commune on Strength of Southern Yellow-Pine Sapwood.* Amer. Wood Preservers' Assoc. Proc. 36: 24-31.

Richards, D. B. 1950. *Decay Resistance and Physical Properties of Wood.* Jour. Forestry 48: 420-422.

Riebold, R. J. 1955a. *Summer Burns for Hardwood Control in Loblolly Pine.* U. S. Forest Serv. Fire Control Notes 16 (1) : 34-36.

————. 1955b. *Prescribed Burning in Loblolly Pine Management.* Fourth Ann. Forestry Symposium Proc., La. State Univ. School Forestry 1955: 92-99.

————. 1956. *Wildlife and Timber, Too,—on the Francis Marion National Forest.* South. Lumberman 193 (2417) : 254, 256-258.

Righter, F. I. 1939. *Early Flower Production Among the Pines.* Jour. Forestry 37: 935-938.

———— and Duffield, J. W. 1951. *Interspecies Hybrids in Pines.* Jour. Hered. 42: 75-80.

Ritter, G. J., and Fleck, L. C. 1930. *Chemistry of Wood, Part IX, Springwood and Summerwood.* U. S. Forest Serv. Forest Prod. Lab. Rpt. R950, 4 pp.

Roberts, E. V., and Cruikshank, J. W. 1941. *The Distribution of Commercial Forest Trees in South Carolina.* U. S. Forest Serv. Appalachian Forest Expt. Sta. Forest Survey Release 9, 20 pp.

Roberts, F. L. 1948. *A Study of the Absorbing Surfaces of the Roots of Loblolly Pine.* Thesis, Duke Univ. School Forestry.

Rosendahl, R., and Korstian, C. F. 1945. *Effect of Fertilizers on Loblolly Pine in a North Carolina Nursery.* Plant Physiol. 20: 19-23.

Roth, E. R. 1949. *Heart Rot in Southern Forests.* Forest Farmer 8 (12) : 5.

———— Buchanan, T. S., and Hepting, G. H. 1948. *A Five-Year Record of Littleleaf on Thirty-One Plots.* U. S. Dept. Agr., Bur. Plant Indus., Soils, and Agr. Engin., Div. Forest Path., Forest Path. Spec. Release 32, 9 pp.

Rothacher, J. S. 1947. *A Basis for Comparing the Value of Southern Yellow Pines for Lumber and Poles.* U. S. Tenn. Val. Authority, Div. Forest Relat. Tech. Note 7, 6 pp.

————. 1948. *Percentage Distribution of Tree Volume by Logs.* Jour. Forestry 46: 115-118.

Rothkugel, M. 1907. *Forest Management in Southern Pines.* Forestry Quart. 5: 1-10.

Rothrock, J. T. 1890. *The Old Field or Loblolly Pine (Pinus Taeda Linnaeus).* Forest Leaves 3 (2): 25.

Rowland, C. A., Jr. 1950. *Effects of Bud-Pruning Upon Slash and Loblolly Pine Trees.* Thesis, Ga. Univ. School Forestry.

Rumbold, C. T. 1931. *Two Blue-Staining Fungi Associated with Bark Beetle Infestation of Pines.* Jour. Agr. Res. 43: 847-873.

Ryan, B. A. 1952. *A Pulpwood Company's Views on Even-Aged Management.* First Ann. Forestry Symposium Proc., La. State Univ. School Forestry 1952: 89-92.

St. George, R. A. 1925. *The Recent Death of Large Quantities of Southern Pine.* Amer. Lumberman 2607: 50-51.

———— and Beal, J. A. 1929. *The Southern Pine Beetle: A Serious Enemy of Pines in the South.* U. S. Dept. Agr. Farmers' Bul. 1586, 18 pp.

Sakornbut, S. S. 1951. *Differentiation of Woods of Southern Pines by Chemical Means.* Jour. Forestry 49: 109-111.

Sargent, C. S. 1884. *Report on the Forests of North America (Exclusive of Mexico).* U. S. Census, 10th, 1880, V. 9, 612 pp. Washington, D. C.

————. 1897. *Coniferae (Pinus), Vol. XII. In* The silva of North America; a description of the trees which grow naturally in North America exclusive of Mexico. 14 v., Boston and New York.

Schafer, E. R. 1949. *Influence of Volume of Summerwood and Rate of Growth on the Specific Gravity of Southern Pine Pulpwood.* South. Pulp and Paper Mfr. 12 (10A): 166-168.

———— Pew, J. C., and Curran, C. E. 1958. *Grinding of Loblolly Pine— Relation of Wood Properties and Grinding Conditions to Pulp and Paper Quality.* U. S. Forest Serv. Forest Prod. Lab. Rpt. 1163, 18 pp. (Revision of the 1937 article.)

———— Pew, J. C., and Knechtges, R. G. 1936. *Effect of High Pit Temperature and Pre-Heating of the Wood on the Grinding of Loblolly Pine.* Paper Trade Jour. 103 (2): 29-32.

Scheffer, T. C., and Lindgren, R. M. 1940. *Stains of Sapwood and Sapwood Products and Their Control.* U. S. Dept. Agr. Tech. Bul. 714, 124 pp.

Schnur, G. L. 1932. *Mortality in Old Field Loblolly Pine.* U. S. Forest Serv. Forest Worker 8 (3): 7.

————. 1934. *Diameter Distribution for Old-Field Loblolly Pine Stands in Maryland.* Jour. Agr. Res. 49: 731-743.

————. 1939. *Volume Tables for Loblolly Pine (Pinus Taeda).* U. S. Forest Serv. Allegheny Forest Expt. Sta. Tech. Note 25, 3 pp.

Schopmeyer, C. S. 1939. *Transpiration and Physico-Chemical Properties of Leaves as Related to Drought Resistance in Loblolly Pine and Shortleaf Pine.* Plant Physiol. 14: 447-462.

Schores, D. D. 1956. *The Effect of Certain Stand Conditions on the Radial Growth of Dominant Loblolly Pine in Southeast Louisiana.* Thesis, La. State Univ. School Forestry.

Schorger, A. W. 1917. *Mannan Content of the Gymnosperms.* Jour. Forestry 15: 197-202.

Schrenk, H. von. 1905. *Some Diseases of Loblolly Pine Timber.* (Abs.) Science 21: 502.

Schumacher, F. X. 1946a. *Stacked and Solid Volume of Southeastern Pulpwood.* Jour. Forestry 44: 579-582.

———. 1946b. *Volume-Weight Ratios of Pine Logs in the Virginia-North Carolina Coastal Plain.* Jour. Forestry 44: 583-586.

——— and Coile, T. S. 1954a. *Growth Prediction of Even-Aged Loblolly Pine Stands.* Duke Univ. School Forestry, 10 pp.

——— and Coile, T. S. 1954b. *Yields of Well Stocked Stands of Coastal Plain Loblolly Pine.* Duke Univ. School Forestry, 5 pp.

——— and Coile, T. S. 1960. *Growth and Yields of Natural Stands of the Southern Pines.* 97 pp. and app. T. S. Coile, Inc., Durham, N. C.

Scott, M. H., and DuPlessis, C. P. 1951. *The Qualities of the Wood of Pinus Taeda Grown in South Africa.* So. African Forestry Assoc. Jour. 20: 19-30.

Segall, G. H., and Purves, D. B. 1946. *Chemical Composition of Wood Barks.* Pulp and Paper Mag. Canada 47 (3): 149-162.

Sentell, N. W. 1949. *Pales Weevil Damages Plantations in Louisiana.* Jour. Forestry 47: 741.

Shaw, G. R. 1914. *The Genus Pinus.* Arnold Arboretum Pub. 5, 96 pp.

Shenefelt, R. D., Liebig, H. R., and Dosen, R. C. 1955. *Protecting Machine Transplanted Trees from White Grubs.* Tree Planters' Notes 20: 14-17.

Shepard, A. L. 1940. *Another Use for Pine Needles.* U. S. Forest Serv. Service Bul. 24 (17): 5.

Shepherd, W. O. 1952. *Highlights of Forest Grazing Research in the Southeast.* Jour. Forestry 50: 280-283.

——— Kaufman, C. M., and Biswell, H. H. 1946. *Forest Grazing in North Carolina.* South. Lumberman 173 (2177): 228-238.

Sherfesee, W. F. 1908. *The Preservative Treatment of Loblolly Pine Cross-Arms.* U. S. Dept. Agr. Forest Serv. Cir. 151, 29 pp.

Sherry, S. P. 1939. *The Rate of Growth and Health of the Southern Pines in the Midland Conservancy.* So. African Forestry Assoc. Jour. 1: 30-40. Forestry Abs. 1 (1): 28.

———. 1947. *The Potentialities of Genetic Research in South African Forestry.* British Empire Forestry Conf., 11 pp. City Printing Works, Ltd., Pietermaritzburg, South Africa.

Shipman, R. D. 1953. *Poisoning Small-Diameter Hardwoods with the Cornell Tool.* U. S. Forest Serv. Southeast. Forest Expt. Sta. Res. Notes 38.

———. 1954. *Release of Loblolly Pine by Various Weeding Methods.* U. S. Forest Serv. Southeast. Forest Expt. Sta. Res. Notes 65.

———. 1958. *Effect of Season of Treatment on Girdling and Chemical Control of Oak and Sweetgum.* Jour. Forestry 56: 33-35.

Shirley, H. L. 1928. *The Influence of Light Intensity and Quality Upon the Growth of Plants.* (Abs.) Amer. Jour. Bot. 15: 621-622.

Shoulders, E. 1952. *Cold Hurts Loblolly in Ozarks.* U. S. Forest Serv. South. Forest Expt. Sta. South. Forestry Notes 82.

————. 1955. *Conserving Louisiana's Loblolly Pine (Pinus Taeda)*. Forests and People 5 (4) : 36-37, 45.

Siggers, P. V. 1948. *Weather and the Southern Fusiform Rust*. Forest Farmer 8 (2) : 8, 10.

————. 1949a. *Fire and the Southern Fusiform Rust*. Forest Farmer 8 (5) : 16, 21.

————. 1949b. *Weather and Outbreaks of the Fusiform Rust of Southern Pines*. Jour. Forestry 47 : 802-806.

————. 1951. *Spray Control of the Fusiform Rust in Forest-Tree Nurseries*. Jour. Forestry 49 : 350-352.

————. 1955. *Control of the Fusiform Rust of Southern Pines*. Jour. Forestry 53 : 442-446.

———— and Lindgren, R. M. 1947. *An Old Disease—a New Problem*. South. Lumberman 175 (2201) : 172-175.

Siggins, H. W. 1933. *Distribution and Rate of Fall of Conifer Seeds*. Jour. Agr. Res. 47 : 119-128.

Silcox, F. A. 1904. *The Lumbering of Loblolly Pine in South Carolina*. Thesis, Yale Univ. School Forestry.

Silker, T. H. 1955a. *Prescribed Burning for the Control of Undesirable Hardwoods in Pine-Hardwood Stands and Slash Pine Plantations*. Tex. Forest Serv. Bul. 46, 19 pp.

————. 1955b. *Forest Grazing in the Pine-Hardwood and Bottomland Hardwood Types of Southeast Texas*. Tex. Forest Serv. Bul. 47, 34 pp.

————. 1956. *Prescribed Burning in the Silviculture and Management of Southern Pine-Hardwood and Slash Pine Stands*. Soc. Amer. Foresters Proc. 1956 : 94-99.

———— and Goddard, R. E. 1953. *Direct Seeding Tests with Slash, Loblolly, and Longleaf Pine in Southeast Texas*. Tex. Forest Serv. Tech. Rpt. 7, 36 pp.

Simmonds, F. A., Kingsbury, R. M., Martin, J. S., and Mitchell, R. L. 1956. *Loblolly Pine High Alpha Prehydrolysis-Sulphate Pulps*. Tappi 39 (9) : 641-647.

Simmons, E. M., and Schnur, G. L. 1937. *Effect of Stand Density on Mortality and Growth of Loblolly Pine*. Jour. Agr. Res. 54 : 47-58.

Sims, I. H., Munns, E. N., and Auten, J. T. 1938. *Management of Forest Soils*. U. S. Dept. Agr. Yearbook 1938 : 737-750.

Sleeth, B. 1943. *Fusiform Rust Control in Forest-Tree Nurseries*. Phytopathology 33 : 33-44.

Slocum, G. K. 1932. *A Seed Study of Loblolly Pine*. Thesis, N. C. State Col. School Forestry.

————. 1951. *Survival of Loblolly Pine Seedlings as Influenced by Depth of Planting*. Jour. Forestry 49 : 500.

———— and Maki, T. E. 1956a. *Some Effects of Depth of Planting Upon Loblolly Pine in the North Carolina Piedmont*. Jour. Forestry 54 : 21-25.

———— and Maki, T. E. 1956b. *Exposure of Loblolly Pine Planting Stock*. Jour. Forestry 54 : 313-315.

Smedberg, W. W. 1947. *Mechanization of Pulpwood Producing Operations in the South*. Thesis, Duke Univ. School Forestry.

Smith, J. H. G. 1954. *The Economics of Pruning*. Forestry Chron. 30 (2) : 197-214.

Smith, L. F. 1947. *Early Results of a Liberation Cutting in a Pine-Hardwood Stand in Northern Louisiana.* Jour. Forestry 45: 278-282.

Smith, R. H. 1954a. *Benzene Hexachloride Controls Black Turpentine Beetle.* South. Lumberman 189 (2369): 155-157.

———. 1954b. *Studies in the Control of the Black Turpentine Beetle in Southern Pine.* (Abs.) Assoc. South. Agr. Workers Proc. 51: 100.

———. 1955. *A Control for the Black Turpentine Beetle in South Georgia and North Florida.* U. S. Forest Serv. Southeast. Forest Expt. Sta. Res. Notes 76. (Revised Oct. 1955.)

Snow, E. A. 1949. *Pine Bark as a Source of Tannin.* Amer. Leather Chem. Assoc. Jour. 44: 504-511.

Snyder, T. E. 1927. *Defects in Timber Caused by Insects.* U. S. Dept. Agr. Bul. 1490, 46 pp.

———. 1935. *The Ips Engraver Beetles in the South.* Naval Stores Rev. 45 (32): 15.

———. 1936. *Bark Beetles in Relation to Selective Cutting.* Naval Stores Rev. 46 (27): 19.

———. 1937. *Damage to Young Pines by a Leaf-Cutting Ant, Atta Texana Buckley, in Louisiana.* La. Conserv. Rev. 6 (1): 14-17.

———. 1940. *The Browning of the Needles of Young Yellow Pine Trees in the Gulf States by a Leaf-Feeding Beetle (Colaspis Pini Barber).* South. Lumberman 160 (2020): 46.

——— and Zetek, J. 1943. *Effectiveness of Wood Preservatives in Preventing Attack by Termites.* U. S. Dept. Agr. Cir. 683, 24 pp.

Society of America Foresters. 1926. *A Forest Type Classification for the Southern Appalachian Mountains and the Adjacent Plateau and Coastal Plain Regions.* South. Appalachian Section, Committee Report, Jour. Forestry 24: 673-684.

South Carolina Commission of Forestry. 1953. *Field Tables and Rules.* 12 pp.

Southeastern Forest Experiment Station. 1948. *Tree Grades for Loblolly and Shortleaf Pine.* U. S. Forest Serv. Southeast. Forest Expt. Sta. Tech. Note 69, 13 pp.

———. 1955. *Annual Report, 1954.* U. S. Forest Serv. Southeast. Forest Expt. Sta. Paper 50, 76 pp.

Southeastern Forest Experiment Station, Southern Piedmont Branch. 1951. *Piedmont Possibilities: Managed Loblolly Does Produce Quality Lumber.* South. Lumber Jour. 55 (7): 33, 34.

Southern Forest Experiment Station. 1933. *Studies on Natural Reproduction and Methods of Cutting by the Southern Forest Experiment Station.* Naval Stores Rev. 43 (49): 6.

———. 1933. *Stand-Improvement Measures for Southern Forests.* Emergency Conserv. Work Forestry Pub. 3, 37 pp.

———. 1955. *Forests of Louisiana, 1953-1954.* U. S. Forest Serv. South. Forest Expt. Sta. Forest Survey Release 75, 64 pp.

Southern Forest Experiment Station, and others. 1953. *Interim Log Grades for Southern Pine.* U. S. Forest Serv. South. Forest Expt. Sta., 18 pp.

Southern Forest Experiment Station, Forest Survey Staff. 1937. *Forest Resources of Southwest Arkansas.* U. S. Forest Serv. South. Forest Expt. Sta. Forest Survey Release 27, 21 pp.

————. 1938a. *Forest Resources of Southwest Alabama.* U. S. Forest Serv. South. Forest Expt. Sta. Forest Survey Release 35, 35 pp.

————. 1938b. *Forest Resources of the Ouachita Mountain Region of Arkansas.* U. S. Forest Serv. South. Forest Expt. Sta. Forest Survey Release 36, 27 pp.

————. 1948. *Florida's Forest Resources, 1934-36.* U. S. Forest Serv. [Unnumbered.] 35 pp.

Speers, C. F. 1955. *Insects which Attack Pine Seedlings in the South.* South. Lumberman 191 (2393) : 147-149.

————. 1956. *Pales Weevil Control with Insecticides: First Year Results.* U. S. Forest Serv. Southeast. Forest Expt. Sta. Res. Notes 96.

————. 1958. *Pales Weevil Rapidly Becoming Serious Pest of Pine Reproduction in the South.* Jour. Forestry 56: 723-726.

Spiers, J. F. 1932. *The Survival and Early Growth of Planted Loblolly Pine in Clarke, Hart, and Banks Counties, Georgia.* The Cypress Knee Ga. State Col. Agr. 10: 44-47, 85-88.

Spillers, A. R. 1935. *Pine Straw Used in Strawberry Culture.* South. Agr. 45 (1) : 23.

————. 1939. *Forest Resources of Southeast Alabama.* U. S. Forest Serv. South. Forest Expt. Sta. Forest Survey Release 47, 32 pp.

————. 1940. *Forest Resources of West Central Alabama.* U. S. Forest Serv. South. Forest Expt. Sta. Forest Survey Release 48, 30 pp.

———— and Eldredge, I. F. 1943. *Georgia Forest Resources and Industries.* U. S. Dept. Agr. Misc. Pub. 501, 70 pp.

Spradling, M. 1936. *Penetration of Trichoderma Lignorum into Sapwood of Pinus Taeda.* Jour. Agr. Res. 52: 541-546.

Spring, S. N. 1902. *Lumbering of Loblolly Pine by the E. P. Burton Lumber Co., South Carolina.* Thesis, Yale Univ. School Forestry.

Spurr, S. H., and Hsiung, W. Y. 1954. *Growth Rate and Specific Gravity in Conifers.* Jour. Forestry 52: 191-200.

Stahelin, R. 1946. *The Conversion of Hardwood to Pine Stands in Alabama.* Ala. Acad. Sci. Jour. 18: 58-59.

————. 1948a. *The Importance of Good Stocking for Maximum Wood Production.* Ala. Acad. Sci. Jour. 20: 58-59.

————. 1948b. *Plantation Spacing and Wood Production.* U. S. Forest Serv. South. Forest Expt. Sta. South. Forestry Notes 56.

————. 1949. *Thinning Even-Aged Loblolly and Slash Pine Stands to Specified Densities.* Jour. Forestry 47: 538-540.

Stanley, G. W. 1954. *Protecting the Young Plantation.* Third Ann. Forestry Symposium Proc., La. State Univ. School Forestry 1954: 93-100.

———— and Shope, H. D. 1956. *What Water Means to the Forest Industries.* Forest Farmer 16 (2) : 10-11, 28, 32, 33.

Steirly, C. C. 1952. *The Red-Cockaded Woodpecker.* Va. Wildlife 13 (8) : 18-19.

Stephenson, G. K. 1956. *Mortality in the Woodpile.* South. Lumberman 193 (2417) : 220-221.

Stern, G. E., and Stoneburner, P. W. 1952. *Design of Nailed Structures.* Va. Polytech. Inst. Engin. Expt. Sta. Ser. 81, 67 pp.

Sternitzke, H. S., and Wheeler, P. R. 1955. *Louisiana Forests Turn the Corner.* Forests and People 5 (2) : 8-9.

Sterrett, W. D. 1914. *Forest Management of Loblolly Pine in Delaware, Maryland, and Virginia.* U. S. Dept. Agr. Bul. 11, 59 pp.

Stockwell, P. 1948. *Pine Breeding Today.* South Lumberman 177 (2225): 279-281.

Stoehr, H. A. 1946. *Estimation of Site Index for Pine in the Lower Piedmont Plateau on the Basis of Certain Soil Characteristics.* Thesis, Duke Univ. School Forestry.

Stoltenberg, C. H. 1956. *Economic Aspects of Type Maintenance and Conversion in Loblolly Pine-Hardwood Region.* Jour. Forestry 54: 371-374.

Stover, W. L., and Christopher, J. F. 1955. *1954 Pulpwood Production in the South.* U. S. Forest Serv. South. Forest Expt. Sta. Forest Survey Release 76, 13 pp.

Strong, O. B. 1950. *A Tree Classification for Even-Aged Immature, Loblolly, Shortleaf, and Slash Pine in Southeast Louisiana.* Thesis, La. State Univ. School Forestry.

Sundberg, U. 1953. *The Use of Power Saws in Forestry Operations.* FAO-EFC Pilot Comm. Logging Tech. 19, 62 pp.

Swain, E. H. F. 1945. *Forestry and the Conservation Imperative in Australian Reconstruction.* N.S.W. Forestry Commission: Rural Reconstruction Commission. 46 pp. Forestry Abs. 7 (3): 378.

Switzer, G. L., and Nelson, L. E. 1956. *The Effect of Fertilization on Seedling Weight and Utilization of N, P, and K by Loblolly Pine Grown in the Nursery.* Soil Sci. Soc. Amer. Proc. 20: 404-408.

Swofford, T. F. 1958. *Stratification Harmful to Some Loblolly and Slash Pine Seed.* Tree Planters' Notes 32: 5-6.

Taber, W. S. 1939. *Delaware Trees.* Del. State Forestry Dept. Pub. 6, 250 pp.

Tannehill, G. F. 1951. *Control of Hardwood Underbrush by Bulldozing.* Jour. Forestry 49: 776-778.

Taras, M. A. 1956. *Buying Pulpwood by Weight—as Compared with Volume Measure.* U. S. Forest Serv. Southeast. Forest Expt. Sta. Paper 74, 11 pp.

Teesdale, C. H. 1914. *Relative Resistance of Various Conifers to Injection with Creosote.* U. S. Dept. Agr. Bul. 101, 43 pp.

Telford, C. J. 1952. *Small Sawmill Operator's Manual.* U. S. Dept. Agr. Handb. 27, 121 pp.

———. 1954. *Small Sawmills: a Pocket Guide.* U. S. Dept. Agr. Handb. 70, 26 pp.

Texas Forest Service. 1945. *Pine Tip Moth.* Tex. Forest Serv. Bul. 35, 4 pp. [rev. 1949.]

———. 1950. *The Southern Pine Beetle—Its Occurrence and Control in East Texas.* Tex. Forest Serv. Cir. 26, 7 pp.

———. 1953a. *Forest Genetic Research for Fiber Production.* South. Pulp and Paper Mfr. 16 (12): 40, 43-46.

———. 1953b. *The Ips Engraver Beetles—Their Indentification and Control.* Tex. Forest Serv. Cir. 33, 5 pp.

Thelen, R. 1923. *Kiln Drying Handbook.* U. S. Dept. Agr. Bul. 1136, 64 pp.

Thomas, J., and Platt, R. B. 1954. *Maximum Temperature Tolerances of*

Loblolly Pine and Sweet Gum Seedlings Under Varying Soil, Moisture, and Light Conditions. (Abs.) Tenn. Acad. Sci. Jour. 29: 186.

Thompson, W. S. 1953. *Fence Post Preservation with Copper Naphthenate by the Cold Soaking Method.* Miss. Agr. Expt. Sta. Cir. 191, 8 pp.

Thomson, R. S. 1914. *The Spur Shoot of the Pines.* Bot. Gaz. 57: 362-385.

Thornthwaite, C. W. 1931. *The Climates of North America According to a New Classification.* Geog. Rev. 21: 633-655.

———. 1941. *Atlas of Climatic Types in the United States 1900-1939.* U. S. Dept. Agr. Misc. Pub. 421, 55 pp.

——— and Mather, J. R. 1955. *The Water Balance.* Drexel Inst. Technol. Climatol. Lab. 8 (1): 104 pp.

Tiemann, H. D. 1906. *Effect of Moisture Upon the Strength and Stiffness of Wood.* U. S. Dept. Agr. Forest. Serv. Bul. 70, 144 pp.

Tissot, A. N. 1932. *Six New Aphids from Florida.* Fla. Ent. 16 (1): 1-13.

Tissue, O. C., Jr. 1953. *Costs and Effects of Several Degrees of Release of Understory Loblolly Pine in Upland Hardwood Stands.* Thesis, N. C. State Col. School Forestry.

Todd, A. S., Jr. 1952a. *Rates of Net Annual Growth in Board Feet Applicable to Large Forested Areas in South Carolina.* U. S. Forest Serv. Southeast. Forest Expt. Sta. Res. Notes 2, 2 pp.

———. 1952b. *Rates of Net Annual Growth in Cords Applicable to Large Forested Areas in South Carolina.* U. S. Forest Serv. Southeast. Forest Expt. Sta. Res. Notes 3, 2 pp.

———. 1953. *Sawmill and Logging Residues in the South Carolina Piedmont: Problems and Methods of Salvage.* U. S. Forest Serv. Southeast. Forest Expt. Sta. Paper 31, 32 pp.

———. 1955. *Pulpwood from Small Sawmill and Logging Residues: Problems and Opportunities.* Jour. Forestry 53: 416-419.

——— and Zirkle, J. J., Jr. 1949. *Marketing Farm Timber in Monroe County, Georgia.* U. S. Forest Serv. Southeast. Forest Expt. Sta. Paper 3, 33 pp.

Tofte, A. L., and Stover, W. S. 1949. *Pulpwood Production in Southern Forest Survey Territory, 1948.* U. S. Forest Serv. South. Forest Expt. Sta. Forest Survey Release 61, 16 pp.

Toole, E. R. 1939. *Relation of Incidence of Needle Disease in Loblolly Pine Plantations to Certain Physical Properties of the Soil.* Jour. Forestry 37: 13-18.

Toole, V. K., and others. 1958. *The Germination and Response of Seeds of Pinus Taeda to Light.* (Abs.) Plant Physiol. 33 (sup.): XXIII.

Toumey, J. W. 1929. *Initial Root Habit in American Trees and Its Bearing on Regeneration.* Internatl. Cong. Plant Sci. Proc. 1926: 713-728.

——— and Stevens, C. L. 1928. *The Testing of Coniferous Tree Seeds at the School of Forestry, Yale University, 1906-1926.* Yale Univ. School Forestry Bul. 21: 1-4.

Townsend, H. E., Jr. 1949. *A Comparison of the Growth and Characteristics of Planted Loblolly Pine and Slash Pine in North Louisiana.* Thesis, La. State Univ. School Forestry.

Trousdell, K. B. 1947. *Some Effects of a Piecework System on Felling and Bucking Costs in Eastern North Carolina.* South. Lumberman 175 (2201): 190-192.

————. 1950a. *A Method of Forecasting Annual Variations in Seed Crop for Loblolly Pine.* Jour. Forestry 48: 345-348.

————. 1950b. *Seed and Seedbed Requirements to Regenerate Loblolly Pine.* U. S. Forest Serv. Southeast. Forest Expt. Sta. Paper 8, 13 pp.

————. 1950c. *Forecasting Loblolly Pine Cone Crops.* South. Lumberman 183 (2297): 137-138.

————. 1950d. *The 1951 Loblolly Pine Cone Crop.* Va. Forests 5 (6): 14, 16.

————. 1952a. *Loblolly Pine Seed Trees Removed with Minor Damage to Seedling Stand.* U. S. Forest Serv. Southeast. Forest Expt. Sta. Res. Notes 8, 2 pp.

————. 1952b. *Bumper Loblolly Cone Crop Forecast for Virginia-North Carolina Area in 1953.* U. S. Forest Serv. Southeast. Forest Expt. Sta. Res. Notes 16, 2 pp.

————. 1954a. *Favorable Seedbed Conditions for Loblolly Pine Disappear 3 Years After Logging.* Jour. Forestry 52: 174-176.

————. 1954b. *A Comparison of Two Systems of Measuring Stocking of Loblolly Pine Seedlings.* U. S. Forest Serv. Southeast. Forest Expt. Sta. Res. Notes 48, 2 pp.

————. 1954c. *Peak Population of Seed-Eating Rodents and Shrews Occurs 1 Year After Loblolly Pine Stands Are Cut.* U. S. Forest Serv. Southeast. Forest Expt. Sta. Res. Notes 68, 2 pp.

————. 1955a. *Hurricane Damage to Loblolly Pine on Bigwoods Experimental Forest.* South. Lumberman 191 (2383): 35-37.

————. 1955b. *Loblolly Pine Seed Tree Mortality.* U. S. Forest Serv. Southeast. Forest Expt. Sta. Paper 61, 11 pp.

———— and Hoover, M. D. 1955. *A Change in Ground Water Level After Clearcutting of Loblolly Pine in the Coastal Plain.* Jour. Forestry 53: 493-498.

Truax, T. R., Harrison, C. A., and Baechler, R. H. 1935. *Experiments in Fireproofing Wood—Fifth Progress Report.* U. S. Forest Serv. Forest Prod. Lab. Rpt. R1118.

Turnbull, J. M. 1943. *A Study in Stem Design.* So. African Forestry Assoc. Jour. 9: 26-30. Forestry Abs. 5 (1): 17.

————. 1947. *Some Factors Affecting Wood Density in Pine Stems.* Pretoria Dept. Forestry, 22 pp. (Fifth Brit. Empire Forestry Conf., Gt. Brit., 1947.)

Turner, L. M. 1936a. *Factors Influencing the Rate of Growth of Pine in Arkansas.* Ecology 17: 227-240.

————. 1936b. *Root Growth of Seedlings of Pinus Echinata and Pinus Taeda.* Jour. Agr. Res. 53: 145-149.

————. 1937a. *Growth of Second Growth Pine on the Coastal Plain Soils of Arkansas.* Ark. Agr. Expt. Sta. Bul. 342, 52 pp.

————. 1937b. *Some Soil Characters Influencing the Distribution of Forest Types and Rate of Growth of Trees in Arkansas.* Jour. Forestry 35: 5-11.

————. 1938. *Some Profile Characteristics of the Pine-Growing Soils of the Coastal-Plain Region of Arkansas.* Ark. Agr. Expt. Sta. Bul. 361, 52 pp.

————. 1943. *Relation of Stand Density to Height Growth.* Jour. Forestry 41: 766.

Tyler, J. S. 1952. *Marking Practice in Even-Aged Management.* First Ann. Forestry Symposium Proc., La. State Univ. School Forestry 1952: 31-35.

Uhlig, H. G., and Bailey, R. W. 1952. *Factors Influencing the Distribution and Abundance of the Wild Turkey in West Virginia.* Jour. Wildlife Mangt. 16: 24-32.

Underhill, G. W. 1943. *Some Insect Pests of Ornamental Plants.* Va. Agr. Expt. Sta. Bul. 349, 38 pp.

Ursic, S. J. 1956a. *Bale Storage of Loblolly Pine Seedlings.* U. S. Forest Serv. South. Forest Expt. Sta. South. Forestry Notes 103.

————. 1956b. *Late Winter Prelifting Fertilization of Loblolly Pine Seedbeds.* Tree Planters' Notes 26: 11-13.

U. S. Forest Service. 1929. *Volume, Yield, and Stand Tables for Second-Growth Southern Pines.* U. S. Dept. Agr. Misc. Pub. 50, 202 pp.

————. 1945. *Guide for Cutting Loblolly Pine of the Eastern Shore.* U. S. Dept. Agr. AIS-2, 8 pp.

————. 1948. *Color Tests for Differentiating Heartwood and Sapwood of Certain Oaks, Pines and Douglas-Fir.* U. S. Forest Serv. Forest Prod. Lab. Tech. Note 253, 2 pp.

————. 1948a. *Woody-Plant Seed Manual.* U. S. Dept. Agr. Misc. Pub. 654, 416 pp.

————. 1951. *Volume Tables, Converting Factors, and Other Information Applicable to Commercial Timber in the South.* U. S. Forest Serv. Div. State and Private Forestry, Region 8, 49 pp.

————. 1953a. *Interim Log Grades for Southern Pine.* U. S. Forest Serv. South. Forest Expt. Sta., 18 pp.

————. 1953b. *A Simple Device for Detecting Compression Wood.* U. S. Forest Serv. Forest Prod. Lab. Rpt. R1390.

————. 1955. *Wood Handbook; Basic Information on Wood As a Material of Construction with Data for Its Use in Design and Specification.* U. S. Dept. Agr. Handb. 72, 528 pp.

————. 1958. *Timber Resources for America's Future.* U. S. Dept. Agr. Forest Resource Rpt. 14, 713 pp.

U. S. Tennessee Valley Authority. 1941. *Forestry Data for the Tennessee Valley. Part I. Area Data for Valley Counties.* U. S. Tenn. Val. Authority, Div. Forestry Relat. Bul. 3, 155 pp.

————. 1955. *Influences of Reforestation and Erosion Control upon the Hydrology of the Pine Tree Branch Watershed, 1941 to 1950.* U. S. Tenn. Val. Authority Tech. Monog. 86, 95 pp.

Vaughan, J. A. 1954. *Controlled-Air Seasoning.* Amer. Wood Preservers' Assoc. Proc. 50: 282-290.

Verrall, A. F. 1939. *Relative Importance and Seasonal Prevalence of Wood-Staining Fungi in the Southern States.* Phytopathology 29: 1031-1051.

————. 1945. *The Control of Fungi in Lumber During Air-Seasoning.* Bot. Rev. 11: 398-415.

————. 1953. *Decay Prevention in Wooden Steps and Porches Through*

Proper Design and Protective Treatments. Forest Prod. Res. Soc. Jour. 3 (4) : 54-60.

———. 1958. *Fusiform Rust of Southern Pines.* U. S. Forest Serv. Forest Pest Leaflet 26, 4 pp.

———and Scheffer, T. C. 1949. *Control of Stain, Mold, and Decay in Green Lumber and Other Wood Products.* Forest Prod. Res. Soc. Proc. 3 : 480-489.

Vincent, P. Y. 1955. *The Use of Fire in the Management of Shortleaf-Loblolly Hardwood Type on the Texas National Forests.* Fourth Ann. Forestry Symposium Proc., La. State Univ. School Forestry 1955 : 86-91.

———. 1956. *Conservation of Timber—and Game.* South. Lumberman 193 (2417) : 252-253.

Wackerman, A. E. 1929. *Why Prairies in Arkansas and Louisiana?* Jour. Forestry 27 : 726-734.

———. 1931. *The Management of Shortleaf and Loblolly Pine for Sawtimber.* Jour. Forestry 29 : 3-10.

———. 1933. *Selective Cutting for Sustained Yield: Good Business.* South. Lumberman 147 (1865) : 74.

———. 1934. *Allocating Cutting Budgets by Means of a Forest Sky Line Graph.* Jour. Forestry 32 : 4-7.

———. 1940. *The Permanence of Southern Pulp Mills.* Mfrs. Rec. 109 (3) : 32-33, 58, 60.

———. 1945. *Forest Products Marketing Problems in the Piedmont Region of North Carolina.* Duke Univ. School Forestry Bul. 12, 62 pp.

Wagener, W. W., and Davidson, R. W. 1954. *Heart Rots in Living Trees.* Bot. Rev. 20 : 61-134.

Wahlenberg, W. G. 1941. *Methods of Forecasting Timber Growth in Irregular Stands.* U. S. Dept. Agr. Tech. Bul. 796, 56 pp.

———. 1948a. *Effect of Forest Shade and Openings on Loblolly Pine Seedlings.* Jour. Forestry 46 : 832-834.

———. 1948b. *Loblolly Seedling Survival in Forest Openings.* U. S. Forest Serv. South. Forest Expt. Sta. South. Forestry Notes 54.

———. 1949. *Forest Succession in the Southern Piedmont Region.* Jour. Forestry 47 : 713-715.

——— and Ostrom, C. E. 1956. *Geographic Variation in Climate in the Loblolly Pine Region.* U. S. Forest Serv. Southeast. Forest Expt. Sta. Res. Notes 94.

Wahlgren, H. E., and Fassnacht, D. L. 1959. *Estimating Tree Specific Gravity from a Single Increment Core.* U. S. Forest Serv. Forest Prod. Rpt. 2146, 24 pp.

Wakeley, P. C. 1928. *Preliminary Observations on the Pine Tip Moth (Rhyacionia Frustrana Comst.) on Southern Pines.* Fourth Internatl. Cong. Ent. Proc. 2 : 865-868.

———. 1929. *Producing Pine Nursery Stock in the South.* U. S. Dept. Agr. Leaflet 35, 8 pp.

———. 1930. *Seed Yield Data for Southern Pines.* Jour. Forestry 28 : 391-394.

———. 1931. *Some Observations on Southern Pine Seed.* Jour. Forestry 29 : 1150-1164.

————. 1931-1941. *Annual Cone Crop Estimates for Southern Pines.* U. S. Forest Serv. South. Forest Expt. Sta. (11 mimeo. reports, 1931-1941).

————. 1935a. *Notes on the Life Cycle of the Nantucket Tip Moth (Rhyacionia Frustrana Comst.) in Southeastern Louisiana.* U. S. Forest Serv. South. Forest Expt. Sta. Occas. Paper 45, 8 pp.

————. 1935b. *Collecting, Extracting, and Marketing Southern Pine Seed.* U. S. Forest Serv. South. Forest Expt. Sta. Occas. Paper 51, 10 pp.

————. 1935c. *Artificial Reforestation in the Southern Pine Region.* U. S. Dept. Agr. Tech. Bul. 492, 115 pp.

————. 1938. *Harvesting and Selling Seed of Southern Pines.* U. S. Dept. Agr. Leaflet 156, 8 pp.

————. 1939. *Storing Southern Pine Seed on a Commercial Scale.* South. Lumberman 159 (2009): 114.

————. 1944a. *Geographic Source of Loblolly Pine Seed.* Jour. Forestry 42: 23-32.

————. 1944b. *Where and How Can the Pines Be Reproduced.* South. Lumberman 169 (2129): 140-145.

————. 1945a. *Planting Wild Seedlings of the Southern Pines.* Forest Farmer 4 (7): 6.

————. 1945b. *How Much Forest Planting Have We To Do?* South. Lumberman 171 (2153): 163-167.

————. 1947a. *Advances in Storing Southern Pine Seed.* U. S. Forest Serv. South. Forest Expt. Sta. South. Forestry Notes 47.

————. 1947b. *The 1947 Cone Crop and Forest Fires.* U. S. Forest Serv. South. Forest Expt. Sta. South. Forestry Notes 51.

————. 1947c. *Loblolly Pine Seed Production.* Jour. Forestry 45: 676-677.

————. 1948a. *Plantation Survival.* La. State Univ. Forestry Dept. Annual Ring 9: 24-25, 44.

————. 1948b. *Storing Southern Pine Planting Stock.* U. S. Forest Serv. South. Forest Expt. Sta. South. Forestry Notes 58.

————. 1948c. *Sun-Dried Seed Keeps Better in Storage.* U. S. Forest Serv. South. Forest Expt. Sta. South. Forestry Notes 57.

————. 1948d. *Collecting Southern Pine Seed.* Forest Farmer 7 (12): 1, 7.

————. 1949. *Physiological Grades of Southern Pine Nursery Stock.* Soc. Amer. Foresters Proc. (1948) 2: 311-322.

————. 1950a. *Directions for Testing Southern Pine Seed at Forest Nurseries.* U. S. Forest Serv. South. Forest Expt. Sta., 11 pp.

————. 1950b. *Plant Loblolly Pines from Local Seed.* U. S. Forest Serv. South. Forest Expt. Sta. South. Forestry Notes 66.

————. 1951. *Storing Southern Pine Seed.* U. S. Forest Serv. South. Forest Expt. Sta. Occas. Paper 123, 13 pp.

————. 1952. *How Seed Source and Seedling Stock Affect Reforestation.* Forest Farmer 12 (2): 16, 28.

————. 1953a. *The South Establishes a Major Pine Geographic Seed Source Study.* Second Tree Impr. Conf. Tech. Rpt. 9, 6 pp.

————. 1953b. *Progress in Study of Pine Races.* South. Lumberman 187 (2345): 139-140.

————. 1954a. *Planting the Southern Pines.* U. S. Dept. Agr. Monog. 18, 233 pp.

————. 1954b. *The Relation of Geographic Race to Forest Tree Improvement.* Jour. Forestry 52: 653.

————. 1957. *A Guide to the Planting of Southern Pines.* Forest Farmer 17 (1): 10-11.

————. 1958. *Five-Year Intercept As Site Index in Southern Pine Plantations.* Jour. Forestry 56: 332-336.

———— and Chapman, R. A. 1937. *A Method of Studying the Factors Affecting Initial Survival in Forest Plantations.* U. S. Forest Serv. South. Forest Expt. Sta. Occas. Paper 69, 19 pp.

———— and Cossitt, F. M. 1950. *What About Our Tree Seed Source.* Forest Farmer 9 (7): 7, 13.

Walker, L. W. 1956. *Controlling Undesirable Hardwoods.* Ga. Forest Res. Council Rpt. 3, 24 pp.

Walker, N. 1956. *Growing Stock Volumes in Unmanaged and Managed Forests.* Jour. Forestry 56: 378-383.

Walter, E. V., Seaton, L., and Mathewson, A. A. 1938. *The Texas Leaf-Cutting Ant and Its Control.* U. S. Dept. Agr. Cir. 494, 19 pp.

Ware, L. M., and Stahelin, R. 1946. *How Far Apart Should Pines Be Planted?* South. Lumberman 173 (2177): 191-193.

———— and Stahelin, R. 1948. *Growth of Southern Pine Plantations at Various Spacings.* Jour. Forestry 46: 267-274.

Waterman, A. M. 1943. *Diplodia Pinea, the Cause of a Disease of Hard Pines.* Phytopathology 33: 1018-1031.

Watson, A. J., and Hodder, I. G. 1954. *Relationship Between Fibre Structure and Handsheet Properties in Pinus Taeda.* Austral. Pulp and Paper Indust. Tech. Proc. 8: 290-310.

Watson, C. J. J., and Moore, D. 1944. *The Suitability of Thinnings of Pinus Taeda and P. Caribaea for Pineapple Cases.* Queensland Forest Serv. Adv. Leaflet 4, 7 pp.

Way, R. D., and Maki, T. E. 1946. *Effects of Pre-Storage Treatment of Hardwood and Pine Seedlings with a-Naphthaleneacetic Acid.* Bot. Gaz. 108: 219-232.

Webb, J. L. 1909. *Some Insects Injurious to Forests. IV. The Southern Pine Sawyer.* U. S. Bur. Ent. Bul. 58, pt. 4, pp. 41-561.

————. 1911. *Injuries to Forests and Forest Products by Roundheaded Borers.* U. S. Dept. Agr. Yearbook 1910: 341-358.

Weber, G. F. 1941. *A Rust of Florida Pines Caused by Cronartium Quercuum (Berk.) Miya.* Fla. Acad. Sci. Proc. 1940: 262-269.

————. 1943. *Needle Rusts of Pine Trees in Florida Caused by Coleosporium Species.* Fla. Acad. Sci. Proc. 6: 131-142.

Weddell, D. J. 1935. *Viable Seed from Nine-Year-Old Southern Pine.* Jour. Forestry 33 (11): 902.

————. 1950. *Harvest Cuttings in the Southern Piedmont Region.* Jour. Forestry 48: 354-356.

———— and Ware, L. M. 1935. *The Effect of Fires of Different Frequencies on the Survival of Different Species of Pines.* Ala. Agr. Expt. Sta. Ann. Rpt. 47: 28-29.

Wells, B. W. 1928. *Plant Communities of the Coastal Plain of North Carolina and Their Successional Relations.* Ecology 9 : 230-242.

———. 1942. *Ecological Problems of the Southeastern United States Coastal Plain.* Bot. Rev. 8 : 533-561.

Wells, S. D., Grabow, R. H., Staidl, J. A., and Bray, M. W. 1923. *Chemistry of the Alkaline Wood Pulp Processes: Part I. Aspen, Loblolly Pine and Jack Pine by the Soda Process.* Paper Trade Jour. 76 (24) : 49-55. U. S. Forest Serv. Forest Prod. Lab. Rpt. R957.

——— and Rue, J. D. 1927. *The Suitability of American Woods for Paper Pulp.* U. S. Dept. Agr. Bul. 1485, 102 pp.

Wellwood, R. W. 1943. *Trend Towards Normality of Stocking for Second-Growth Loblolly Pine Stands.* Jour. Forestry 41 : 202-209.

Wenger, K. F. 1950. *The Mechanical Effect of Fusiform Rust Cankers on Stems of Loblolly Pine.* Jour. Forestry 48 : 331-333.

———. 1952. *Effect of Moisture Supply and Soil Texture on the Growth of Sweetgum and Pine Seedlings.* Jour. Forestry 50 : 862-864.

———. 1953a. *The Effect of Fertilization and Injury on the Cone and Seed Production of Loblolly Pine Seed Trees.* Jour. Forestry 51 : 570-573.

———. 1953b. *How to Estimate the Number of Cones in Standing Loblolly Pine Trees (Pinus Taeda).* U. S. Forest Serv. Southeast. Forest Expt. Sta. Res. Notes 44, 2 pp.

———. 1953c. *Preharvest Release of Loblolly Pine Seed Trees Will Increase Seed Supply at Harvest.* U. S. Forest Serv. Southeast. Forest Expt. Sta. Res. Notes 45, 2 pp.

———. 1954. *The Stimulation of Loblolly Pine Seed Trees by Preharvest Release.* Jour. Forestry 52 : 115-118.

———. 1955a. *Loblolly Pine Reproduction: Success or Failure?* South. Lumberman 190 (2373) : 68, 70, 72.

———. 1955b. *Height Growth of Loblolly Pine Seedlings in Relation to Seedling Characteristics.* Forest Sci. 1 : 158-163.

———. 1955c. *Growth and Prospective Development of Hardwoods and Loblolly Pine Seedlings on Clear-Cut Areas.* U. S. Forest Serv. Southeast. Forest Expt. Sta. Paper 55, 19 pp.

———. 1955d. *Light and Mycorrhiza Development.* Ecology 36 : 518-520.

———. 1955e. *Seed Tree Requirements in Loblolly Pine.* South. Lumberman 191 (2393) : 116-118.

———. 1956. *Growth of Hardwoods After Clear-Cutting Loblolly Pine.* Ecology 37 : 735-742.

———. 1957. *Annual Variation in the Seed Crops of Loblolly Pine.* Jour. Forestry 55 : 567-569.

———. 1958. *Silvical Characteristics of Loblolly Pine.* U. S. Forest Serv. Southeast. Forest Expt. Sta. Paper 98, 32 pp.

——— Evans, T. C., Lotti, T., Cooper, R. W., and Brender, E. V. 1958. *The Relation of Growth to Stand Density in Natural Loblolly Pine Stands.* U. S. Forest Serv. Southeast. Forest Expt. Sta. Paper 72, 10 pp.

——— and Trousdell, K. B. 1958. *Natural Regeneration of Loblolly Pine in the South Atlantic Coastal Plain.* U. S. Dept. Agr. Prod. Res. Rpt. 13, 78 pp.

Westberg, D. L. 1950. *From Scrub Hardwood to Pine in Alabama.* Forest Farmer 10 (3): 8.

Whalen, E. J. 1956. *A Folding Spudder for Tree Planting.* Tree Planters' Notes 25: 20-21.

Wheeler, P. R. 1952. *Effect of Cutting Upon Growth.* The Unit, Newsletter 43, South. Pine Conser. Assoc., 23-26.

————. 1956. *Forests of East Texas, 1953-55.* U. S. Forest Serv. South. Forest Expt. Sta. Forest Survey Release 77, 51 pp.

———— and Reynolds, R. R. 1952. *Forest Management Pays Off in Southern Arkansas.* Jour. Forestry 50: 395-396.

Wherry, E. T. 1922. *Soil Acidity Preferences of Eastern Conifers.* Jour. Forestry 20: 488-496.

Wiesehuegel, E. G. 1955. *Loblolly Pine Geographic Seed Source Tests—Five-Year Results.* U. S. Tenn. Val. Authority, Div. Forest Relat., 9 pp.

Williams, W. K. 1928. *Growing Pine Pulpwood as a Farm Crop.* Ark. Agr. Col. Ext. Cir. 249, 23 pp.

Williston, H. L. 1949a. *Sprouting Following August Girdling.* U. S. Forest Serv. South. Forest Expt. Sta. South. Forestry Notes 64.

————. 1949b. *Damage from Long-Length Logging.* U. S. Forest Serv. South. Forest Expt. Sta. South. Forestry Notes 63.

————. 1950. *Mortality Following Thinning.* U. S. Forest Serv. South. Forest Expt. Sta. South. Forestry Notes 68.

————. 1951. *Height Growth of Pine Seedlings.* U. S. Forest Serv. South. Forest Expt. Sta. South. Forestry Notes 71.

————. 1958a. *Cost of Pruning Loblolly and Shortleaf.* U. S. Forest Serv. South. Forest Expt. Sta. South. Forestry Notes 114.

————. 1958b. *Shortleaf Versus Loblolly Pine in North Mississippi.* Jour. Forestry 56: 761.

————. 1959. *Cost of Pruning Loblolly and Shortleaf Pine.* South. Lumberman 198 (2470): 43.

———— and Rawls, I. W. 1947. *Building Up a Poorly Stocked Farm Forest.* U. S. Forest Serv. South. Forest Expt. Sta. Occas. Paper 110, 7 pp.

Wilson, C. C. 1953. *The Response of Two Species of Pine to Various Levels of Nutrient Zinc.* Science 117: (231- 233).

Wilson, T. R. C. 1930. *Moisture in Wood in Its Relation to Strength.* South. Lumberman 140 (1785): 58, 60.

————. 1932. *Strength-Moisture Relations for Wood.* U. S. Dept. Agr. Tech. Bul. 282, 88 pp.

————. 1934. *Guide to the Grading of Structural Timbers and the Determination of Working Stresses.* U. S. Dept. Agr. Misc. Pub. 185, 27 pp.

Winters, R. K., Ward, G. B., Jr., and Eldredge, I. F. 1943. *Louisiana Forest Resources and Industries.* U. S. Dept. Agr. Misc. Pub. 519, 44 pp.

Wishart, J. E. 1946. *Some of the Economics of Southern Pine.* Thesis, Yale Univ. School Forestry.

Wood, J. E., Davis, D. E., and Komarek, E. V. 1958. *Distribution of Fox Populations in Relation to Vegetation in Southern Georgia.* Ecology 39 (1): 160-162.

Wood, L. W. 1950. *Southern Pine and the Density Rule.* South. Lumberman 181 (2273) : 236-238.

Wood, O. M. 1936. *Early Survival of Some Pine Interplantings in Southern New Jersey.* Jour. Forestry 34: 873-878.

Worrell, A. C. 1953a. *Costs of Practising Forestry in the South.* South. Lumberman 186 (2325) : 43-44.

———. 1953b. *Financial Maturity: a Questionable Concept in Forest Management.* Jour. Forestry 51: 711-714.

———. 1955a. *Forest Production in a Dynamic Economy.* Jour. Forestry 53: 447-450.

———. 1955b. *Economics of Fire Detection in the South.* Jour. Forestry 53: 639-644.

———. 1955c. *The Economic Combination of Towers and Air Patrol in Fire Detection.* Fourth Ann. Forestry Symposium Proc., La. State Univ. School Forestry 1955: 46-54.

———. 1956. *Optimum Intensity of Forest Land Use on a Regional Basis.* Forest Sci. 2: 199-240.

———. 1957. *Short Rotation Management on Small Forest Properties.* Forest Farmer 16 (11) : 10-12, 14; and 16 (12) : 11, 18.

Worthington, N. 1954. *The Loblolly Pine of the South Versus the Douglas Fir of the Pacific Northwest.* Pulp and Paper 28 (10) : 84-85, 87-88, 90.

Worthington, R. E. 1939. *Costs of Tractor Logging in Southern Pine.* U. S. Dept. Agr. Tech. Bul. 700, 64 pp.

Wright, C. E. 1955. *Growing Trend to Pallet Loading of Southern Pulpwood.* Paper Trade Jour. 139 (12) : 24-26.

Wright, E., and Wells, H. R. 1948. *Tests on the Adaptability of Trees and Shrubs to Shelterbelt Planting on Certain Phymatotrichum Root Rot Infested Soils of Oklahoma and Texas.* Jour. Forestry 46: 256-262.

Wyman, L. 1932. *How to Combat the Pine Beetles' Damage to the Pine Trees.* Naval Stores Rev. 41 (48) : 10.

Yandle, D. O. 1956. *Statistical Evaluation of the Effect of Age on Specific Gravity in Loblolly Pine.* U. S. Forest Serv. Forest Prod. Lab. Rpt. R2049, 4 pp.

Yarham, E. R. 1946. *North American Species Thriving in New Zealand.* Brit. Columbia Lumberman 29: 69-70. Forestry Abs. 7 (3) : 285.

———. 1947. *Exotics in New Zealand.* Wood 11 (8) : 216-218. Forestry Abs. 8 (3) : 369.

Yocom, H. A. 1951. *How Late Can Pines Be Planted in North Alabama?* Forest Farmer 10 (6) : 15.

———. 1952. *Estimating the Time Needed for Girdling Hardwoods.* Jour. Forestry 50: 484.

———. 1954. *Machine Faster Than Ax for Girdling.* U. S. Forest Serv. South. Forest Expt. Sta. South. Forestry Notes 94.

Young, H. E. 1940. *Fused Needle Disease and Its Relation to the Nutrition of Pinus.* Queensland Forest Serv. Bul. 13, 108 pp.

———. 1947. *Carbohydrate Absorption by Roots of Pinus Taeda.* Queensland Jour. Agr. Sci. 4 ($\frac{1}{2}$) : 1-6.

———. 1948. *The Response of Loblolly and Slash Pines to Phosphate Manures.* Queensland Jour. Agr. Sci. 5: 77-105.

Young, Harold E. 1948. *The Effect of Pruning on the Height and Diameter Growth of Loblolly Pine*. Thesis, Duke Univ. School Forestry.

———. 1952. *Differential Time of Change from Earlywood to Latewood Along the Bole of Young Loblolly Pine Trees*. Jour. Forestry 50: 614-615.

——— and Kramer, P. J. 1952. *The Effect of Pruning on the Height and Diameter Growth of Loblolly Pine*. Jour. Forestry 50: 474-479.

Young, V. 1950. *Gaylord Pine Plantations and Forestry Policy*. South. Pulp and Paper Mfr. 13 (3): 42.

Young, W. D. 1931. *Loblolly Pine Production*. Ga. Forest Serv. Leaflet 14, 8 pp.

Zahner, R. 1953. *The Effect of Soil Properties on Site Quality for Loblolly Pine in the Gulf Coastal Plain*. Thesis, Duke Univ. School Forestry.

———. 1954. *Estimating Loblolly Pine Sites in the Gulf Coastal Plain*. Jour. Forestry 52: 448-449.

———. 1955a. *Soil Water Depletion by Pine and Hardwood Stands During a Dry Season*. Forest Sci. 1: 258-264.

———. 1955b. *Effect of Interrupted Dark Period on Height Growth of Two Tree Species*. Forest Sci. 1: 193-195.

———. 1955c. *Plantation Exhausts Soil Water Rapidly*. U. S. Forest Serv. South. Forest Expt. Sta. South. Forestry Notes 95.

———. 1956. *Evaluating Summer Water Deficiencies*. U. S. Forest Serv. South. Forest Expt. Sta. Occas. Paper 150, 18 pp.

———. 1957a. *Mapping Soils for Pine Site Quality in South Arkansas and North Louisiana*. Jour. Forestry 55: 430-433.

———. 1957b. *Field Procedures for Soil-Site Classification of Pine Land in South Arkansas and North Louisiana*. U. S. Forest Serv. South. Forest Expt. Sta. Occas. Paper 155, 17 pp.

———. 1958. *Site-Quality Relationships of Pine Forests in Southern Arkansas and Northern Louisiana*. Forest Sci. 4: 162-176.

Zak, B. 1956. *Experimental Air Layering of Shortleaf and Loblolly Pine*. U. S. Forest Serv. Southeast. Forest Expt. Sta. Paper 69, 12 pp.

Zeller, S. M. 1917. *Studies in the Physiology of the Fungi: III. Physical Properties of Wood in Relation to Decay Induced by Lenzites Sepiaria, Freis*. Mo. Bot. Gard. Ann. 4: 93-164.

Ziegler, E. A. 1931. *Where and When Does Timber Growing Pay?* Agr. Bul. Atlanta and West Point Rail Road, Western Railway of Alabama, and Georgia Railroad. Winter issue, pp. 25-28.

———. 1942. *Cost of Growing Pulpwood on Southern Pine Land*. Southern Pulp and Paper Jour. 5 (5): 40, 44, 46, 48.

——— and Bond, W. E. 1932. *Financial Aspects of Growing Pine in the South*. Jour. Forestry 30: 284-297.

——— Spillers, A. E., and Coulter, C. H. 1931. *Financial Aspects of Growing Southern Pine in Washington County, Florida*. Fla. Forest Serv. Bul. 7, 77 pp.

Zobel, B. J. 1953. *Are There Natural Loblolly-Shortleaf Pine Hybrids?* Jour. Forestry 51: 494-495.

———. 1955. *Research on Certain Properties of Loblolly Pine (Pinus Taeda)*. Paper Mill News 78 (39): 60.

———. 1956. *Genetic, Growth, and Environmental Factors Affecting Specific Gravity of Loblolly Pine.* Forest Prod. Res. Soc. Jour. 6: 442-447.

——— and Goddard, R. E. 1954. *Pine Flowering and Seed Ripening in Texas.* Tex. Forest Serv. Res. Note 8, 12 pp.

——— and Goddard, R. E. 1955. *Preliminary Results on Tests of Drought Hardy Strains of Loblolly Pine (Pinus Taeda L.).* Tex. Forest Serv. Res. Note 14, 23 pp.

——— and McElwee, R. L. 1958a. *Natural Variation in Wood Specific Gravity of Loblolly Pine, and an Analysis of Contributing Factors.* Tappi 41 (4): 158-161.

——— and McElwee, R. L. 1958b. *Variation of Cellulose in Loblolly Pine.* Tappi 41 (4): 167-170.

——— and Rhodes, R. R. 1955. *Relationship of Wood Specific Gravity in Loblolly Pine to Growth and Environmental Factors.* Tex. Forest Serv. Tech. Rpt. 11, 32 pp.

——— and Rhodes, R. R. 1956. *Specific Gravity Estimations of Mature Loblolly Pine from Juvenile Wood and Seedling Limb Sections.* Forest Sci. 2: 107-112.

——— and Rhodes, R. R. 1957. *Specific Gravity Indices for Use in Breeding Loblolly Pine.* Forest Sci. 3: 281-285.

Zon, R. 1905. *Loblolly Pine in Eastern Texas, with Special Reference to the Production of Cross-Ties.* U. S. Dept. Agr. Forest Serv. Bul. 64, 53 pp.

———. 1941. *Climate and the Nation's Forests.* U. S. Dept. Agr. Yearbook 1941: 477-498.

INDEX OF AUTHORS

SUBJECT INDEX[148]

[148] See CONTENTS for list of sections in the text. Use BIBLIOGRAPHY to locate original source material in literature. Refer to INDEX OF AUTHORS for monograph pages where citations appear.

This SUBJECT INDEX lists detailed topics included, but locates geographic sources of information by states only.